More Medicode Products

Coder-Tested And Coder-Approved

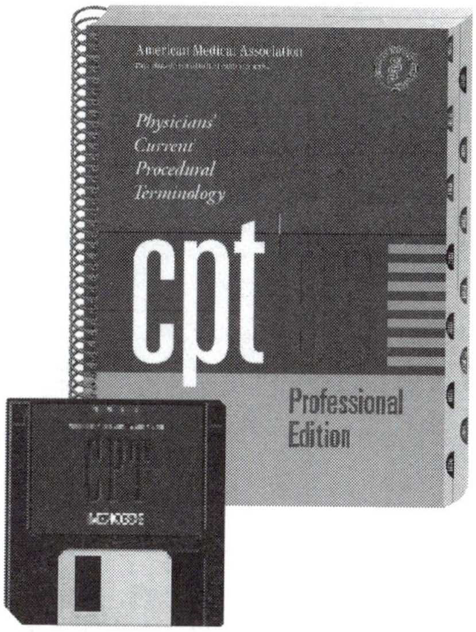

Color Keys And Illustrations For 1996

Using updated codes is essential. That's why *CPT 1996* is a must for every office. Easy to use, *CPT 1996* is the most comprehensive coding reference available for CPT codes.

New CPT 1996 Professional Edition

The AMA's new *Professional Edition of CPT 1996* delivers the features of the standard edition, plus:

- **Color Keys.** These easy-to-see keys support precision coding.
- **Anatomical Illustrations.** They make coding more manageable.
- **Medical Terminology.** Defines and clarifies complex meanings.
- **Spiral Binding And Thumb-Index Tabs.** Facilitate handling and use.

CPT On Disk

With *Medicode's Relative Values And CPT 1996 On Disk* you'll get CPT codes, abbreviated descriptions and Medicode's relative values. DOS ASCII file imports easily into your software.

New Color-Coding For Ease-Of-Use

You'll need our *HCPCS 1996* to bill Medicare and many private payers. It's the most user-friendly, most comprehensive edition on the market. And new features for this year:

- New color coding of Medicare coverage instructions with a helpful legend.
- Expanded index that includes product name references. Find products, even if you don't know the manufacturer.
- Thinner size and free spiral binding.

Plus these existing features:

- Pharmacist-verified table of drugs with brand names, generics, dosage, route of administration and correct J or K codes.
- Instructions preceding each section to guide you through information.

HCPCS On Disk

With *HCPCS 1996 On Disk* you'll get HCPCS Level II codes and full descriptions. DOS ASCII file imports easily into your software.

MEDICODE®

OWER TO MAKE THE RIGHT DECISIONS.™

Available from your medical bookstore or distributor. For a free catalog, call 1-800-999-4600.

More Medicode Products

Coder-Tested And Coder-Approved

Coding With An Outdated ICD•9 Is Risky

Not a single *Medicode ICD•9* goes out until every one of the government's code changes are included. So only Medicode dares to offer this risk-free guarantee: "Use any *Medicode 1996 ICD•9*. If you make a coding error based on an outdated code, Medicode will give you next year's *ICD•9* absolutely free!" But that's not all.

Receive Our New Specialty Minibook Free!

Order a *Deluxe or Compact 1996 ICD•9* and get our handy new *ICD•9 Minibook*, free. It organizes codes by specialty (eight in all).

Minibook Specialties Available:
Cardiology • General Surgery • Primary Care • Ophthalmology • Obstetrics And Gynecology • OMS And Reconstructive Surgery • Orthopedics • Urology

New for 1996, our *Compact ICD•9* is easier to handle, at just 6" x 9" and with thumb-index tabs. Our *Deluxe 1996 ICD•9* offers thumb-index tabs and spiral binding. And, our *Standard 1996 ICD•9* has regular binding at the most economical price.

Largest Billing Directory Available

Find the latest on more than 5,000 third-party payers and self-administered corporations. Simply open up a copy of our *1996 Insurance Directory* for the most accurate listings, we phone-check each and every one. No other company keeps such a watchful eye. New features include:

- Symbols that identify types of claims paid by each company. New symbols for 1996 include home health services and prescription claims.
- A listing of Medicare "Part A" Intermediaries for each state. You save time.
- More listings than any other directory, along with "800" and FAX numbers.
- Identification of companies that electronically process claims.
- Ready-to-use claim management forms.
- Instructions for completing the HCFA-1500 form.
- Index of companies listed by state.

With our new *1996 Insurance Directory On Disk* you'll get a listing of company names, addresses, phone numbers, fax numbers and the types of claims processed. It's in a DOS ASCII file to import easily into your software.

MEDICODE®

OWER TO MAKE THE RIGHT DECISIONS.™

Available from your medical bookstore or distributor. For a free catalog, call 1-800-999-4600.

Fee & Coding Standard

MEDICODE®

First Printing — February 1996

For additional copies of this publication, please call 1 800 999-4600.

MEDICODE PUBLICATIONS STAFF

Susan P. Seare	Publisher
Lynn Speirs	Editorial Director
Sheri P. Bernard	Managing Editor
Jerry G. Seare, M.D.	Medical Director
Charlene Neeshan	Clinical Editor/Writer
Kerrie Hornsby	Designer/Typesetter
Robert J. Welsh	Project Manager

Contents

Introduction

Medicode's *Fee & Coding Standard* is designed to assist and prepare clinicians and their staffs to manage successfully today's dramatic changes in healthcare. Its purpose is two-fold: to help physicians develop a reasonable and equitable fee schedule for their practices, and to provide accepted industry and Medicare coding standards as they apply to *Physicians' Current Procedural Terminology* (*CPT '96*), the most commonly used procedure coding system in the country. Included are helpful insights and suggestions on coding, auditing, contracting with payers, cosmetic surgery reimbursement, Medicare fragmentation, subsidiary codes, and other issues important to the financial success of a medical practice.

In today's competitive and dynamic healthcare environment, being a good clinician is vital, but being a good administrator may be just as important. Billers, coders, and office staff need the physician's help to be successful, and this in turn ensures the success of a practice. Not keeping up with the administrative demands can mean the difference between a successful practice and a "clinic closed" sign.

This book provides the tools to compete successfully in this fast-paced environment. Admittedly, more of the physician's time may be required in the beginning, but in time the office staff will be able to carry on with very little guidance. Get involved now. Be sure your office staff is trained on setting fees, coding, and billing accurately; it will facilitate a successful practice. Then, everyone can share in the rewards of receiving correct payment for services provided.

KEY TO PROPER REIMBURSEMENT

Providers are frequently underpaid by payers for services rendered. The cause of low reimbursement, however, lies not only with the payer (many are trying honestly to contain costs without sacrificing quality of care), but also with improper coding and documentation by the provider. Proper reimbursement for services depends largely on:

Communication between the physician and office staff;

Communication between the physician and the URN/Case Manager;

Communication between the office staff and hospital or other facilitiy providing documentation;

Communication between the physician and resident/non-resident responsible for dictation of operative and other reports;

Communication between the office staff and the payer;

Communication between the physician and insurance contract negotiator;

Communication between the physician or office staff and the patient;

Communication in writing of what has been done for the patient in the medical record, and;

Communication of laboratory, x-ray, and other diagnostic/therapeutic procedure results into the medical records. These results must be secured and initialed by the physician. (You can do all the tests in the world, but if the results are not in the record they were not "officially" done.) Payers are, justifiably, suspicious of loose sheets not in the record and found after the fact, and often will deny payment for such claims.

THE MEDICAL CODING SYSTEM

As simple as it sounds, if you want to get paid for what you do you have to speak the language of coding. Physicians use a common language of names, numbers, and terminology (nomenclature) to communicate with other physicians and with the organizations that reimburse them for the services they perform. This coding nomenclature greatly reduces verbiage and paperwork and is recognized and accepted by most insurance payers. The codes represent diagnoses, physician services and procedures, and medical services and supplies. To receive fair and adequate reimbursement in a timely fashion by third-party payers, providers and their reimbursement specialists must understand and use these codes correctly.

There are three primary references in the medical coding system. The first is the diagnostic reference, *International Classification of Diseases, 9th Revision, Clinical Modification*, referred to as ICD-9-CM or, more commonly, as ICD-9. Within this system, and by way of example, the code for an open fracture of malar and maxillary bones is 802.5, and vesicoureteral reflux is coded as 593.7. Reimbursement is often tied to the medical necessity established by proper use of ICD-9 codes.

The second reference, and the one around which this book is constructed, is CPT. CPT is published annually by the American Medical Association and contains codes for physician services and procedures. Continuing with the diagnostic examples above, an open treatment of palatal or maxillary fracture would be reported with CPT code 21422, and cystotomy for excision, incision, or repair of ureterocele with code 51535. CPT coding is discussed in greater detail in Chapter 1.

The third reference is the Health Care Financing Administration's (HCFA) *Common Procedure Coding System*, commonly called HCPCS (pronounced "hick-picks") Level II codes. Codes in this system are accepted in Medicare claims, but are not as widely accepted among private payers. Their use is growing. HCPCS Level II codes identify medical services and supplies not specifically identified in CPT, including drugs administered by injection and durable medical equipment.

Understanding and using these references correctly is essential for achieving accurate compensation for what you do.

WHAT THIS BOOK HAS TO OFFER

Medicode's Fee & Coding Standard provides in-depth information to help you evaluate the fee schedule you are currently using. Useful applications include:

- Comparison of your current charges to those of other physicians nationwide.
- Development of fees for new or seldom-performed procedures.
- Modification of current high or low fees,with relative values.

CODING INSIGHT

The clinical and coding professionals at Medicode present their guidelines and suggestions to help enhance your coding accuracy. Information about modifiers, bilateral and unilateral procedures, payer attitudes and methodologies, seldom-performed procedures, and a variety of other special considerations and comments about particular codes are presented under this heading. Not every code has a specific comment — to do so would have produced a book three times this size. Rather, we have grouped and commented on the codes in ranges.

COSMETIC WARNING

A number of codes in the surgery section of CPT are commonly done for cosmetic purposes only. This is an important reimbursement issue. This book points out those codes which, 85 percent of the time or more, are considered cosmetic by payers.

Subsidiary Codes
This information relates to codes which are not usually reported alone, but "in addition to" a primary code. Subsidiary codes have values that do not require any further adjustment, so they are an important reimbursement issue.

Medicare Alert
Medicare is unique in the payer community. Under this heading we have attempted to "alert" you to a host of issues regarding Medicare: modifiers and how they will affect reimbursement, starred procedures, surgical destruction, unbundling/fragmentation, and many others. Additional detailed information regarding Medicare issues is found in the introduction to the surgery section.

CPT Code Descriptions and Data
Establishing fees for medical services is a difficult practice management task. Fees that are too high can result in both loss of patients and disputes with payers, and fees that are too low will, naturally, result in inadequate reimbursement for the medical services provided Striking a balance between the two is essential. We have included national 50th and 75th percentile relative values, regional conversion factors, as well as a Medicare national average, to help you evaluate your current charges.

Relative Values
The relative values reported in this section are proprietary to Medicode. They were developed and are maintained by Medicode's committee of clinical and coding experts. A relative value is a numeric ranking assigned to a procedure relating it to other procedures in terms of the time, work, and costs associated with the procedure. The relative values for surgical procedures are not on the same numeric scale as those assigned to nonsurgical procedures and therefore cannot be compared.

The relative value columns in *Medicode's Fee & Coding Standard* present a blend of two different methodologies. The RVS weighs medical procedures relative to one another on a scale linked to difficulty, work, risk, and the material costs of the procedure. The second ingredient can be characterized as a simple statistical profiling of charges.

While profiling alone has the benefit of reporting actual charges, the method presupposes coding accuracy, and the required data volume is very high. The accuracy of the analysis is strictly limited to the quality and quantity of the data set and does not address the question of whether the charges are reasonable. Since 80 percent of procedures billed are represented by less than 5 percent of codes, many statistical holes develop where the quantity of data is insufficient for confident analysis. Furthermore, studies show that up to 30 percent of all medical bills are coded inaccurately — a further compromise to good data analysis.

Medicode feels this method of combining the approaches merges the benefits of a relative value scale with the better features of actual charge data. This combination is further enhanced by the company's tremendous number of charges (now approximately 300 million), which allows us to array the data confidently by zip code areas.

Please note that while thousands of payers and providers contribute to the data used in this product, no individual physician, clinic, or payer schedules appear in the data.

National 50th and 75th Percentile Amounts
The 50th and 75th percentile amounts were calculated from Medicode's national database of submitted charge data using a relative value and conversion factor methodology. The charges are for medical services performed during the 18-month period of April 1994 to November 1995. The charge data has been trended forward to November 1995 using the CPI for physician services.

Modifier -26

For some codes, especially in the Radiology and Pathology & Laboratory sections, you will see -26 listed under the code number with amounts on the same line in the percentile columns. Modifier -26 indicates the professional component portion of a procedure that has both professional and technical components. If this amount is the same as the total above it, the procedure is entirely professional. Otherwise, simply subtract the professional portion from the total to arrive at the technical portion.

MEDICARE AMOUNTS

The amounts in this column represent the average amount allowed by each of the Medicare carriers for each locality in 1995. For most of the laboratory codes, Medicare carrier information is not available. For these codes Medicare's national lab fee schedule was utilized.

GEOGRAPHIC AREAS

Conversion factors for U.S. geographic areas are included in appendix A, and Medicare "geo-zip" conversion factors are listed in appendix B.

A NOTE ON MEDICARE

National Medicare policies do not exist for every medical service. HCFA, through Carrier Medical Advisory committees and the Carrier Medical Director, allows carriers to establish local medical policies for services where no national policy exists. Providers are notified of these local medical policies through their carrier newsletter.

Under contract to AdminaStar Federal, HCFA established a new Correct Coding Initiative. Two main types of code combinations effective in January 1996 are:

- Comprehensive and component code combinations
- "Mutually exclusive" coding combinations (that represent services or procedures that would not or could not be performed at the same time, based on CPT code description or standard medical practice)

The intiative is too large to include in this publication. A copy of the *Correct Coding Policy Manual* version 2 (available in hard copy and on diskette) can be obtained from NTIS. Call (703) 487-4650 for more information.

If you have questions about how to use Medicode's *Fee & Coding Standard*, please call Medicode Client Services at 800-765-6818.

CPT Coding and Use of Modifiers

CPT is a standardized system of five-digit codes and descriptive terms used to report the medical services and procedures performed by physicians. It was developed and is updated and published annually by the AMA and includes procedures that are consistent with contemporary medical practice by physicians in many locations. CPT codes provide an effective language for nationwide communication among physicians, insurance payers, and patients.

CPT is arranged in six major sections as follows:

Evaluation and Management	99201–99499
Anesthesiology	00100–01999 and 99100–99140
Surgery	10040–69979
Radiology (including nuclear medicine and diagnostic ultrasound)	70010–79999
Pathology and Laboratory	80002–89399
Medicine	90701–99199

CPT is the most widely accepted procedure coding system. In fact, Medicare and state Medicaid carriers are required by law to use these codes for the payment of health insurance claims, and most commercial insurance payers likewise use CPT. Common exceptions are state medical associations and workers' compensation plans that have developed their own procedure coding systems or use relative value studies for claims payment. These other systems vary, so request information as needed from the plans or associations in your area.

Although required by most insurance companies, the mere existence of CPT procedure codes does not imply coverage under any given insurance plan. In other words, just because there is a CPT code for a current medical procedure does not mean that a payer is obligated to reimburse physicians for that service.

CPT INDEX

The CPT coding process begins with a careful examination of the medical record to determine primary and secondary procedures as well as any modifying or extenuating circumstances. The alphabetical CPT index is the starting point of all CPT coding, but do not select codes solely on the basis of information in the index — it is only a reference to the full listing of codes. Procedures are listed in the CPT index by:

- Procedure or service
- Organ or other anatomic site
- Condition
- Key synonyms
- Key eponyms (disease or procedure named after a person, e.g., Moh's technique)
- Abbreviations

CPT CONVENTIONS

Effective CPT coding depends upon thorough familiarity with the system's contents and conventions.

FORMAT

Because many of the codes within a given section repeat some common portion of a procedure's description, CPT's format has been designed to save space. In the example below, codes 42104 and 42106 share some common descriptive words. The difference between the codes is that 42104 does not include closure of the incision, while 42106 includes simple primary closure.

42104 *Excision, lesion of palate, uvula; without closure*
42106 *with simple primary closure*

The key to interpreting these codes correctly is the semicolon (;) in 42104 which separates the common portion of the description from the information unique to that code. Then, the indented 42106 code does not repeat the common portion (that part immediately before the semicolon), but instead supplies unique or special information. You should refer to the previous code for the common portion of the description. Therefore, the complete description of code 42106 is "Excision, lesion of palate, uvula; with simple primary closure."

GUIDELINES

Guidelines appear at the beginning of each of the six major sections of CPT. This information provides definitions, explanations of terms, and factors relevant to that specialty area. Each guideline must be reviewed for complete understanding of that section of codes because necessary information is often listed only in the guidelines. Additionally, subsections provide information unique to that specific subsection.

Information specific to a given code may be included as a parenthetical phrase following the code.

67335 *Placement of adjustable suture(s) during strabismus surgery, including postoperative adjustment(s) of suture(s) (Report in addition to code for specific strabismus surgery)*

(Use also code for conventional muscle surgery, 67311–67334 to identify number of muscles involved)

CODE CHANGES

To keep up with the dynamic nature of medicine, the AMA revises and publishes CPT on an annual basis. Appendix B always consists of a summary of additions, deletions, and revisions to the current edition. Of these three types of changes, only the descriptions of new codes appear in appendix B, so you must compare the new edition to the previous one to identify how the code descriptions have been revised. These changes are indicated as follows in CPT:

New codes are identified by a solid circle.

● 49428 *Ligation of peritoneal-venous shunt*

Revised codes are identified by a solid triangle.

▲ 60100 *Biopsy thyroid, percutaneous core needle*

Deleted codes are enclosed within parentheses.

(38090 has been deleted. To report, use 38999)

Once you have updated the codes used in your office by referring to the newest edition of CPT, don't neglect to evaluate the fees assigned to all codes, not just the new codes.

MODIFIERS

CPT modifiers indicate that a service was altered in some way from the stated CPT description without actually changing the basic definition of the service. Separate five-digit codes provided by CPT may be used instead of the two-digit modifier. When using the code, the three-digit prefix 099 precedes the assigned modifier number. Documentation should always support the use of the modifier/code.

Modifiers can indicate:

- A service or procedure has both a professional and a technical component
- A service or procedure was performed by more than one physician
- Only part of a service was performed
- An adjunctive service was performed
- A bilateral procedure was performed
- A service or procedure was provided more than once
- Unusual events occurred

MODIFIER IMPACT ON REIMBURSEMENT

The correct use of modifiers is frequently the only way to increase payment for a procedure. Billing personnel must know how to use modifiers correctly.

Modifiers that usually affect reimbursement include :

-21 Prolonged Evaluation and Management Services
-22 Unusual Procedural Services
-26 Professional Component
-47 Anesthesia by Surgeon
-50 Bilateral Procedure
-51 Multiple Procedures
-52 Reduced Services
-54 Surgical Care Only
-55 Postoperative Management Only
-62 Cosurgery
-66 Surgical Team
-80 Assistant Surgeon
-81 Minimum Assistant Surgeon
-82 Assistant Surgeon (when qualified resident surgeon not available)

Modifiers that may or may not affect reimbursement, depending upon the payer, include:

-20 Microsurgery
-23 Unusual Anesthesia
-56 Preoperative Management Only

-78 Return to the Operating Room for a Related Procedure During the Postoperative Period

The following modifiers are informational in nature and do not affect reimbursement. Since payers seldom have specific guidelines for these modifiers, you must bill them consistently. It is a good idea to monitor the reimbursements received when using these modifiers.

-24 Unrelated Evaluation and Management Service by the Same Physician During a Postoperative Period

-25 Significant, Separately Identifiable Evaluation and Management Service by the Same Physician on the Day of a Procedure (Use of this modifier may allow reimbursement for both a surgical and E/M service.)

-32 Mandated Services

-57 Decision for Surgery (Use of this modifier does not allow two codes to be reported.)

-58 Staged or Related Procedure or Service by the Same Physician During the Postoperative Period

-76 Repeat Procedure by Same Physician

-77 Repeat Procedure by Another Physician

-79 Unrelated Procedure or Service by the Same Physician During the Postoperative Period

-90 Reference (Outside) Laboratory

-99 Multiple Modifiers

MODIFIERS THAT USUALLY AFFECT REIMBURSEMENT

The proper use of modifiers may or may not have an impact on reimbursement. The modifiers listed below affect payment and are not usually profiled. This means the charge can be higher or lower than the usual fee without affecting the area geographic charge percentiles maintained by Medicare and other payers.

-21 Prolonged Evaluation and Management Services

Modifier -21 reports services that take more time or are greater than the highest level E/M code in a category.

- Modifier -21 may be reported with CPT codes 99205, 99215, 99223, 99233, 99245, 99255, 99263, 99285, 99303, and 99313
- Modifier -21 is used to report physician face-to-face or floor/unit service(s); do not report with nonphysician service(s)
- Increased usual charge should be determined by the provider. (Note: an additional value for this modifier has not been established)

Payers will determine a percentage increase based upon individual contracts, medical necessity, and documentation.

Medicare and Modifier -21

The carrier will determine from review of the records if the services were appropriate.

The evaluation and management service (99205, 99215, 99223, 99233, 99245, 99255, 99263, 99285, 99303, or 99313) will be allowed and will include up to 30 minutes of time in excess of the code description. Submit a report with the claim.

-22 Unusual Procedural Services

Modifier -22 is not appropriate if "simple" is part of the code description. Rather, modifier -22 is used to indicate that a procedure was complicated, complex, difficult, or took significantly more time than usually required by the provider to complete the procedure. Documentation should be provided with the billing and kept in the medical record when this modifier is used. When modifier -22 is used, an operative report should always be attached to the claim.

Payment for modifier -22 should be 20 percent to 30 percent of the contract rate for the procedure performed. If modifier -22 is appended to a code that is not the primary code, and a modifier -51 has been appended, modifier -22 should be paid in full in addition to the cut contract rate paid for the code.

Modifier -22 often produces an automatic review or audit by payers. If the operative report attached to the claim does not indicate appropriate use of the modifier, the 20 percent to 30 percent increase in payment will be denied. The difficulty here is that the physician is not always the one who dictates operative reports, and the person who does the dictation may not realize the impact insufficient documentation has on reimbursement. Periodic orientations for all involved in the coding process are advised from both a legal and reimbursement perspective.

Because modifier -22 is often used when complications are encountered during surgical procedures, medical necessity is substantiated by additional diagnostic codes that identify the complication. These diagnostic codes should reflect the operative condition and the complication(s) encountered during the surgery.

Medicare and Modifier -22

Use of modifier -22 can be applied to all codes with a global period of 0, 10, or 90 days. It also includes services that are not surgical; for example, code 90945. Modifier -22 may generate an increased payment amount if the claim is sufficiently documented. An operative report should be submitted with the claim.

-26 Professional Component

Modifier -26 identifies the physician's component of a two-component service, usually associated with radiology services. The technical component includes reimbursement for the facility, equipment, film processing, and the technician. The professional component is reserved for the physician who interprets the procedure. See Radiology section for information regarding specific use of modifier -26 in radiology.

Medicare and Modifier -26

Modifier -26 affects the amount a provider is paid. The Medicare Fee Schedule contains different payment amounts for professional components. See Medicare RBRVS and payment components in the *Federal Register*.

-47 Anesthesia By Surgeon

Modifier -47 identifies regional or general (not local) anesthesia administered by the surgeon. The charge for anesthesia by a surgeon is usually based on time increments instead of a percentage of the total charge for the surgical service. Reimbursement policies for these situations vary dramatically. The predominant attitude of most payers is that a physician should perform the role of the operating surgeon or the anesthesiologist, but not both. Contact frequently billed payers for specific instructions.

Medicare and Modifier -47

This modifier is not a Medicare covered benefit.

-50 Bilateral Procedure

Modifier -50 identifies an identical procedure performed bilaterally during a single operative session. Depending upon payer rules, you will either have to (1) list the procedure twice and append modifier -50 to the second procedure, or (2) only list the code once with the bilateral modifier appended. Do not use modifier -50 when a procedure code description specifically states that the procedure is bilateral, such as code 58700 *Salpingectomy, complete or partial, unilateral or bilateral (separate procedure)*. Unless specified by the carrier or Medicare, do not reduce the second procedure — let the claims adjudication process reduce the procedure. There is a much greater chance that the adjudication process will apply a reduction to the procedure beyond what you have already applied than of the carrier overpaying you for the second procedure.

Medicare and Modifier -50

Comparable HCPCS Level II (Medicare) modifiers are -LT and -RT, but Medicare carriers have been directed to accept either CPT or Level II modifiers.

Bilateral procedures can be billed when the services are provided by the same surgeon, on the same patient, on the same day. Attach modifier -50 to the procedure code as a one-line item to indicate the bilateral nature of the surgery. Medicare allows payment for both procedures at a total of 150 percent of the usual amount for one procedure (200 percent for x-rays). The physician's fee should reflect this adjustment.

Some codes have the bilateral aspect built into the description. Bilateral codes receive no additional payment and may not be billed with modifier -50.

Nota Bene: Medicare and many national payers are moving toward the single line entry to identify a bilateral situation. However, careful monitoring will ensure correct reimbursement for both sides. Some payers allow 100 percent for each side if a separate incision is involved. Payers that do not allow 100 percent for the second side usually allow from 50 to 75 percent. Because of the varying allowances, monitor your reimbursement to determine the percentage allowed for the second side. When billing Medicare, special rules apply. If contracts are not specific or a contract is not in force, establish policies for handling balances above third-party payer reimbursements and make patients aware of your policies.

-51 Multiple Procedures

Modifier -51 designates multiple procedures rendered at the same operative session or on the same day. CPT states that modifier -51 should be used when a combination of surgical services, medical services, or surgical and medical services are provided. It is applicable when unrelated procedures are performed at the same operative session or when multiple related procedures are performed and there is no single inclusive code available. List the primary procedure first on the HCFA-1500 claim form, then attach modifier -51 to each secondary procedure code.

The following guidelines make good billing and coding practice for modifier -51:

- List the procedure code with the highest value first when billing Medicare and commercial payers
- List additional procedures by descending value
- Clearly state in your operative reports which procedures were accomplished through separate incisions and which were done through the same incision
- Do not combine charges when coding multiple, unrelated procedures. List each procedure separately on the claim form and indicate each charge
- If a comprehensive procedure has a single CPT code, report that code rather than "unbundling" or listing the individual components

Nota Bene: Some payers use modifier -51 to mean "through the same incision or in the same area," and use modifier -50 to mean "bilateral or when performed at the same surgical session at separate and remote sites." When reporting procedures or negotiating a contract, it is important that you know the payer's rules for these two modifiers. Payer rules should be used when a contract is in force — the way a payer has interpreted modifier rules can be an advantage to you if your billing reflects their guidelines and they are higher than average.

Medicare and Modifier -51
Multiple surgeries are separate procedures performed by a physician on the same patient at the same operative session or on the same day for which separate payment may be allowed. Co-surgeons, surgical teams, or assistants-at-surgery may participate in performing multiple surgeries on the same patient on the same day.

Multiple surgeries are distinguished from procedures that are components of or incidental to a primary procedure. These intraoperative services, incidental surgeries, or components of more major surgeries are not separately billable.

Medicare pays the lesser of the actual charge or 100 percent of the fee schedule amount for the highest priced procedure. Payment for the second highest valued procedure is based on the lesser of the actual charge or 50 percent of the fee schedule amount. Payment for the third to fifth highest valued procedure(s) is based on the lesser of the actual charges or 50 percent of the fee schedule amount. Surgical procedures beyond the fifth procedure continue to be "by report" and based on documentation of the services performed.

-52 Reduced Services
Modifier -52 identifies situations in which the physician elects to reduce or eliminate a portion of a service or procedure. Cover letters and/or operative reports are not necessary when modifier -52 is used since these claims are not usually sent to medical review. Cover letters and operative reports may even impede claims processing. However, physicians may find it helpful to provide the payer with an explanation of the reduced fee compared to the usual fee. The reduction in charge reflects the reduction or elimination of a portion of the service. Modifier -52 is used to indicate an aborted surgical procedure (e.g., code a laparotomy if that is as far as the surgery went instead of the complete procedure as it had been planned).

Medicare and Modifier -52
Modifier -52 should be billed to Medicare when appropriate. However, for exams that are considered global, this modifier is informational only and does not affect payment amount. For other situations, such as aborted procedures, a reduction in payment may occur. Under these circumstances, the service provided can be identified by its usual procedure code with modifier -52 attached. Documentation should be furnished explaining the reduction.

-54 Surgical Care Only
Modifier -54 is used when one physician performs a surgical procedure and another provides preoperative and/or postoperative management. The surgeon who performs the procedure reports modifier -54. Both physicians need to determine what percentage of the overall fee each will bill for their individual services (for example, 70 percent for the surgery and 30 percent for the postoperative care). Do not bill over 100 percent for the service provided.

Medicare and Modifier -54
Payment will be limited to the amount allotted to the preoperative and intraoperative services only. Use only with surgical codes. Medicare has split global surgery package relative values into preoperative, intraoperative, and postoperative percentages. The percentages are necessary to calculate fees when different physicians provide separate phases of care. This information is part of the Medicare Fee Schedule database and is available from your Medicare carrier.

-55 Postoperative Management Only

Modifier -55 is used when one physician provides postoperative management after another physician has performed the surgical procedure. The physician providing postoperative management bills the surgical procedure code at the percentage agreed upon (see modifier -54) with modifier -55 attached.

Medicare and Modifier -55

Payment will be limited to the amount allotted postoperative services only. (See Medicare modifier -54 for information on Medicare's split global surgery package). If more than one physician bills for the postoperative care, apportion the postoperative percentage according to the number of days each physician was responsible for the patient's care.

-62 Two Surgeons (Cosurgery)

Modifier -62 indicates that the skills of two or more surgeons (sometimes with different skills) are required to manage a specific surgical procedure. Multiple-surgeon procedures may be related or unrelated. When the procedures are unrelated, identify the separate services performed by each surgeon. List multiple related procedures as though one physician performed all procedures and add modifier -62. The surgeons should agree on charges, procedure codes, and reimbursement percentage splits prior to submission. Because of many variables, be sure to coordinate the physicians' billing and submit complete and detailed documentation. Patient knowledge of the situation is essential; inform the patient of the cosurgery aspects and the billing issues.

Medicare and Modifier -62

According to Medicare guidelines, "Cosurgery refers to a single surgical procedure which requires two surgeons. It may also apply when a surgical procedure involves two surgeons performing parts of the procedure simultaneously, e.g., heart transplant, bilateral knee replacements." Cosurgery is allowed at 125 percent of the global procedure amount divided equally between the two surgeons, so each surgeon is allowed 62.5 percent of the global surgery amount. Each surgeon bills the procedure with a modifier -62. No payment is allowed for an assistant surgeon.

-66 Surgical Team

Modifier -66 identifies complex procedures that require concomitant services. Several physicians, from the same or different specialties, other highly skilled and specially trained personnel, and different types of complex equipment may be used in the surgery. Team surgery is usually confined to organ transplants and replantations. Identify these circumstances for team surgery by listing all procedures as though performed by one physician and add modifier -66 to each procedure code used. The surgeons should agree on charges, procedure codes, and reimbursement splits prior to claims submission. Because of many variables, carefully coordinate the physicians' billing and submit complete and detailed documentation. Also, include a cover letter explaining the reimbursement distribution for each member of the team. The total of charges for all procedures performed may be increased up to 50 percent for team surgery. The reimbursement is divided among the surgeons contingent upon actual fees, complexity of procedures, and medical review.

Medicare and Modifier -66

Medicare guidelines state, "Team surgery refers to a single procedure which requires more than two surgeons of different specialties. If surgeons of different specialties are each performing a different procedure (with specific CPT codes), multiple surgery rules do not apply. If one of the surgeons performs multiple procedures, the multiple procedure pricing rule applies to that surgeon's services." Each surgeon bills the service with a modifier -66.

Carriers price this type of surgery modification "By Report." Documentation of the medical necessity for team surgeons is required for some surgeries.

-80 Assistant Surgeon

Modifier -80 identifies surgical assistant services and is applied to the surgical procedure code(s). Assisting physicians usually charge 16 percent to 30 percent of their normal fee for performing the surgery alone. Be aware that payers may use the surgeon's contract rate to figure the assistant's percentage and usually will not pay a resident for an assistant surgeon fee.

Although this modifier is usually preferred by most payers to report assistant surgeon, always monitor EOBs and keep a list of carrier preferences.

Medicare and Modifier -80

Medicare restricts the use of this modifier to the primary procedure performed. Where payment for an assistant surgeon is allowed, payment is based on 16 percent of the fee schedule payment amount.

Medicare publishes a list of procedures which specifies (1) procedures where a surgical assist is allowed, (2) procedures where a surgical assist is not allowed and payment will be denied (and the patient cannot be billed for the assistant surgeon charge), and (3) procedures where surgical assist might be allowed upon carrier review.

Ask your Medicare carrier for a copy of the assistant surgeon list.

-81 Minimum Assistant Surgeon

Modifier -81 identifies minimal surgical assistant services. Minimal assistant surgeons usually charge from 10 percent to 15 percent for their services. This modifier is frequently used to indicate that a nurse or other nonphysician provided the assist. Be aware that not all payers will allow this modifier to be used for that purpose. Always bill for nonphysician assistants at surgery as instructed by the payer. Be sure to negotiate a contract percentage rate for this modifier. Track reimbursement from all payers to determine how your charge for this service is being paid and adjust as appropriate.

Medicare and Modifier -81

Medicare does not recognize modifier -81.

-82 Assistant Surgeon (when qualified resident surgeon not available)

Modifier -82 identifies situations when a qualified resident is unavailable to assist in surgery and another physician must be brought in to assist. Assisting physicians usually charge 16 percent to 30 percent of their normal fee for performing the surgery alone. Be aware that modifier -80 is used more frequently than modifier -82 by surgeon assistants. Bill according to the payer's rules for assistant surgery modifiers.

Medicare and Modifier -82

Refer to modifier -80 above for assistant surgeon guidelines.

Modifiers That May Not Affect Reimbursement

Modifiers that may not affect reimbursement, depending on the payer, include:

- -20 Microsurgery
- -23 Unusual Anesthesia
- -56 Preoperative Management Only
- -78 Return to the Operating Room for a Related Procedure During the Postoperative Period

-20 Microsurgery

Modifier -20 identifies surgical services performed with an operating microscope. This modifier is not appropriate with use of a magnifying surgical loupe or eyeglasses. Reimbursement policies for modifier -20 vary among payers; some allow a percentage (20 percent to 30 percent) of the surgical fee as increased reimbursement, while others base additional reimbursement on the actual time spent using the operating microscope.

Note the following in regard to modifier -20:

- The use of an operating microscope should only be recognized as an additional service with procedures where its use is documented
- Modifier -20 is not appropriate with codes that already include the term "operating microscope." For example, 31526 *Laryngoscopy direct, with or without tracheoscopy; diagnostic, with operating microscope* has a relative value adjusted to reflect the additional time and skill required associated with the use of an operating microscope

Modifier -20 is not appropriate if microsurgery is not warranted for performance of a specific procedure; for example, with 11401 *Excision, benign lesion, except skin tag (unless listed elsewhere), trunk, arms, legs; lesion diameter 0.6 to 1.0 cm.*

Modifier -20 is not appropriate when the use of an operating microscope is inherent. For example, the codes for ocular surgery, inner ear and middle ear, should not be reported with modifier -20, nor should codes 61712 *Microdissection, intracranial or spinal procedure (list separately in addition to code for primary repair)* or 64830 *Microdissection and/or microrepair of nerve (list separately in addition to code for nerve repair)* or 64727 *Internal neurolysis, requiring use of operating microscope (list separately in addition to code for neuroplasty) (Neuroplasty includes external neurolysis).*

Reimbursement for modifier -20 may be based on either a variable percentage increase (typically 20 percent) for the procedure(s) performed with the use of an operating microscope, or an assigned dollar amount based on increments of time (e.g., $100 per hour for time spent using the operating microscope).

In multiple surgery situations modifier -20 should only be appended to the code(s) where microsurgery was performed.

Medicare and Modifier -20

Modifier -20 does not affect the level of reimbursement allowed by Medicare.

-23 Unusual Anesthesia

Modifier -23 is not appropriate with codes that state "without anesthesia" in the code description, nor with codes that report procedures or services usually performed under general anesthesia.

Modifier -23 is appropriate with codes that report procedures or services usually performed under local anesthesia.

-56 Preoperative Management Only

Modifier -56 identifies the physician providing preoperative care during the preoperative time clause established by the payer but not performing the actual surgery. Use this modifier only with codes from the Surgery and Medicine sections of CPT. It does not appear in the guidelines of the evaluation and management codes.

Medicare and Modifier -56

Medicare does not recognize the use of modifier -56.

-78 Return to the Operating Room for a Related Procedure During the Postoperative Period

Modifier -78 reports related procedures performed in the operating room within the assigned postoperative period of a surgical procedure. CPT does not specify that the related procedure be performed by the initial physician.

Medicare and Modifier -78

When an unlisted procedure is billed because no code exists to describe the treatment for complications, base payment on a maximum of 50 percent of the value of the intra-operative services originally performed. If multiple surgeries were originally performed, base payment on no more than 50 percent of the value of the intra-operative services of the surgery for which the complications occurred.

INFORMATIONAL MODIFIERS

The following modifiers are informational in nature and do not affect reimbursement. Since payers generally do not have specific guidelines for these modifiers, you must bill them consistently. Monitor the reimbursements received when using these modifiers.

- -24 Unrelated Evaluation and Management Service by the Same Physician During a Postoperative Period
- -25 Significant, Separately Identifiable Evaluation and Management Service by the Same Physician on the Day of a Procedure (This modifier may allow additional reimbursement when submitted to Medicare.)
- -32 Mandated Services
- -57 Decision for Surgery
- -58 Staged or Related Procedure or Service by the Same Physician During the Postoperative Period
- -76 Repeat Procedure by Same Physician
- -77 Repeat Procedure by Another Physician
- -79 Unrelated Procedure or Service by the Same Physician During the Postoperative Period
- -90 Reference (Outside) Laboratory
- -99 Multiple Modifiers

-24 Unrelated Evaluation and Management Service by the Same Physician During a Postoperative Period

Modifier -24 should be billed with an E/M code. Do not use this modifier with a CPT surgical code. Assign the proper E/M code and amount as appropriate for service rendered.

Medicare and Modifier -24

This modifier has no effect on the Medicare payment amount and should be used only with E/M codes. Use modifier -24 to indicate that an E/M service performed during the postoperative period was not related to the original procedure.

-25 Significant, Separately Identifiable Evaluation and Management Service by the Same Physician on the Same Day of the Procedure or Other Service

This modifier is not appropriate with an E/M code that has a minimum level of service. Assign the proper E/M code and amount as appropriate for service rendered. Most payers will allow payment for significant E/M services on the day of a procedure. Documentation of unusual circumstances should be submitted with the claim.

Medicare and Modifier -25

Modifier -25 is used to report that on the day a procedure was performed, the patient's condition required significant, separately identifiable E/M service above and beyond the usual pre- and postoperative care associated with the procedure.

-32 Mandated Services

Modifier -32 identifies services that are mandated by Medicare, a peer review organization, a state, local, or government agency, and private payers. Reimbursement may be made at 100 percent of the allowable amount for the service or procedure (such as confirmatory consultations and related diagnostic services). Deductibles or copayments may also be waived by the payer. Keep in mind, however, that not all payers cover services when they are mandated and often expect the government agency to pay for the service (e.g., an examination to determine abuse/rape).

Medicare and Modifier -32

Mandated services have no effect on Medicare's payment amount.

-57 Decision For Surgery

Modifier -57 identifies an evaluation and management service that resulted in the initial decision to perform surgery. Even though modifier -57 is included in the guidelines for E/M, Surgery, and Medicine services, it should only be reported with E/M codes. Because CPT does not designate whether the surgery decided upon is major or minor, diagnostic or therapeutic, use modifier -57 to identify when the decision for any surgery is made.

Note the following in regard to Modifier -57:

- Use modifier -57 in cases in which the decision for surgery was made during the preoperative period of a nonstarred surgical procedure
- The provider may use modifier -57, regardless of when the surgical procedure is performed, to ensure that it is always used during the preoperative period
- Payers may allow payment for the E/M service when it occurs prior to the preoperative period of the surgery based on individual contracts, medical necessity, and/or the level of intensity of the service provided
- Modifier -57 may be used with E/M visits furnished during the global period of minor procedures (0 to 10 day global)
- Providers rarely need to report modifier -57 to identify that the decision for surgery was made during the preoperative period of a minor procedure. Many payers do not have preoperative time clauses assigned to minor procedures
- Providers are more likely to use modifier -25 to identify that a significant, separately reportable E/M service was provided on the same day a minor procedure was performed

Medicare and Modifier -57

Modifier -57 replaces HCPCS alpha-numeric modifier QI (decision for major surgery).

Modifier -57 should be used only in cases in which the decision for surgery was made during the preoperative period (the day before and the day of) a major surgical procedure (procedures with 90 days of follow-up).

Modifier -57 should not be used with E/M visits furnished during the global period of minor procedures (0 to 10 day global) unless the purpose of the visit was to make the decision for major surgery. Use modifier -25 to report a significant, separately identifiable evaluation and management service by the same physician on the day of a procedure.

-58 Staged Procedure or Service by the Same Physician During the Postoperative Period

When reporting modifier -58, the physician may need to indicate that the procedure or service was: (1) planned prospectively at the time of the original procedure, or staged, (2) more extensive than the original procedure, or (3) for therapy following a diagnostic surgical procedure. Do not use this modifier to report the treatment of a problem that requires a return to the operating room (see modifier -78). Modifier -58 is included in the guidelines for E/M, Surgery, Radiology, and Medicine services.

Note the following in regard to modifier -58:

- Do not use Modifier -79 (Unrelated Procedure or Service by the Same Physician During the Postoperative Period) with CPT codes to report staged procedures
- The existence of CPT modifier -58 does not negate the global fee concept; therefore, services that are included in CPT as multiple sessions or are otherwise defined as including multiple services or events may not be billed with this modifier
- Modifier -58 should not alter the amount charged or paid for subsequent unrelated or staged procedures performed during the postoperative period of a previous procedure. Modifier -78 may drive a reduction because it is for management of a resulting complication of the previous procedure

Medicare and Modifier -58

This modifier does not affect Medicare payment. Use only on surgery codes to indicate a related surgery that is due to a progression of the disease.

-76 Repeat Procedure By Same Physician

Modifier -76 indicates that a basic procedure with no follow-up days had to be repeated by the same physician. Use this modifier to identify the procedure as a repeat rather than a duplicate service or billing error. Payers may require additional documentation to establish medical necessity. Modifier -76 is easily misused, so note the following applications of other modifiers:

- A staged or related procedure or service by the same physician during the postoperative period is reported with modifier -58
- A return to the operating room for a related procedure during the postoperative period is reported with modifier -78
- An unrelated procedure or service by the same physician during the postoperative period is reported with modifier -79

Medicare and Modifier -76

This modifier does not affect Medicare payment; it is used for informational purposes only.

-77 Repeat Procedure by Another Physician

Modifier -77 indicates that a basic procedure performed by one physician was repeated by a different physician. This modifier is usually used during the postoperative period of the basic procedure. The second physician adds the modifier to the procedure code used by the first physician.

It is appropriate to use modifier -22 when the procedure is unusually complicated, or modifier -52 when only a portion of the procedure is repeated. The ICD-9 diagnostic codes must substantiate the medical necessity of repeating the procedure. Because payers often require additional documentation to establish medical necessity, it is advisable to submit the operative report with a cover letter.

Medicare and Modifier -77
This modifier does not affect Medicare payment; it is used for informational purposes only.

-79 Unrelated Procedure or Service by the Same Physician During the Postoperative Period
Modifier -79 was added to CPT to notify payers that the procedure was performed during a postoperative period of another procedure but is not related to that surgery. The diagnostic codes must document the medical necessity of the service, so the ICD-9 codes are usually different for this service from those reported with the initial procedure. Do not use modifier -79 to report staged or related procedures or services performed by the same physician during the assigned postoperative period of a procedure.

Medicare and Modifier -79
This modifier has no effect on the Medicare payment amount. Use only on surgical codes. Payment will not be allowed for this service without use of the modifier.

-90 Reference (Outside) Laboratory
Modifier -90 identifies laboratory procedures performed by a party other than the treating or reporting physician. HMOs and private payers will often allow a fee for a blood draw (arterial and/or venous) and a fee for transport to an outside facility. Use codes 99000–99001 to report this type of service — not modifier -90.

Medicare and Modifier -90
Do not report this modifier on Medicare claims; the performing laboratory should bill Medicare directly.

-99 Multiple Modifiers
Modifier -99 identifies circumstances when two or more modifiers are necessary to delineate a service. Attach modifier -99 to the procedure code and list all appropriate modifiers as subsequent line items.

Medicare and Modifier -99
Enter all applicable modifiers when modifier -99 is used. If modifier -99 is entered on multiple line items of a single claim form, all applicable modifiers for each line item containing a -99 modifier should be listed as follows: 1= (mod). Here, "1" represents the line item and "mod" represents all modifiers applicable to the referenced line item.

Unlisted Procedures
Each section of CPT — Evaluation and Management, Anesthesiology, Surgery, Radiology, Pathology and Laboratory, and Medicine — contains unlisted procedure codes. Use these codes when the overall procedure and outcome of the surgery is not adequately described by an existing code. If an existing CPT description closely describes the procedure performed, report that code with modifier -22 Unusual Services or -52 Reduced Services.

Unlisted codes are billed "by report," and extensive documentation is required for proper reimbursement. Insurance claims with unlisted codes take longer to process since they are usually sent to medical review for individual consideration. Include cover notes and comprehensive operative reports in the claims submission. Documentation should include:

- A definition or description of the nature, extent, and medical necessity for the procedure
- A statement of the time and effort necessary to provide the service
- A comparison of the procedure to existing procedure codes and descriptions

Reimbursement Issues

SETTING MEDICAL FEES

Healthcare providers have some flexibility when setting private fees. Unlike Medicare, private payers employ a variety of payment methodologies and generally do not establish limiting charges. By choosing a pricing philosophy, gathering available charge information, developing a pricing strategy, and conducting an impact analysis, you can establish an equitable and rational fee schedule for your office. Establishing fees based on measurable work performed, standard decision-making processes, a national fee comparison, and exposure to risk — rather than on the type of guesswork that spawns erratic fees — will help generate proper reimbursement.

Step 1: Choose several commonly performed services and compare your current fees to the fee ranges presented in this book.

Step 2: If your fees are dramatically higher or lower than those offered here, you may want to adjust them accordingly. Before adjusting your fees, however, consider the following:

- How will the new fees compare with what payers are willing to reimburse?
- How will your patients react to a change in charges?
- Do the new fees accurately reflect the cost and worth of your services?
- Realize that you may be restricted in adjusting some fees by the Medicare Fee Schedule limiting charge, PPO and HMO schedules, as well as workers' compensation schedules.

Step 3: After evaluating your fees using the criteria in step two, make the necessary adjustments and prepare a list of your updated fees.

Do not simply select a given percentile and assume that it will translate into an appropriate fee in your practice. For example, if the financial and marketing goals of your practice call for mid-range fees, compare your current fee schedule to the area's 50th percentile. You may find several charges that fall well below the area 50th percentile requiring gradual adjustment up to a more acceptable level. However, other fees may exceed the 75th percentile and require adjustment downward. The resulting fee schedule diminishes your patient's out-of-pocket expenses while placing your new charges in the "safety zone" for acceptance and payment by most commercial and managed care payers.

CHOOSE A PRICING PHILOSOPHY FOR FEES

Two basic pricing philosophies are seen in medical fees: a market-driven approach and a relative value approach.

Market Driven Fees

The market-driven approach, known also as UCR (usual, customary, reasonable) ties medical prices to the perceived skills and respective charges found within a pool of providers. Under a market-driven approach, fees stay current with industry trends as they emerge in the local community. A market-driven fee schedule relies partially on the assumption that patients are price-sensitive and aware of cost differences among physicians.

Relative Values

With a relative value approach, fees are tied to the intrinsic "worth" of a procedure and are structured according to the physician skill, time, and risk involved in rendering the service. A relative value approach facilitates the pricing of new and emerging procedures and services that have little or no historic market charge data. Relative values are easy to use and the methodologies behind relative value studies are accepted by most private payers.

Blending Philosophies

Carefully consider the advantages and disadvantages of each approach when selecting a pricing philosophy. One option is to blend data from both market and relative value sources. Many practices adopt a market-driven philosophy and "gap fill" with relative value fees, or use relative values to correct discrepancies in market-based fees.

AREA CHARGE INFORMATION

To learn what private payers are authorizing for reimbursement, look at your charge information. The information gathering process can usually begin in your office files. Charge information specific to your area and practice is of greatest value. The data listed below can be found in most offices; arranging it together will give you a picture of pricing strengths and weaknesses.

- Begin with your current fee schedule
- Get the Medicare Fee Schedule amount for participating or nonparticipating physicians from your local carrier
- If participating in a managed care group, ask for the HMO/PPO fee schedule
- Obtain from the state's workers' compensation division or industrial commission a fee schedule or relative value study with the specific conversion factor for your area
- Ask colleagues what they charge, but keep in mind that this may result in subjective estimates; remember, too, that setting prices in collusion with colleagues is illegal

Notice that most of the fees cluster around an average number. A few fees, called "outliers," may be exceedingly high or low. Outliers usually reflect an error in the data, such as an incorrect use of the code, and should be discarded.

Once the available charge information has been analyzed, the next step is to develop a pricing strategy.

DEVELOPING A PRICING STRATEGY

Regardless of which pricing philosophy you choose, develop a pricing strategy. Consider the following guidelines when developing fees:

- Compile available area charge data into high, low, and middle ranges
- Determine where your practice should be relative to the market — at the higher end (75th–95th percentile) or the lower end (40th–50th percentile)
- Compare current fees to the compiled charge data. Do the fees fall above, below, or within the designated range? If existing fees lie above the designated percentile but are being reimbursed by private payers, consider retaining them
- Consider pricing on an individual basis those services a patient is likely to "shop" for, such as new patient office visits

With a market-driven pricing philosophy, the fee schedule is complete once your practice gathers and analyzes available charge data and develops a pricing strategy. If your pricing philosophy relies on a relative value approach, calculate an average conversion factor — a monetary figure that is calculated by dividing the current fee (or a fee based on compiled charge data) by a relative value from a relative value study. Use this average conversion factor to turn relative units into fees for given services. The average conversion factor calculated for E/M services should not be used to develop fees for other sections of CPT, such as Surgery, because of differences in work, risk, and skill.

CONDUCTING AN IMPACT ANALYSIS

After your fees are established, an impact analysis can help determine whether the new fees achieve the desired annual financial goals. Compare the new fee schedule amounts with your practice's existing fee schedule and/or the area charge data gathered. Established fees should be:

- No lower than the dollar amount calculated using the conversion factor, unless competitive pricing demands such a fee
- Competitive with area fees, unless physician skill or expertise justifies a significantly higher fee
- Reflective of general administrative expenses, practice costs, and desirable profit

SUMMARY CHECKLIST

- ❑ Check your fees twice each year. Because the healthcare marketplace is so volatile, this check will help you avoid over- or underpricing your services
- ❑ Develop and maintain a tracking system for claims to ensure accurate reimbursement
- ❑ Medicare continually changes its reimbursement methodology. Stay informed of these developments and remember that the Medicode Helpline is a source for understanding how Medicare works
- ❑ Please note that the *Fee & Coding Standard* is not a fee schedule, but a useful tool to assist you in fee comparisons and determining an equitable fee for a specific procedure

CONTRACTS

Other issues besides clinical coding and setting fees can affect reimbursement in a practice. Contracts, whether or not to sign with a PPO or HMO, capitation, etc., are some issues worth consideration for most healthcare practitioners. This chapter addresses noncoding elements associated with achieving fair and adequate reimbursement for medical services rendered.

Due to enormous changes in healthcare, many practitioners have found it worthwhile to contract with more than one payer. These can be health maintenance organizations (HMOs), preferred provider organizations (PPOs), independent practice associations (IPAs), managed care organizations, capitated plans, self-funded plans, Medicare, and a variety of other types of payers. One of the most important things any practitioner can do is to take time to review existing contracts with the office staff. Be certain everyone understands the differences between the contractual arrangements currently in place and those likely to be negotiated in the future. The following information may help in this process.

RISK CONTRACT

A risk contract is an agreement between payers and a physician or group of physicians. The physician or group gets paid a set amount for providing care of a patient base. If costs exceed the amount negotiated, patients still receive care during the term of the contract, but this can affect adversely the reimbursement due to the practice or group. If the cost for care of the patient base is lower than the negotiated amount, the practice/group benefits. Some payers pay a bonus for coming in under the contracted amount of the plan since they will not have to raise significantly the amount of the next contract (e.g., over the medical inflation rate, plus a negotiated percentage).

HMO (Health Maintenance Organization)

An HMO health plan typically uses primary care physicians as "gatekeepers," with the emphasis on preventive care. Utilization of services is the key to their profit margin, and referrals are sent to other provider specialists who are also contracted with the payer. (Nearly all of the providers use ancillary services such as radiology, laboratory, home health, and hospitals that have favorable contracts with the payer).

PPO (Preferred Provider Organization)

Preferred provider plans contract with providers on a discounted basis. Members must stay within the plan or pay a significant co-payment — sometimes as much as 50 percent. The increased co-pay takes risk away from the payer, who may not be contracted with the out of plan provider, hospital, and/or the ancillary service resources it uses. The PPO panel of providers may have a risk or nonrisk contract with the payer. PPOs are frequently set up and marketed by a third-party group. The panel of providers each pay a set amount for them to negotiate contracts, settle disputes, and provide some administrative functions.

IPA (Independent Practice Association)

An IPA organization is made up of providers and groups who contract with payers at a discounted fee-for-service, capitated, or set amount risk contract. The group of providers may market themselves as a group, and perform their own administrative functions. Payers may also set up an IPA from a panel of contracted providers. In either case, several members of the panel serve at one time as a committee that regularly meets with payer representatives to settle provider or payer problems, sanction providers within the group, add or delete panel members, and re-negotiate the contract.

Managed Care

Managed care involves the concept of managing a case while in progress to ensure care is the most appropriate, efficient, and cost effective (which is not always the least expensive). Contracted physicians participate in the management of health care costs, and bonus systems may be in place if the plan is cost-effective. Utilization, prior authorization, and cost containment are key components of managed care. The care may be provided by HMO, PPO, IPA, or other contracted providers.

Capitated Plan

Capitation is a system in which a set amount of money is received or paid out based on membership — per member per month (PMPM) — rather than on the number of services rendered. All of the payer's membership may be capitated with a provider/group or a capitated area, such as an assigned geographical area. If a geographical area is assigned and the provider(s) sees a member who is not within the assigned criteria, the provider may (1) not be paid for seeing the member, or (2) be paid at a discounted fee-for-service or other pre-negotiated amount.

RBRVS (Resource Based Relative Value Scale)

This type of contract is based on a relative value scale originally developed by Harvard University for use by HCFA for Medicare. The scale assigns value to procedures by their resource relatedness rather than based on historical data. Many managed care payers are currently negotiating contracts that use the RBRVS because it is easy to obtain. They may use different conversion factors. (See RBRVS below for more information on this type of contract).

Medicare and Medicaid

Medicare is the national program that provides medical care to the elderly and qualified disabled persons, and Medicaid is a federal-state health insurance program for qualified low-income individuals and families.

CHAMPUS (Civilian Health Medical Program of the Uniformed Services)
CHAMPUS is a federal medical benefits reimbursement program for dependents of military personnel, military retirees, and others.

Flat Rate
As the name implies, this arrangement is a set amount paid for a service, regardless of the cost of the actual service. Payers contract with providers to render services to their members at a flat rate. The reason providers are willing to accept this type of contract is simple: large payer organizations have huge patient bases that will significantly add to the number of patients the provider will have available to see.

Self-Insured/Self-Funded Plans
In these plans the risk is assumed by the employer rather than an insurer, although they may use a third-party administrator to administer the plan (pay claims, etc.).

Nota Bene: Self-insured policies are exempt from state regulation. If a self-insured policy denies your claim, it falls under the jurisdiction of the U.S. Department of Labor's Pension and Welfare Benefits Administration. The administration has regional offices to arbitrate claims. To find the number of your pension and welfare benefits administration regional office, call 1–800–359–3997.

FFS (Fee For Service)
In a fee-for-service plan the payer does not have a contract with the provider and must pay full charges for medical services rendered to its members.

In addition to the above plans, there are many that are a combination of several types of contracts, some even paying a percentage of a DRG contract for hospital-based services. Do your homework before committing to any plan.

THE BIG TWO: RBRVS AND CAPITATION
Currently, two types of contracts are especially popular with payers today — the Resource Based Relative Value Scale (RBRVS) and capitation. The following discussion provides more detail and a better understanding of some of the advantages of these contracts.

RBRVS
A giant transformation not seen since 1992 is occurring in physician offices across the country. The Resource Based Relative Value Scale (RBRVS), adopted by HCFA as part of the Medicare Fee Schedule, is now being utilized by payers to establish their own fee schedules for use in contracting with providers. Up to 75 percent of non-Medicare payers are currently or will soon be using RBRVS. While many payers establish their own conversion factors to be used with the RBRVS (often higher than Medicare's), others use the Medicare conversion factors. How this new wave of payer contracting might affect your practice depends on how prepared you are when RBRVS comes knocking at your door.

Initially, payers may have set up RBRVS fee schedules in order to compare prices with Medicare; the price comparison was often used to detect possible cost shifting by providers as Medicare started using RBRVS. But it didn't take long for payers to realize that RBRVS spelled the opportunity of using a low cost, easily accessed and converted relative value study that was accepted for use by one of the countries largest payers — Medicare.

The use of RBRVS by non-Medicare payers has been in two forms, each with its own set of rewards or drawbacks, depending upon whether you are on the provider or payer side. The advantages and disadvantages can be seen in the following discussion.

The RBRVS Fee Schedule with a Payer or Medicare's Conversion Factor
Advantages

Payer

- RBRVS is resource based and accepted by Medicare
- Published and updated in the *Federal Register*, the fee schedule represents a small charge if purchased (the *Federal Register* on diskette costs $20 for a personal computer and $8 for a printed copy.) A national tape costs approximately $1,100 for fee schedule transition to national locality specific pricing for every state and includes carrier, locality, procedure, and modifier information. There is also a tape available for $400 that lists relative value units and the national Medicare edits
- Comparison with existing fee schedules is relatively simple. Although it is time consuming it is well worth the effort, especially for large payers
- It adapts easily to a spreadsheet format so that different conversion factors can be inserted and changed as necessary, depending upon specialty and other factors
- More contracts using the same fee schedule allows easier access when trying to locate specialty-specific conversion factors in databases. A significant amount of time is saved over dealing with several different fee schedules and conversion factors
- It can be used as a national fee schedule instead of just in a local area

Provider

- It is a fee schedule that is familiar to providers and is currently used by Medicare for compensation
- Published and updated in the *Federal Register*, the fee schedule is easy to access for a reasonable fee
- Comparison with a provider's current fee schedule is relatively simple if the provider has the personnel to do the work (or, an RBRVS conversion can be purchased). However, some conversion will be necessary with any product
- Can be updated by the provider quickly, especially if entered into a spreadsheet format
- It is advantageous to a provider when most contracts are based on the same fee schedule by making it easier to compare reimbursement from various payers and to assign an equitable conversion factor

Disadvantages
Payer

- Providers may be suspicious of the fee schedule if they do not have the time and resources available to do fee schedule comparisons
- Questions from providers about the compensation and coding rules associated with the Medicare RBRVS fee schedule may slow down the processing of claims
- It is difficult to get providers to accept RBRVS if the Medicare conversion factor is used because of the low reimbursement rate
- Providers who do accept the fee schedule may feel they are being inadequately reimbursed and have bad feelings about the payer when asked to accept Medicare rates, especially if they are in an area where an HMO has a large member base. Providers may feel they are forced to accept the Medicare rate, or wind up without enough patients to keep their practice viable

Provider

- Providers may not have personnel available for the labor intensive time required to do the fee schedule comparison
- The negotiated contract may only be updated yearly and, depending upon the payer, may be late in being updated (even though Medicare publishes quarterly updates)
- Providers seldom have the resources (e.g., information) that large payers have, such as the average conversion factor for a given specialty in a community. Thus, providers do not know where they stand in relationship to other providers in the same specialty and are often left with taking the payer's word that the proposed reimbursement rate is fair.
- Providers feel that if payers base fee schedules on the RBRVS they should also adopt Medicare's payment guidelines. Otherwise, providers may feel that payers are not only reimbursing at a low rate, but that they are also taking advantage of old global surgery and other rules which further discount the services providers perform. They do not necessarily understand that RBRVS is a relative value study and was only adopted by Medicare; the fee schedule did not have Medicare's coding guidelines with it. They were added after for their own use
- Primary care and other providers with RBRVS contracts based totally on Medicare, including the Medicare conversion factor, may feel that they should also be able to utilize Medicare's payment guidelines, especially those that deal with modifiers and the global surgery rule

How to Convert a Fee Schedule to RBRVS

Chances are good that many contracts offered in the future will be based on RBRVS. The best thing healthcare providers can do to make sure they are adequately compensated is to prepare ahead and have a RBRVS "crosswalk" in place.

RBRVS Crosswalk

A crosswalk is one method to determine how a practice might be affected by an RBRVS contract. It allows providers to compare fees between the type of fee schedule they are using now and one based on RBRVS. The best way to make the comparison is to enter your current fee schedule in a software spreadsheet program, then add other columns with RBRVS data and compare them. Current contracted fee rates can also be added to allow an overall comparison to RBRVS. Use column A to represent the code, column B the code description, column C the RBRVS relative value units (read carefully to make sure you include all of the factors built into the relative value units (i.e., work, etc.), leave column D blank to insert a conversion factor, and in column E insert your present fee for service rate (rounded to the nearest dollar). To arrive at the conversion factor, divide the fee in column E by the RBRVS/RVUs.

Example

A	B	C	D	E
Code	Code Desc.	RBRVS/RVUs	Conv. Factor	Your Fee
99201	OFF/OUTPT EXAM	.79	72.15	$57
99202	OFF/OUTPT EXAM	1.25	72.80	$91
99203	OFF/OUTPT EXAM	.72	72.68	$125
99211	OFF/OUTPT EXAM	.38	73.69	$28
99212	OFF/OUTPT EXAM	.68	72.06	$49
99213	OFF/OUTPT EXAM	.96	2.92	$70

At this point, unused columns to the right of your fee can be used to list other contracts. Leave a blank column (column F) to figure the conversion factor; be sure to enter the same code for the contract you are checking. In column G list the payer contract fee, then divide the fee by the RBRVS/RVUs to fill in column F. To find the percentage being paid at the contract rate divide your fee by the payer contract fee. In the example listed below, payment would be at 79 percent of your fee for service charge.

To find the percentage you are being paid per contract over what you are charging:

Example

A	F	G	H
Code	Conv. Factor	Payer Contract Fee	% Contract Payment
99201	54.43	$43	79%

Contracts based on RBRVS can have a tremendous impact on profitability. To ensure the impact will be a good one, be prepared for potential changes. Knowing your rates and how any contract might affect them is important, especially when a large shift to this type of contract may be imminent. Figure the different fees based on RBRVS, then determine the appropriate conversion factor. In other words, use your new information to negotiate the best contract possible.

Capitation

Many managed care and other payers are negotiating contracts that are based on the number of members assigned to them instead of the number of members they actually see. This type of contract is called a "capitated" contract. In this type of arrangement, the physician or a group of physicians is assigned a number of members who belong to a certain insurance plan. Depending upon the plan, the provider may be responsible for the emergency care of all members of the plan or, if the members are spread in different locations, they may be responsible for part of the members in the group (in which case the membership may be divided by zip codes or other methods of determining the capitated [per head] group membership).

Providers are paid a set amount of money per member per month (PMPM), whether or not they see the member for care during the month. The providers may also be responsible for the emergency care of the assigned group and, depending upon the plan, may be responsible for members who go out of plan (e.g., the member is on vacation and needs emergency services). In such a situation, the amount paid by the payer for the out-of-plan expense may be deducted from the capitated rate paid to the provider during the month the out-of-plan expense was incurred. Some plans may take into account different factors, such as the age of the plan members (which may affect the utilization of emergency services), when they compute the amount that will be paid for each member.

Effects of Capitation on Providers

Depending upon several different factors, providers can be affected positively or negatively by signing a capitated agreement. Some of these factors include:

Billing of Services

Individual billing of services is often eliminated. In its place, utilization tracking by use of a computer generated list of the member, member plan identification number, date of service, the normal CPT code that would have been assigned for the service to the member if they were not capitated, and the physician's normal fee for the service may be employed.

This tracking allows the payer and provider to determine if the capitated rate needs to be adjusted higher or lower for the next contract period.

Monthly Capitated Payment

In a capitated plan, payment is generally made monthly by check for a set amount for each member as defined in the agreement. Providers may also be eligible to bill the plan separately for any members given care who are not within their assigned membership (e.g., not within the assigned zip code or other area definition of the plan). The rate, prior authorization requirements, time period for payment of claims, and any restrictions to seeing these members should be clearly defined in the contract.

When capitated, providers may also be responsible for members who go out of plan. The amount, if any, which will be withheld from the capitated payment should also be negotiated and then clearly defined in the contract. Keep in mind that when members are seen outside of the payer's normal area of operation, the services will frequently be paid at a fee-for-service rate because the provider most likely will not be contracted.

One advantage of capitation which should be mentioned here is the cash flow this type of agreement can generate. It is an amount the provider can rely on each month, give or take a few members.

Prior Authorization

In a capitated agreement, prior authorization of services is eliminated — unless the patient is admitted as an inpatient or the member is out of the plan capitated area.

Number of Members Assigned to Providers

The number of members assigned to the provider is an important element in a capitated agreement. If the membership is too low, the provider may not be able to provide adequate care for the patients on the amount received as a capitated payment. Certain key expenses, such as malpractice expense (if self-paid), may make the payment too low. Also, the number of members can fluctuate each month as members change jobs/plans or during the payer's open enrollment periods (generally, this is not a significant issue). Before signing on, ask the payer for the membership enrollment history and negotiate a stop loss number of members.

Amount the Provider Is Paid PMPM

Obviously, the rate of PMPM payment must be at a certain level for a provider to be able to render services and stay in business. Keep in mind that capitated rates can seem low when they are first looked at especially in certain specialty areas.

Capitated payments are usually calculated in cents. Multiply the number of members times the payment for each member in the plan to determine the amount that will be paid.

Utilization Patterns of the Plan Group

When contracting using capitation, the provider usually does not have a database that indicates the utilization patterns of the proposed plan group. This is one area that is very important for the provider to scrutinize closely since it is generally the payer who provides this information. Know the payer well. How much capitated experience has it had in the past? Does it have a good reputation for making timely payments? Are they able to show utilization patterns for the group? (Try negotiating a penalty fee for payments not made or postmarked within a specified period of time.) There are many factors that can affect how well the capitated arrangement works out.

Consider, too, that while some members would never use an emergency provider unless the condition is life threatening, others will use the emergency room for almost all services.

When negotiating the set amount for the plan, it is a good idea to contract for a prearranged amount to be added or an early renegotiation clause should costs exceed the capitated agreement to a significant degree.

Member Co-pays

Member co-pays may be collected in capitated plans, though the co-pays may be split between the facility and the provider, and as such are not typically a consideration (because of the small amount) in the contract agreement unless there are unusual circumstances.

Facility Location and Fees

Facility location and fees may be a consideration when deciding on a capitated agreement. How well the administrators of the facility get along with the payer, the location and ease of access for members to the facility, and the control the payer exerts over the utilization of services at emergency rooms (e.g., it may lower the number of emergency visits and the per member payment) are factors to be kept in mind. Generally, payers try to contract with emergency room providers based in a facility that their members frequently use; they may also contract with the facility, not just with the provider.

Summary of Capitation

Capitated agreements can make good business sense and save a great deal of time and consternation in billing, prior authorization, payment for services, and a host of other issues. Be sure you understand this type of contract. Many providers who are prepared seem to like this type of contractual agreement.

AUDITING

Another important element in the overall reimbursement and practice management process is auditing; which should include auditing yourself as well as understanding what happens when you are audited.

Auditing Your Charts

The medical record serves a variety of purposes and is essential to the proper functioning of any medical practice — especially in today's complicated healthcare environment. Charts should detail information pertinent to the care of the patient, document the performance of reportable services, and serve as a legal document that describes a course of treatment. Periodic audits help ensure that the record adequately serves these purposes.

Auditing charts can be a valuable learning experience; it helps in assessing the completeness of the medical record and the accuracy of the physician's documentation, and may turn up sources of and reasons for lost revenue. An auditor, whether an employee or a hired consultant, examines the documentation to determine whether or not it adequately substantiates the service reported and identifies the medical necessity. Check charts on an ongoing basis for incorrect or inappropriate documentation and coding practices, as well as to determine areas of noncompliance with government and private payer guidelines.

Audit Objectives

Before performing a chart audit, identify specific goals by dividing the audit objectives into two main categories: revenue and compliance.

Revenue

An audit's revenue objectives involve examining coding practices for lost revenue due to the improper use of codes. This process can also reveal inappropriate reporting to increase reimbursement — an open invitation for a payer audit. When considering revenue, look at nonreported services, overreported or underreported services, undocumented services, and denied or downcoded services.

- *Nonreported Services*. Compare the medical record to what was actually reported to identify services that are documented in the medical record but may not have been coded. This is often caused by ineffective communication between the clinicians and the billing staff or a lack of knowledge on the part of the coders.
- *Overreported or Underreported Services*. As with nonreported services, the search for over- or under-reported services begins with comparing the chart documentation to the reported codes. All services, including evaluation and management and surgical

procedures, should be explained in sufficient detail in the documentation to allow coders to choose the proper code.

- *Undocumented Services*. A good audit will identify instances in which codes are reported without proper supporting documentation. When a payer, either Medicare or a private insurance company, requests written proof of reported charges, the provider must be able to substantiate the service. The most commonly misplaced information is laboratory test results and x-ray reports.
- *Denied or Downcoded Services*. Analyze those services that are denied or downcoded by payers to discover the cause of the denial. This can be effected by comparing the reported services to the explanation of benefits (EOB) or explanation of Medicare benefits (EOMB) portion of the payer's statement.

Compliance
The second set of audit objectives involves evaluating the documentation for compliance with Medicare, Medicaid, and private payer standards. Not only are compliance issues important to the overall good management of patients, they are also important for timely and accurate reimbursement. When looking at compliance issues, consider current patient data, physician signatures, signed consent forms, Medicare limitation of liability waiver, and insurance forms.

- *Current Patient Data*. Examine the patient information sheet to verify that all important information about the patient such as allergies (allergies should be listed with each encounter), date of birth, address, nearest living relative, and insurance information has been recorded. The patient information sheet should be updated regularly. Request that patients with insurance sign an Assignment of Benefits form to ensure direct payment of insurance benefits to the provider. Update this record yearly. Medicare offers a lifetime signature form which must also be kept on file by the provider.

Nota Bene: Billing your Medicare carrier electronically allows access to patient Medicare numbers, primary and secondary payer, and other beneficiary eligibility information. The National Standard Format (NSF) or American National Standard Institute (ANSI) Format, which use is required as of July 1995, allows access to areas that can provide answers to many questions you may have. Call your local Medicare carrier for more information.

- *Physician Signatures*. A thorough audit will verify that all services and procedures provided to a patient are signed by the physician. The signature of the physician acknowledges that he or she has performed or supervised the service or procedure. Do not forget to sign or initial laboratory and x-ray results; this shows auditors that the physician has reviewed the information.

  One of the most common problems seen in an audit is the lack of documentation. Physician or nursing calls to patients with test results, refill requests for medication, case management services, etc., are frequently absent from the medical record. In an audit situation the medical record often has no entries other than those services performed in the provider's office. A lab slip may have a note for the nurse from the doctor stating, "call results to patient," but there is rarely a note from the nurse stating a call was made. Such unsigned and/or incomplete entry in a medical record may be viewed by a payer as nonperformance of that service.

  Chart entries that are not in the physician's handwriting should be countersigned by the attending physician. This includes medical services performed by a nurse or telephone conversations between patients and staff members.

- *Signed Consent Forms*. The medical record of each patient who undergoes a procedure involving significant risk should contain a written consent form. Always obtain consent before conducting an invasive procedure. The consent should state that the patient has been informed about the procedure, its risks and benefits, and the alternatives. It should also indicate the patient understood the issues discussed and gave consent to treatment.

- *Medicare Limitation of Liability*. The government has published a list of services it classifies as medically unnecessary under the Medicare program. When providing these services to a Medicare beneficiary, obtain a signed waiver known as the Limitation of Liability. This notification informs the patient in advance that the services he or she seeks may be denied, and he or she is responsible to pay the bill.
- *Insurance Forms*. An auditor should check claim forms, whether submitted electronically or by hard copy, to see that they are completed correctly. Include all pertinent dates and diagnostic and procedural coding information necessary for payers to generate reimbursement.

Performing the Chart Audit

The initial steps of performing a chart audit include assembling the necessary materials for the analysis and comparing the documentation to the procedural and diagnostic codes. The auditor should have a list of the objectives and keep a tally of various findings.

Step 1: *Gather Reference Materials*

The auditor must use current CPT and ICD-9 coding books as well as the previous year's edition of each book. A HCPCS Level II book will be required when reviewing supplies and equipment billed to Medicare.

Step 2: *Select Charts to Be Reviewed*

Start by reviewing 10 charts for each physician to get a good sample of each physician's services. Another method is to target specific services. In either case, the charts selected should contain examples of services performed by each physician. Since the focus should be on current coding, review only those services less than one year old.

Step 3: *Obtain Insurance Information*

Gather insurance information, either copies of submitted HCFA-1500 forms or computerized insurance data, for each date of service assessed. Review the insurance information for completeness.

Step 4: *Obtain EOBs and EOMBs*

Reviewing the explanation of benefits (EOBs) or explanation of Medicare benefits (EOMBs) statements provided by payers is a valuable way for providers to discover unacceptable code use or incorrect sequencing of codes. When a certain service results in consistent denial or substantial reduction in payment by more than one payer, the coding practice should be analyzed and corrected. This review may reveal a claim form with codes that are transposed, outdated, or improperly sequenced.

The EOB and EOMB statements can provide a method to track payers' usual, customary, and reasonable (UCR) amounts. Compare the UCRs of different insurance companies for insight into keeping fees current and in line with the market.

Unfortunately, EOBs and EOMBs can be difficult to read because the wide variety of payer formats. Whenever possible, ask the payer to provide specific information or break down the charges paid. Ideally, the explanation provided by the payer would identify the date of service being reimbursed, the charges submitted, the allowed payment determined by the payer, and whether the patient's deductible is subtracted from the payment made to the payer.

Step 5: *Develop a Tally Sheet*
The auditor will need a form to record the frequency of correct and incorrect coding and documentation errors. The following is an overview of information that should be recorded on the tally sheet, with the issues divided between compliance and revenue:

Compliance

- Allergies
- Patient chart number and physician name
- Date of service
- Patient's consent
- Physician's signature (signature/initials on laboratory, x-ray results and other tests)
- Patient's signature (for release of medical information and assignment of benefits)
- Signed documentation for calls to patients and requests for prescription refills
- Insurance information (e.g., Medicare or private), including primary and secondary

Revenue

- Correct, incorrect, and corrected CPT codes
- CPT codes coded but not documented
- CPT codes documented but not coded
- Patient co-pay
- Total amount billed
- Corrected amount billed — be sure to use payer contracts for correct amounts
- Contractual write-off
- Total percentage over- or underpaid (should be within 3 percent; if over 3 percent your claims may be audited until they are within an acceptable range)
- Correct, incorrect, and corrected ICD-9 codes
- ICD-9 codes coded but not documented
- ICD-9 codes documented but not coded

Don't forget to check the number of denials for incorrect coding or reporting and figure the cost of reprocessing and resubmitting claims.

WHAT HAPPENS WHEN YOU ARE AUDITED

Mutual trust and respect are the key to any type of business arrangement. Once trust is broken on either side it is a very difficult to re-establish it. This applies to both the payer and provider. In the long run it is not worth it to report services or try to increase revenue by submitting claims that are questionable. Revenue can be legitimately increased by negotiating contracts mutually beneficial to both the provider and the payer and by proper coding and reporting for services. It is not just a matter of getting caught by payers; your reporting could be labeled as fraudulent, causing a loss of contracts and your removal from panels.

CODING RESOURCES AND PAYER GUIDELINES

It can be very frustrating when a claim is denied based on payer reimbursement guidelines, especially if the coder feels he or she has applied the correct code, interpretation of that code, and sound coding rules. To solve this type of problem go back to the basics and determine how the code and the applicable rules are being interpreted versus how the payer is viewing them. Where did you get your information? What resource did the payer use?

Payer rules are generally established from guidelines published in the various coding sections throughout CPT. Problems occur because a specific guideline cannot or does not address every issue. Because each use of a guideline cannot be listed, payers frequently base their "interpretation" on what is written within the guideline or on some other resource.

As payers set up their guidelines they have several choices: they can (1) set up and clinically interpret each guideline for their company, or (2) they can purchase a software or consult package that has guideline interpretations programmed into it. Because of these options, payers sometimes seem to have inconsistent and even contradictory guidelines.

Coders, too, can add to the problem. When information is obtained from the same source as the payer there is less likelihood of conflict. However, when information and clarification about specific codes or rule interpretations are obtained from a different coding resource (such as the AMA or a specialty society, e.g., the American College of Gynecologists Committee on Coding and Nomenclature), payers and providers are less likely to be in agreement.

Appealing a Denial

Hence, a multitude of outdated guidelines may remain in place for both the payer and provider that causes reimbursement to be denied in many instances.

When appealing a denial, do not just appeal a single claim but the actual coding guideline the denial is based on. In order to do this, first determine where exactly the discrepancy is in the way you and the payer interpret a guideline. Once this determination has been made and you're confident your position can be supported, the rest of the appeal is relatively easy and consists of a few basic steps as follows:

- Write a letter explaining precisely the reason why you do not agree with the denial of the claim listed on the EOB
- Back up your reason with excerpts from the coding resource you are consulting and attach a copy of the article; include the name of the article, the coding resource, and the date of the publication
- Make copies of all documentation in case they must be submitted more than once
- Call the payer and try to speak with someone with decision-making authority. Explain that you would like to resubmit an appeal directly to them and what you are trying to accomplish with the appeal

If you win your appeal but must submit a copy of the same documents for the same issue over and over again, don't get discouraged. Even when a payer agrees to reverse a denial, it does not mean every claim with the same issue will be paid correctly in the future. Remember, payers process tens of thousands of claims a month on an established system, and unless they are able easily to change their system to accommodate the new guideline, the same problem might well arise again.

MEDICAL SERVICES PROVIDED BY NONPHYSICIANS

According to an article in *Part B News*, Medicare covers the following services furnished by nonphysician practitioners (e.g., physician assistants) as "incident to" a physician's care:

- Minor surgery
- Setting casts or simple fractures
- Reading x-rays and other activities involving the evaluation and management of a patient ordinarily performed by a physician

The physician must be "physically present in the same office suite and be immediately available to render assistance if that becomes necessary."

HCFA has determined that nonphysicians are not limited to low level office visits, since the employing physician is responsible for billing the services furnished by the PA, he/she determines the most accurate code for the specific treatment furnished.

The following are policy considerations proffered by Medicode:

- The PA cannot report an initial visit where the physician did not see the patient. Some PAs do the initial work-up and order lab and x-rays. The patient returns for a follow-up visit to see the physician
- The physician must actively participate in each service provided by the physician assistant. If the physician sees the patient initially and the follow-up visit(s) is provided by a physician assistant, the service may be reported as 99211 (the physician does not need to see the patient; however, the physician should oversee the PA and sign the chart notes)
- Use HCPCS Level II modifier -AN when the PA performs subsequent hospital visits or nursing home visits

SURGICAL SERVICES PROVIDED BY NONPHYSICIANS

CPT modifiers -80, -81, and -82 are for use when reporting the services of an assistant surgeon. The AMA has stated that these modifiers should not be used to report surgical assistant services provided by nonphysicians.

Physicians billing non-Medicare payers should consider the following:

- Use an unlisted code from the appropriate surgical section for the procedure performed
- Use the procedure code for the procedure performed with the use of modifier -80 and state in the comments field for EMC or write a statement on the claim form that the assistant surgery services were performed by a nonphysician (e.g., physician assistant)
- Use HCPCS Level II modifier -AS when reporting surgical assistant services of PAs

LOCAL VS. NATIONAL MEDICARE POLICY

If you prepare Medicare claims for more than one state you know that some Medicare policies are specific to a certain state or region. Medicare carriers use both national and local policies to make medical coverage decisions. Early in 1995, HCFA updated the guidelines that carriers use to develop national and local medical review policy. A national coverage policy outlines Medicare coverage decisions that apply to all states and regions. National coverage policy indicates whether and under what circumstances items/services are covered. These policies are published in HCFA regulations in the *Federal Register*, contained in HCFA rulings, or issued as program instructions (such as manual issuances in the Coverage Issues Manual or Medicare Carriers Manual.

A local medical review policy is used to make local Medicare coverage decisions when needed and/or in the absence of a national coverage policy. The process of developing local Medicare policy includes creating a draft policy based on review of medical literature, understanding local practice, soliciting comments from the medical community and carrier advisory committee, responding to and incorporating into final local policy comments received, and notifying providers of the policy effective date. It is the responsibility of the carrier medical director, with assistance from carrier staff, to determine when a local policy is needed.

Here are the Medicare guidelines for the development of national and local medical review policy, as listed in the Medicare Carriers Manual, Section 7501.1 and part of 7501.2:

NATIONAL COVERAGE POLICY

A. Definition of National Coverage Policy

The primary authority for all coverage provisions is the statute. A national coverage policy is a statement of national policy regarding Medicare coverage which is:

- Published in HCFA regulations,
- Contained in a HCFA ruling, or
- Issued as a program instruction, such as manual issuances in the Coverage Issues Manual or Medicare Carriers Manual.

National coverage policy indicates whether and under what circumstances items/services are covered. Apply all pertinent statutory provisions, regulations, and national coverage policy when adjudicating claims.

When a national coverage policy indicates that a given item/service is covered under specific circumstances, cover the item/service under those circumstances. The authority and responsibility to interpret national coverage policy and apply it to individual cases is retained by you (the carrier). However, when making individual case determinations, you have no discretion to deviate from national policy if absolute words such as "never" or "only if" are used in the policy.

Requirements for prerequisite therapies listed in national coverage policy (e.g., "conservative treatment has been tried, but failed") must be adhered to when making decisions to cover an item/service.

When new national coverage policy is published, notify the provider community as soon as possible of the effective date. Do not solicit comments or in any way alter or revise the national coverage policy.

B. Statutory Exclusions from Coverage

The statutory authority for the majority of MR is §1862(a)(1)(A) of the Act, which excludes coverage for "items or services that are not reasonable and necessary for the diagnosis or treatment of illness or injury or to improve the functioning of a malformed body member."

These are statutory exceptions to this exclusion which are specified in the full text of §1862(a) for the following items and services:

- Pneumococcal, influenza, and hepatitis B vaccines are not covered if they are not reasonable and necessary for the prevention of illness
- Screening mammography is not covered if it exceeds frequency limits or does not meet quality standards
- Screening Pap smears are not covered if they exceed frequency limits

C. Least Costly Alternative

This national policy provision must be applied when determining payment for all durable medical equipment (DME). (See §2100.2.) You (the carrier) have the discretion to apply this principle to payment for non-DME items and services as well.

D. Local MR Policy (LMRP)

LMRPs are those policies which are used to make local medical coverage decisions. When needed and in the absence of a national coverage policy for a particular item/service, develop an LMRP to indicate whether the item/service is covered and under what clinical circumstances it is considered to be reasonable, necessary, and appropriate. The process for developing an LMRP includes the development of a draft policy based on review of medical literature and your understanding of local practice, soliciting comments from the medical community, including the Carrier Advisory Committee (CAC), responding to and incorporating into final policy comments received, and notifying providers of the policy effective date. (See §7503.)

Your (the carrier's) LMRP must be clear, concise, and not restrict or conflict with national policy. If a national policy states that a given time is "covered for diagnoses/conditions A, B and C," you may not use that as a basis to develop an LMRP to cover only "diagnoses/conditions A, B and C." When a national policy does not exclude coverage for other diagnoses/conditions, you must allow for individual consideration unless your LMRP supports automatic denial for some or all of those other diagnoses/conditions.

E. Identify Items/Services for which an LMRP Is Needed

It is the responsibility of the Carrier Medical Director (CMD), with assistance from your staff, to determine when an LMRP is needed. The CMD may use any or all of the following sources, as well as other sources, in deciding which items or services require an LMRP:

- Your data (such as reports that identify items/services with a significant increase in utilization in the past year)
- National claims history FMR report from the Part B Extract Statistical System (BESS)
- Information obtained from national or regional medical director conferences
- Recommended model policy developed by national or regional medical director work groups
- Recommendations from internal sources (MR staff, fraud unit, etc.)

Evaluation and Management (E/M) Codes

Evaluation and Management (E/M) codes are structured according to a common formula: the extent or intensity of select components of a medical encounter, coupled with the risk and complexities associated with the diagnosis and medical decision, determine the code selection.

E/M GUIDELINES

NEW AND ESTABLISHED PATIENT SERVICE

Several code subcategories in the E/M section are based on the patient's status as being either new or established. CPT guidelines clarify this distinction by providing the following time references:

- New patient: one who has not received any services from that physician, or other physician of the same specialty in the same practice, within three years
- Established patient: one who has received services from that physician, or other physician of the same specialty in the same practice, within three years

If one physician is on call or covering for another physician, classify the patient encounter new or established as if for the physician who is unavailable.

E/M SERVICE COMPONENTS

The components of history, examination, and medical decision making are considered the keys to selecting the correct level of E/M codes. In most cases, all three components must be addressed in the documentation. However, in established, subsequent, and follow-up categories, only two of the three must be met or exceeded for a given code.

The history component is categorized by four levels:

Problem Focused — chief complaint; brief history of present illness or problem

Expanded Problem Focused — chief complaint; brief history of present illness; problem-pertinent system review

Detailed — chief complaint; extended history of present illness; problem-pertinent system review (with limited related systems); pertinent past, family, and/or social history directly related to the patient's problems

Comprehensive — chief complaint; extended history of present illness; system review related to present illness (with review of all related systems); complete past, family, and social history

The physical examination component is similarly divided into four levels of complexity:

Problem Focused — an exam limited to the affected body area or organ system

Expanded Problem Focused — an examination of the affected body area or organ system and of other symptomatic or related organ systems

Detailed — an extended examination of the affected body area(s) and other symptomatic or related organ system(s)

Comprehensive — a complete single system specialty examination or a general multi-system examination of systems (the extent of which is based on age and identified risk factors)

Medical decision making is the final piece of the current E/M coding puzzle, and is a bit more complicated to determine than are the history and examination components. Three subcomponents must be evaluated to determine the overall complexity level of the medical decision.

E/M Documentation Guidelines

The AMA and HCFA developed documentation guidelines for evaluation and management (E/M) services. These guidelines supplement the information already found in CPT and are summarized here. For the full text regarding the three key E/M components (history, examination, and medical decision making), please refer to *CPT '96*.

First Key Component — History

The chief complaint, review of systems, and the past, family, and/or social history may be included as separate elements of the history. This information may also be included in the description of the history of the present illness.

A review of systems and/or a past, family, and/or social history obtained during an earlier encounter does not need to be re-recorded if there is evidence that the physician reviewed and updated the previous information. This may occur when a physician updates his or her own record, or in an institutional setting or group practice where many physicians use a common record. The review and update may be documented by (1) describing any new review of systems and/or past, family, and/or social history information or noting there has been no change in the information, and (2) noting the date and location of the earlier review of systems and/or past, family, and/or social history.

The review of systems and/or past, family, and/or social history may be recorded by ancillary staff or on a form completed by the patient. To document that the physician reviewed the information, there must be a notation supplementing or confirming the information recorded by others.

If the physician cannot obtain a history from the patient or other source, the record should describe the patient's condition or other circumstance that precludes obtaining a history.

The medical record should clearly reflect the chief complaint, describe one to three elements of the present illness (brief history of present illness), and describe four or more elements of the present illness or associated co-morbidities (extended history of present illness).

- The patient's positive responses and pertinent negatives for the system related to the problem should be documented (problem pertinent review of systems)
- The patient's positive responses and pertinent negatives for two to nine systems should be documented (expanded review of systems)
- At least ten organ systems must be reviewed. Those systems with positive or pertinent negative responses must be individually documented. For the remaining systems, a notation indicating all other systems are negative is permissible. In the absence of such a notation, at least ten systems must be individually documented (complete review of systems)

At least one specific item from any of the three history areas must be documented for a pertinent past, family, and/or social history.

At least one specific item from two of the three history areas must be documented for a complete past, family, and/or social history for the following categories of E/M services:

- Office or other outpatient services, established patient
- Emergency department
- Subsequent nursing facility care
- Domiciliary care, established patient
- Home care, established patient

At least one specific item from each of the three history areas must be documented for a complete past, family, and/or social history for the following categories of E/M services:

- Office or other outpatient services, new patient
- Hospital observation services
- Hospital inpatient services, initial care
- Consultations
- Comprehensive nursing facility assessments
- Domiciliary care, new patient
- Home care, new patient

Second Key Component — Examination

Specific abnormal findings and relevant negative findings of the examination of the affected or symptomatic body area(s) or organ system(s) should be documented. A notation of "abnormal" without elaboration is insufficient.

Abnormal or unexpected findings of the examination of the unaffected or asymptomatic body area(s) or organ system(s) should be described.

A brief statement or notation indicating "negative" or "normal" is sufficient to document normal findings related to unaffected area(s) or asymptomatic organ system(s).

The medical record for a general multi-system examination should include findings about eight or more of the twelve organ systems.

Third Key Component — Medical Decision Making

An assessment, clinical impression, or diagnosis should be documented for each encounter. This information may be explicitly stated or implied in documented decisions regarding management plans and/or further evaluation.

The initiation of, or changes in, treatment should be documented. Treatment includes a wide range of management options including patient instructions, nursing instructions, therapies, and medications.

If referrals are made, consultations requested, or advice sought, the record should indicate who receives the advice, who requests the advice, and where the referral or consultation is made.

If a diagnostic service (test or procedure) is ordered, planned, scheduled, or performed at the time of the E/M encounter, the type of service (e.g., laboratory or x-ray) should be documented.

The review of laboratory, radiology, and/or other diagnostic tests should be documented. An entry in a progress note such as "WBC elevated" or "chest x-ray unremarkable" is acceptable. Alternatively, the review may be documented by initialing and dating the report containing the test results.

Document any decision to obtain old records or to obtain additional history from the family, caretaker, or other source to supplement that obtained from the patient and note any relevant finding from the old records or interviews. If there is no relevant information beyond that already obtained, that fact should be documented. A notation of "old records reviewed" or "additional history obtained from family" without elaboration is insufficient.

Document the results of discussion of laboratory, radiology, or other diagnostic tests with the physician who performed or interpreted the study in addition to the direct visualization and independent interpretation of an image, tracing, or specimen previously or subsequently interpreted by another physician.

Document co-morbidities, underlying diseases, or other factors that increase the complexity of medical decision making by increasing the risk of complications, morbidity, or mortality.

If a surgical or invasive diagnostic procedure is ordered, planned, or scheduled at the time of the E/M encounter, the type of procedure (e.g., laparoscopy) should be documented. A surgical or invasive diagnostic procedure performed at the time of the E/M encounter should also be documented.

Document the referral for or decision to perform a surgical or invasive diagnostic procedure on an urgent basis.

If the physician elects to report the level of service based on counseling and/or coordination of care, the total length of time of the encounter (face-to-face or floor time) should be documented and the record should describe the counseling and/or activities to coordinate care.

Contributory Components

Counseling, coordination of care, and the nature of the presenting problem are not major considerations in most encounters, but they generally provide contributory information to the code selection process. The exception arises when counseling or coordination of care dominates (more than 50 percent of the encounter). In these cases, time determines the proper code. Documentation of the exact amount of time spent will verify and substantiate your selected code. Along with the time, spell out what was discussed during the encounter. If a physician coordinates care with an interdisciplinary team of physicians or health professionals/agencies without a patient encounter, report it as a case management service.

Counseling is defined in CPT as a discussion with a patient and/or family concerning one or more of the following areas:

- Diagnostic results, impressions, and recommended diagnostic studies
- Prognosis
- Risks and benefits of treatment options
- Instructions for treatment and/or follow-up
- Importance of compliance with chosen treatment options
- Risk factor reduction
- Patient and family education

The editors of CPT designed the E/M codes to report actual work performed, not time spent. But, when counseling or coordination of care dominates the encounter, time overrides the other factors and determines the proper code. For office encounters, count only the time spent face-to-face with the patient and/or family; for hospital or other inpatient encounters, count the time spent in the patient's unit or on the patient's floor. The time assigned to each code is an average and varies by physician.

A presenting problem is a disease, condition, illness, injury, symptom, sign, finding, complaint, or other reason for the patient to seek out physician services. Five types of presenting problems are defined in CPT. Review these definitions, but remember, this information merely contributes to code selection — the presenting problem is not a key factor.

E/M Guidelines Summary

Don't let this brief overview be your only experience with the E/M section of CPT. Carefully read the complete guidelines in CPT; much information is presented regarding aspects of a family history and the associated body areas and organ systems. The modifiers that apply to the E/M section are also listed in the guidelines.

PLACE OF SERVICE DISTINCTIONS

The E/M code section is divided into subsections by type and place of service. Keep the following in mind when coding each service setting:

- A patient is considered an outpatient at a healthcare facility until formal inpatient admission occurs
- All physicians use codes 99281–99285 for reporting emergency department services, regardless of hospital-based or nonhospital-based status
- Consultation codes are linked to location
- Admission to a hospital or nursing facility includes evaluation and management services provided elsewhere (office or emergency department) by the admitting physician on the same day

The E/M section is broken down into subcategories by type of service. The following is an overview of these codes.

99201–99215
Office or Other Outpatient Services

Coding Insight

Office or Other Outpatient Services codes report the services for most patient encounters. Multiple new patient office or outpatient visits provided on the same calendar date are billable if medically necessary. Support the claim with documentation and indicate the time of each occurrence.

Note that in this subcategory, code 99211 is the equivalent of the old level of service code 90030. It is unique (even in the subcategory) because it does not require the key components. The service must be supervised by the physician, who does not have to be in the room but must be available on the premises.

Code	Description	Medicode RVU	50th	75th	Medicare Nat'l Avg
99201	Office or other outpatient visit for the evaluation and management of a new patient, which requires these three key components: a problem focused history; a problem focused examination; and straightforward medical decision making. Counseling and/or coordination of care with other providers or agencies are provided consistent with the nature of the problem(s) and the patient's and/or family's needs. Usually, the presenting problems are self limited or minor. Physicians typically spend 10 minutes face-to-face with the patient and/or family.	34.50	46	54	29

Code	Description	Medicode RVU	50th	75th	Medicare Nat'l Avg
99202	Office or other outpatient visit for the evaluation and management of a new patient, which requires these three key components: an expanded problem focused history; an expanded problem focused examination; and straightforward medical decision making. Counseling and/or coordination of care with other providers or agencies are provided consistent with the nature of the problem(s) and the patient's and/or family's needs. Usually, the presenting problem(s) are of low to moderate severity. Physicians typically spend 20 minutes face-to-face with the patient and/or family.	43.00	57	67	45
99203	Office or other outpatient visit for the evaluation and management of a new patient, which requires these three key components: a detailed history; a detailed examination; and medical decision making of low complexity. Counseling and/or coordination of care with other providers or agencies are provided consistent with the nature of the problem(s) and the patient's and/or family's needs. Usually, the presenting problem(s) are of moderate severity. Physicians typically spend 30 minutes face-to-face with the patient and/or family.	56.00	75	87	60
99204	Office or other outpatient visit for the evaluation and management of a new patient, which requires these three key components: a comprehensive history; a comprehensive examination; and medical decision making of moderate complexity. Counseling and/or coordination of care with other providers or agencies are provided consistent with the nature of the problem(s) and the patient's and/or family's needs. Usually, the presenting problem(s) are of moderate to high severity. Physicians typically spend 45 minutes face-to-face with the patient and/or family.	80.00	107	125	91
99205	Office or other outpatient visit for the evaluation and management of a new patient, which requires these three key components: a comprehensive history; a comprehensive examination; and medical decision making of high complexity. Counseling and/or coordination of care with other providers or agencies are provided consistent with the nature of the problem(s) and the patient's and/or family's needs. Usually, the presenting problem(s) are of moderate to high severity. Physicians typically spend 60 minutes face-to-face with the patient and/or family.	108.0	144	169	111
99211	Office or other outpatient visit for the evaluation and management of an established patient, that may not require the presence of a physician. Usually, the presenting problem(s) are minimal. Typically, 5 minutes are spent performing or supervising these services.	19.00	26	30	14
99212	Office or other outpatient visit for the evaluation and management of an established patient, which requires at least two of these three key components: a problem focused history; a problem focused examination; straightforward medical decision making. Counseling and/or coordination of care with other providers or agencies are provided consistent with the nature of the problem(s) and the patient's and/or family's needs. Usually, the presenting problem(s) are self limited or minor. Physicians typically spend 10 minutes face-to-face with the patient and/or family.	27.00	37	42	24

Code	Description	Medicode RVU	50th	75th	Medicare Nat'l Avg
99213	Office or other outpatient visit for the evaluation and management of an established patient, which requires at least two of these three key components: an expanded problem focused history; an expanded problem focused examination; medical decision making of low complexity. Counseling and coordination of care with other providers or agencies are provided consistent with the nature of the problem(s) and the patient's and/or family's needs. Usually, the presenting problem(s) are of low to moderate severity. Physicians typically spend 15 minutes face-to-face with the patient and/or family.	34.50	47	54	34
99214	Office or other outpatient visit for the evaluation and management of an established patient, which requires at least two of these three key components: a detailed history; a detailed examination; medical decision making of moderate complexity. Counseling and/or coordination of care with other providers or agencies are provided consistent with the nature of the problem(s) and the patient's and/or family's needs. Usually, the presenting problem(s) are of moderate to high severity. Physicians typically spend 25 minutes face-to-face with the patient and/or family.	50.00	68	78	52
99215	Office or other outpatient visit for the evaluation and management of an established patient, which requires at least two of these three key components: a comprehensive history; a comprehensive examination; medical decision making of high complexity. Counseling and/or coordination of care with other providers or agencies are provided consistent with the nature of the problem(s) and the patient's and/or family's needs. Usually, the presenting problem(s) are of moderate to high severity. Physicians typically spend 40 minutes face-to-face with the patient and/or family.	80.00	109	125	82

99217–99220

Hospital Observation Services

CODING INSIGHT

Code 99217 reports observation care discharge services only if discharge from observation status occurs on a date other than the initial date of observation status. The code includes final examination of the patient, discussion of the hospital stay, instructions for continuing care, and preparation of discharge records. If a patient is admitted to and subsequently discharged from observation status on the same date, report only the Initial Observation Services code.

Codes 99217–99220 report E/M services provided to patients admitted to observation status in a hospital. However, it is not necessary that the patient be located in a designated observation area. Any other related E/M services provided on the same date as the observation are included in the observation code and cannot be billed separately.

The instructional notes for Initial Hospital Observation Care include the following instructions:

- Use these codes to report the encounter by the supervising physician when the patient is designated as "observation status"
- These codes include initiation of observation status, supervision of the healthcare plan for observation, and performance of periodic reassessments

- See Office and Other Outpatient Consultation codes to report observation encounters by other physicians

When a patient is admitted to observation status in the course of an encounter in another site of service (e.g., hospital emergency department, physician's office, nursing facility), all E/M services provided by that physician on the same day are included in the admission for hospital observation. Only one physician can report initial observation services.

Do not use these observation codes for post-recovery of a procedure that is considered a global surgical service.

Observation services are included in the inpatient admission service when provided on the same date. Use Initial Hospital Care codes for services provided to a patient who, after receiving observation services, is admitted to the hospital on the same date — the observation service is not reported separately.

Nota Bene: What determines an outpatient observation status versus and inpatient hospital stay is the physician's intention. In an audit situation the physician's written orders are what determines whether the stay will be considered outpatient or inpatient.

If a patient is admitted to outpatient observation, report a second visit when the patient is not discharged and stays overnight. Some payers have criteria that specifies when the start of a second day occurs. It is possible to report two visits when the physician orders observation at 8:00 p.m. on one day and discharges the patient 10 hours later at 6:00 a.m. the next day.

Medicare Alert

Only the physician who admits the patient to hospital observation and is responsible for the patient's care during the stay in observation, or a physician who does not have inpatient admitting privileges but is authorized to admit a patient to observation, may report the hospital observation codes.

Physicians reporting observation codes must maintain an observation record for the patient containing dated and timed admitting orders, nursing notes, and progress notes prepared by the physician while the patient was in observation status.

Hospital Observation payment includes the care rendered by the admitting physician on the date the patient was admitted to observation status. Other physicians providing services to the patient while in observation status must bill the appropriate outpatient services codes or outpatient consultation codes.

Only the Observation Care code may be reported if the patient is discharged on the same day he or she was admitted to observation status. For patients remaining in observation status after the first night's count and discharged the next day, the physician must report 99217.

The physician must report an initial hospital visit for any E/M services provided when a patient is admitted to inpatient status from observation status on the same day. Medicare payment for the initial hospital visit includes all services provided by that physician on the date of admission, regardless of site of service.

Typically, the global surgical fee includes payment for hospital observation services and any additional payments can be made only if (1) the hospital observation services can be reported with modifier -24, -25, or -57; and (2) the observation services provided by the surgeon meet all criteria for the code reported.

Code	Description	Medicode RVU	50th	75th	Medicare Nat'l Avg
99217	Observation care discharge day management	60.00	77	93	54

Code	Description	Medicode RVU	50th	75th	Medicare Nat'l Avg
99218	Initial observation care, per day, for the evaluation and management of a patient which requires these three key components: a detailed or comprehensive history; a detailed or comprehensive examination; and medical decision making that is straightforward or of low complexity. Counseling and/or coordination of care with other providers or agencies are provided consistent with the nature of the problem(s) and the patient's and/or family's needs. Usually, the problem(s) requiring admission to "observation status" are of low severity.	75.00	96	117	62
99219	Initial observation care, per day, for the evaluation and management of a patient, which requires these three key components: a comprehensive history; a comprehensive examination; and medical decision making of moderate complexity. Counseling and/or coordination of care with other providers or agencies are provided consistent with the nature of the problem(s) and the patient's and/or family's needs. Usually, the problem(s) requiring admission to "observation status" are of moderate severity.	102.0	130	159	99
99220	Initial observation care, per day, for the evaluation and management of a patient, which requires these three key components: a comprehensive history; a comprehensive examination; and medical decision making of high complexity. Counseling and/or coordination of care with other providers or agencies are provided consistent with the nature of the problem(s) and the patient's and/or family's needs. Usually, the problem(s) requiring admission to "observation status" are of high severity.	128.0	164	199	125

99221–99239
Hospital Inpatient Services

CODING INSIGHT

The codes for Hospital Inpatient Services report admission to a hospital setting, follow-up care provided in a hospital setting, and hospital discharge day management. For inpatient care, the time component includes not only face-to-face time with the patient but also the physician's time spent in the patient's unit or on the patient's floor. This time may include family counseling or discussing the patient's condition with the family; establishing and reviewing the patient's record; documenting within the chart; and communicating with other healthcare professionals, such as other physicians, nursing staff, respiratory therapists, and so on.

These codes identify services provided on the day of admission by the admitting physician. Only one physician can bill the initial hospital service (generally referred to as the "admit"), and only one initial hospital service can be billed for a patient for each hospital stay.

All three initial hospital care codes 99221–99223 include a comprehensive history and examination, so the complexity of the medical decision making component usually determines the code. Code 99221 includes a detailed or comprehensive history and examination. Use this code when the hospital does not require a comprehensive history or examination either for initial service or for a readmission following a recent discharge.

Initial hospital care includes all related evaluation and management services provided by the physician in a calendar day, not a 24-hour period.

If the patient is admitted to a facility on the same day as any related outpatient encounter (office, ED, nursing facility, etc.), report the total care as one service with the appropriate Initial Hospital Care code.

Codes 99231– 99233 report total services provided on each day in the hospital following the day of admission, including reviewing medical records and analyzing diagnostic studies and test results. The physician must provide some patient care to qualify as a reportable service.

Report the discharge services of a multiple-day stay with 99238. When an admission and discharge occur on the same day, bill only the admission. The discharge service includes final hospital care, final examination, discussion of the hospital stay, instructions for continuing care, and preparation of discharge records. Code 99238 reports hospital discharge day management, but excludes discharge of a patient from observation status (see 99217). When concurrent care is provided on discharge day by a physician other than the attending physician, report these services using Subsequent Hospital Care codes.

Nota Bene: Code 99238 in this range has been revised in *CPT '96*. The words "30 minutes or less" have been added. A new code, 99239, has been added to report "hospital day discharge management; more than 30 minutes." The instructional paragraph following 99239 has been completely changed and a new parenthetical phrase has been added: "(For discharge services provided to newborns admitted and discharged on the same date, see 99435)." Read the nomenclature for 99238–99239 and the CPT notes carefully before making your code selection.

Code	Description	Medicode RVU	50th	75th	Medicare Nat'l Avg
99221	Initial hospital care, per day, for the evaluation and management of a patient which requires these three key components: a detailed or comprehensive history; a detailed or comprehensive examination; and medical decision making that is straightforward or of low complexity. Counseling and/or coordination of care with other providers or agencies are provided consistent with the nature of the problem(s) and the patient's and/or family's needs. Usually, the problem(s) requiring admission are of low severity. Physicians typically spend 30 minutes at the bedside and on the patient's hospital floor or unit.	83.50	107	130	61
99222	Initial hospital care, per day, for the evaluation and management of a patient, which requires these three key components: a comprehensive history; a comprehensive examination; and medical decision making of moderate complexity. Counseling and/or coordination of care with other providers or agencies are provided consistent with the nature of the problem(s) and the patient's and/or family's needs. Usually, the problem(s) requiring admission are of moderate severity. Physicians typically spend 50 minutes at the bedside and on the patient's hospital floor or unit.	112.5	144	175	100
99223	Initial hospital care, per day, for the evaluation and management of a patient, which requires these three key components: a comprehensive history; a comprehensive examination; and medical decision making of high complexity. Counseling and/or coordination of care with other providers or agencies are provided consistent with the nature of the problem(s) and the patient's and/or family's needs. Usually, the problem(s) requiring admission are of high severity. Physicians typically spend 70 minutes at the bedside and on the patient's hospital floor or unit.	138.0	176	214	126
99231	Subsequent hospital care, per day, for the evaluation and management of a patient, which requires at least two of these three key components: a problem focused interval history; a problem focused examination; medical decision making that is straightforward or of low complexity. Counseling and/or coordination of care with other providers or agencies are provided consistent with the nature of the problem(s) and the patient's and/or family's needs. Usually, the patient is stable, recovering or improving. Physicians typically spend 15 minutes at the bedside and on the patient's hospital floor or unit.	44.00	56	68	32

	Code	Description	Medicode RVU	50th	75th	Medicare Nat'l Avg
	99232	Subsequent hospital care, per day, for the evaluation and management of a patient, which requires at least two of these three key components: an expanded problem focused interval history; an expanded problem focused examination; medical decision making of moderate complexity. Counseling and/or coordination of care with other providers or agencies are provided consistent with the nature of the problem(s) and the patient's and/or family's needs. Usually, the patient is responding inadequately to therapy or has developed a minor complication. Physicians typically spend 25 minutes at the bedside and on the patient's hospital floor or unit.	60.00	77	93	46
	99233	Subsequent hospital care, per day, for the evaluation and management of a patient, which requires at least two of these three key components: a detailed interval history; a detailed examination; medical decision making of high complexity. Counseling and/or coordination of care with other providers or agencies are provided consistent with the nature of the problem(s) and the patient's and/or family's needs. Usually, the patient is unstable or has developed a significant complication or a significant new problem. Physicians typically spend 35 minutes at the bedside and on the patient's hospital floor or unit.	88.50	113	138	64
▲	**99238**	Hospital discharge day management; 30 minutes or less	52.00	66	81	53
●	**99239**	Hospital discharge day management; more than 30 minutes	65.00	83	101	–

99241–99275
Consultations

CODING INSIGHT

Consultations fall under four subcategories: Office or Other Outpatient Consultations, Initial Inpatient Consultations, Follow-up Consultations, and Confirmatory Consultations. Again, if counseling dominates the encounter, time determines the correct code in three of the four subcategories. Confirmatory consultations have no times established.

Code subcategory 99241–99245 makes no distinction between new and established patients. If the attending physician requests an additional opinion or advice for the same or for a new problem, these codes are appropriate for that service.

The services for codes 99251–99255 apply to either new or established patients in a hospital or nursing facility. Report only one initial consultation per admission. If the attending physician requests additional opinions on the same patient, report these services as follow-up inpatient consultations.

Codes 99261–99263 apply exclusively to established patients and report services that either complete the initial consultation or were subsequent consultative services requested by the attending physician. These services include monitoring progress, recommending modifications in management, and giving advice on a new care plan in response to changes in a patient's status.

More than one follow-up inpatient consult may be billed per calendar day if medically necessary.

Use 99271–99275 if the consultation is a known second or third opinion on the necessity or appropriateness of a previously recommended medical treatment or surgical procedure. In these cases, the requesting party is usually not a physician, but rather the patient or the payer.

Confirmatory consultations are not linked to a location. Report any services subsequent to the visit with established patient or subsequent care codes. When this consultation is required by a payer, list the proper code with modifier -32.

Consultations vs. Referrals

In medical coding, the difference between a consultation and a referral can be confusing. Confusion can be kept to a minimum by remembering that a consultation is a physician's advice for treatment of a patient, while a referral is a physician's direct involvement in the treatment of a patient. Here are some other tips that may help:

- CPT defines a consultation as "a type of service provided by a physician whose opinion or advice regarding evaluation and/or management of a specific problem is requested by another physician or other appropriate source"
- If the intent is for the physician to see the patient and give an opinion, but not to become actively involved at that point, then consultation codes are appropriate
- Most requests for consultation come from an attending physician or other appropriate source. The need and request for a consultation must be documented in the patient's medical record. The consultant's opinion and any services ordered or performed should also be documented and communicated to the requesting (referring) physician prior to the performance of any therapeutic services. Medicare requires the name of the physician referring or ordering the consultation to be listed in item 17 of the HCFA-1500 claim form; it also requires the physician UPIN number in item 17 and 17a
- The consultant may initiate diagnostic and/or therapeutic services, such as writing orders or prescriptions and initiating treatment plans
- Confirmatory consultations may be requested by the patient and/or family or may result from the second (or third) opinion required by the patient's insurance company
- Consultation codes should not be used if the intent is for the physician to get involved and the patient is referred for evaluation and treatment of a condition
- When the physician assumes responsibility for the management of any or all of the patient's care subsequent to an encounter with the patient, then consultation codes are no longer appropriate. Depending on the location, identify the correct subsequent or established patient codes
- Report separately any identifiable procedure or service performed on, or subsequent to, the date of the initial consultation
- When a patient is referred for management of an aspect of the patient's condition, an appropriate office or outpatient visit code or initial or subsequent hospital visit code should be used

Code	Description	Medicode RVU	50th	75th	Medicare Nat'l Avg
99241	Office consultation for a new or established patient, which requires these three key components: a problem focused history; a problem focused examination; and straightforward medical decision making. Counseling and/or coordination of care with other providers or agencies are provided consistent with the nature of the problem(s) and the patient's and/or family's needs. Usually, the presenting problem(s) are self limited or minor. Physicians typically spend 15 minutes face-to-face with the patient and/or family.	60.00	81	95	45

Code	Description	Medicode RVU	50th	75th	Medicare Nat'l Avg
99242	Office consultation for a new or established patient, which requires these three key components: an expanded problem focused history; an expanded problem focused examination; and straightforward medical decision making. Counseling and/or coordination of care with other providers or agencies are provided consistent with the nature of the problem(s) and the patient(s) and/or family's needs. Usually, the presenting problem(s) are of low severity. Physicians typically spend 30 minutes face-to-face with the patient and/or family.	76.50	104	122	67
99243	Office consultation for a new or established patient, which requires these three key components: a detailed history; a detailed examination; and medical decision making of low complexity. Counseling and/or coordination of care with other providers or agencies are provided consistent with the nature of the problem(s) and the patient's and/or family's needs. Usually, the presenting problem(s) are of moderate severity. Physicians typically spend 40 minutes face-to-face with the patient and/or family.	97.50	132	155	87
99244	Office consultation for a new or established patient, which requires these three key components: a comprehensive history; a comprehensive examination; and medical decision making of moderate complexity. Counseling and/or coordination of care with other providers or agencies are provided consistent with the nature of the problem(s) and the patient's and/or family's needs. Usually, the presenting problem(s) are of moderate to high severity. Physicians typically spend 60 minutes face-to-face with the patient and/or family.	127.5	173	203	121
99245	Office consultation for a new or established patient, which requires these three key components: a comprehensive history; a comprehensive examination; and medical decision making of high complexity. Counseling and/or coordination of care with other providers or agencies are provided consistent with the nature of the problem(s) and the patient's and/or family's needs. Usually, the presenting problem(s) are of moderate to high severity. Physicians typically spend 80 minutes face-to-face with the patient and/or family.	161.0	218	256	161
99251	Initial inpatient consultation for a new or established patient, which requires these three key components: a problem focused history; a problem focused examination; and straightforward medical decision making. Counseling and/or coordination of care with other providers or agencies are provided consistent with the nature of the problem(s) and the patient's and/or family's needs. Usually, the presenting problem(s) are self limited or minor. Physicians typically spend 20 minutes at the bedside and on the patient's hospital floor or unit.	71.00	96	113	46
99252	Initial inpatient consultation for a new or established patient, which requires these three key components: an expanded problem focused history; an expanded problem focused examination; and straightforward medical decision making. Counseling and/or coordination of care with other providers or agencies are provided consistent with the nature of the problem(s) and the patient's and/or family's needs. Usually, the presenting problem(s) are of low severity. Physicians typically spend 40 minutes at the bedside and on the patient's hospital floor or unit.	91.00	123	145	68

Code	Description	Medicode RVU	50th	75th	Medicare Nat'l Avg
99253	Initial inpatient consultation for a new or established patient, which requires these three key components: a detailed history; a detailed examination; and medical decision making of low complexity. Counseling and/or coordination of care with other providers or agencies are provided consistent with the nature of the problem(s) and the patient's and/or family's needs. Usually, the presenting problem(s) are of moderate severity. Physicians typically spend 55 minutes at the bedside and on the patient's hospital floor or unit.	112.0	152	178	89
99254	Initial inpatient consultation for a new or established patient, which requires three key components: a comprehensive history; a comprehensive examination; and medical decision making of moderate complexity. Counseling and/or coordination of care with other providers or agencies are provided consistent with the nature of the problem(s) and the patient's and/or family's needs. Usually, the presenting problem(s) are of moderate to high severity. Physicians typically spend 80 minutes at the bedside and on the patient's hospital floor or unit.	140.0	189	222	122
99255	Initial inpatient consultation for a new or established patient, which requires these three key components: a comprehensive history; a comprehensive examination; and medical decision making of high complexity. Counseling and/or coordination of care with other providers or agencies are provided consistent with the nature of the problem(s) and the patient's and/or family's needs. Usually, the presenting problem(s) are of moderate to high severity. Physicians typically spend 110 minutes at the bedside and on the patient's hospital floor or unit.	176.0	238	280	162
99261	Follow-up inpatient consultation for an established patient, which requires at least two of these three key components: a problem focused interval history; a problem focused examination; medical decision making that is straightforward or of low complexity. Counseling and/or coordination of care with other providers or agencies are provided consistent with nature of the problem(s) and the patient's and/or family's needs. Usually, the patient is stable, recovering or improving. Physicians typically spend 10 minutes at the bedside and on the patient's hospital floor or unit.	38.00	51	60	25
99262	Follow-up inpatient consultation for an established patient which requires at least two of these three key components: an expanded problem focused interval history; an expanded problem focused examination; medical decision making of moderate complexity. Counseling and/or coordination of care with other providers or agencies are provided consistent with the nature of the problem(s) and the patient's and/or family's needs. Usually, the patient is responding inadequately to therapy or has developed a minor complication. Physicians typically spend 20 minutes at the bedside and on the patient's hospital floor or unit.	60.00	81	95	42
99263	Follow-up inpatient consultation for an established patient which requires at least two of these three key components: a detailed interval history; a detailed examination; medical decision making of high complexity. Counseling and/or coordination of care with other providers or agencies are provided consistent with the nature of the problem(s) and the patient's and/or family's needs. Usually, the patient is unstable or has developed a significant complication or a significant new problem. Physicians typically spend 30 minutes at the bedside and on the patient's hospital floor or unit.	87.00	118	138	64

Code	Description	Medicode RVU	50th	75th	Medicare Nat'l Avg
99271	Confirmatory consultation for a new or established patient, which requires these three key components: a problem focused history; a problem focused examination; and straightforward medical decision making. Counseling and/or coordination of care with other providers or agencies are provided consistent with the nature of the problem(s) and the patient's and/or family's needs. Usually, the presenting problem(s) are self limited or minor.	60.00	81	95	41
99272	Confirmatory consultation for a new or established patient, which requires these three key components: an expanded problem focused history; an expanded problem focused examination; and straightforward medical decision making. Counseling and/or coordination of care with other providers or agencies are provided consistent with the nature of the problem(s) and the patient's and/or family's needs. Usually, the presenting problem(s) are of low severity.	76.50	104	122	57
99273	Confirmatory consultation for a new or established patient, which requires these three key components: a detailed history; a detailed examination; and medical decision making of low complexity. Counseling and/or coordination of care with other providers or agencies are provided consistent with the nature of the problem(s) and the patient's and/or family's needs. Usually, the presenting problem(s) are of moderate severity.	97.50	132	155	79
99274	Confirmatory consultation for a patient, which requires these three key components: a comprehensive history; a comprehensive examination; and medical decision making of moderate complexity. Counseling and/or coordination of care with other providers or agencies are provided consistent with the nature of the problem(s) and the patient's and/or family's needs. Usually, the presenting problem(s) are of moderate to high severity.	127.5	173	203	104
99275	Confirmatory consultation for a patient, which requires these three key components: a comprehensive history; a comprehensive examination; and medical decision making of high complexity. Counseling and/or coordination of care with other providers or agencies are provided consistent with the nature of the problem(s) and the patient's and/or family's needs. Usually, the presenting problem(s) are of moderate to high severity.	161.0	218	256	142

99281–99288
Emergency Department Services

Coding Insight

Emergency Department (ED) service codes do not differentiate new and established patients and are used by hospital-based and nonhospital-based physicians. The notes define an emergency department as a hospital-based facility for the provision of unscheduled services to patients requesting immediate attention. An ED must operate around the clock. Care provided in the ED for convenience should not be coded as an ED service. More than one ED service can be reported per calendar day if medically necessity has been documented.

Associated with ED services is 99288 *Physician direction of emergency medical systems (EMS) emergency care, advanced life support*. The physician must be located in the ED or critical care department; be in two-way voice communication with the ambulance or rescue personnel outside the hospital; and direct the performance of necessary medical procedures.

Code	Description	Medicode RVU	50th	75th	Medicare Nat'l Avg
99281	Emergency department visit for the evaluation and management of a patient, which requires these three key components: a problem focused history; a problem focused examination; and straightforward medical decision making. Counseling and/or coordination of care with other providers or agencies are provided consistent with the nature of the problem(s) and the patient's and/or family's needs. Usually, the presenting problem(s) are self limited or minor.	39.00	55	62	21
99282	Emergency department visit for the evaluation and management of a patient, which requires these three key components: an expanded problem focused history; an expanded problem focused examination; and medical decision making of low complexity. Counseling and/or coordination of care with other providers or agencies are provided consistent with the nature of the problem(s) and the patient's and/or family's needs. Usually, the presenting problem(s) are of low to moderate severity.	52.50	74	83	32
99283	Emergency department visit for the evaluation and management of a patient, which requires these three key components: an expanded problem focused history; an expanded problem focused examination; and medical decision making of moderate complexity. Counseling and/or coordination of care with other providers or agencies are provided consistent with the nature of the problem(s) and the patient's and/or family's needs. Usually, the presenting problem(s) are of moderate severity.	79.00	111	125	57
99284	Emergency department visit for the evaluation and management of a patient, which requires these three key components: a detailed history; a detailed examination; and medical decision making of moderate complexity. Counseling and/or coordination of care with other providers or agencies are provided consistent with the nature of the problem(s) and the patient's and/or family's needs. Usually, the presenting problem(s) are of high severity, and require urgent evaluation by the physician but do not pose an immediate significant threat to life or physiologic function.	118.0	165	186	86
99285	Emergency department visit for the evaluation and management of a patient, which requires these three key components within the constraints imposed by the urgency of the patient's clinical condition and mental status: a comprehensive history; a comprehensive examination; and medical decision making of high complexity. Counseling and/or coordination of care with other providers or agencies are provided consistent with the nature of the problem(s) and the patient's and/or family's needs. Usually, the presenting problem(s) are of high severity and pose an immediate significant threat to life or physiologic function.	176.0	247	278	132
99288	Physician direction of emergency medical systems (EMS) emergency care, advanced life support	0.00	0	0	–

99291–99292
Critical Care Services

Coding Insight

Critical Care Services report treatment of critically ill patients in emergencies that require the constant attendance of the physician as in the case of shock, cardiac arrest, bleeding, respiratory failure, or postoperative complications. Critical care is not specific to a location.

Rather, it is determined by the patient's critically ill condition requiring this type of physician care. Therefore, routine visits to a stabilized patient in an ICU are not necessarily critical care.

Several instructional guidelines for the Critical Care Services codes are as follows:

- Critical care codes include evaluation and management of the critically ill or injured patient, requiring constant attendance of the physician
- Care provided to a patient who is not critically ill but happens to be in a critical care unit should be identified using Subsequent Hospital Care codes or Inpatient Consultation codes as appropriate
- Critical care of less than 30 minutes should be reported using an appropriate hospital service code
- Critical care codes identify the total duration of time spent by a physician on a given date, even if the time is not continuous. Code 99291 reports the first hour of critical care and is used only once per date. Code 99292 reports each additional 30 minutes of critical care per date
- Critical care of less than 15 minutes beyond the first hour or less than 15 minutes beyond the final 30 minutes should not be reported

Critical care is a global procedure and includes the performance of a variety of procedures attendant to the emergency care of the critical patient.

When providing critical care of less than 30 minutes total duration on a given date, report the services with the appropriate Subsequent Hospital Care code (99232 or 99233).

Critical care is coded by time only.

Emergency Room Critical Care
The ED physician is often the first person involved in the care of a trauma or critically ill patient. During the care of the patient other providers are frequently called to treat injuries to various body systems. Because CPT specifies that critical care is not specific to a location (e.g., ICU or CCU), it can become confusing when reporting for this type of care, especially when trying to determine if ED or critical care codes apply.

Payers will allow two physicians to identify critical care codes when it is necessary for each physician to manage critical episodes at different periods during the same day, but they generally will not pay for two physicians billing for critical care during the same hour. The ED physician may do the initial evaluation of the patient, but an internist may be called in to assume the major role in the care of the patient, including directing care provided by other specialists. To identify the concurrent medical services, the ED physician would report an ED E/M code and the internist would report a critical care code.

The ED physician may identify critical care when he/she is the person who assumes the care of and directs others in the critical care of the patient (i.e., when another physician is not responsible for or coordinating the care). This may include calling in specialists, such as a cardiologist for Swan-Ganz insertion and/or an orthopedic surgeon for fracture evaluation. However, because ED physicians do not generally have admitting privileges at most hospitals, the critical care would occur in the ED. When critical care is required upon presentation to the ED or the ED physician attends to and directs the care of the patient, ED codes are not reported in addition to the critical care service.

Although *CPT '96* specifies that critical care requires the constant attendance of the physician, it does not mean the physician is required to be at the bedside. The physician may be recording in the medical record, obtaining opinions or advice from other consultants, or reviewing laboratory or other data as necessary to care for the patient. All time spent and service(s) rendered by the emergency department physician should be clearly recorded in the patient's medical record to support the claim for critical care services.

Services included when reporting critical care codes are listed on pages 27 and 28 of *CPT '96*; any other services performed should be reported in addition to the code for critical care. Some payers, however, may determine that other services — such as IV fluid or drug therapy or interpretation of ECGs (93000, 93010, 93040, 93042) or pulse oximetry determination — are incidental to critical care and are not reimbursable.

Examples illustrating the correct reporting of critical care services by total duration of care are listed on pages 27 and 28 of *CPT '96*. Be sure to read the directions listed on these pages; they provide important information.

Medicare and Critical Care

Medicare has recently clarified its policy for the use of critical care codes. Critical care includes the care of patients who might not be in a "medical emergency" but who nonetheless require constant physician attention because they are unstable and critically ill, or unstable and critically injured. The care of such patients involves decision making of high complexity to assess, manipulate, and support circulatory, respiratory, central nervous, metabolic, or other vital system functions to prevent or treat single or multiple vital organ system failure. It often requires extensive interpretation of multiple databases and the application of advanced technology to manage the patient.

This expanded definition does not mean that the care of a patient who happens to be in a critical care, intensive care, or other specialized care unit should be reported with the critical care codes. In such a unit, the care of a patient who is not unstable and critically injured is reported using the appropriate subsequent hospital care code (99231–99233) or inpatient consultation code (99251–99263).

"Constant Attendance" as a Prerequisite for Use of Critical Care Codes

There are no absolute limits on the amount of critical care services that can be reported per day or per hospital. A physician must be prepared to demonstrate that the service billed meets the definition of critical care. Medicare may request documentation for cases in which it is implausible that the amount of critical care billed was provided (e.g., more than a total of 12 hours of critical care billed by the physician for one or more patients on the same day).

Critical Care and Aftercare Days

Critical care cannot be paid on the day the physician also bills a procedure code with a global surgical period unless the critical care is billed with modifier -25 to indicate that the critical care is a significant, separately identifiable E/M service that is above and beyond the usually pre- and postoperative care associated with the procedure that is performed.

If denials for critical care are occurring, they may relate to a misunderstanding of what services are included or bundled into critical care. Prior to 1993, the CPT definition of critical care bundled a number of fairly significant procedures into the critical care codes, including endotracheal intubation and placement of catheters. At that time, it would have been consistent, with the CPT definition, for Medicare to deny payment for those procedures when they were billed on the same date as the critical care codes. However, beginning in 1993 the CPT definition of critical care in CPT was revised, and HCFA assigned relative value units to the critical care codes to be consistent with the revised definition. The following services are included in reporting critical care when performed during the critical care period by the physician providing critical care:

The interpretation of:

- Cardiac output measurements (93561 & 93562)
- Chest x-rays (71010 & 71020)

- Blood gases
- Information stored in computers (e.g., ECGs, blood pressures, hematological data) (99090), gastric intubation (91105), temporary transcutaneous pacing (92953), ventilator management (94656, 94657, 94660, 94662), and vascular access procedures (36000, 36410, 36415, 36600)

Any services performed that are not listed above should be reported separately. Services such as endotracheal intubation (31500) and the insertion and placement of a flow directed catheter (e.g., Swan-Ganz, 93503) are no longer bundled into the critical care codes. Therefore, separate payment may be made for critical care in addition to these services if the critical care was a significant, separately identifiable service and it was reported with modifier -25. The time spent performing these other unbundled services is excluded from the determination of the time spent providing critical care.

This policy applies to any procedure with a 0, 10, or 90 day global period, including cardiopulmonary resuscitation (92950). CPR has a global period of 0 days and is not bundled into the critical care codes. Therefore, critical care may be billed in addition to CPR if critical care was a significant, separately identifiable service and was reported with modifier -25. The time spent performing CPR is excluded from the time spent providing critical care.

Nota Bene: Claims adjudication systems were for a long time incapable of determining how many different physicians were billing for a service on a given day. Consequently, auditing was one of the only ways of applying coding rules across a set of physicians who billed on the same date of service. Payer systems are now becoming more sophisticated, and edits can be performed in ever-increasing numbers to identify coding and billing errors by more than one provider. In the future, coders may find a claim denied or that a claim has had the code changed to meet definitions of coding rules. Critical care will be one of the areas experiencing tighter restrictions on how many times in a day different physicians can bill critical care.

Subsidiary Codes

Subsidiary codes have relative values that require no further adjustment:

99292 is "in addition" to 99291

Because these are subsidiary or "in addition to" codes, reimbursement reduction and CPT modifier -51 do not apply.

Medicare Alert

Medicare rebundles certain codes in the E/M section when the listed codes are considered components of a more comprehensive service.

G0001 will not be reimbursed when reported with 99291–99292
36000 will not be reimbursed when reported with 99291–99292
36410 will not be reimbursed when reported with 99291–99292
36600 will not be reimbursed when reported with 99291–99292
71010 will not be reimbursed when reported with 99291–99292
71020 will not be reimbursed when reported with 99291–99292
91105 will not be reimbursed when reported with 99291–99292
92953 will not be reimbursed when reported with 99291–99292
93561 will not be reimbursed when reported with 99291–99292
93562 will not be reimbursed when reported with 99291–99292
94656 will not be reimbursed when reported with 99291–99292
94657 will not be reimbursed when reported with 99291–99292
94760 will not be reimbursed when reported with 99291–99292
94761 will not be reimbursed when reported with 99291–99292
94762 will not be reimbursed when reported with 99291–99292

Code	Description	Medicode RVU	50th	75th	Medicare Nat'l Avg
▲ 99291	Critical care, evaluation and management of the unstable critically ill or unstable critically injured patient, requiring the constant attendance of the physician; first hour	200.0	274	313	170
▲ 99292	Critical care, evaluation and management of the critically ill or critically injured patient, requiring the constant attendance of the physician; each additional 30 minutes	100.0	137	156	83

99295–99297
Neonatal Intensive Care

Coding Insight

CPT codes 99295–99297 report services provided by a physician directing the care of a neonate or infant in a neonatal intensive care unit (NICU). These codes represent care starting on the date of admission to the NICU, and only one code may be reported once per patient per date. Once the neonate is no longer considered to be critically ill, report services with Subsequent Hospital Care codes.

The three codes to report neonatal intensive care services are not broken into components as are the previous E/M codes. Instead, 99295 reports the initial care, 99296 reports subsequent care provided to a critically ill unstable neonate, and 99297 reports the subsequent care provided to a critically ill stable neonate.

Initial NICU care does not include services provided prior to admission to the NICU, and all three codes are to be used in addition to the codes for prolonged physician services (99356 and 99357), physician standby services (99360), and newborn resuscitation (99440) when the physician is present for the delivery and resuscitation is required.

Neonatal intensive care includes management; monitoring and treatment of the patient, including nutritional, metabolic, and hematologic maintenance; patient counseling; and direct supervision of the healthcare team in the performance of cognitive and procedural activities. Also included are umbilical, central, or peripheral vessel catheterization; endotracheal intubation; lumbar puncture; suprapubic bladder aspiration; and any additional services referred to in the parenthetical note following each NICU code. Report separately any services provided that are not specifically mentioned with each code or in the instructional notes.

Nota Bene: neonatal intensive care notes and codes *in CPT '96* have been revised. Read these changes/revisions carefully before making a code selection.

Code	Description	Medicode RVU	50th	75th	Medicare Nat'l Avg
▲ 99295	Initial neonatal intensive care, per day, for the evaluation and management of a critically ill neonate or infant	750.0	1026	1173	774
▲ 99296	Subsequent neonatal intensive care, per day, for the evaluation and management of a critically ill and unstable neonate or infant	500.0	684	782	363
▲ 99297	Subsequent neonatal intensive care, per day, for the evaluation and management of a critically ill though stable neonate or infant	340.0	465	532	186

99301–99313
Nursing Facility Services

CODING INSIGHT

Nursing facility E/M services have been grouped into two subcategories: Comprehensive Nursing Facility Assessments and Subsequent Nursing Facility Care. Included in these codes are E/M services provided to patients in psychiatric residential treatment centers. These facilities must provide a 24-hour professionally staffed therapeutic group living and learning environment. Report other services, such as medical psychotherapy, separately when provided in addition to E/M services.

Comprehensive assessments (99301–99303) may be performed in various locations such as hospital, office, nursing facility, domiciliary/non-nursing facility, or the patient's home. Nursing facility codes apply to new and established patients, and more than one comprehensive assessment may be needed during the course of patient confinement.

All E/M services provided on the same day as the comprehensive assessment are included in that care, such as care provided in the ED or physician's office. The only exception is when a patient is discharged from the hospital and admitted to a nursing facility on the same day. In this situation, the discharge services may be reported separately.

Subsequent Nursing Facility Care codes (99311–99313) describe the services provided to patients who do not require a comprehensive assessment, i.e., patients who have had no major or permanent change in status. All subsequent care services include reviewing the medical record, noting any changes since the last visit, and reviewing and signing orders.

Code	Description	Medicode RVU	50th	75th	Medicare Nat'l Avg
99301	Evaluation and management of a new or established patient involving an annual nursing facility assessment which requires these three key components: a detailed interval history; a comprehensive examination; and medical decision making that is straightforward or of low complexity. Counseling and/or coordination of care with other providers or agencies are provided consistent with the nature of the problem(s) and the patient's and/or family's needs. Usually, the patient is stable, recovering or improving. The review and affirmation of the medical plan of care is required. Physicians typically spend 30 minutes at the bedside and on the patient's facility floor or unit.	45.00	62	70	54
99302	Evaluation and management of a new or established patient involving a nursing facility assessment which requires these three key components: a detailed interval history; a comprehensive examination; and medical decision making of moderate to high complexity. Counseling and/or coordination of care with other providers or agencies are provided consistent with the nature of the problem(s) and the patient's and/or family's needs. Usually, the patient has developed a significant complication or a significant new problem and has had a major permanent change in status. The creation of a new medical plan of care is required. Physicians typically spend 40 minutes at the bedside and on the patient's facility floor or unit.	56.00	77	88	75
99303	Evaluation and management of a new or established patient involving a nursing facility assessment at the time of initial admission or readmission to the facility, which requires these three key components: a comprehensive history; a comprehensive examination; and medical decision making of moderate to high complexity. Counseling and/or coordination of care with other providers or agencies are provided consistent with the nature of the problem(s) and the patient's and/or family's needs. The creation of a medical plan of care is required. Physicians typically spend 50 minutes at the bedside and on the patient's facility floor or unit.	83.50	114	131	113

Code	Description	Medicode RVU	50th	75th	Medicare Nat'l Avg
99311	Subsequent nursing facility care, per day, for the evaluation and management of a new or established patient, which requires at least two of these three key components: a problem focused interval history; a problem focused examination; medical decision making that is straightforward or of low complexity. Counseling and/or coordination of care with other providers or agencies are provided consistent with the nature of the problem(s) and the patient's and/or family's needs. Usually, the patient is stable, recovering or improving. Physicians typically spend 15 minutes at the bedside and on the patient's facility floor or unit.	32.00	44	50	32
99312	Subsequent nursing facility care, per day, for the evaluation and management of a new or established patient, which requires at least two of these three key components: an expanded problem focused interval history; an expanded problem focused examination; medical decision making of moderate complexity. Counseling and/or coordination of care with other providers or agencies are provided consistent with the nature of the problem(s) and the patient's and/or family's needs. Usually, the patient is responding inadequately to therapy or has developed a minor complication. Physicians typically spend 25 minutes at the bedside and on the patient's facility floor or unit.	38.00	52	59	46
99313	Subsequent nursing facility care, per day, for the evaluation and management of a new or established patient, which requires at least two of these three key components: a detailed interval history; a detailed examination; medical decision making of moderate to high complexity. Counseling and/or coordination of care with other providers or agencies are provided consistent with the nature of the problem(s) and the patient's and/or family's needs. Usually, the patient has developed a significant complication or a significant new problem. Physicians typically spend 35 minutes at the bedside and on the patient's facility floor or unit.	48.00	66	75	58

99321–99333

Domiciliary, Rest Home, or Custodial Care Services

Coding Insight

These codes report care given to patients residing in a long-term care facility that provides room and board as well as other personal assistance services. The facility's services do not include a medical component, and typical times have not been established.

These new patient codes are used when a patient has not received any professional services from the physician or another physician of the same specialty who belongs to the same group practice, within the past three years.

Code	Description	Medicode RVU	50th	75th	Medicare Nat'l Avg
99321	Domiciliary or rest home visit for the evaluation and management of a new patient which requires these three key components: a problem focused history; a problem focused examination; and medical decision making that is straightforward or of low complexity. Counseling and/or coordination of care with other providers or agencies are provided consistent with the nature of the problem(s) and the patient's and/or family's needs. Usually, the presenting problem(s) are of low severity.	43.00	59	67	40

Code	Description	Medicode RVU	50th	75th	Medicare Nat'l Avg
99322	Domiciliary or rest home visit for the evaluation and management of a new patient, which requires these three key components: an expanded problem focused history; an expanded problem focused examination; and medical decision making of moderate complexity. Counseling and/or coordination of care with other providers or agencies are provided consistent with the nature of the problem(s) and the patient's and/or family's needs. Usually, the presenting problem(s) are of moderate severity.	62.00	85	97	55
99323	Domiciliary or rest home visit for the evaluation and management of a new patient, which requires these three key components: a detailed history; a detailed examination; and medical decision making of high complexity. Counseling and/or coordination of care with other providers or agencies are provided consistent with the nature of the problem(s) and the patient's and/or family's needs. Usually, the presenting problem(s) are of high complexity.	82.00	112	128	74
99331	Domiciliary or rest home visit for the evaluation and management of an established patient, which requires at least two of these three key components: a problem focused interval history; a problem focused examination; medical decision making that is straightforward or of low complexity. Counseling and/or coordination of care with other providers or agencies are provided consistent with the nature of the problem(s) and the patient's and/or family's needs. Usually, the patient is stable, recovering or improving.	35.00	48	55	31
99332	Domiciliary or rest home visit for the evaluation and management of an established patient, which requires at least two of these three key components: an expanded problem focused interval history; an expanded problem focused examination; medical decision making of moderate complexity. Counseling and/or coordination of care with other providers or agencies are provided consistent with the nature of the problem(s) and the patient's and/or family's needs. Usually, the patient is responding inadequately to therapy or has developed a minor complication.	43.00	59	67	41
99333	Domiciliary or rest home visit for the evaluation and management of an established patient, which requires at least two of these three key components: a detailed interval history; a detailed examination; medical decision making of high complexity. Counseling and/or coordination of care with other providers or agencies are provided consistent with the nature of the problem(s) and the patient's and/or family's needs. Usually, the patient is unstable or has developed a significant complication or a significant new problem.	54.00	74	84	51

99341–99353
Home Services

CODING INSIGHT
Services and care provided at the patient's home are coded from this subcategory. Typical times have not been established for this code group.

Code	Description	Medicode RVU	50th	75th	Medicare Nat'l Avg
99341	Home visit for the evaluation and management of a new patient, which requires these three key components: a problem focused history; a problem focused examination; and medical decision making that is straightforward or of low complexity. Counseling and/or coordination of care with other providers or agencies are provided consistent with the nature of the problem(s) and the patient's and/or family's needs. Usually, the presenting problem(s) are of low severity.	58.00	79	91	59
99342	Home visit for the evaluation and management of a new patient, which requires these three key components: an expanded problem focused history; an expanded problem focused examination; and medical decision making of moderate complexity. Counseling and/or coordination of care with other providers or agencies are provided consistent with the nature of the problem(s) and the patient's and/or family's needs. Usually, the presenting problem(s) are of moderate severity.	74.00	101	116	75
99343	Home visit for the evaluation and management of a new patient, which requires these three key components: a detailed history; a detailed examination; and medical decision making of high complexity. Counseling and/or coordination of care with other providers or agencies are provided consistent with the nature of the problem(s) and the patient's and/or family's needs. Usually, the presenting problem(s) are of high severity.	94.00	129	147	98
99351	Home visit for the evaluation and management of an established patient, which requires at least two of these three key components: a problem focused interval history; a problem focused examination; medical decision making that is straightforward or of low complexity. Counseling and/or coordination of care with other providers or agencies are provided consistent with the nature of the problem(s) and the patient's and/or family's needs. Usually, the patient is stable, recovering or improving.	55.00	75	86	46
99352	Home visit for the evaluation and management of an established patient, which requires at least two of these three key components: an expanded problem focused interval history; an expanded problem focused examination; medical decision making of moderate complexity. Counseling and/or coordination of care with other providers or agencies are provided consistent with the nature of the problem(s) and the patient's and/or family's needs. Usually, the patient is responding inadequately to therapy or has developed a minor complication.	60.00	82	94	58
99353	Home visit for the evaluation and management of an established patient, which requires at least two of these three key components: a detailed interval history; a detailed examination; medical decision making of high complexity. Counseling and/or coordination of care with other providers or agencies are provided consistent with the nature of the problem(s) and the patient's and/or family's needs. Usually, the patient is unstable or has developed a significant complication or a significant new problem.	72.00	99	113	73

99354–99360
Prolonged Services

Coding Insight
This section of E/M codes includes three service categories:

Prolonged Physician Service with Direct Patient Contact
These codes report services involving direct patient contact beyond the usual service, with separate codes for office or outpatient encounters (99354 and 99355) and for inpatient encounters (99356 and 99357). Prolonged physician services are reportable in addition to other physician services, including any level of E/M service. The codes report the total duration of face-to-face time spent by the physician on a given date, even if the time is not continuous. The physician must be dedicated to the management of the patient and should not be performing unrelated services.

Code 99354 or 99356 reports the first hour of prolonged service on a given date, depending upon the place of service, with 99355 or 99357 used to report each additional 30 minutes for that date. Services lasting less than 30 minutes are not reportable in this category, and the services must extend 15 minutes or more into the next time period to be reportable. For example, services lasting one hour and twelve minutes are reported by code 99354 or 99356 alone. Services lasting one hour and seventeen minutes are reported by the code for the first hour plus the code for an additional 30 minutes. *CPT '96* provides a table on page 34 illustrating correct coding by time spent.

Prolonged Physician Service without Direct Patient Contact
These prolonged physician services without direct patient contact may include review of extensive records and tests and communication (other than telephone calls, 99371–99373) with other professionals and/or the patient and family. These are beyond the usual services and include both inpatient and outpatient settings. Report these services in addition to other services provided, including any level of E/M service.

Use 99358 to report the first hour and 99359 for each additional 30 minutes. All aspects of time reporting are the same as explained above for direct patient contact services.

Physician Standby Service
Code 99360 reports the situation when a physician is requested by another physician to be on standby, and the standby physician has no direct patient contact. The standby physician may not provide services to other patients or be proctoring another physician for the time to be reportable. Also, if the standby physician ultimately provides services subject to a surgical package, the standby is not separately reportable.

This code reports cumulative standby time by date of service. Less than 30 minutes is not reportable, and a full 30 minutes must be spent for each unit of service reported. For example, 25 minutes is not reportable, and 50 minutes is reported as one unit (99360 x 1).

SUBSIDIARY CODES
Subsidiary codes have relative values that require no further adjustment:

99355 is "in addition" to 99354
99357 is "in addition" to 99356
99359 is "in addition" to 99358

Because these are subsidiary or "in addition to" codes, reimbursement reduction and CPT modifier -51 do not apply.

MEDICARE ALERT
Under Medicare rules, Physician Standby Services (99360) are considered to be hospital services and are not payable under the physician fee schedule. No RVUs are assigned to code 99360.

Code	Description	Medicode RVU	50th	75th	Medicare Nat'l Avg
99354	Prolonged physician service in the office or other outpatient setting requiring direct (face-to-face) patient contact beyond the usual service (eg, prolonged care and treatment of an acute asthmatic patient in an outpatient setting); first hour	115.0	157	180	84
99355	Prolonged physician service in the office or other outpatient setting requiring direct (face-to-face) patient contact beyond the usual service (eg, prolonged care and treatment of an acute asthmatic patient in an outpatient setting); each additional 30 minutes	57.50	79	90	84
99356	Prolonged physician service in the inpatient setting, requiring direct (face-to-face) patient contact beyond the usual service (eg, maternal fetal monitoring for high risk delivery or other physiological monitoring, prolonged care of an acutely ill inpatient); first hour	150.0	205	235	81
99357	Prolonged physician service in the inpatient setting, requiring direct (face-to-face) patient contact beyond the usual service (eg, maternal fetal monitoring for high risk delivery or other physiological monitoring, prolonged care of an acutely ill inpatient); each additional 30 minutes	75.00	103	117	81
99358	Prolonged evaluation and management service before and/or after direct (face-to-face) patient care (eg, review of extensive records and tests, communication with other professionals and/or the patient/family); first hour	110.0	150	172	–
99359	Prolonged evaluation and management service before and/or after direct (face-to-face) patient care (eg, review of extensive records and tests, communication with other professionals and/or the patient/family); each additional 30 minutes	55.00	75	86	–
99360	Physician standby service, requiring prolonged physician attendance, each 30 minutes (eg, operative standby, standby for frozen section, for cesarean/high risk delivery for newborn care, for monitoring EEG)	75.00	103	117	–

99361–99373
Case Management Services

CODING INSIGHT

Physician case management is the process of physician-directed care. This includes coordinating and controlling access to the patient or initiating and/or supervising other necessary healthcare services.

The Case Management codes in CPT for team conferences and telephone calls are currently reported with codes 99361–99373.

Medicare considers these services "bundled" into other medical services such as an office or hospital visit, and, therefore, never pays for them separately. Private payers vary in their policies regarding these codes. Medicode recommends that you submit these codes to establish a billing pattern and draw attention to the need for these services.

MEDICARE ALERT

Medicare allows separate payment for these services reported by 99375. Services must be furnished to beneficiaries receiving Medicare-covered home health and hospice services.

Code	Description	Medicode RVU	50th	75th	Medicare Nat'l Avg
99361	Medical conference by a physician with interdisciplinary team of health professionals or representatives of community agencies to coordinate activities of patient care (patient not present); approximately 30 minutes	63.00	86	99	–
99362	Medical conference by a physician with interdisciplinary team of health professionals or representatives of community agencies to coordinate activities of patient care (patient not present); approximately 60 minutes	110.0	150	172	–
99371	Telephone call by a physician to patient or for consultation or medical management or for coordinating medical management with other health care professionals (eg, nurses, therapists, social workers, nutritionists, physicians, pharmacists); simple or brief (eg, to report on tests and/or laboratory results, to clarify or alter previous instructions, to integrate new information from other health professionals into the medical treatment plan, or to adjust therapy)	10.00	14	16	–
99372	Telephone call by a physician to patient or for consultation or medical management or for coordinating medical management with other health care professionals (eg, nurses, therapists, social workers, nutritionists, physicians, pharmacists); intermediate (eg, to provide advice to an established patient on a new problem, to initiate therapy that can be handled by telephone, to discuss test results in detail, to coordinate medical management of a new problem in an established patient, to discuss and evaluate new information and details, or to initiate new plan of care)	25.00	34	39	–
99373	Telephone call by a physician to patient or for consultation or medical management or for coordinating medical management with other health care professionals (eg, nurses, therapists, social workers, nutritionists, physicians, pharmacists); complex or lengthy (eg, lengthy counseling session with anxious or distraught patient, detailed or prolonged discussion with family members regarding seriously ill patient, lengthy communication necessary to coordinate complex services of several different health professionals working on different aspects of the total patient care plan)	50.00	68	78	–

99375–99376
Care Plan Oversight Services

Coding Insight

These codes report the services of a physician providing ongoing review and revision of a patient's care plan involving complex or multi-disciplinary care modalities. Only one physician may report this code per patient per 30-day period, and only then if more than 30 minutes is spent during the 30 days. Do not use this code for supervision of patients in nursing facilities or under the care of home health agencies unless the patient requires recurrent supervision of therapy. Also, low intensity and infrequent supervision services are not reported separately.

Codes 99375 and 99376 identify physician supervision of a patient under the care of a home health agency, in a hospice, or in a nursing facility (if the patient is not present). The patient's condition must require recurrent supervision of therapy and complex or multi-disciplinary care modalities.

Code	Description	Medicode RVU	50th	75th	Medicare Nat'l Avg
99375	Physician supervision of patients under care of home health agencies, hospice or nursing facility patients (patient not present) requiring complex or multidisciplinary care modalities involving regular physician development and/or revision of care plans, review of subsequent reports of patient status, review of related laboratory and other studies, communication (including telephone calls) with other health care professionals involved in patient's care, integration of new information into the medical treatment plan and/or adjustment of medical therapy, within a 30-day period; 30-60 minutes	83.50	114	131	58
99376	Physician supervision of patients under care of home health agencies, hospice or nursing facility patients (patient not present) requiring complex or multidisciplinary care modalities involving regular physician development and/or revision of care plans, review of subsequent reports of patient status, review of related laboratory and other studies, communication (including telephone calls) with other health care professionals involved in patient's care, integration of new information into the medical treatment plan and/or adjustment of medical therapy, within a 30-day period; greater than 60 minutes	0.00	0	0	–

99381–99429
Preventive Medicine Services

Coding Insight

With added emphasis on preventive care, these codes report services provided to healthy patients to promote health and prevent illness or injury. These services include routine examinations performed in the absence of patient complaints or symptoms and counseling or risk factor reduction intervention. The instructional notes in code range 99381–99387 were changed in CPT in 1995.

Nota Bene: Risk factor reduction interventions, counseling, and anticipatory guidance are included in the listed codes and should not be identified separately unless they are provided at a separate encounter. Immunizations, laboratory, radiology, or other procedures are still billed separately. The definition of these codes as routine examinations performed in the absence of patient complaints or symptoms has also been changed; the codes now include a comprehensive history and examination. Patients are still categorized by new or established status and by age.

If a pre-existing problem or abnormality is encountered and requires additional work to perform the key components of a problem-oriented E/M service, a code from the 99201–99215 range, with modifier -25 appended, and the preventive medicine code both should be reported. However, if a trivial and/or insignificant problem is encountered during a preventive medicine visit, it should not be reported separately.

Codes 99401–99404 report counseling provided to healthy individuals at a separate encounter for issues such as family problems, diet and exercise, substance abuse, sexual practices, and so forth. Do not use these codes to report counseling and risk factor reduction services provided to patients with symptoms or illnesses. For patients with symptoms, use the appropriate office, hospital, or consultation codes.

The codes are divided into individual and group counseling, with time as the determining factor. Code 99420 describes the "administration and interpretation of health risk assessment instrument." This subcategory also has its own unlisted service code (99429).

MEDICARE ALERT

Medicare policy dictates that when a physician schedules both a routine physical examination (preventive service) and a Medicare-covered service (E/M service) during the same office visit, the covered service is payable but the routine service is not. Under Medicare policy, you are not required to give the beneficiary written advance notice of noncoverage. HCFA has revised their policy to permit the physician to bill the patient for the noncovered part of the visit. To bill for this service properly you must:

- Determine your usual fee for the noncovered, routine physical examination
- Determine your fee for the covered portion of the examination (nonparticipating physicians use their limiting charge)
- Bill the covered portion using the appropriate E/M visit code (99201–99215) and charge (nonparticipating physicians use their limiting charge)
- Bill the balance (the difference between the noncovered and covered fees) using the preventive medicine codes (99381–99397)

Code	Description	Medicode RVU	50th	75th	Medicare Nat'l Avg
99381	Initial preventive medicine evaluation and management of an individual including a comprehensive history, a comprehensive examination, counseling/anticipatory guidance/risk factor reduction interventions, and the ordering of appropriate laboratory/diagnostic procedures, new patient; infant (age under 1 year)	39.00	53	61	–
99382	Initial preventive medicine evaluation and management of an individual including a comprehensive history, a comprehensive examination, counseling/anticipatory guidance/risk factor reduction interventions, and the ordering of appropriate laboratory/diagnostic procedures, new patient; early childhood (age 1 through 4 years)	42.00	57	66	–
99383	Initial preventive medicine evaluation and management of an individual including a comprehensive history, a comprehensive examination, counseling/anticipatory guidance/risk factor reduction interventions, and the ordering of appropriate laboratory/diagnostic procedures, new patient; late childhood (age 5 through 11 years)	45.00	62	70	–
99384	Initial preventive medicine evaluation and management of an individual including a comprehensive history, a comprehensive examination, counseling/anticipatory guidance/risk factor reduction interventions, and the ordering of appropriate laboratory/diagnostic procedures, new patient; adolescent (age 12 through 17 years)	48.00	66	75	–
99385	Initial preventive medicine evaluation and management of an individual including a comprehensive history, a comprehensive examination, counseling/anticipatory guidance/risk factor reduction interventions, and the ordering of appropriate laboratory/diagnostic procedures, new patient; 18-39 years	65.00	89	102	–
99386	Initial preventive medicine evaluation and management of an individual including a comprehensive history, a comprehensive examination, counseling/anticipatory guidance/risk factor reduction interventions, and the ordering of appropriate laboratory/diagnostic procedures, new patient; 40-64 years	71.00	97	111	–
99387	Initial preventive medicine evaluation and management of an individual including a comprehensive history, a comprehensive examination, counseling/anticipatory guidance/risk factor reduction interventions, and the ordering of appropriate laboratory/diagnostic procedures, new patient; 65 years and over	80.00	109	125	–

Code	Description	Medicode RVU	50th	75th	Medicare Nat'l Avg
99391	Periodic preventive medicine reevaluation and management of an individual including a comprehensive history, comprehensive examination, counseling/anticipatory guidance/risk factor reduction interventions, and the ordering of appropriate laboratory/diagnostic procedures, established patient; infant (age under 1 year)	32.00	44	50	–
99392	Periodic preventive medicine reevaluation and management of an individual including a comprehensive history, comprehensive examination, counseling/anticipatory guidance/risk factor reduction interventions, and the ordering of appropriate laboratory/diagnostic procedures, established patient; early childhood (age 1 through 4 years)	34.00	47	53	–
99393	Periodic preventive medicine reevaluation and management of an individual including a comprehensive history, comprehensive examination, counseling/anticipatory guidance/risk factor reduction interventions, and the ordering of appropriate laboratory/diagnostic procedures, established patient; late childhood (age 5 through 11 years)	37.00	51	58	–
99394	Periodic preventive medicine reevaluation and management of an individual including a comprehensive history, comprehensive examination, counseling/anticipatory guidance/risk factor reduction interventions, and the ordering of appropriate laboratory/diagnostic procedures, established patient; adolescent (age 12 through 17 years)	40.00	55	63	–
99395	Periodic preventive medicine reevaluation and management of an individual including a comprehensive history, comprehensive examination, counseling/anticipatory guidance/risk factor reduction interventions, and the ordering of appropriate laboratory/diagnostic procedures, established patient; 18-39 years	54.00	74	84	–
99396	Periodic preventive medicine reevaluation and management of an individual including a comprehensive history, comprehensive examination, counseling/anticipatory guidance/risk factor reduction interventions, and the ordering of appropriate laboratory/diagnostic procedures, established patient; 40-64 years	59.00	81	92	–
99397	Periodic preventive medicine reevaluation and management of an individual including a comprehensive history, comprehensive examination, counseling/anticipatory guidance/risk factor reduction interventions, and the ordering of appropriate laboratory/diagnostic procedures, established patient; 65 years and over	67.00	92	105	–
99401	Preventive medicine counseling and/or risk factor reduction intervention(s) provided to an individual (separate procedure); approximately 15 minutes	17.50	24	27	–
99402	Preventive medicine counseling and/or risk factor reduction intervention(s) provided to an individual (separate procedure); approximately 30 minutes	35.00	48	55	–
99403	Preventive medicine counseling and/or risk factor reduction intervention(s) provided to an individual (separate procedure); approximately 45 minutes	46.50	64	73	–
99404	Preventive medicine counseling and/or risk factor reduction intervention(s) provided to an individual (separate procedure); approximately 60 minutes	64.00	88	100	–
99411	Preventive medicine counseling and/or risk factor reduction intervention(s) provided to individuals in a group setting (separate procedure); approximately 30 minutes	25.00	34	39	–

Code	Description	Medicode RVU	50th	75th	Medicare Nat'l Avg
99412	Preventive medicine counseling and/or risk factor reduction intervention(s) provided to individuals in a group setting (separate procedure); approximately 60 minutes	50.00	68	78	–
99420	Administration and interpretation of health risk assessment instrument (eg, health hazard appraisal)	0.00	0	0	–
99429	Unlisted preventive medicine service	0.00	0	0	–

99431–99440
Newborn Care

Coding Insight
This series of codes describes care provided to normal or high-risk newborns. The codes identify specific locations such as the hospital or birthing room, other than hospital or birthing room, and the office.

There is no separate code for the hospital discharge of a newborn, so report 99238 for this service.

Codes 99431 and 99432 report initial newborn care. Use 99431 for the infant born in a hospital setting (including birthing room). This code includes the initiation of diagnostic and treatment programs as well as the preparation of hospital records. Use 99432 when an infant is born in a location other than the hospital or birthing room (such as the infant born at home), including the examination and conference held with the parents.

Code 99433 identifies each day's subsequent hospital visit. This code reports the total day's service and is billed only once per day.

Code 99435 is a new code added to *CPT 1996*. It reports history and examination of the normal newborn infant and includes the preparation of medical records. The code specifies that it should only be used when newborns are assessed and discharged from the hospital or birthing room on the same day.

Code 99440 for newborn resuscitation has been changed in *CPT 1996*. It now describes provision of positive pressure ventilation and/or chest compressions in the presence of acute inadequate ventilation and/or cardiac output.

Note that codes 99431, 99432, 99433, and 99440 report newborn services. If an infant is readmitted to the hospital, use 99221– 99233.

Code	Description	Medicode RVU	50th	75th	Medicare Nat'l Avg
99431	History and examination of the normal newborn infant, initiation of diagnostic and treatment programs and preparation of hospital records. (This code should also be used for birthing room deliveries.)	90.00	123	141	84
99432	Normal newborn care in other than hospital or birthing room setting, including physical examination of baby and conference(s) with parent(s)	48.00	66	75	90
99433	Subsequent hospital care, for the evaluation and management of a normal newborn, per day	42.00	57	66	44

	Code	Description	Medicode RVU	50th	75th	Medicare Nat'l Avg
●	**99435**	History and examination of the normal newborn infant, including the preparation of medical records (this code should only be used for newborns assessed and discharged from the hospital or birthing room on the same date)	90.00	123	141	–
▲	**99440**	Newborn resuscitation: provision of positive pressure ventilation and/or chest compressions in the presence of acute inadequate ventilation and/or cardiac output	170.0	233	266	210

99450–99456
Special Evaluation and Management Services

Coding Insight

This series of codes was introduced in CPT in 1995 to report physician evaluations in order to establish baseline information for insurance certification and/or work related or medical disability. These services can be performed in the office or other setting, and no distinction is made between new or established patient.

Codes 99450–99456 should not be used to indicate any active management of problems or conditions. If other E/M services and/or procedures are performed on the same date, report them with the appropriate E/M code in addition to the special evaluation code.

Code 99450 is a basic life or disability examination that includes: a medical history; height, weight, and blood pressure measurement; collecting blood and urine specimens; and filling out the necessary forms and reports.

Codes 99455 and 99456 are used for work-related or medical disability. Use code 99455 for the treating physician and 99456 for other than the treating physician.

When reporting E/M services within a postoperative period by the same physician, append either modifier -24 or modifier -25.

Code	Description	Medicode RVU	50th	75th	Medicare Nat'l Avg
99450	Basic life and/or disability examination that includes: •measurement of height, weight and blood pressure; •completion of a medical history following a life insurance pro forma; •collection of blood sample and/or urinalysis complying with "chain of custody" protocols; and •completion of necessary documentation/certificates	0.00	0	0	–
99455	Work related or medical disability examination by the treating physician that includes: •completion of a medical history commensurate with the patient's condition; •performance of an examination commensurate with the patient's condition; •formulation of a diagnosis, assessment of capabilities and stability, and calculation of impairment; •development of future medical treatment plan; and *completion of necessary documentation/certificates and report.	0.00	0	0	–
99456	Work related or medical disability examination by other than the treating physician that includes: •completion of a medical history commensurate with the patient's condition; •performance of an examination commensurate with the patient's condition; •formulation of a diagnosis, assessment of capabilities and stability, and calculation of impairment; •development of future medical treatment plan; and •completion of necessary documentation/certificates and report.	0.00	0	0	–

99499
Other Evaluation and Management Services

Coding Insight
This is an unlisted code to report services not specifically defined in CPT.

Code	Description	Medicode RVU	50th	75th	Medicare Nat'l Avg
99499	Unlisted evaluation and management service	0.00	0	0	–

Anesthesia Codes 00100-02020

Although the underlying premise for coding anesthesia services is universal, the coding methodologies used to report the services to payers vary. The differences in coding methodology and in payer guidelines, along with the combination of codes used to report anesthesia services, complicate the coding of these services. To report anesthesia services accurately it is necessary to understand the main terms, concepts, and logic behind anesthesia coding as well as the resources available for code selection.

CODING RESOURCES

The two main resources available for coding anesthesia are:

- The American Medical Association's *Physicians' Current Procedural Terminology* (CPT), published and updated yearly by the American Medical Association
- The American Society of Anesthesiologists (ASA) *Relative Value Guide* (RVG), published and updated yearly by the society

ANESTHESIA CODES AND GUIDELINES

CPT guidelines remark that reporting anesthesia services is appropriate under the supervision of a physician. The services include but are not limited to general, regional, supplementation of local anesthesia, or other services considered necessary by the anesthesiologist to provide the patient with the required anesthesia care during any procedure. Anesthesia services include the usual preoperative and postoperative visits, the care during the procedure, the administration of fluids and/or blood, and the usual monitoring services such as temperature, blood pressure, and so forth. Unusual forms of monitoring are not included.

The ASA and CPT descriptions and guidelines for anesthesia services are similar.

Codes 00100-01999 are designated in CPT as the Anesthesia Section, but codes from other areas of CPT may also be used by anesthesiologists (e.g., arterial line insertion, Swan-Ganz insertion, etc.). However, some payers require the use of a CPT code from the Surgery Section (10040-69979) when reporting anesthesia services. This makes reporting anesthesia more difficult since many surgery codes can apply to a single anesthesia code. And, there are codes in the Surgery Section that do not apply to anesthesia, such as code 16020 *Dressings and/or debridement, initial or subsequent; without anesthesia, office or hospital, small*. Since the CPT code description states "without" anesthesia, anesthesia would not be appropriate.

The ASA has designated codes 00100-99199 for use in reporting anesthesia services in its *Relative Value Guide*.

CPT AND ASA CODE DIFFERENCES

The difference between the methodologies, as stated, is not great. Following are the ASA only codes that do not appear in CPT:

00636

00863

01112

01216

01997 (No time is added to this code)

02000

02010

02020 (No time is added to this code)

The CPT only code that does not appear in the ASA guide is:

00865

The descriptor for codes 00863 and 00865 is the same in *CPT '96* and the ASA *Relative Value Guide*.

HOW TO CODE ANESTHESIA

Understanding certain main concepts and terms is essential to report anesthesia services. Keep in mind, however, that neither CPT nor the ASA addresses reimbursement issues (such as a recommended dollar conversion factor charge). CPT also does not recommend any number of units for the base value, time, or modifying units, nor does it list a formula for use in calculating anesthesia services.

STANDARD FORMULA BASED ON UNITS

Each anesthesia service is calculated by units or a relative value unit. Typically, a unit of anesthesia is reported by calculating the total number of units and multiplying them by a dollar amount (conversion factor). The dollar conversion factor can vary, depending upon the location (state/city) where the service was rendered and what the UCR (usual, customary, and reasonable) charge is for the service in the area. Another method is to negotiate a set amount (or accept a mandated amount — required by federal and state programs such as Medicare, Medicaid, and workers compensation programs).

FORMULA

A standard anesthesia formula consists of basic value (units) + time units + modifying units (e.g., physical status and qualifying circumstances) + other* allowed unit charges.

The addition of the base, time, modifying, and other allowed units equals the total amount of anesthesia for the service. This total is then multiplied by a dollar amount (conversion factor) for the area to arrive at a billed amount. As an example:

Base		7
Time	+	6
Modifying units		3
Other units		3
Total units	x	19
Multiplied by Dollar amount (conversion factor)		$25.00
The total amount billed	=	$475.00

*Other codes may be reported in addition to the basic value (units), time, and modifying units (e.g., as Swan-Ganz insertion or daily management of patient controlled analgesia) on a case-by-case basis, depending upon the services rendered. Report these codes in the same manner as other codes from CPT or the RVG.

Nota Bene: Many managed care payers contract for anesthesia services by negotiating a discounted dollar conversion factor for each reported unit of anesthesia. Contracts with managed care organizations for these services should include other anesthesia reporting issues such as how qualifying circumstances, physical status, and pain management will be paid. Be sure to clarify what is and is not covered in the definition of anesthesia services and when will prior authorization be necessary.

Base Units

Base units for anesthesia listed in the RVG are widely accepted across the United States. However, some payers, especially government or agency payers, such as Medicaid or workers compensation programs may use different relative value scales developed exclusively for their use. Other payers may utilize "national relative value guides" generally available in the marketplace, which may or may not be based on the ASA *Relative Value Guide*.

Check with the individual payers to know how they will calculate payment for base units. When two or more procedures are performed, the most widely accepted policy is the ASA *Relative Value Guide* recommendation:

> The Basic Value for anesthesia when multiple surgical procedures are performed during a single anesthetic administration is the Basic Value for the procedure with the highest unit value. The appropriate basic value units, modifying units, and time units may be applied to each anesthetic administration.

Time Units

Time units for anesthesia vary across the country. They may be based on (1) the usual, customary, and reasonable charge for a given area, (2) studies purchased from different vendors, or (3) on data payers have gathered to create their own databases. The ASA recommends "time units will be added to the basic value and modifying units as is customary in the local area." Most time units are based on 15-minute increments, but can be calculated on increments of 10-30 minutes. The following are examples of how time units might be calculated:

Based on 15-Minute Increments

Anesthesia provided from 8:00 a.m. to 10:08 a.m.

Time equals two hours and eight minutes, or 128 minutes

Time		128
	÷	15-minute time increments
	=	
Total anesthesia time units billed	=	8.53 units

Based on 12-Minute Increments

Anesthesia provided from 8:00 a.m. to 10:08 a.m.

Time equals two hours and eight minutes, or 128 minutes

Time		128
	÷	12-minute time increments
	=	
Total anesthesia time units billed	=	10.66 units

Nota Bene: Some payers allow a fraction of anesthesia time to be rounded up to the next whole number, while others require that actual time be reported. Check payer guidelines on time units. The time units in *Fee & Coding Standard* are the HCFA national averages.

Anesthesia time begins when the anesthesiologist is present in the operating room and ends when he or she is no longer in attendance. Anesthesiologists may elect to follow some patients during all or a portion of their stay in the recovery room, in which case the time does not end until the patient is released from the anesthesiologist's care. Medical records should clearly indicate when the patient is released by the anesthesiologist. To qualify for time, the anesthesiologist must be present continuously.

Anesthesia Codes Without Time

Time is not a factor for the following codes. The formula for payment calculation is, typically, the dollar conversion factor multiplied by the number of base units assigned to the code.

01995	Regional IV administration of local anesthetic agent
01996	Daily hospital management of epidural or subarachnoid drug
01997*	Daily hospital management patient - controlled analgesia
02020	Each additional 9% TBSA or part thereof
99100	Anesthesia for patient under 1 year or over 70
99116	Anesthesia complicated - total body hypothermia
99135	Anesthesia complicated - controlled hypotension
99140	Anesthesia complicated by emergency conditions - specify

MODIFYING UNITS

Physical status modifiers and qualifying circumstances, with unit values assigned, are as follows in the ASA *Relative Value Guide*:

Physical Status

Physical status modifiers are represented with an initial letter P followed by a single digit from 1-6 (e.g., P1, P2).

Modifier	*Description*	*Relative Value*
P1	Normal healthy patient	0
P2	Patient with mild systemic disease	0
P3	Patient with severe systemic disease	1
P4	Patient with severe systemic disease that is a constant threat to life	2
P5	Moribund patient who is not expected to survive without the operation	3
P6	A declared brain-dead patient whose organs are being removed for donor purposes	0

Qualifying Circumstances

99100	Anesthesia for patient of extreme age, under one year and over seventy	1
99116	Anesthesia complicated by utilization of total body hypothermia	5
99135	Anesthesia complicated by utilization of controlled hypotension	5
99140	Anesthesia complicated by emergency conditions (specify)	2

(Emergency conditions exist when delay in treatment would lead to a significant increase in the threat to life or body part.)

Both physical status (PS) and qualifying circumstances are listed in CPT and the ASA RVG. However, only the ASA guide assigns units to them.

Nota Bene: Many payers allow reimbursement for physical status and qualifying circumstances. List the applicable modifier or code (alone) on a separate line, when reporting them.

Unusual Monitoring

Unusual forms of monitoring are reported by most anesthesiologists and many payers allow benefits beyond the basic anesthesia service. Codes 36488-36491 (insertion of a central venous catheter), 36620-36625 (insertion of an intra-arterial catheter), and 93503 (Swan-Ganz insertion) represent unusual forms of monitoring that may be rendered by an anesthesiologist.

MEDICARE AND ANESTHESIA CODING

When coding for Medicare reimbursement, it is important to note that HCFA (Health Care Financing Administration) was mandated by OBRA '89 (Omnibus Budget Reconciliation Act [Public Law 1-1-239, enacted December 19, 1989]) to adopt a "uniform relative value guide." The designated guide was the ASA's 1988 RVG — with a few modifications.

Medicare pays for medical and surgical services furnished by an anesthesiologist if rebundling provisions do not preclude separate payment. The services may be furnished in conjunction with the anesthesia procedure or as single services, e.g., during the day of or the day before the anesthesia service. These services include the insertion of a Swan Ganz catheter, the insertion of central venous pressure lines, emergency intubation, and critical care visits.

Medicare and Multiple Anesthesia Procedures

Medicare pays for anesthesia services associated with multiple surgical procedures or multiple bilateral procedures. Payment is determined based on the base unit of the anesthesia procedure with the highest base unit value and time units based on the actual anesthesia time of the multiple procedures.

Most anesthesiologists utilize base units from the ASA *Relative Value Guide*; other relative value guides may differ significantly in the amount of base units — sometimes as much as three or more units difference — in the same codes. How much this affects reimbursement depends upon how time units and other factors are calculated in a given area.

Medicare Policy for Time Units

Currently, Medicare calculates one anesthesia time unit as equivalent to 15 minutes when a physician personally performs an anesthesia procedure. Less than 15 minutes of anesthesia, in total or as part of the total anesthesia time, will be converted to a fraction of 1 time unit (i.e., 12 minutes of anesthesia equals .8 time units).

Beginning January 1, 1996 both the physician medical direction allowance and the medically directed CRNA allowance will be calculated at 55 percent of the allowance that would be recognized if an anesthesiologist performs the procedure.

Time units involve the continuous presence of the physician (or of the medically directed qualified anesthetist or resident) and start when he or she begins preparing the patient for anesthesia care and ends when the anesthesiologist (or medically directed CRNA) is no longer in personal attendance and the patient may be safely placed under postoperative care.

Medicare Policy for Modifying Units

Medicare does not allow additional unit values for physical status modifiers or qualifying circumstances (OBRA '89). Other ASA/CPT anesthesia modifiers are usually recognized by Medicare carriers, but no additional value is allowed.

The following modifiers are currently recognized by HCFA:

- AA Anesthesia services performed personally by anesthesiologist
- AB Medical direction of own employee(s) by anesthesiologist (not more than four employees)

AC Medical direction of other than own employee(s) by anesthesiologist (not more than four individuals)

AD Medical supervision by a physician: more than four concurrent anesthesia procedures

AE Direction of residents in furnishing not more than two concurrent anesthesia services - attending physician relationship met

QJ Two concurrent procedures, medically directed by physician

QS Monitored anesthesiology care services (CRNA or physician; informational only)

QX CRNA with medical direction by physician

QZ CRNA without medical direction by physician

MEDICARE AND UNUSUAL MONITORING

Currently Medicare allows separate payment for specialized procedures such as Swan-Ganz catheters and central venous pressure line furnished by anesthesiologists. The procedures must be reasonable and necessary and not included as services paid under the global surgical fee.

BILLING FOR ANESTHESIA

Billing for anesthesia services should be based on what is customary in the local area. Exceptions to billing for what is customary in the area may be necessary depending on contracts with payers, Medicare, or other mandated billing guidelines.

UNUSUAL ANESTHESIA

CPT defines unusual anesthesia as follows:

> Occasionally, a procedure, which usually requires either no anesthesia or local anesthesia, because of unusual circumstances must be done under general anesthesia. This circumstance may be reported by adding the modifier -23 to the procedure code of the basic service or by use of the separate five-digit modifier code 09923.

Although it is generally inappropriate to report anesthesia with some E/M, Medicine, and Radiology codes, there are situations wherein medical necessity requires anesthesia be used (e.g., a baby, small child, or hard to control patient needs dressings and/or debridement). Under these unusual circumstances payers will usually allow the anesthesia charge. Submit an operative report and cover letter with the claim explaining the need for any unusual anesthesia.

ANESTHESIA AND COSMETIC PROCEDURES

When anesthesia is provided for procedures that may be considered cosmetic, be aware of what the payer has authorized for the service. Anesthesia for cosmetic procedures may be paid in full, partially paid, or denied as patient responsibility. In the event part of a procedure is for cosmetic reasons, the anesthesiologist and surgeon should clearly document when one procedure or portion of a procedure ends and another begins. Claims reviewers/auditors base the patient responsibility and provider payment on the documentation in the medical records, so be certain that all records clearly define procedures performed.

Billing services that submit anesthesia claims to payers in more than one location must be clear on the methodologies and anesthesia coding guidelines to be used. Claims submitted using guidelines from one state will not necessarily apply to another state or locality.

COMMON BILLING ERROR

Incorrect ICD-9 or CPT coding is a frequent problem encountered in anesthesia reporting. The code(s) may be incorrect because they do not match the diagnosis or procedure reported by the surgeon. Make certain when submitting claims that the anesthesiologist's report reflects the same diagnosis and procedure(s) as the surgeon's.

CHOOSING AN ANESTHESIA CODE BY A SURGICAL CODE

Certain codes in the Surgery Section of CPT are subsidiary codes, i.e., a procedure that is secondary to a more primary code. Choose the primary code to determine an appropriate anesthesia cross-code when submitting claims.

For example, code 11001 is a subsidiary code. The primary procedure code is 11000 *Debridement of extensive eczematous or infected skin; up to 10% of body surface*. Code 11001 should not be reported alone but always with or "in addition to" 11000 because its description states "each additional 10% of the body surface." In this case, the appropriate CPT code for determining anesthesia payment guidelines is 11000.

00100-00222
Head

MEDICARE ALERT

Medicare unbundles certain codes in the Anesthesia section when the listed codes are considered a component of a more comprehensive service.

36400-36410, 36430, 36600, 64443, 67500, 92950, 94700, 94710, G0001 will not be reimbursed when reported with 00140

36430, 36600, 94700, 94710 will not be reimbursed when reported with 00142

Code	Description	RVU	Time Unit
00100	Anesthesia for procedures on integumentary system of head and/or salivary glands, including biopsy; not otherwise specified	5	7.26
00102	Anesthesia for procedures on integumentary system of head and/or salivary glands, including biopsy; plastic repair of cleft lip	6	8.53
00103	Anesthesia for procedures on integumentary system of head and/or salivary glands, including biopsy; blepharoplasty	6	N/A
00104	Anesthesia for electroconvulsive therapy	4	1.55
00120	Anesthesia for procedures on external, middle, and inner ear including biopsy; not otherwise specified	5	8.11
00124	Anesthesia for procedures on external, middle, and inner ear including biopsy; otoscopy	4	3.62
00126	Anesthesia for procedures on external, middle, and inner ear including biopsy; tympanotomy	4	3.49
00140	Anesthesia for procedures on eye; not otherwise specified	5	5.87
00142	Anesthesia for procedures on eye; lens surgery	6	4.74
00144	Anesthesia for procedures on eye; corneal transplant	6	7.91
00145	Anesthesia for procedures on eye; vitrectomy	6	8.93
00147	Anesthesia for procedures on eye; iridectomy	6	5.94
00148	Anesthesia for procedures on eye; ophthalmoscopy	4	5.53
00160	Anesthesia for procedures on nose and accessory sinuses; not otherwise specified	5	7.05

Code	Description	RVU	Time Unit
00162	Anesthesia for procedures on nose and accessory sinuses; radical surgery	7	9.32
00164	Anesthesia for procedures on nose and accessory sinuses; biopsy, soft tissue	4	5.68
00170	Anesthesia for intraoral procedures, including biopsy; not otherwise specified	5	6.11
00172	Anesthesia for intraoral procedures, including biopsy; repair of cleft palate	6	8.74
00174	Anesthesia for intraoral procedures, including biopsy; excision of retropharyngeal tumor	6	6.62
00176	Anesthesia for intraoral procedures, including biopsy; radical surgery	7	20.52
00190	Anesthesia for procedures on facial bones; not otherwise specified	5	9.67
00192	Anesthesia for procedures on facial bones; radical surgery (including prognathism)	7	18.46
00210	Anesthesia for intracranial procedures; not otherwise specified	11	15.20
00212	Anesthesia for intracranial procedures; subdural taps	5	6.38
00214	Anesthesia for intracranial procedures; burr holes	9	7.82
00215	Anesthesia for intracranial procedures; elevation of depressed skull fracture, extradural (simple or compound)	9	N/A
00216	Anesthesia for intracranial procedures; vascular procedures	15	21.05
00218	Anesthesia for intracranial procedures; procedures in sitting position	13	14.48
00220	Anesthesia for intracranial procedures; spinal fluid shunting procedures	10	8.76
00222	Anesthesia for intracranial procedures; electrocoagulation of intracranial nerve	6	5.93

00300-00352
Neck

Coding Insight
The ASA *Relative Value Guide* lists five base units for field avoidance: when a procedure is performed around the head, neck, or shoulder girdle, or when the patient is positioned other than lithotomy or supine. For more information on ASA guidelines consult the ASA RVG.

Medicare Alert
Medicare unbundles certain codes in the Anesthesia section when the listed codes are considered a component of a more comprehensive service.

36430, 36600, 94700, 94710 will not be reimbursed when reported with 00320, 00350

92585 will not be reimbursed when reported with 00350

Code	Description	RVU	Time Unit
00300	Anesthesia for all procedures on integumentary system of neck, including subcutaneous tissue	5	6.54
00320	Anesthesia for all procedures on esophagus, thyroid, larynx, trachea and lymphatic system of neck; not otherwise specified	6	6.50
00322	Anesthesia for all procedures on esophagus, thyroid, larynx, trachea and lymphatic system of neck; needle biopsy of thyroid	3	6.97
00350	Anesthesia for procedures on major vessels of neck; not otherwise specified	10	10.98
00352	Anesthesia for procedures on major vessels of neck; simple ligation	5	4.89

00400-00474
Thorax (Chest Wall and Shoulder Girdle)

Code	Description	RVU	Time Unit
00400	Anesthesia for procedures on anterior integumentary system of chest, including subcutaneous tissue; not otherwise specified	3	5.03
00402	Anesthesia for procedures on anterior integumentary system of chest, including subcutaneous tissue; reconstructive procedures on breast (eg, reduction or augmentation mammoplasty, muscle flaps)	5	10.87
00404	Anesthesia for procedures on anterior integumentary system of chest, including subcutaneous tissue; radical or modified radical procedures on breast	5	8.80
00406	Anesthesia for procedures on anterior integumentary system of chest, including subcutaneous tissue; radical or modified radical procedures on breast with internal mammary node dissection	13	9.11
00410	Anesthesia for procedures on anterior integumentary system of chest, including subcutaneous tissue; electrical conversion of arrhythmias	4	2.03
00420	Anesthesia for procedures on posterior integumentary system of chest, including subcutaneous tissue	5	6.27
00450	Anesthesia for procedures on clavicle and scapula; not otherwise specified	5	6.74
00452	Anesthesia for procedures on clavicle and scapula; radical surgery	6	10.14
00454	Anesthesia for procedures on clavicle and scapula; biopsy of clavicle	3	5.81
00470	Anesthesia for partial rib resection; not otherwise specified	6	8.24
00472	Anesthesia for partial rib resection; thoracoplasty (any type)	10	11.39
00474	Anesthesia for partial rib resection; radical procedures (eg, pectus excavatum)	13	12.75

00500-00580
Intrathoracic

Coding Insight
When more than one anesthesiologist must be present during a surgery, payers often apply the ASA guideline for five base units plus time units.

In cases where hospital policy requires that a second anesthesiologist be present payers may allow both anesthesiologists the actual base units for the surgery. Know the payer's policy regarding this issue before submitting a claim.

Payers often deny a ventilation assist and management code when reported for a procedure that routinely requires transfer of the patient to ICU.

The word "diagnostic" was added to 00520–00528, and the words "(including surgical thoracoscopy)" were added to the description of 00540–00548 in *CPT '96*.

MEDICARE ALERT

Medicare unbundles certain codes in the Anesthesia section when the listed codes are considered a component of a more comprehensive service.

36430, 36600, 92585, 94700, 94710 will not be reimbursed when reported with 00562

	Code	Description	RVU	Time Unit
	00500	Anesthesia for all procedures on esophagus	15	21.13
▲	**00520**	Anesthesia for closed chest procedures (including esophagoscopy, bronchoscopy, diagnostic thoracoscopy); not otherwise specified	6	5.32
▲	**00522**	Anesthesia for closed chest procedures (including esophagoscopy, bronchoscopy, thoracoscopy); needle biopsy of pleura	4	5.44
▲	**00524**	Anesthesia for closed chest procedures (including esophagoscopy, bronchoscopy, thoracoscopy); pneumocentesis	4	4.36
▲	**00528**	Anesthesia for closed chest procedures (including esophagoscopy, bronchoscopy, thoracoscopy); mediastinoscopy	8	7.39
	00530	Anesthesia for transvenous pacemaker insertion	4	6.92
	00532	Anesthesia for access to central venous circulation	4	4.97
	00534	Anesthesia for transvenous insertion or replacement of cardioverter/defibrillator	7	N/A
▲	**00540**	Anesthesia for thoracotomy procedures involving lungs, pleura, diaphragm, and mediastinum (including surgical thoracoscopy); not otherwise specified	13	12.99
▲	**00542**	Anesthesia for thoracotomy procedures involving lungs, pleura, diaphragm, and mediastinum; decortication	15	13.32
▲	**00544**	Anesthesia for thoracotomy procedures involving lungs, pleura, diaphragm, and mediastinum; pleurectomy	15	14.00
▲	**00546**	Anesthesia for thoracotomy procedures involving lungs, pleura, diaphragm, and mediastinum; pulmonary resection with thoracoplasty	15	15.59
▲	**00548**	Anesthesia for thoracotomy procedures involving lungs, pleura, diaphragm, and mediastinum; intrathoracic repair of trauma to trachea and bronchi	15	14.86
	00560	Anesthesia for procedures on heart, pericardium, and great vessels of chest; without pump oxygenator	15	10.89
	00562	Anesthesia for procedures on heart, pericardium, and great vessels of chest; with pump oxygenator	20	22.27
	00580	Anesthesia for heart transplant or heart/lung transplant	20	27.01

00600-00670
Spine and Spinal Cord

CODING INSIGHT
Codes for reporting chronic pain management, trigger point injections, nerve blocks, destruction by neurolytic agent, spinal cord injections, and neurostimulators are found in CPT; refer to the index to find the proper code.

MEDICARE ALERT
Medicare unbundles certain codes in the Anesthesia section when the listed codes are considered a component of a more comprehensive service.

36430, 36600, 62278, 62289, 64440-64442, 92585, 94700, 94710 will not be reimbursed when reported with 00630

Code	Description	RVU	Time Unit
00600	Anesthesia for procedures on cervical spine and cord; not otherwise specified	10	14.31
00604	Anesthesia for procedures on cervical spine and cord; posterior cervical laminectomy in sitting position	13	13.44
00620	Anesthesia for procedures on thoracic spine and cord; not otherwise specified	10	15.34
00622	Anesthesia for procedures on thoracic spine and cord; thoracolumbar sympathectomy	13	10.08
00630	Anesthesia for procedures in lumbar region; not otherwise specified	8	11.30
00632	Anesthesia for procedures in lumbar region; lumbar sympathectomy	7	7.95
00634	Anesthesia for procedures in lumbar region; chemonucleolysis	10	1.92
00670	Anesthesia for extensive spine and spinal cord procedures (eg, Harrington rod technique)	13	21.82

00700-00796
Upper Abdomen

MEDICARE ALERT
Medicare unbundles certain codes in the Anesthesia section when the listed codes are considered a component of a more comprehensive service.

36430, 36600, 62278, 94700, 94710 will not be reimbursed when reported with 00790

Code	Description	RVU	Time Unit
00700	Anesthesia for procedures on upper anterior abdominal wall; not otherwise specified	3	5.99
00702	Anesthesia for procedures on upper anterior abdominal wall; percutaneous liver biopsy	4	7.67
00730	Anesthesia for procedures on upper posterior abdominal wall	5	6.94
00740	Anesthesia for upper gastrointestinal endoscopic procedures	5	3.29
00750	Anesthesia for hernia repairs in upper abdomen; not otherwise specified	4	6.62

Code	Description	RVU	Time Unit
00752	Anesthesia for hernia repairs in upper abdomen; lumbar and ventral (incisional) hernias and/or wound dehiscence	6	7.45
00754	Anesthesia for hernia repairs in upper abdomen; omphalocele	7	9.12
00756	Anesthesia for hernia repairs in upper abdomen; transabdominal repair of diaphragmatic hernia	7	11.55
00770	Anesthesia for all procedures on major abdominal blood vessels	15	18.01
00790	Anesthesia for intraperitoneal procedures in upper abdomen including laparoscopy; not otherwise specified	7	9.88
00792	Anesthesia for intraperitoneal procedures in upper abdomen including laparoscopy; partial hepatectomy (excluding liver biopsy)	13	19.03
00794	Anesthesia for intraperitoneal procedures in upper abdomen including laparoscopy; pancreatectomy, partial or total (eg, Whipple procedure)	8	23.85
00796	Anesthesia for intraperitoneal procedures in upper abdomen including laparoscopy; liver transplant (recipient)	30	41.76

00800-00884
Lower Abdomen
Obstetrical Anesthesia Codes

Coding Insight
Obstetrical anesthesia can be accomplished by epidural or general anesthesia and are as follows:

Epidural obstetrical anesthesia codes are: 00857 *Continuous epidural analgesia, for labor and C-section*, and 00955 *Continuous epidural analgesia, for labor and vaginal delivery*.

General obstetrical anesthesia codes are 00850 *Anesthesia for C-section*, 00855 *Anesthesia for cesarean hysterectomy*, and 00946 *Anesthesia for vaginal delivery*.

Calculation of time units for epidural obstetrical anesthesia for vaginal deliveries may vary, but are generally based on the amount of documented time actually spent at the patient's bedside.

When labor for a vaginal delivery fails and a cesarean is necessary, code only the base units (highest) for the cesarean, not the base units for both procedures. This guideline applies to epidural anesthesia during the entire labor and delivery or when the labor portion is under an epidural and the delivery portion is under a general anesthetic.

Calculate time units for the labor portion of a continuous epidural anesthesia for a vaginal delivery by what is customary in the area or by payer preference (usually only the actual time the anesthesiologist spent at the bedside is reimbursable). For a general anesthetic, calculate time in full because the provider must be continuously present.

Medicare Alert
Medicare unbundles certain codes in the Anesthesia section when the listed codes are considered a component of a more comprehensive service.

36430, 36600, 62278, 94700, 94710 will not be reimbursed when reported with 00830, 00840

Code	Description	RVU	Time Unit
00800	Anesthesia for procedures on lower anterior abdominal wall; not otherwise specified	3	5.88
00802	Anesthesia for procedures on lower anterior abdominal wall; panniculectomy	5	10.47
00810	Anesthesia for intestinal endoscopic procedures	6	3.74
00820	Anesthesia for procedures on lower posterior abdominal wall	5	6.56
00830	Anesthesia for hernia repairs in lower abdomen; not otherwise specified	4	6.69
00832	Anesthesia for hernia repairs in lower abdomen; ventral and incisional hernias	6	7.55
00840	Anesthesia for intraperitoneal procedures in lower abdomen including laparoscopy; not otherwise specified	6	10.27
00842	Anesthesia for intraperitoneal procedures in lower abdomen including laparoscopy; amniocentesis	4	7.45
00844	Anesthesia for intraperitoneal procedures in lower abdomen including laparoscopy; abdominoperineal resection	7	14.94
00846	Anesthesia for intraperitoneal procedures in lower abdomen including laparoscopy; radical hysterectomy	8	13.06
00848	Anesthesia for intraperitoneal procedures in lower abdomen including laparoscopy; pelvic exenteration	8	19.41
00850	Anesthesia for intraperitoneal procedures in lower abdomen including laparoscopy; cesarean section	7	7.15
00855	Anesthesia for intraperitoneal procedures in lower abdomen including laparoscopy; cesarean hysterectomy	8	11.61
00857	Continuous epidural analgesia, for labor and cesarean section	7	10.33
00860	Anesthesia for extraperitoneal procedures in lower abdomen, including urinary tract; not otherwise specified	6	10.22
00862	Anesthesia for extraperitoneal procedures in lower abdomen, including urinary tract; renal procedures, including upper 1/3 of ureter, or donor nephrectomy	7	13.01
00864	Anesthesia for extraperitoneal procedures in lower abdomen, including urinary tract; total cystectomy	8	24.43
● 00865	Anesthesia for extraperitoneal procedures in lower abdomen, including urinary tract; radical prostatectomy (suprapubic, retropubic)	7	N/A
00866	Anesthesia for extraperitoneal procedures in lower abdomen, including urinary tract; adrenalectomy	10	14.86
00868	Anesthesia for extraperitoneal procedures in lower abdomen, including urinary tract; renal transplant (recipient)	10	18.32
00870	Anesthesia for extraperitoneal procedures in lower abdomen, including urinary tract; cystolithotomy	5	6.79
00872	Anesthesia for lithotripsy, extracorporeal shock wave; with water bath	7	6.77
00873	Anesthesia for lithotripsy, extracorporeal shock wave; without water bath	5	6.63
00880	Anesthesia for procedures on major lower abdominal vessels; not otherwise specified	15	18.84

Code	Description	RVU	Time Unit
00882	Anesthesia for procedures on major lower abdominal vessels; inferior vena cava ligation	10	5.81
00884	Anesthesia for procedures on major lower abdominal vessels; transvenous umbrella insertion	5	5.58

00900-00955
Perineum

Medicare Alert

Medicare unbundles certain codes in the Anesthesia section when the listed codes are considered a component of a more comprehensive service.

36430, 36600, 62278, 94700, 94710 will not be reimbursed when reported with 00910–00914

Code	Description	RVU	Time Unit
00900	Anesthesia for procedures on perineal integumentary system (including biopsy of male genital system); not otherwise specified	3	5.02
00902	Anesthesia for procedures on perineal integumentary system (including biopsy of male genital system); anorectal procedure (including endoscopy and/or biopsy)	4	4.49
00904	Anesthesia for procedures on perineal integumentary system (including biopsy of male genital system); radical perineal procedure	7	15.41
00906	Anesthesia for procedures on perineal integumentary system (including biopsy of male genital system); vulvectomy	4	7.78
00908	Anesthesia for procedures on perineal integumentary system (including biopsy of male genital system); perineal prostatectomy	6	13.65
00910	Anesthesia for transurethral procedures (including urethrocystoscopy); not otherwise specified	3	4.19
00912	Anesthesia for transurethral procedures (including urethrocystoscopy); transurethral resection of bladder tumor(s)	5	4.85
00914	Anesthesia for transurethral procedures (including urethrocystoscopy); transurethral resection of prostate	5	6.31
00916	Anesthesia for transurethral procedures (including urethrocystoscopy); post-transurethral resection bleeding	5	5.57
00918	Anesthesia for transurethral procedures (including urethrocystoscopy); with fragmentation and/or removal of ureteral calculus	5	6.01
00920	Anesthesia for procedures on male external genitalia; not otherwise specified	3	5.26
00922	Anesthesia for procedures on male external genitalia; seminal vesicles	6	6.36
00924	Anesthesia for procedures on male external genitalia; undescended testis, unilateral or bilateral	4	5.22
00926	Anesthesia for procedures on male external genitalia; radical orchiectomy, inguinal	4	5.14
00928	Anesthesia for procedures on male external genitalia; radical orchiectomy, abdominal	6	6.63
00930	Anesthesia for procedures on male external genitalia; orchiopexy, unilateral or bilateral	4	5.41

Code	Description	RVU	Time Unit
00932	Anesthesia for procedures on male external genitalia; complete amputation of penis	4	8.57
00934	Anesthesia for procedures on male external genitalia; radical amputation of penis with bilateral inguinal lymphadenectomy	6	13.73
00936	Anesthesia for procedures on male external genitalia; radical amputation of penis with bilateral inguinal and iliac lymphadenectomy	8	15.15
00938	Anesthesia for procedures on male external genitalia; insertion of penile prosthesis (perineal approach)	4	9.43
00940	Anesthesia for vaginal procedures (including biopsy of labia, vagina, cervix or endometrium); not otherwise specified	3	3.78
00942	Anesthesia for vaginal procedures (including biopsy of labia, vagina, cervix or endometrium); colpotomy, colpectomy, colporrhaphy	4	7.93
00944	Anesthesia for vaginal procedures (including biopsy of labia, vagina, cervix or endometrium); vaginal hysterectomy	6	10.16
00946	Anesthesia for vaginal procedures (including biopsy of labia, vagina, cervix or endometrium); vaginal delivery	5	11.28
00948	Anesthesia for vaginal procedures (including biopsy of labia, vagina, cervix or endometrium); cervical cerclage	4	4.28
00950	Anesthesia for vaginal procedures (including biopsy of labia, vagina, cervix or endometrium); culdoscopy	5	4.83
00952	Anesthesia for vaginal procedures (including biopsy of labia, vagina, cervix or endometrium); hysteroscopy	4	3.95
00955	Continuous epidural analgesia, for labor and vaginal delivery	5	15.56

01000-01190
Pelvis (Except Hip)

Code	Description	RVU	Time Unit
01000	Anesthesia for procedures on anterior integumentary system of pelvis (anterior to iliac crest), except external genitalia	3	6.17
01110	Anesthesia for procedures on posterior integumentary system of pelvis (posterior to iliac crest), except perineum	5	7.05
01120	Anesthesia for procedures on bony pelvis	6	8.38
01130	Anesthesia for body cast application or revision	3	5.81
01140	Anesthesia for interpelviabdominal (hindquarter) amputation	15	16.21
01150	Anesthesia for radical procedures for tumor of pelvis, except hindquarter amputation	8	15.54
01160	Anesthesia for closed procedures involving symphysis pubis or sacroiliac joint	4	6.34
01170	Anesthesia for open procedures involving symphysis pubis or sacroiliac joint	8	10.39
01180	Anesthesia for obturator neurectomy; extrapelvic	3	7.70
01190	Anesthesia for obturator neurectomy; intrapelvic	4	5.72

01200-01274
Upper Leg (Except Knee)

Medicare Alert
Medicare unbundles certain codes in the Anesthesia section when the listed codes are considered a component of a more comprehensive service.

36430, 36600, 62278, 94700, 94710 will not be reimbursed when reported with 01210–01214, 01230, 01270

64441 will not be reimbursed when reported with 01230, 01270

Code	Description	RVU	Time Unit
01200	Anesthesia for all closed procedures involving hip joint	4	4.22
01202	Anesthesia for arthroscopic procedures of hip joint	4	8.83
01210	Anesthesia for open procedures involving hip joint; not otherwise specified	6	8.54
01212	Anesthesia for open procedures involving hip joint; hip disarticulation	10	11.20
01214	Anesthesia for open procedures involving hip joint; total hip replacement or revision	9	12.45
01220	Anesthesia for all closed procedures involving upper 2/3 of femur	4	6.55
01230	Anesthesia for open procedures involving upper 2/3 of femur; not otherwise specified	6	8.51
01232	Anesthesia for open procedures involving upper 2/3 of femur; amputation	5	6.97
01234	Anesthesia for open procedures involving upper 2/3 of femur; radical resection	8	10.09
01240	Anesthesia for all procedures on integumentary system of upper leg	3	5.82
01250	Anesthesia for all procedures on nerves, muscles, tendons, fascia, and bursa of upper leg	4	6.35
01260	Anesthesia for all procedures involving veins of upper leg, including exploration	3	8.79
01270	Anesthesia for procedures involving arteries of upper leg, including bypass graft; not otherwise specified	8	15.31
01272	Anesthesia for procedures involving arteries of upper leg, including bypass graft; femoral artery ligation	4	7.55
01274	Anesthesia for procedures involving arteries of upper leg, including bypass graft; femoral artery embolectomy	6	9.29

01300-01444
Knee and Popliteal Area

Medicare Alert
Medicare unbundles certain codes in the Anesthesia section when the listed codes are considered a component of a more comprehensive service.

36430, 36600, 62278, 64441, 94700, 94710 will not be reimbursed when reported with 01402

Code	Description	RVU	Time Unit
01300	Anesthesia for all procedures on integumentary system of knee and/or popliteal area	3	5.66
01320	Anesthesia for all procedures on nerves, muscles, tendons, fascia, and bursa of knee and/or popliteal area	4	6.71
01340	Anesthesia for all closed procedures on lower 1/3 of femur	4	7.33
01360	Anesthesia for all open procedures on lower 1/3 of femur	5	10.45
01380	Anesthesia for all closed procedures on knee joint	3	3.23
01382	Anesthesia for arthroscopic procedures of knee joint	3	6.08
01390	Anesthesia for all closed procedures on upper ends of tibia, fibula, and/or patella	3	6.00
01392	Anesthesia for all open procedures on upper ends of tibia, fibula, and/or patella	4	8.83
01400	Anesthesia for open procedures on knee joint; not otherwise specified	4	7.65
01402	Anesthesia for open procedures on knee joint; total knee replacement	7	11.58
01404	Anesthesia for open procedures on knee joint; disarticulation at knee	5	7.22
01420	Anesthesia for all cast applications, removal, or repair involving knee joint	3	6.31
01430	Anesthesia for procedures on veins of knee and popliteal area; not otherwise specified	3	12.92
01432	Anesthesia for procedures on veins of knee and popliteal area; arteriovenous fistula	5	9.49
01440	Anesthesia for procedures on arteries of knee and popliteal area; not otherwise specified	5	12.62
01442	Anesthesia for procedures on arteries of knee and popliteal area; popliteal thromboendarterectomy, with or without patch graft	8	13.36
01444	Anesthesia for procedures on arteries of knee and popliteal area; popliteal excision and graft or repair for occlusion or aneurysm	8	16.95

01460-01522
Lower Leg (Below Knee)

MEDICARE ALERT

Medicare unbundles certain codes in the Anesthesia section when the listed codes are considered a component of a more comprehensive service.

36430, 36600, 62278, 64441, 94700, 94710 will not be reimbursed when reported with 01480

Code	Description	RVU	Time Unit
01460	Anesthesia for all procedures on integumentary system of lower leg, ankle, and foot	3	5.29
01462	Anesthesia for all closed procedures on lower leg, ankle, and foot	3	5.45
01464	Anesthesia for arthroscopic procedures of ankle joint	3	7.91

Code	Description	RVU	Time Unit
01470	Anesthesia for procedures on nerves, muscles, tendons, and fascia of lower leg, ankle, and foot; not otherwise specified	3	5.82
01472	Anesthesia for procedures on nerves, muscles, tendons, and fascia of lower leg, ankle, and foot; repair of ruptured Achilles tendon, with or without graft	5	8.07
01474	Anesthesia for procedures on nerves, muscles, tendons, and fascia of lower leg, ankle, and foot; gastrocnemius recession (eg, Strayer procedure)	5	8.69
01480	Anesthesia for open procedures on bones of lower leg, ankle, and foot; not otherwise specified	3	7.10
01482	Anesthesia for open procedures on bones of lower leg, ankle, and foot; radical resection	4	7.07
01484	Anesthesia for open procedures on bones of lower leg, ankle, and foot; osteotomy or osteoplasty of tibia and/or fibula	4	8.80
01486	Anesthesia for open procedures on bones of lower leg, ankle, and foot; total ankle replacement	7	11.48
01490	Anesthesia for lower leg cast application, removal, or repair	3	5.28
01500	Anesthesia for procedures on arteries of lower leg, including bypass graft; not otherwise specified	8	15.19
01502	Anesthesia for procedures on arteries of lower leg, including bypass graft; embolectomy, direct or catheter	6	9.69
01520	Anesthesia for procedures on veins of lower leg; not otherwise specified	3	8.88
01522	Anesthesia for procedures on veins of lower leg; venous thrombectomy, direct or catheter	5	8.24

01600-01682
Shoulder and Axilla

Code	Description	RVU	Time Unit
01600	Anesthesia for all procedures on integumentary system of shoulder and axilla	3	5.60
01610	Anesthesia for all procedures on nerves, muscles, tendons, fascia, and bursa of shoulder and axilla	5	7.88
01620	Anesthesia for all closed procedures on humeral head and neck, sternoclavicular joint, acromioclavicular joint, and shoulder joint	4	4.03
01622	Anesthesia for arthroscopic procedures of shoulder joint	4	9.10
01630	Anesthesia for open procedures on humeral head and neck, sternoclavicular joint, acromioclavicular joint, and shoulder joint; not otherwise specified	5	9.17
01632	Anesthesia for open procedures on humeral head and neck, sternoclavicular joint, acromioclavicular joint, and shoulder joint; radical resection	6	10.85
01634	Anesthesia for open procedures on humeral head and neck, sternoclavicular joint, acromioclavicular joint, and shoulder joint; shoulder disarticulation	9	11.49
01636	Anesthesia for open procedures on humeral head and neck, sternoclavicular joint, acromioclavicular joint, and shoulder joint; interthoracoscapular (forequarter) amputation	15	10.53

Code	Description	RVU	Time Unit
01638	Anesthesia for open procedures on humeral head and neck, sternoclavicular joint, acromioclavicular joint, and shoulder joint; total shoulder replacement	10	13.28
01650	Anesthesia for procedures on arteries of shoulder and axilla; not otherwise specified	6	8.44
01652	Anesthesia for procedures on arteries of shoulder and axilla; axillary-brachial aneurysm	10	10.49
01654	Anesthesia for procedures on arteries of shoulder and axilla; bypass graft	8	13.32
01656	Anesthesia for procedures on arteries of shoulder and axilla; axillary-femoral bypass graft	10	17.67
01670	Anesthesia for all procedures on veins of shoulder and axilla	4	5.98
01680	Anesthesia for shoulder cast application, removal or repair; not otherwise specified	3	5.04
01682	Anesthesia for shoulder cast application, removal or repair; shoulder spica	4	6.93

01700-01784
Upper Arm and Elbow

Code	Description	RVU	Time Unit
01700	Anesthesia for all procedures on integumentary system of upper arm and elbow	3	5.60
01710	Anesthesia for procedures on nerves, muscles, tendons, fascia, and bursa of upper arm and elbow; not otherwise specified	3	5.83
01712	Anesthesia for procedures on nerves, muscles, tendons, fascia, and bursa of upper arm and elbow; tenotomy, elbow to shoulder, open	5	6.47
01714	Anesthesia for procedures on nerves, muscles, tendons, fascia, and bursa of upper arm and elbow; tenoplasty, elbow to shoulder	5	9.46
01716	Anesthesia for procedures on nerves, muscles, tendons, fascia, and bursa of upper arm and elbow; tenodesis, rupture of long tendon of biceps	5	7.93
01730	Anesthesia for all closed procedures on humerus and elbow	3	5.46
01732	Anesthesia for arthroscopic procedures of elbow joint	3	7.99
01740	Anesthesia for open procedures on humerus and elbow; not otherwise specified	4	8.42
01742	Anesthesia for open procedures on humerus and elbow; osteotomy of humerus	5	9.48
01744	Anesthesia for open procedures on humerus and elbow; repair of nonunion or malunion of humerus	5	12.16
01756	Anesthesia for open procedures on humerus and elbow; radical procedures	6	10.89
01758	Anesthesia for open procedures on humerus and elbow; excision of cyst or tumor of humerus	5	6.92
01760	Anesthesia for open procedures on humerus and elbow; total elbow replacement	7	15.83

Code	Description	RVU	Time Unit
01770	Anesthesia for procedures on arteries of upper arm and elbow; not otherwise specified	6	9.30
01772	Anesthesia for procedures on arteries of upper arm and elbow; embolectomy	6	7.52
01780	Anesthesia for procedures on veins of upper arm and elbow; not otherwise specified	3	6.25
01782	Anesthesia for procedures on veins of upper arm and elbow; phleborrhaphy	4	9.36
01784	Anesthesia for repair of arterio-venous (A-V) fistula, congenital or acquired	6	8.50

01800-01860
Forearm, Wrist and Hand

Anesthesia Provided by Hand Surgeon

Regional or general anesthesia provided by a surgeon can be reported by appending modifier -47 to the surgery code. Payment for this service varies and may be based on time only or on base units only.

Code	Description	RVU	Time Unit
01800	Anesthesia for all procedures on integumentary system of forearm, wrist, and hand	3	5.57
01810	Anesthesia for all procedures on nerves, muscles, tendons, fascia, and bursa of forearm, wrist, and hand	3	5.26
01820	Anesthesia for all closed procedures on radius, ulna, wrist, or hand bones	3	4.85
01830	Anesthesia for open procedures on radius, ulna, wrist, or hand bones; not otherwise specified	3	7.69
01832	Anesthesia for open procedures on radius, ulna, wrist, or hand bones; total wrist replacement	6	10.03
01840	Anesthesia for procedures on arteries of forearm, wrist, and hand; not otherwise specified	6	8.25
01842	Anesthesia for procedures on arteries of forearm, wrist, and hand; embolectomy	6	7.00
01844	Anesthesia for vascular shunt, or shunt revision, any type (eg, dialysis)	6	8.50
01850	Anesthesia for procedures on veins of forearm, wrist, and hand; not otherwise specified	3	5.93
01852	Anesthesia for procedures on veins of forearm, wrist, and hand; phleborrhaphy	4	5.60
01860	Anesthesia for forearm, wrist, or hand cast application, removal, or repair	3	4.47

01900-01922
Radiological Procedures

Code	Description	RVU	Time Unit
01900	Anesthesia for injection procedure for hysterosalpingography	3	5.15
01902	Anesthesia for burr hole(s) for ventriculography	9	7.15
01904	Anesthesia for injection procedure for pneumoencephalography	7	3.02
01906	Anesthesia for injection procedure for myelography; lumbar	5	4.85
01908	Anesthesia for injection procedure for myelography; cervical	5	5.28
01910	Anesthesia for injection procedure for myelography; posterior fossa	9	4.48
01912	Anesthesia for injection procedure for diskography; lumbar	5	3.66
01914	Anesthesia for injection procedure for diskography; cervical	6	3.99
01916	Anesthesia for arteriograms, needle; carotid, or vertebral	5	6.95
01918	Anesthesia for arteriograms, needle; retrograde, brachial or femoral	5	4.72
01920	Anesthesia for cardiac catheterization including coronary arteriography and ventriculography (not to include Swan-Ganz catheter)	7	5.19
01921	Anesthesia for angioplasty	7	5.73
01922	Anesthesia for non-invasive imaging or radiation therapy	7	6.05

01990-01999
Other Procedures

Coding Insight

Consults should not be reported on the same day as the anesthesia code for daily management of epidural or subarachnoid drug administration.

At the end of surgery when an injection for pain management is utilized, be certain to document the actual end of the anesthesia for the procedure. Auditors will usually not pay for an injection for pain when a catheter is already in place and they are paying the provider for his/her actual time. Careful documentation stating what was actually done to prepare, administer, and set-up for the pain management will help distinguish between the two procedures.

Code	Description	RVU	Time Unit
01990	Physiological support for harvesting of organ(s) from brain-dead patient	7	0.12
01995	Regional IV administration of local anesthetic agent (upper or lower extremity)	5	0.10
01996	Daily management of epidural or subarachnoid drug administration	3	0.00
01999	Unlisted anesthesia procedure(s)	0	N/A

Surgery Introduction

Reimbursement guidelines, often different among carriers, make The Surgery Section of CPT a challenge for even experienced coders; but, carrier reimbursement rates are not necessarily low and audits and "red tape" do not have to cause undue problems. Think of coding and reimbursement as being a game of skill, not a game of chance. The skill is in knowing how to code, report, and get reimbursed correctly for your services. Doing so will enable you to receive the maximum possible reimbursement within the guidelines established by the federal government and private payers.

Be sure to read and follow all the guidelines in this section. Contrary to widely-held beliefs, correct coding and reporting frequently increases rather than decreases reimbursement.

SURGERY SECTION ARRANGEMENT

The surgery section of CPT includes three types of procedures: (1) package, (2) diagnostic, and (3) starred services. They are presented in subsections, listed by body system or anatomical site. Several subsections contain notes, which give instructions, directions, and point out the special needs associated with codes within that subsection. Follow the directions carefully within the notes and other coding rules to ensure accurate coding and maximum reimbursement.

Integumentary System	10040–19499
Musculoskeletal System	20000–29909 *
Respiratory System	30000–32960
Cardiovascular System	33010–37799 *
Hemic and Lymphatic System	38100–38999
Mediastinum and Diaphragm	39000–39545
Digestive System	40490–49999
Urinary System	50010–53675
Male Genital System	54000–55899
Intersex Surgery	55970–55980
Laparoscopy/Peritoneoscopy/Hysteroscopy	56300–56399 *
Female Genital System	46405–59350
Maternity Care and Delivery	59000–59899 *
Endocrine System	60000–60699
Nervous System	61000–64999
Eye and Adnexa	65091–65114
Auditory System	69000–69979

* Contain notes

SURGICAL CODING METHODOLOGY

Use a step-by-step approach for determining the correct fees for surgical procedures. Correct coding will generally increase revenue and the level of confidence the payer has in the claims you submit. It will also decrease turn-around time in processing, which increases cash flow and decreases the likelihood of appeals, denials, and audits. Checking each claim you submit against the guidelines listed below will help improve coding accuracy.

1. Read the surgery guidelines at the beginning of the surgery section.
2. Locate in the index the code that most accurately describes the procedure(s) performed.
3. Read the descriptive nomenclature of that code carefully, and read any information before and after the code that might give directions. Make sure your documentation or operative report justifies the use of the code.
4. Page back as necessary to the subheading for the code and read any notes or directions for that section that apply to the code.
5. Watch for notes or see references that apply to the code you wish to use. Does a note specify the code cannot be used with another code; does it send you to another area for a more correct code; or does it explain additional procedures that may be reported with the code?
6. Consider the code and what is included in it. Do not unbundle, but do not miss the opportunity to code additional procedures not included in the code.
7. Enter the code correctly onto the claim form, always listing the most revenue intensive code first.
8. If more than one code is used, apply the correct modifier(s) that apply to the second and additional codes. Never cut the cost of codes appended with modifiers; let the payer make any necessary adjustments.
9. On the HCFA-1500 claim form, apply the correct diagnostic codes and indicate next to the CPT code in the correct box every diagnosis that applies to the surgery or procedure.
10. Attach operative reports to all claims unless instructed to do otherwise by the payer, and follow any contractual arrangements you may have with the entity you are billing.

When coding, never use just the index; references may be for a code that has been deleted. And, do not just "flip" to a code and use it. Always go to the beginning of the subheading and read and apply any directions listed.

Do not rely completely on a computerized coding system to give you the correct code. While computer systems were meant to speed up coding time, they were not meant to replace the coding books from which the information came. The most sophisticated coding programs are not capable of applying the correct codes and rules every time.

If the code has been deleted or a note below the code sends you to another code, always look it up — an older reference may not have been deleted. Look also at other codes in the area; you may find a code that more accurately describes the procedure(s) performed.

Look for key phrases both in the operative report and within the code description that can help determine the correct code (e.g., with or without, includes, separate procedure, eponym [procedure name], single, unilateral, bilateral, excludes, primary, secondary, in addition, open, closed, etc.).

If you encounter persistent problems with a particular type of claim (and if the payer's claims department cannot satisfactorily resolve the problem) contact the provider relations individual responsible for your contract. Although there may be a CPT code describing a procedure, payers may not be obligated to reimburse a physician for that service. Insurance companies have a variety of payment guidelines for surgery services, and a particular code may not be covered. Following is an explanation of some of the most common CPT surgical terminology.

GLOBAL SURGERY OR SURGICAL PACKAGE

In CPT, global surgery or the surgical package consists of normal performance of specific surgical services, i.e., without any complications. The assumption is that "on average, all surgical procedures of a given type are similar with respect to skill level, duration, and length of normal follow-up care." The majority of the CPT surgical codes are package services and include related minor procedures and normal follow-up. Reimbursement for package procedures listed in CPT includes the actual surgical service, local or topical anesthesia, metacarpal or digital block, and an allowance for normal postoperative care.

When a patient is seen for a routine follow-up postoperative visit within the normal follow-up period, use 99024 for documentation purposes only.

The surgical package does not include the following:

- Preoperative care (under certain circumstances)
- Postoperative complications
- Care unrelated to the surgery

PREOPERATIVE CARE

Although CPT does not list preoperative examination and care of the patient in its designation of "Listed Surgical Procedures," it is discussed in the introduction to the surgical section and mentioned again in Appendix A in connection with modifier -25 and modifier -57. Modifier -25 concerns separate E/M services provided on the same day as other services or procedures, and modifier -57 indicates the decision for surgery. However, the rules about preoperative care performed before the day of surgery without mention of a "decision for surgery" — even on the day of surgery — are varied. Many payers assume it is included in the global surgery package. Some carriers have strict guidelines that identify not only the number of preoperative days included, but also the number of hours. Other payers are more liberal and allow a separate payment for care prior to surgery or even same-day care. (These payers, however, may change their policies as they attempt to find ways to cut expenditures).

Because of the different interpretations of preoperative care by payers, it is necessary to understand and negotiate the best possible contract with the carrier. In other words, take advantage of any extra benefits that you may be able to negotiate. For other noncontracted payers it is a good idea to develop a written policy regarding these types of issues. It will help your office staff to have specific billing rules they can reference that lets insurance auditors know your billing protocol is consistent. And, it makes it easier for your staff to appeal denials.

Existing contracts should specify a payer's rules. Make note of these rules for contracted payers and for those most frequently billed

POSTOPERATIVE CARE

Postoperative care only includes normal, uncomplicated follow-up care. Treatment of complications such as wound dehiscence, infection, and bleeding can be reported separately. Report inpatient and outpatient services for these postoperative complications in addition to the surgical service. The diagnostic code and all medical records documentation should reflect the exacerbation or acute nature of the problem being treated. Use modifier -78 to identify a return to the operating room to manage postoperative complications.

Unrelated Care

Always code services unrelated to the operative problem, such as care for other diseases or injuries, with an appropriate inpatient or outpatient level of service and corresponding diagnostic code that identifies a problem other than the surgical diagnosis.

Negotiating Contracts

When negotiating contracts try to stipulate that preoperative services will be paid separately. Because CPT rules are somewhat unclear in this area, both parties should know what to expect, both in the reporting and the in payment of this type of claim. If the payer believes it should be included in the global surgical package, have the circumstances under which it would be paid specified. Each additional preoperative service for which you get paid can add significant revenue to your practice.

Make sure that the same service is not redone at a later date before or on the day of surgery or that another provider does not perform the same service. You don't want to appear to be "gouging." If you change the way you have been doing business, document it, and give reasons why the change was made. That way, if you are audited (or in future contract negotiations) you can explain why you have reviewed and changed your policy.

FRAGMENTED BILLING

The process of coding incidental services separately from a major surgical procedure is called "unbundling" or "fragmenting." If the component is considered part of the surgery package, do not code it individually. In other words, ask yourself what usually happens with the service or procedure. Examples of minor procedures that are always included in the package for a primary surgical service include:

- Local infiltration of medication
- Closure of surgically created wounds, minor debridement, and wound culture
- Exploration of operative area
- Intra-operative photos and video imaging
- Lysis of moderate amounts of adhesions and fulguration of bleeding points
- Application of dressings and most splints

As payers become increasingly more proficient in interpreting reimbursement codes, you must exercise caution when reporting incidental procedures, even when benefits are allowed for those services. Medicare and Medicaid closely monitor physician reporting practices for possible abusive or fraudulent billing. Private payers also have mechanisms in place for careful scrutiny of all claims.

When physicians contract with health maintenance organizations (HMOs) and preferred provider organizations (PPOs), they agree to report according to the guidelines established by those groups. There appears to be no firm incentive for physicians to refrain from unbundling their services when billing commercial payers. Payers can, however, ask for refunds when services are reported incorrectly. In addition, private payers are obligated to report abusive billing practices to local peer review organizations.

How to Avoid Fragmented Billing

Your practice can take some easy steps to avoid problems with fragmented or unbundled reporting. Although they may not completely eliminate the problem in your office, they can help control it.

Step 1: Have a current CPT book available in your office, as well as the rules and regulations and provider manuals for Medicare and for the private payers with whom you have contractual arrangements.

Step 2: Educate all staff and physicians regarding the guidelines to CPT as well as the rules and regulations of your payers.

Step 3: When using a preprinted charge ticket or routing sheet, specify the exact CPT description. Always have an area on the charge ticket that can be checked to indicate that you want the service hand coded or coded from the operative report or medical record. (Many providers feel they are reimbursed better by having coding done directly from the record or operative report).

Step 4: Create your charge tickets or routing sheets to avoid fragmented billing. Adding the abbreviation "SP" to codes such as 49000 *Exploratory laparotomy, exploratory celiotomy with or without biopsy(s) (separate procedure)* alerts the coder that this is a "separate procedure" and cannot be reported when it is related to, or integral to, a major procedure.

Step 5: Learn to provide documentation that offers complete and concise information to the coder.

Medicare and "Fragmentation"

The Medicare code editor rebundles codes which HCFA feels have been unbundled or fragmented. The list is updated periodically every year. The unbundled or fragmented codes are identified in this publication in each section under the heading **Medicare Alert**, as well as other pertinent Medicare information.

GLOBAL SURGERY AND MEDICARE

Preoperative Care

The surgeon's initial evaluation or consultation to determine the necessity for surgery is not considered part of the global payment; a separate allowance is made. Modifier -57 has been created to identify when the decision for surgery is made. Once the decision for surgery has been made, preoperative visits for care of the surgical problem, other than the initial evaluation, are usually included in the surgical package. Preoperative visits for care of the surgical problem other than the initial evaluation beginning one day prior to surgery, regardless of location, are included in the surgical fee.

Postoperative Care

Medicare's policy defines the postoperative period for nearly all major surgical services as 90 days following the date of surgery. (Minor surgeries have either a zero- or a 10-day postoperative period. See Medicare's Minor and Nonincisional Procedures Policy.) The following are included in postoperative care:

- Dressing change and local incisional care
- Removal of operative packs
- Removal of cutaneous sutures, staples, lines, wires, tubes, drains, casts, and splints
- Insertion, irrigation, and removal of urinary catheters
- Insertion and removal of routine peripheral IV line, NG, and rectal tubes
- Change and removal of tracheostomy tubes

Medicare's position on unrelated problems is unchanged. When a patient is seen during the postoperative period for an unrelated problem, services such as the following are paid separately:

- The initial consultation or evaluation by the surgeon to determine the need for surgery
- Services of other physicians except where there is an agreed upon transfer of care. This agreement may be in the form of a letter or an annotation in the discharge summary, hospital record, or ASC record
- Visits unrelated to the diagnosis for which the surgical procedure is performed, unless the visits occur due to complications of the surgery
- Treatment for the underlying condition or an added course of treatment that is not part of normal recovery from surgery
- Diagnostic tests and procedures, including diagnostic radiological procedures
- Clearly distinct surgical procedures during the postoperative period that are not re-operations or treatment for complications. (A new postoperative period begins with the subsequent procedure.) This includes procedures done in two or more parts for which the decision to stage the procedure is made prospectively or at the time of the first procedure. Examples of this are procedures to diagnose and treat epilepsy (61533, 61534–61536, 61539, 61541, and 61543), which may be performed in succession within 90 days of each other
- Treatment for postoperative complications that requires a return trip to the operating room (OR). An OR in this instance is defined as a place of service specifically equipped and staffed for the sole purpose of performing procedures. The term includes a cardiac catheterization suite, laser suite, treatment room, recovery room, or an intensive care unit (unless the patient's condition was so critical that there is insufficient time for transportation to an OR)
- If a less extensive procedure fails, and a more extensive procedure is required, the second procedure is payable separately. They must be identified clearly by the ICD-9 code for the problem
- Certain services performed in a physician's office requiring use of a surgical tray. Splints and casting supplies are also payable separately under the reasonable charge payment methodology
- Immunosuppressive therapy for organ transplants
- Critical care services (99291 and 99292) unrelated to the surgery where a seriously injured or burned patient is critically ill and requires constant attendance of the physician

COMPLICATIONS

Medicare allows reimbursement for postoperative complications requiring a return trip to the operating room. These services are denoted with modifier -78 Return to the operating room for a related procedure during the postoperative period. The payment level for these "re-operations" for complication is set at the value of the intra-operative portion of the procedure described by the CPT code. If there is no code, payment cannot exceed 50 percent of the intra-operative portion of the service originally performed.

MEDICARE AND MINOR PROCEDURES

Included in this list of procedures are many of the "starred" procedures as well as some diagnostic and therapeutic endoscopy procedures.

Same-Day Evaluation or Consultation

Same-day services are included unless they are unrelated to, or can be identified separately from, the procedure.

Postoperative Care

Minor surgeries have either a zero- or a 10-day postoperative period. Those with 10-day periods include all services related to the recovery from surgery. Other services during that period, whether for the underlying condition or for an unrelated condition, are paid separately.

Endoscopic procedures performed through an existing body orifice have no postoperative days. Incisional procedures, such as laparoscopy, include 10 or 90 days of postoperative care, depending upon the complexity of the procedure.

DIAGNOSTIC SERVICES

Diagnostic services are not strictly global procedures. Code the care for the condition for which the diagnostic service was performed, or other concomitant conditions, separately. Diagnostic services may be performed with consultative services. However, the diagnostic services are then part of the overall assessment and should not be the treatment of the patient. The consultant does not assume the patient's medical management. It is important to understand the difference between diagnostic and therapeutic services.

Diagnostic services are performed to determine or establish a patient's diagnosis. This could be, for example, diagnostic arthroscopy or injection procedures for radiography. Diagnostic services include performance of the procedure and recovery of the patient after the procedure. Additional care of the underlying disease or injury may be coded separately. The follow-up period for diagnostic procedures is variable. Check with frequently-billed payers for their policies.

THERAPEUTIC SERVICES

Therapeutic services are performed for definitive treatment of a specific diagnosis. These services include performance of the procedure, various incidental elements, and normal follow-up care related to the procedure.

ENDOSCOPIC PROCEDURES

Endoscopic procedures are often performed through an existing orifice. The procedure is considered diagnostic when the scope is placed into a body cavity to visualize an abnormality or to determine the extent of a disease. When the endoscope is placed for visualization and treatment of the abnormality or disease, the procedure is considered therapeutic.

When reporting for endoscopic procedures, adhere to these general guidelines:

- A diagnostic endoscope is reported only when performed alone.
- The diagnostic endoscopic procedure is incidental to the therapeutic endoscopic procedure.
- A diagnostic endoscopy can be reported when it leads to incisional therapeutic services.
- When an endoscopic procedure has been aborted or is incomplete, use modifier -52 (reduced services) to identify this unique service.

Endoscopic procedures include minor related functions. For example:

- IV sedation. Components of performing sedation include: 36000 *Introduction of needle or intracatheter, vein,* 90782 *Therapeutic or diagnostic injection; subcutaneous or intramuscular,* 90784 *Therapeutic or diagnostic injection (specify material injected).*

- Placement of the endoscope
- Diagnostic evaluation
- Videotaping/monitoring
- Irrigation and suction
- Control of minor bleeding

Medicare Endoscopy

Special payment rules apply when multiple endoscopy procedures are rendered at the same session. HCFA has identified "families" of related endoscopies and has developed a "base" endoscopy for each family. The rules apply to services performed after December 31, 1994.

Payment for multiple related endoscopies is determined as follows: 100 percent for the primary endoscopy plus the difference between the Medicare Fee Schedule amount for the next highest procedure and the base endoscopy amount. No payment is made for a secondary procedure if the base procedure has a higher value. This payment adjustment applies only when the related multiple procedures are performed through the same orifice. Medicare will not pay for any portion of a diagnostic procedure when it is reimbursing for other secondary surgical procedures performed through the same orifice and at the same time.

Multiple Endoscopy Groupings

Base Code	Related Procedure Codes
29815	29819–29823, 29825–29826
29830	29834–29838
29840	29843–29847
29870	29871, 29874–29877, 29879–29887
31237	31238–31240, 31254–31256, 31267
31245	31246–31249, 31251
31250	31252, 31258
31260	31263, 31265, 31268
31261	31262, 31264, 31266, 31269, 31271
31270	31275, 31277
31280	31281–31284, 31286
31287	31288
31292	31293–31294
31505	31510–31513
31525	31527–31530, 31535, 31540, 31560, 31570
31526	31531, 31536, 31541, 31561, 31571
31575	31576–31579
31622	31625, 31628–31631, 31635, 31640–31641, 31645
43200	43202, 43204–43205, 43215–43217, 43219–43220, 43226–43228
43235	43239, 43241, 43243–42347, 42349–42351, 43255, 43258–43259
43260	3261–43265, 43267–43269, 43271–43272
44360	44361, 44363–44366, 44369, 44372–44373
44376	44377–44378
44388	44389–44394
45300	45303, 45305, 45307–45309, 45315, 45317, 45320–45321
45330	45331–45334, 45337–45339
45378	45379–45380, 45382–45385
46600	46604, 46606, 46608, 46610–46612, 46614–46615
47522	47553–47556
50551	50555, 50557, 50559, 50561
50570	50572, 50574–50576, 50578, 50580

Base Code	Related Procedure Codes
50951	50953, 50955, 50957, 50959, 50961
50970	50974, 50976
52000	52007, 52010, 52204, 52214, 52224, 52250, 52260, 52265, 52270, 52275–52277, 52281, 52283, 52285, 52290, 52300, 52305, 52310, 52315, 52317–52318
52205	52320, 52325, 52327, 52330, 52332, 52334
52335	52336–52339
56300	56301–56309, 56311
56350	56351–56356
57452	57454, 57460

Special reimbursement rules apply to multiple endoscopic procedures. The payment for multiple procedures depends upon the endoscopic procedures performed on one day.

"Stand Alone" endoscopy procedures (procedures that do not have a base code) and single endoscopy procedures from several different code families are reimbursed under the multiple surgery guidelines at 100 percent for the first endoscopy procedure, 50 percent for the second through fifth procedures. Subsequent procedures are by report.

An example of Medicare's payment rules is as follows:

In the course of performing a fiberoptic colonoscopy (45378), a physician performs a biopsy on a lesion (45380) and removes a polyp (45385) from a different part of the colon. The physician reports 45380 and 45385. Codes 45380 and 45385 both have the value of the diagnostic colonoscopy (45387) built in. Rather than paying 100 percent for the highest valued procedure (45385) and 50 percent for the next (45380), the full value of the higher valued endoscopy (45385) is paid, plus the difference between the next highest endoscopy (45380) and the base endoscopy (45378).

Assume the following fee schedule amounts for these codes:

45385	=	$374.56 (Not on base list — pay at full value)
45378	=	$255.40
Plus		
45380	=	$285.98
		$ 30.58 (On base list — pay difference between 45378 and 45380)
Total payment		$405.14

MATERIALS SUPPLIED BY A PHYSICIAN

Some CPT services do not include any provision for medications and sterile trays. Therefore, you can code them separately. Additionally, those supplies and services over and above those usually included with the office visit or service rendered may be reported separately using 99070.

Many insurers reimburse only for supplies that are excessive or extraordinarily expensive. Do not report supplies that are customarily included in surgical packages, such as gauze, sponges, applicators, or steri-strips. Applicable CPT codes are the following:

99070	for supplies, including reusable and disposable items. Specify the supply or type of medication and the amount that was provided.
96545	for the "provision of chemotherapy agent."

92330 and 92335	for ocular prostheses. Additional supplies relating to the eye (including contact lens and spectacles) are identified with 92390–92396.
78990 and 79900	for radiopharmaceutical(s), diagnostic or therapeutic respectively.

Billing Medicare and Medicaid

To report injectable medications, use HCPCS Level II "J" codes and specify the type of medication and amount used. Other HCPCS codes report more specifically the supplies your practice uses.

Attach a statement to the billing form, as indicated, informing the payer of the physician's cost, including a reasonable charge for handling, and provide a description of the supply used.

Since many payers do not reimburse supplies provided by physicians, monitor EOBs to assure that charges for supplies were allowed and reimbursed. Monitoring also alerts you to payers who recognize HCPCS codes or have an internal coding system for medicines and supplies. With the deletion of the narrative space following the code on the HCFA-1500 form, payers may be more likely to recognize HCPCS Level II codes to avoid the need for contacting the patient or provider for additional information.

Medicare's Supply Policy

Medicare makes no special allowance for supplies routinely furnished in the course of patient care in the office. Included here are supplies used in laceration repairs and when administering chemotherapy. Chemotherapy drugs, however, are not considered routine supplies. Splints, casting supplies, and surgical dressings are allowed separately.

Exceptions are made for certain expensive, and mostly disposable, supplies used in the performance of facility-based procedures in a physician's office. The facility-based national list has 72 procedures (listed below), including bunion correction, endoscopy (esophagus, upper GI, and operative upper GI), colonoscopy, and several others. When the physician performs one of these procedures in the office, report HCPCS code A4550. The following trays are a few of those included under that code:

- Lumbar puncture tray
- Thoracentesis tray
- Cystoscopy tray
- Surgical tray
- Catheter insertion tray
- Bone marrow aspiration tray
- Venous access catheter

The reimbursement by Medicare for A4550 is limited and does not offer much of a financial advantage to the physician. In deciding whether to provide these services in your office, consider the convenience factor for your practice, as well as the proportions of your practice that are Medicare and non-Medicare. Private payers may be more liberal in their allowance for surgical supplies.

Physicians may receive separate reimbursement for A4263 *Permanent, long-term, nondissolvable lacrimal duct implant, each* when reported with 68761.

Reimbursement may also be made for A4300 *Implantable access portal/catheter (venous, arterial, epidural, or peritoneal)* when reported with 36533.

Medicare Facility-based National List
Medicare will pay for the surgical tray associated with the following CPT codes:

19101	A4550	36533	A4300	45382	A4550	52276	A4550
19120	A4550	37609	A4550	45383	A4550	52277	A4550
19125	A4550	38500	A4550	45384	A4550	52283	A4550
19126	A4550	43200	A4550	45385	A4550	52290	A4550
20200	A4550	43202	A4550	49080	A4550	52300	A4550
20205	A4550	43220	A4550	49081	A4550	52305	A4550
20220	A4550	43226	A4550	52005	A4550	52310	A4550
20225	A4550	43234	A4550	52007	A4550	52315	A4550
20240	A4550	43235	A4550	52010	A4550	57520	A4550
25111	A4550	43239	A4550	52204	A4550	57522	A4550
28290	A4550	43245	A4550	52214	A4550	58120	A4550
28292	A4550	43247	A4550	52224	A4550	62270	A4550
28293	A4550	43249	A4550	52234	A4550	68761	A4263
28294	A4550	43250	A4550	52235	A4550	85095	A4550
28296	A4550	43251	A4550	52240	A4550	85102	A4550
28297	A4550	43458	A4550	52250	A4550	95028	G0025
28298	A4550	45378	A4550	52260	A4550	96440	A4550
28299	A4550	45379	A4550	52270	A4550	96445	A4550
32000	A4550	45380	A4550	52275	A4550	96450	A4550

MULTIPLE PROCEDURES

Multiple procedures are defined by CPT as occurring on the same day or at the same session. To report multiple procedures, list the highest dollar value code as the primary procedure and appending modifier -51 to subsequent procedures. Although definitions of just what a multiple procedure is vary widely among payers (some use modifier -51 to mean through the same incision or in the same area, while some use modifier -50 to mean bilateral or when performed at the same surgical session at separate and remote sites), most generally agree on the terminology on the same day, during the same operative session. This is one area where your practice should have a clearly documented policy. Know how the various payers you bill interpret these rules and bill accordingly. Define what is a multiple procedure in your contracts, and monitor payments by the contracted and noncontracted payers.

MEDICARE'S POLICY CLAIMS FOR MULTIPLE SURGERIES

Co-surgeons, surgical teams, or assistants at surgery may participate in performing multiple surgeries on the same patient on the same day.

Multiple surgeries are distinguished from procedures that are components of or incidental to a primary procedure. These intra-operative services, incidental surgeries, or components of more major surgeries are not separately reportable.

Medicare will pay the lesser of the actual charge or 100 percent of the fee schedule amount for the highest priced procedure. Payment for the second through fifth procedures is based on the lesser of the actual charge or 50 percent of the fee schedule amount. Surgical procedures beyond the fifth procedure continue to be "by report" and based on documentation of the services performed.

The standard multiple surgery policy is now the same as the policy that applies to multiple dermatology procedures. Because Medicare estimated this new policy would result in increased 1995 Medicare payments of approximately $35 million, the relative value units were reduced in an effort to remain budget-neutral. It was thought that the reduction would result in approximately 0.1 percent reduction to the relative value units. However, Medicare states that "[g]iven the increase in the CFs for all services, we do not believe that physicians will see a reduction in payment as a result of this payment policy change."

SEPARATE PROCEDURES

Separate procedure codes are often misread and improperly coded as related cases. Related cases refer to procedures with the same diagnosis, same operative area, and same indication. Reporting a separate procedure in addition to the larger procedure to which it is related produces fragmented billing because it is actually a component of, or incidental to, the larger related procedure.

To reduce fragmented billing, review the surgical codes you report that include the notation (separate procedure), and apply the following guidelines:

- Code separate procedures only when the procedure is performed alone rather than in conjunction with related procedures
- When a procedure that is ordinarily a component of a larger procedure is performed alone for a specific purpose, list it by itself or as a multiple procedure with modifier -51 attached. In other words, it is unrelated to the other procedure(s) performed in a multiple setting. The operative report and associated ICD-9 code must substantiate reporting a separate procedure in conjunction with another major surgical procedure

UNLISTED SERVICE OR PROCEDURE

Unlisted procedures should only be used when the overall procedure and outcome of the surgery is not adequately described by an existing CPT code. If an existing CPT description closely describes the procedure performed, report that code with modifier -22 Unusual Services or -52 Reduced Services.

Unlisted codes are reported "by report." Extensive documentation is required for proper reimbursement. Insurance claims with unlisted codes take longer to process since they are usually sent to medical review for individual claims submission. Documentation should include the following:

- A definition or description of the nature, extent, and medical necessity of the procedure
- A statement of the time and effort necessary to provide the service
- A comparison of the procedure to existing procedure codes and descriptions

SETTING FEES FOR UNLISTED PROCEDURES

Pricing of procedures is far from an exact science — particularly when it comes to setting fees for by report, unlisted, or new procedures with no historical fee-for-service data or relative values. Without historical pricing data or relative values to fall back on, it may be difficult to persuade payers to reimburse medically necessary procedures at a fair and full level. To receive fair reimbursement for services performed, substantiate that procedures are appropriately priced. Two techniques can be used to price most by report, unlisted, or new procedure(s):

1. Break down the procedure into identifiable and mutually exclusive component procedures.

   This first technique assumes that the component procedures are listed as identifiable CPT codes for which historical fee-for-service data or relative values are established. These amounts serve as a good basis for setting fees. In turn, fees for each of the component procedures can be added to arrive at a total fee for the whole procedure. If the first technique is applicable, you should carefully select the component procedures to avoid fragmentation.

2. Compare the service with a known CPT procedure that is similar in nature.

   The second technique may be more appropriate if component procedures of the service are not identifiable or do not have established fee-for-service data or relative values. In comparing the service with a known CPT procedure, consider such factors as risk, time, pre- and postoperative management, and the required level of technical training.

When reporting any new or unlisted procedure, remember to include documentation that shows service and pricing rationale.

PRICING EXAMPLE: BREAKING THE SERVICE INTO COMPONENTS

This example demonstrates how to set fees by breaking down an unlisted service into identifiable and mutually exclusive component procedures.

Scenario

In performing intercranial surgery for a 47-year-old man, a neurosurgeon asks a vascular surgeon to induce hypothermia in the patient to slow down all body systems. To initiate the hypothermia, the vascular surgeon places arterial and venous catheters in a lower extremity and initiates extracorporeal cooling. The vascular surgeon takes additional time to monitor the patient for three hours during the remainder of the surgery. Following surgery, the vascular surgeon rewarms the patient, removes the catheters, and repairs the artery and veins. The vascular surgeon then spends three additional hours monitoring the patient in postoperative critical care.

Setting a Fee for the Service

To set a fee for the service, identify the mutually exclusive (unfragmented) components. It is important that no services overlap. The induced hypothermia can be broken down into the following identifiable procedures:

Procedural Components	*CPT Code*	*50th**	*90th*
Arterial catheterization for monitoring, cutdown	36625	$183	$260
Venipuncture, cutdown	36425	$100	$150
Prolonged detention, 3 hours			
first hour	99356	$190	$262
additional hours	99357x 4	$380	$524
Arterial repair, lower extremity	35226	$2,055	$2,780
Venous repair, lower extremity	35226	$2,055	$2,780
Post-operative critical care, 3 hours			
first hour	99291	$253	$34
additional 2 hours	99292x 4	$508	$700

* Average fees at the 50th and 90th percentiles for geographic zip code for example purposes only.

Breaking the Service into Component Procedures

The induced hypothermia should be reported with 99199 *Unlisted special service or report*. Code 99186 identifies total body hypothermia; however, this code only represents cooling of a patient by immersion in cold water or ice (i.e., by external means), and does not accurately represent the procedure. To substantiate the pricing methodology, code the component procedures with appropriate modifiers, if applicable. Using the 90th percentile average reimbursement, the procedure may be coded and priced as follows:

(Note: The following pricing breakdown is for example purposes only and does not reflect co-surgery splits, reporting of other modifiers, etc.)

35226	$2,780
35226-51	$1,390
36625-51	$130
36425-51	$75
99356	$262
99357 x 4	$524
99291	$349
99292 x 4	$700
Total fee:	$6,210

SPECIAL REPORT

Special reports are required for surgeries that are rare, unusual, or that vary from normal services. They require special handling to determine both medical necessity and reimbursement. All pertinent information, like time and effort, description, unusual or special equipment, and the reason for the surgery, should be reported. Include diagnosis, symptoms (and their complexity), other major/minor procedures, size, shape, location of lesion(s), other problems that ran concurrently, complex symptoms, prior authorization, previous or exacerbating problems, and any other pertinent documentation that will aid the reviewer in making a determination about the claim.

STARRED PROCEDURES OR SERVICES

Some surgical services are characterized by indefinite pre- and postoperative services. Because of these indefinite parameters, the usual package concept for surgical services cannot be applied. Such procedures are identified by a star (*) following the procedure code.

When a star (*) follows a surgical procedure code, the service listed includes only the surgical procedure, no associated pre- and postoperative services. This is the guideline as stated in CPT. Medicare national policy for starred procedures may differ from this, so contact your Medicare carrier directly for this listing.

Observe the following guidelines when using starred codes:

- When the starred procedure is the major service, use 99025 as a second line entry to identify the medical care when it is a new patient service. An established patient visit would not be charged unless a separate, identifiable service is performed. Note that Medicare bundles 99025 into the procedure performed
- When the starred procedure is not the major service being provided, use an appropriate level of E/M service as an additional code, regardless of new or established patient status. Use modifier -25 with the code for the procedure. (Some payers may unbundle new patient services and transfer the E/M code to 99025.)
- Use an emergency care code as an additional code, where appropriate, if the patient is treated on an emergency basis
- Report all postoperative care on a service-by-service basis
- Code separately any complications requiring additional services. Identify the complications with the correct ICD•9 code

- When a physician provides supplies that are not included in the surgical package, such as injectable medications and supplies, code these items separately at the physician's discretion. Follow payer guidelines

Medicare and Starred Procedures

Medicare views starred procedures generally as minor surgeries and are not traditionally paid using a global surgery policy.

SURGICAL DESTRUCTION

Surgical destruction methods are usually not listed separately. If the technique significantly alters the standard management, separate code numbers are provided in CPT to indicate the exception.

Many payers consider laser use a technical function that does not significantly change the desired outcome of a primary procedure. This is demonstrated by a change in terminology for many CPT codes. The words "destruction by any method" imply that the result is what the code is intending to describe, not the method of performance of the procedure. When laser use significantly alters procedure performance, CPT has included codes that specifically identify laser in the description.

Medicare and Surgical Destruction

Medicare recognizes the use of lasers for many medical indications. In the absence of a specific noncoverage instruction, and where a laser has been approved for marketing by the Food and Drug Administration, the contractor must determine whether a laser procedure is reasonable and necessary and, consequently, covered.

COSMETIC WARNING

In sections where certain procedures within the section are considered cosmetic 85 percent of the time or more, you will see this heading. When this message appears, the codes that are considered cosmetic will be listed.

Negotiating with Payers

Always negotiate in good faith. If you do not have a contract with the payer and you are asked to give a discount for the service, try to come to a mutual decision for a fair discount.

Get prior authorization. If you think a procedure could result in an improved appearance, even if that is not necessarily the reason for the surgery, request prior authorization either by phone or in writing from the payer. Make sure you obtain a prior authorization number and that any claims submitted or inquiries made concerning the claim include that number.

When the payer determines a percentage of the surgery will be considered cosmetic and the remainder will be considered therapeutic, and if you agree with the percentages, be sure to state clearly in the operative report how much time, resources, number of days in the hospital stay, etc., is assigned to which procedure. If you disagree with the percentages discuss the point with the person who made the decision concerning the breakdown of the services.

In the event of a claim denial, have the insured or your office staff check the member handbook to determine if the procedure is covered. If the handbook states coverage is dependent upon written protocols, ask for a copy of the protocol and the resources used to determine the protocols. If you disagree with the guidelines the payer has established, submit in writing to the medical director why you disagree and any medical association or other literature that may substantiate your position. It may take a little longer to go through this process, but if it is a frequently used payer your letter may help change the protocols for the better.

Always appeal a denied claim. Once again, this may take a little extra time, but appeals are typically handled by departments other than the ones who made the original decision. If you win an appeal it may establish the basis for you to perform a service that has a broader scope than it did before the appeal. Although each case is unique, there are usually enough similarities for a decision to be of value to you. Winning an appeal may also give you the argument you need to win with other payers.

SUBSIDIARY (IN-ADDITION) CODES

Key phrases are used throughout CPT to indicate that a code is to be used "in-addition" to the primary code. Phrases that help identify subsidiary codes include, but are not limited to, the following: each additional; list in addition to; and done at time of other major procedure. Subsidiary or in-addition codes are identified in this publication under the heading Subsidiary Codes.

Subsidiary codes usually are not reported alone, the exception being co-surgery situations, though they can be used in multiple surgeon situations without changing the rules for the use of subsidiary codes. Services represented by subsidiary codes are not included as part of the primary procedure.

These codes have relative values that require no further adjustment, and, due to the nature of subsidiary codes, the use of modifier -51 would be redundant. When a subsidiary code has a higher value than the corresponding primary procedure, the primary procedure code is not reduced. The primary procedure code would be subject to reduction as a multiple procedure, however, if additional, higher valued procedures were also performed at the same session.

Subsidiary codes are generally related to their corresponding principle procedure code(s). They may have distinct ICD•9 diagnostic codes and unbundle relationships consistent with and/or independent of the corresponding primary procedure code(s).

Note the following about subsidiary codes:

- They have follow-up days independent of the primary code(s), although the follow-up days may or may not be the same as the primary code
- They are performed at the same operative session as the primary procedure; subsidiary medicine and E/M services are performed on the same date as the primary service
- One subsidiary code may be a trigger code for another subsidiary code
- Some subsidiary codes may have a "By Report" classification. As with any other code classified as By Report, review by the payer or reviewer is required
- There may be scenarios where it would be appropriate to use modifier -20, -22, or -52 with a subsidiary code. In those situations, appropriate additional values would be allowed for modifiers -20 and -22, and a lesser value allowed for modifier -52, depending upon how much of the procedure was performed
- If a subsidiary code represents a procedure that allows modifier -80, -81, or -82, then use of these modifiers and appropriate reductions would apply to the subsidiary code

Medicodes' *Fee & Coding Standard* lists subsidiary codes for each code range. Due to the large number of codes which may have a corresponding subsidiary code, and the number of code ranges that may be affected, the coder must give individual consideration to the subsidiary code. It may apply to all of the codes in the range listed or only to part of the codes listed.

Surgery Codes 10040–19499

10040

Coding Insight

This code is used for specific types of acne surgery, e.g., marsupialization. For acne surgery performed by cryotherapy, see 17340, and by chemical exfoliation, see 17360.

Benign lesion excision codes (11400–11446) may be denied by payers when they are billed with this code.

Subsidiary Codes

Subsidiary codes have relative values that require no further adjustment.

20920 is "in addition" to 10040
20922 is "in addition" to 10040
20926 is "in addition" to 10040

Because these are subsidiary or "in addition to" codes, reimbursement reduction and modifier -51 do not apply.

Code		Description	Medicode RVU	50th	75th	Medicare Nat'l Avg
10040	*	Acne surgery (eg, marsupialization, opening or removal of multiple milia, comedones, cysts, pustules)	2.00	48	56	61

10060–10180

Coding Insight

Codes in this section are reported only for incision and drainage or removal of foreign bodies from the skin and subcutaneous tissue. For incision and drainage or incision and removal of abscess, foreign body, or hematoma of deeper structures, you must go to the appropriate anatomical area in CPT; for example:

- Incision of soft tissue abscess, (e.g., secondary to osteomyelitis); superficial, see 20000*; deep or complicated, see 20005
- Removal of foreign body in muscle or tendon sheath, simple, see 20520*; deep or complicated, see 20525
- Incision and drainage of deep abscess, infected bursa, or hematoma, thigh or knee region, see 27301

According to *CPT '96* "wound exploration due to penetrating trauma without laparotomy or thoracotomy"shoud be reported by selection of a code from the new 20100–20103 series.

CPT also specifies 10060 or 10061 be used "for drainage of paronychia or onychia." See 11770–11772 if pilonidal cyst is excised instead of incised. For reporting secondary wound closure see 12020, 12021, 13160.

Subsidiary Codes

Subsidiary codes have relative values that require no further adjustment:

20920 is "in addition" to 11060–10180
20922 is "in addition" to 11060–10180
20926 is "in addition" to 11060–10180

Because these are subsidiary or "in addition to" codes, reimbursement reduction and modifier -51 do not apply.

Medicare Alert

Medicare rebundles certain codes in the surgery section when the listed codes are considered a component of a more comprehensive service.

64450 will not be reimbursed when reported with 10060 or 10061

Code		Description	Medicode RVU	50th	75th	Medicare Nat'l Avg
10060	*	Incision and drainage of abscess (eg, carbuncle, suppurative hidradenitis, cutaneous or subcutaneous abscess, cyst, furuncle, or paronychia); simple or single	3.25	79	92	59
10061		Incision and drainage of abscess (eg, carbuncle, suppurative hidradenitis, cutaneous or subcutaneous abscess, cyst, furuncle, or paronychia); complicated or multiple	10.00	242	282	119
10080	*	Incision and drainage of pilonidal cyst; simple	5.00	121	141	70
10081		Incision and drainage of pilonidal cyst; complicated	12.00	290	338	142
10120	*	Incision and removal of foreign body, subcutaneous tissues; simple	4.00	91	109	63
10121		Incision and removal of foreign body, subcutaneous tissues; complicated	12.00	274	326	141
10140	*	Incision and drainage of hematoma, seroma or fluid collection	6.00	137	163	72
10160	*	Puncture aspiration of abscess, hematoma, bulla, or cyst	3.25	74	88	57
10180		Incision and drainage, complex, postoperative wound infection	18.00	411	488	136

11000–11044
Debridement Codes

Coding Insight

Codes 11040–11044 report extensive debridement of soft tissue and/or bone. Procedures that meet the criteria listed in the repair section of CPT for prolonged decontamination and/or debridement are rare and may be denied by payers when billed with wound repair unless (1) documentation is submitted with the claim explaining the unusual circumstances or (2) an appeal is made after denial by the payer when charges are warranted and documentation supports the additional use of a debridement code.

Debridement is reportable with repair only when contamination requires prolonged cleansing, when appreciable amounts of devitalized or contaminated tissue are removed, or when debridement done separately without immediate primary closure of the wound.

Nota Bene: *CPT '96* added information to the notes under Repair (Closure). The additional notes describe circumstances that would allow the use of the new codes 20100–20103 for wound exploration — trauma with repair codes.

Read the new notes carefully listed under repair and the new wound exploration codes in the musculoskeletal system. Use the codes as directed in CPT, "as appropriate."

If significant time and effort were required, weigh the length of time to determine if modifier -22 or a debridement code is warranted. Remember, the debridement code will be reduced with modifier -51 appended, but modifier -22 should not be reduced. Although modifier -22 is reviewed by most payers, if the documentation supports the charge, use the modifier.

SUBSIDIARY CODES

Subsidiary codes have relative values that require no further adjustment:

11001 is "in addition" to 11000
20920 is "in addition" to 11000–11044
20922 is "in addition" to 11000–11044
20926 is "in addition" to 11000–11044

Because these are subsidiary or "in addition to" codes, reimbursement reduction and modifier -51 do not apply.

MEDICARE ALERT

Medicare rebundles certain codes in the surgery section when the listed codes are considered a component of a more comprehensive service.

64450 will not be reimbursed when reported with 11000, 11040, 11041, 11042, 11043, 11044
11040 will not be reimbursed when reported with 11041, 11042, 11043, 11044
11041 will not be reimbursed when reported with 11042, 11043, 11044
11042 will not be reimbursed when reported with 11043, 11044
11043 will not be reimbursed when reported with 11044

Code		Description	Medicode RVU	50th	75th	Medicare Nat'l Avg
11000	*	Debridement of extensive eczematous or infected skin; up to 10% of body surface	2.75	62	75	51
11001		Debridement of extensive eczematous or infected skin; each additional 10% of the body surface	2.25	51	61	29
11040		Debridement; skin, partial thickness	3.00	68	82	37
11041		Debridement; skin, full thickness	7.00	159	191	64
11042		Debridement; skin, and subcutaneous tissue	12.25	278	334	87
11043		Debridement; skin, subcutaneous tissue, and muscle	22.00	499	599	176
11044		Debridement; skin, subcutaneous tissue, muscle, and bone	27.00	613	736	245

11050–11052
Paring or Curettement Codes

Coding Insight
These codes are specific for removal of lesion(s) that do not extend through the stratum corneum (the first layer of skin). For removal of deeper lesions, see other lesion removal codes.

Subsidiary Codes
Subsidiary codes have relative values that require no further adjustment:

20920 is "in addition" to 11050–11052
20922 is "in addition" to 11050–11052
20926 is "in addition" to 11050–11052

Because these are subsidiary or "in addition to" codes, reimbursement reduction and modifier -51 do not apply.

Code		Description	Medicode RVU	50th	75th	Medicare Nat'l Avg
11050	*	Paring or curettement of benign hyperkeratotic skin lesion with or without chemical cauterization (such as verrucae or clavi) not extending through the stratum corneum (eg, callus or wart) with or without local anesthesia; single lesion	2.00	46	55	32
11051		Paring or curettement of benign hyperkeratotic skin lesion with or without chemical cauterization (such as verrucae or clavi) not extending through the stratum corneum (eg, callus or wart) with or without local anesthesia; two to four lesions	2.50	57	69	47
11052		Paring or curettement of benign hyperkeratotic skin lesion with or without chemical cauterization (such as verrucae or clavi) not extending through the stratum corneum (eg, callus or wart) with or without local anesthesia; more than four lesions	4.00	91	110	51

11100–11101
Biopsy Codes

Coding Insight
Codes 11100 and 11101 are separate procedures and by definition are usually components of more complex services and not identified separately. When they are performed alone and for a specific and documented purpose, they may be reported.

It is not appropriate to report a biopsy and a lesion excision of the same anatomic location during the same surgical session. If a tumor is removed (a biopsy), and evaluation of a frozen section indicates the need for excision of additional tissue during the same operative session, report only the greater of the two procedures (in this case, excision of the lesion). It would be proper, however, to code both a biopsy and a later excision of the same lesion, provided the procedures are done during separate surgical sessions.

Use biopsy codes to report the removal of a small amount of tissue to determine the extent of a disease, confirm a diagnosis, or estimate the outcome of a disease. A single tissue sample may be lifted or picked out with forceps, or a portion of the lesion may be biopsied by incising the lesion and applying a few sutures. Biopsy codes are appropriate for needle aspiration for biopsy, incisional biopsy, and partial excision, as well as for scraping, curetting, and using a skin punch.

Biopsy codes are arranged by anatomic site of the lesion or cyst. Use integumentary codes when the biopsy is of skin, subcutaneous tissue, or mucous membrane only.

Subsidiary Codes

Subsidiary codes have relative values that require no further adjustment:

11101 is "in addition" to 11100
20920 is "in addition" to 11100–11101
20922 is "in addition" to 11100–11101
20926 is "in addition" to 11100–11101

Because these are subsidiary or "in addition to" codes, reimbursement reduction and modifier -51 do not apply.

Code	Description	Medicode RVU	50th	75th	Medicare Nat'l Avg
11100	Biopsy of skin, subcutaneous tissue and/or mucous membrane (including simple closure), unless otherwise listed (separate procedure); single lesion	3.80	86	100	53
11101	Biopsy of skin, subcutaneous tissue and/or mucous membrane (including simple closure), unless otherwise listed (separate procedure); each separate/additional lesion	2.80	63	74	28

11200–11201
Removal of Skin Tags

Coding Insight

Skin tags are removed with scissors or other sharp instruments. They may also be removed by strangulation — tied off, causing the tissue to die. Codes in this section include cauterization of the wound (chemical or hot). Although the wound created with this type of removal usually does not require any sutures (CPT specifies no suture is required), one stitch would be included in the code and would not be reported separately. Note that up to and including 15 skin or fibrocutaneous tags, in any area, are included in code 11200, but for each additional 10 lesions after 15 you are instructed to report code 11201.

Subsidiary Codes

Subsidiary codes have relative values that require no further adjustment:

11201 is "in addition" to 11200
20920 is "in addition" to 11200–11201
20922 i "in addition" to 11200–11201
20926 is "in addition" to 11200–11201

Because these are subsidiary or "in addition to" codes, reimbursement reduction and modifier -51 do not apply.

Medicare Alert

Medicare rebundles certain codes in the surgery section when the listed codes are considered a component of a more comprehensive service.

12001–12018 will not be reimbursed when reported with codes 11200 or 11201

Code		Description	Medicode RVU	50th	75th	Medicare Nat'l Avg
11200	*	Removal of skin tags, multiple fibrocutaneous tags, any area; up to and including 15 lesions	3.50	80	95	46
11201		Removal of skin tags, multiple fibrocutaneous tags, any area; each additional ten lesions	2.75	63	75	19

11300–11313
Shaving of Epidermal or Dermal Lesions

CODING INSIGHT
Shaving is accomplished by slicing horizontally or by transverse incision with a sharp instrument. Layers removed can include the epidermis and superficial dermis. This type of lesion removal does not require suturing. Typically, hot cautery or a cotton-like material impregnated with chemicals is applied to stop the bleeding and protect the wound. Local anesthesia is used and is included in the surgery.

Note the starred (*) procedures in this section and apply correct coding rules.

SUBSIDIARY CODES
Subsidiary codes have relative values that require no further adjustment:

20920, 20922, 20926 are "in addition" to 11300–11313

Because these are subsidiary or "in addition to" codes, reimbursement reduction and modifier -51 do not apply.

MEDICARE ALERT
Medicare rebundles certain codes in the surgery section when the listed codes are considered a component of a more comprehensive service.

12001–12018 will not be reimbursed when reported with 11300–11313

Code		Description	Medicode RVU	50th	75th	Medicare Nat'l Avg
11300	*	Shaving of epidermal or dermal lesion, single lesion, trunk, arms or legs; lesion diameter 0.5 cm or less	3.25	74	88	44
11301		Shaving of epidermal or dermal lesion, single lesion, trunk, arms or legs; lesion diameter 0.6 to 1.0 cm	4.00	91	109	63
11302		Shaving of epidermal or dermal lesion, single lesion, trunk, arms or legs; lesion diameter 1.1 to 2.0 cm	4.75	108	129	81
11303		Shaving of epidermal or dermal lesion, single lesion, trunk, arms or legs; lesion diameter over 2.0 cm	6.00	137	163	118
11305	*	Shaving of epidermal or dermal lesion, single lesion, scalp, neck, hands, feet, genitalia; lesion diameter 0.5 cm or less	3.50	80	95	50
11306		Shaving of epidermal or dermal lesion, single lesion, scalp, neck, hands, feet, genitalia; lesion diameter 0.6 to 1.0 cm	4.25	97	116	71
11307		Shaving of epidermal or dermal lesion, single lesion, scalp, neck, hands, feet, genitalia; lesion diameter 1.1 to 2.0 cm	5.00	114	136	88
11308		Shaving of epidermal or dermal lesion, single lesion, scalp, neck, hands, feet, genitalia; lesion diameter over 2.0 cm	5.75	131	157	127

Code		Description	Medicode RVU	50th	75th	Medicare Nat'l Avg
11310	*	Shaving of epidermal or dermal lesion, single lesion, face, ears, eyelids, nose, lips, mucous membrane; lesion diameter 0.5 cm or less	4.00	91	109	60
11311		Shaving of epidermal or dermal lesion, single lesion, face, ears, eyelids, nose, lips, mucous membrane; lesion diameter 0.6 to 1.0 cm	4.75	108	129	79
11312		Shaving of epidermal or dermal lesion, single lesion, face, ears, eyelids, nose, lips, mucous membrane; lesion diameter 1.1 to 2.0 cm	5.50	125	150	98
11313		Shaving of epidermal or dermal lesion, single lesion, face, ears, eyelids, nose, lips, mucous membrane; lesion diameter over 2.0 cm	6.25	143	170	136

11400–11646
Excision of Benign and Malignant Lesions

Coding Insight

Lesion excision includes many codes that are selected on the basis of precise anatomical locations and procedure descriptions.

Codes in this section are used to report full-thickness excision (through the dermis) of a lesion of the skin (e.g., hypertrophic or cicatricial scars, burns, etc.). Lesion excision includes simple repair and excludes intermediate and complex repair, grafts, and flaps. Lesion excision includes adjacent tissue transfer. Lesion excision includes only simple closure; the following are reported separately:

- Layered (intermediate) repair (12031–12057)
- Complex or reconstructive closure (13100–13300)
- Free skin graft (15000–15400)

Flaps (skin and/or deep tissues) include the recipient site when the flap is being attached in transfer or to a final site, and include the donor site when a tube is formed for later or when delay of flap is prior to transfer. Lesion excision may be separately reported, as appropriate, but adjacent tissue transfer (14000–14300) is not reported separately.

Pathology reports are used to determine if the lesion is benign or malignant. They can also be used to establish the depth of the lesion (e.g., fascia, muscle); however, do not use the pathology report for the size of the lesion because the lesion will shrink when introduced into a solution that preserves the tissue.

Excision of lesion codes are assigned according to the diameter of the lesion excised to a full-thickness depth. Different anatomical sites listed vary widely in the lesion sizes assigned to them, especially when performed on the head or neck, so choose the correct code.

The excision of benign lesion codes includes lesions of the skin or subcutaneous tissues such as cicatricial, fibrous, inflammatory, congenital, and cystic. They do not include excision of deeper structures. To find the excision of benign lesion codes of deeper structures you must go to the correct anatomical section in CPT, examples are:

- Excision, tumor, thigh or knee area; subcutaneous, 27327; deep, subfascial, or intramuscular, 27328
- Excision, tumor, forearm and/or wrist area; subcutaneous, 25075; deep, subfascial, or intramuscular, 25076

- Excision, abdominal wall tumor, subfascial (e.g., desmoid), 22900

Malignant lesion excision codes do not take into consideration the invasiveness of a tumor and the underlying surfaces it has invaded or to which it has rooted. For radical excision of tumors go to the correct anatomical section in CPT; examples are:

- Radical resection of tumor (e.g., malignant neoplasm), soft tissue of upper arm or elbow area, 24077
- Radical resection of tumor (e.g., malignant neoplasm), soft tissue of leg or ankle area, 27615
- Radical resection of tumor (e.g., malignant neoplasm), soft tissue of back or flank, 21935

Radical excisions are of deeper structures, beyond the full-thickness layer. They may include a wide excision but they also include removal of the tumor as well as surrounding soft tissues such as muscle, fascia, and neurovascular structures. When the bone is involved, codes are found under the anatomical site listed by the name of the bone. Examples are:

- Radical resection of tumor, bone, femur or knee, 27365
- Radical resection for tumor, radius or ulna, 25170

If the lesion excision is complicated, append modifier -22. Closure of surgical wound by use of flap or skin graft is used in addition to the code for the excision of the lesion. Local anesthesia is included in the listed service.

If benign, premalignant, or malignant lesions are destroyed instead of excised, see 17000–17105 and 17260–17286.

A complex repair may be required following a lesion excision. Most commonly, a large defect is closed in this manner to achieve "maximum functional and cosmetic" results. Other complicated closures may be required, depending upon the size and/or location of the lesion removed. Refer to the section on repairs and tissue transfers for selecting codes.

Subsidiary Codes

Subsidiary codes have relative values that require no further adjustment:

20920 is "in addition" to 11400–11646
20922 is "in addition" to 11400–11646
20926 is "in addition" to 11400–11646

Because these are subsidiary or "in addition to" codes, reimbursement reduction and modifier -51 do not apply.

Medicare Alert

Medicare rebundles certain codes in the surgery section when the listed codes are considered a component of a more comprehensive service.

12001–12018 will not be reimbursed when reported with 11400–11446
12001–12057 will not be reimbursed when reported with 11450, 11462, 11470
12001–13300 will not be reimbursed when reported with 11451, 11463, 11471
12001–12018 will not be reimbursed when reported with 11600–11640, 11641–11646

Code	Description	Medicode RVU	50th	75th	Medicare Nat'l Avg
11400	Excision, benign lesion, except skin tag (unless listed elsewhere), trunk, arms or legs; lesion diameter 0.5 cm or less	4.75	108	129	56

Code	Description	Medicode RVU	50th	75th	Medicare Nat'l Avg
11401	Excision, benign lesion, except skin tag (unless listed elsewhere), trunk, arms or legs; lesion diameter 0.6 to 1.0 cm	6.00	137	163	78
11402	Excision, benign lesion, except skin tag (unless listed elsewhere), trunk, arms or legs; lesion diameter 1.1 to 2.0 cm	8.00	182	218	99
11403	Excision, benign lesion, except skin tag (unless listed elsewhere), trunk, arms or legs; lesion diameter 2.1 to 3.0 cm	10.25	234	279	124
11404	Excision, benign lesion, except skin tag (unless listed elsewhere), trunk, arms or legs; lesion diameter 3.1 to 4.0 cm	14.50	331	395	147
11406	Excision, benign lesion, except skin tag (unless listed elsewhere), trunk, arms or legs; lesion diameter over 4.0 cm	20.50	467	558	196
11420	Excision, benign lesion, except skin tag (unless listed elsewhere), scalp, neck, hands, feet, genitalia; lesion diameter 0.5 cm or less	5.25	120	143	61
11421	Excision, benign lesion, except skin tag (unless listed elsewhere), scalp, neck, hands, feet, genitalia; lesion diameter 0.6 to 1.0 cm	6.75	154	184	87
11422	Excision, benign lesion, except skin tag (unless listed elsewhere), scalp, neck, hands, feet, genitalia; lesion diameter 1.1 to 2.0 cm	8.50	194	231	107
11423	Excision, benign lesion, except skin tag (unless listed elsewhere), scalp, neck, hands, feet, genitalia; lesion diameter 2.1 to 3.0 cm	12.50	285	340	141
11424	Excision, benign lesion, except skin tag (unless listed elsewhere), scalp, neck, hands, feet, genitalia; lesion diameter 3.1 to 4.0 cm	16.00	365	436	161
11426	Excision, benign lesion, except skin tag (unless listed elsewhere), scalp, neck, hands, feet, genitalia; lesion diameter over 4.0 cm	22.00	502	599	228
11440	Excision, other benign lesion (unless listed elsewhere), face, ears, eyelids, nose, lips, mucous membrane; lesion diameter 0.5 cm or less	6.25	143	170	72
11441	Excision, other benign lesion (unless listed elsewhere), face, ears, eyelids, nose, lips, mucous membrane; lesion diameter 0.6 to 1.0 cm	8.25	188	225	96
11442	Excision, other benign lesion (unless listed elsewhere), face, ears, eyelids, nose, lips, mucous membrane; lesion diameter 1.1 to 2.0 cm	11.00	251	299	119
11443	Excision, other benign lesion (unless listed elsewhere), face, ears, eyelids, nose, lips, mucous membrane; lesion diameter 2.1 to 3.0 cm	14.00	319	381	156
11444	Excision, other benign lesion (unless listed elsewhere), face, ears, eyelids, nose, lips, mucous membrane; lesion diameter 3.1 to 4.0 cm	18.00	410	490	196
11446	Excision, other benign lesion (unless listed elsewhere), face, ears, eyelids, nose, lips, mucous membrane; lesion diameter over 4.0 cm	25.75	587	701	247
11450	Excision of skin and subcutaneous tissue for hidradenitis, axillary; with simple or intermediate repair	30.00	684	817	232

Code	Description	Medicode RVU	50th	75th	Medicare Nat'l Avg
11451	Excision of skin and subcutaneous tissue for hidradenitis, axillary; with complex repair	34.00	775	925	280
11462	Excision of skin and subcutaneous tissue for hidradenitis, inguinal; with simple or intermediate repair	26.00	593	708	205
11463	Excision of skin and subcutaneous tissue for hidradenitis, inguinal; with complex repair	29.50	673	803	241
11470	Excision of skin and subcutaneous tissue for hidradenitis, perianal, perineal, or umbilical; with simple or intermediate repair	26.00	593	708	253
11471	Excision of skin and subcutaneous tissue for hidradenitis, perianal, perineal, or umbilical; with complex repair	29.50	673	803	283
11600	Excision, malignant lesion, trunk, arms, or legs; lesion diameter 0.5 cm or less	7.75	179	209	102
11601	Excision, malignant lesion, trunk, arms, or legs; lesion diameter 0.6 to 1.0 cm	8.50	197	230	134
11602	Excision, malignant lesion, trunk, arms, or legs; lesion diameter 1.1 to 2.0 cm	11.25	260	304	160
11603	Excision, malignant lesion, trunk, arms, or legs; lesion diameter 2.1 to 3.0 cm	14.00	324	378	194
11604	Excision, malignant lesion, trunk, arms, or legs; lesion diameter 3.1 to 4.0 cm	18.50	428	500	219
11606	Excision, malignant lesion, trunk, arms, or legs; lesion diameter over 4.0 cm	27.00	624	729	298
11620	Excision, malignant lesion, scalp, neck, hands, feet, genitalia; lesion diameter 0.5 cm or less	11.00	254	297	113
11621	Excision, malignant lesion, scalp, neck, hands, feet, genitalia; lesion diameter 0.6 to 1.0 cm	13.00	301	351	157
11622	Excision, malignant lesion, scalp, neck, hands, feet, genitalia; lesion diameter 1.1 to 2.0 cm	15.50	358	419	194
11623	Excision, malignant lesion, scalp, neck, hands, feet, genitalia; lesion diameter 2.1 to 3.0 cm	19.00	439	513	238
11624	Excision, malignant lesion, scalp, neck, hands, feet, genitalia; lesion diameter 3.1 to 4.0 cm	24.00	555	648	283
11626	Excision, malignant lesion, scalp, neck, hands, feet, genitalia; lesion diameter over 4.0 cm	30.00	694	810	339
11640	Excision, malignant lesion, face, ears, eyelids, nose, lips; lesion diameter 0.5 cm or less	12.00	278	324	138
11641	Excision, malignant lesion, face, ears, eyelids, nose, lips; lesion diameter 0.6 to 1.0 cm	15.50	358	419	191
11642	Excision, malignant lesion, face, ears, eyelids, nose, lips; lesion diameter 1.1 to 2.0 cm	19.50	451	527	235
11643	Excision, malignant lesion, face, ears, eyelids, nose, lips; lesion diameter 2.1 to 3.0 cm	25.00	578	675	276
11644	Excision, malignant lesion, face, ears, eyelids, nose, lips; lesion diameter 3.1 to 4.0 cm	29.00	671	783	337
11646	Excision, malignant lesion, face, ears, eyelids, nose, lips; lesion diameter over 4.0 cm	36.00	833	972	438

11700–11765
Nails

Coding Insight
Controversy exists between some providers and payers in the excision of nail and nail matrix codes. Some providers code partial or complete excisions per side of each toe, using procedure code 11750 x 2 for one great toe, or 11750 x 4 for two great toes. Payers feel there is only one nail involved and only one code per toe should be used. Track EOBs for reimbursement for these procedures and appeal any reimbursement decision you feel is unfair.

Subsidiary Codes
Subsidiary codes have relative values that require no further adjustment:

11701 is "in addition" to 11700
11711 is "in addition" to 11710
11731 is "in addition" to 11730
11732 is "in addition" to 11730, 11731
20920 is "in addition" to 11700–11765
20922 is "in addition" to 11700–11765
20926 is "in addition" to 11700–11765

Because these are subsidiary or "in addition to" codes, reimbursement reduction and modifier -51 do not apply.

Medicare Alert
Medicare rebundles certain codes in the surgery section when the listed codes are considered a component of a more comprehensive service.

64450 will not be reimbursed when reported with 11700–11732
11730 will not be reimbursed when reported with 11750–11752
11750 will not be reimbursed when reported with 11752

Code		Description	Medicode RVU	50th	75th	Medicare Nat'l Avg
11700	*	Debridement of nails, manual; five or less	1.80	42	49	26
11701		Debridement of nails, manual; each additional, five or less	1.20	28	33	19
11710	*	Debridement of nails, electric grinder; five or less	1.75	41	48	26
11711		Debridement of nails, electric grinder; each additional, five or less	1.20	28	33	16
11730	*	Avulsion of nail plate, partial or complete, simple; single	3.80	88	104	61
11731		Avulsion of nail plate, partial or complete, simple; second nail plate	2.75	64	75	41
11732		Avulsion of nail plate, partial or complete, simple; each additional nail plate	2.00	47	55	25
11740		Evacuation of subungual hematoma	3.00	70	82	32
11750		Excision of nail and nail matrix, partial or complete, (eg, ingrown or deformed nail) for permanent removal;	13.50	314	370	159

Code	Description	Medicode RVU	50th	75th	Medicare Nat'l Avg
11752	Excision of nail and nail matrix, partial or complete, (eg, ingrown or deformed nail) for permanent removal; with amputation of tuft of distal phalanx	19.00	442	520	233
11755	Biopsy of nail unit, any method (eg, plate, bed, matrix, hyponychium, proximal and lateral nail folds) (separate procedure)	6.00	140	164	94
11760	Repair of nail bed	16.50	384	452	107
11762	Reconstruction of nail bed with graft	24.00	559	657	229
11765	Wedge excision of skin of nail fold (eg, for ingrown toenail)	9.00	209	246	50

11770–11772
Excision of Pilonidal Cyst or Sinus

Coding Insight
Incision and drainage of these cysts are often performed more than once. For incision and drainage, see 10080–10081.

Subsidiary Codes
Subsidiary codes have relative values that require no further adjustment:

20920, 20922, 20926 are "in addition" to 11770–11772

Because these are subsidiary or "in addition to" codes, reimbursement reduction and modifier -51 do not apply.

Code	Description	Medicode RVU	50th	75th	Medicare Nat'l Avg
11770	Excision of pilonidal cyst or sinus; simple	26.50	617	726	234
11771	Excision of pilonidal cyst or sinus; extensive	38.00	884	1041	427
11772	Excision of pilonidal cyst or sinus; complicated	42.75	995	1171	487

11900–11977
Injections, Tattoos, Tissue Expanders, and Contraceptive Capsules

Coding Insight
Multiple codes should not be used to report subcutaneous injection of filling material (11950–11954). When more than one code from this coding range is used it may be rebundled by the payer.

Cosmetic Warning
This section contains codes (11920–11954) which are considered cosmetic 85 percent of the time or more.

SUBSIDIARY CODES

Subsidiary codes have relative values that require no further adjustment:

11922 is "in addition" to 11921
20920 is "in addition" to 11900–11977
20922 is "in addition" to 11900–11977
20926 is "in addition" to 11900–11977

Because these are subsidiary or "in addition to" codes, reimbursement reduction and modifier -51 do not apply.

Code		Description	Medicode RVU	50th	75th	Medicare Nat'l Avg
11900	*	Injection, intralesional; up to and including seven lesions	2.50	57	67	30
11901	*	Injection, intralesional; more than seven lesions	3.75	85	100	47
11920		Tattooing, intradermal introduction of insoluble opaque pigments to correct color defects of skin, including micropigmentation; 6.0 sq cm or less	25.00	568	669	117
11921		Tattooing, intradermal introduction of insoluble opaque pigments to correct color defects of skin, including micropigmentation; 6.1 to 20.0 sq cm	50.00	1135	1338	140
11922		Tattooing, intradermal introduction of insoluble opaque pigments to correct color defects of skin, including micropigmentation; each additional 20.0 sq cm	25.00	568	669	36
11950		Tattooing, intradermal introduction of insoluble opaque pigments to correct color defects of skin, including micropigmentation; subcutaneous injection of "filling" material (eg, collagen); 1 cc or less	11.00	250	294	83
11951		Tattooing, intradermal introduction of insoluble opaque pigments to correct color defects of skin, including micropigmentation; 1.1 to 5.0 cc	12.00	272	321	97
11952		Tattooing, intradermal introduction of insoluble opaque pigments to correct color defects of skin, including micropigmentation; 5.1 to 10.0 cc	13.00	295	348	116
11954		Tattooing, intradermal introduction of insoluble opaque pigments to correct color defects of skin, including micropigmentation; over 10.0 cc	0.00	0	0	123
11960		Insertion of tissue expander(s) for other than breast, including subsequent expansion	0.00	0	0	610
11970		Replacement of tissue expander with permanent prosthesis	88.00	1998	2356	701
11971		Removal of tissue expander(s) without insertion of prosthesis	17.00	386	455	256
11975		Insertion, implantable contraceptive capsules	8.25	187	221	–
11976		Removal, implantable contraceptive capsules	8.25	187	221	114
11977		Removal with reinsertion, implantable contraceptive capsules	9.00	204	241	–

12001–13300
Simple, Intermediate, Complex Repair

Coding Insight

Closure
Repair codes usually indicate closure of lacerations or reconstructive surgery. Closure of surgically created wounds is usually an integral part of procedures and is not reported separately.

The sums of the length of the repairs should be added together and reported for each separate site listed. For example, under simple repair there may be a 1.0 cm repair of the scalp, a 1.5 cm repair of the eyelid, and a 1.5 cm repair of the face. In this instance, two codes would be reported — 12001 for the 1.0 cm repair of the scalp, and 12013 for the 1.5 cm repair of the eyelid and the 1.5 cm repair of the face (1.5 cm + 1.5 cm = 3.0 cm reportable for the same area). Sums are always reported in centimeters (cm). To convert inches to centimeters, multiply the number of inches by 2.54.

Keep the following guidelines in mind when using wound closure codes:

- Wound closures are classified according to location, size, and tissue involvement
- The lengths of lacerations are combined within the same classification and location and coded as a single item
- Surgical procedures include closure of the surgically created wound
- Lesion excision includes simple closure of the skin and subcutaneous tissue
- Repair of underlying nerves, blood vessels, and tendons includes simple or intermediate repair of the overlying wound. Complex wound repair can be reported separately. Simple exploration as part of the essential treatment of the wound is included

If, when repairing a laceration, the physician performs adjacent tissue transfer or rearrangement, see adjacent tissue transfer or rearrangement rules and 14000–14350.

Simple
Simple repair codes are used for the repair of wounds but are not coded in addition to the codes used for wound excision.

Simple repair is performed when the wound involves partial or full-thickness damage to the skin and/or subcutaneous tissues. It is superficial; there is no significant involvement of deeper structures and only simple, primary suturing is required. Placement of adhesive strips are reported as an office visit, according to the level of service performed.

Because of the unusual length of the repair listed in the highest level codes in this section, it is advisable to submit an operative report and cover letter with the claim submission.

For extensive or complicated secondary wound closure, see 13160.

Intermediate
Wound repair codes only include simple closure. If intermediate repair is required when a lesion is excised it is reported separately along with the excision code.

Intermediate repair is performed for wounds and lacerations where one or more of the deeper layers of subcutaneous tissue and nonmuscle fascia are repaired in addition to the skin and subcutaneous tissue. Single-layer closure can also be coded as an intermediate repair if the wound is heavily contaminated and requires extensive cleaning or removal of particulate matter.

Complex

Wound repair codes only include simple closure. When complex repair is required it is reported separately, along with an excision code, using a code from this section.

Complex repair includes the repair of wounds requiring reconstructive surgery, complicated wound closure, debridement, skin grafting, or intricate, unusual, and time-consuming techniques to obtain the maximum functional and cosmetic result. Complex repairs include the creation of a defect, (e.g., extending excisions), necessary preparations for repairs, and moderate debridement of complicated lacerations, avulsions, and other wounds.

Because of the complexity of the repairs listed in 13100–13300 it is advisable to submit an operative report and cover letter with the claim submission. These code are usually scrutinized closely by auditors because they are more costly and frequently lack documentation.

SUBSIDIARY CODES

Subsidiary codes have relative values that require no further adjustment:

20920 is "in addition" to 12001–13300
20922 is "in addition" to 12001–13300
20926 is "in addition" to 12001–13300

Because these are subsidiary or "in addition to" codes, reimbursement reduction and modifier -51 do not apply.

Code		Description	Medicode RVU	50th	75th	Medicare Nat'l Avg
12001	*	Simple repair of superficial wounds of scalp, neck, axillae, external genitalia, trunk and/or extremities (including hands and feet); 2.5 cm or less	4.75	110	128	72
12002	*	Simple repair of superficial wounds of scalp, neck, axillae, external genitalia, trunk and/or extremities (including hands and feet); 2.6 cm to 7.5 cm	6.00	139	162	87
12004	*	Simple repair of superficial wounds of scalp, neck, axillae, external genitalia, trunk and/or extremities (including hands and feet); 7.6 cm to 12.5 cm	7.75	180	209	114
12005		Simple repair of superficial wounds of scalp, neck, axillae, external genitalia, trunk and/or extremities (including hands and feet); 12.6 cm to 20.0 cm	9.50	221	256	148
12006		Simple repair of superficial wounds of scalp, neck, axillae, external genitalia, trunk and/or extremities (including hands and feet); 20.1 cm to 30.0 cm	11.50	267	310	189
12007		Simple repair of superficial wounds of scalp, neck, axillae, external genitalia, trunk and/or extremities (including hands and feet); over 30.0 cm	0.00	0	0	238
12011	*	Simple repair of superficial wounds of face, ears, eyelids, nose, lips and/or mucous membranes; 2.5 cm or less	6.00	139	162	81
12013	*	Simple repair of superficial wounds of face, ears, eyelids, nose, lips and/or mucous membranes; 2.6 cm to 5.0 cm	7.25	169	195	101
12014		Simple repair of superficial wounds of face, ears, eyelids, nose, lips and/or mucous membranes; 5.1 cm to 7.5 cm	9.75	227	263	123
12015		Simple repair of superficial wounds of face, ears, eyelids, nose, lips and/or mucous membranes; 7.6 cm to 12.5 cm	12.75	296	343	163
12016		Simple repair of superficial wounds of face, ears, eyelids, nose, lips and/or mucous membranes; 12.6 cm to 20.0 cm	15.75	366	424	216

Code		Description	Medicode RVU	50th	75th	Medicare Nat'l Avg
12017		Simple repair of superficial wounds of face, ears, eyelids, nose, lips and/or mucous membranes; 20.1 cm to 30.0 cm	31.50	732	848	284
12018		Simple repair of superficial wounds of face, ears, eyelids, nose, lips and/or mucous membranes; over 30.0 cm	0.00	0	0	431
12020		Treatment of superficial wound dehiscence; simple closure	10.25	238	276	155
12021		Treatment of superficial wound dehiscence; with packing	10.75	250	290	108
12031	*	Layer closure of wounds of scalp, axillae, trunk and/or extremities (excluding hands and feet); 2.5 cm or less	6.50	149	177	106
12032	*	Layer closure of wounds of scalp, axillae, trunk and/or extremities (excluding hands and feet); 2.6 cm to 7.5 cm	8.75	201	239	133
12034		Layer closure of wounds of scalp, axillae, trunk and/or extremities (excluding hands and feet); 7.6 cm to 12.5 cm	11.25	258	307	171
12035		Layer closure of wounds of scalp, axillae, trunk and/or extremities (excluding hands and feet); 12.6 cm to 20.0 cm	15.25	350	416	214
12036		Layer closure of wounds of scalp, axillae, trunk and/or extremities (excluding hands and feet); 20.1 cm to 30.0 cm	19.75	453	539	263
12037		Layer closure of wounds of scalp, axillae, trunk and/or extremities (excluding hands and feet); over 30.0 cm	24.75	567	675	321
12041	*	Layer closure of wounds of neck, hands, feet and/or external genitalia; 2.5 cm or less	8.00	183	218	104
12042		Layer closure of wounds of neck, hands, feet and/or external genitalia; 2.6 cm to 7.5 cm	10.00	229	273	131
12044		Layer closure of wounds of neck, hands, feet and/or external genitalia; 7.6 cm to 12.5 cm	13.00	298	355	164
12045		Layer closure of wounds of neck, hands, feet and/or external genitalia; 12.6 cm to 20.0 cm	17.00	390	464	204
12046		Layer closure of wounds of neck, hands, feet and/or external genitalia; 20.1 cm to 30.0 cm	22.00	504	600	291
12047		Layer closure of wounds of neck, hands, feet and/or external genitalia; over 30.0 cm	26.00	596	709	312
12051	*	Layer closure of wounds of face, ears, eyelids, nose, lips and/or mucous membranes; 2.5 cm or less	10.00	229	273	133
12052		Layer closure of wounds of face, ears, eyelids, nose, lips and/or mucous membranes; 2.6 cm to 5.0 cm	12.50	286	341	166
12053		Layer closure of wounds of face, ears, eyelids, nose, lips and/or mucous membranes; 5.1 cm to 7.5 cm	16.50	378	450	194
12054		Layer closure of wounds of face, ears, eyelids, nose, lips and/or mucous membranes; 7.6 cm to 12.5 cm	21.50	493	587	245
12055		Layer closure of wounds of face, ears, eyelids, nose, lips and/or mucous membranes; 12.6 cm to 20.0 cm	27.50	630	750	316
12056		Layer closure of wounds of face, ears, eyelids, nose, lips and/or mucous membranes; 20.1 cm to 30.0 cm	35.00	802	955	418
12057		Layer closure of wounds of face, ears, eyelids, nose, lips and/or mucous membranes; over 30.0 cm	0.00	0	0	464
13100		Repair, complex, trunk; 1.1 cm to 2.5 cm	9.50	225	263	165

Code	Description	Medicode RVU	50th	75th	Medicare Nat'l Avg
13101	Repair, complex, trunk; 2.6 cm to 7.5 cm	17.00	402	470	239
13120	Repair, complex, scalp, arms, and/or legs; 1.1 cm to 2.5 cm	15.00	355	415	180
13121	Repair, complex, scalp, arms, and/or legs; 2.6 cm to 7.5 cm	23.00	544	636	280
13131	Repair, complex, forehead, cheeks, chin, mouth, neck, axillae, genitalia, hands and/or feet; 1.1 cm to 2.5 cm	17.50	414	484	227
13132	Repair, complex, forehead, cheeks, chin, mouth, neck, axillae, genitalia, hands and/or feet; 2.6 cm to 7.5 cm	34.00	805	940	359
13150	Repair, complex, eyelids, nose, ears and/or lips; 1.0 cm or less	15.50	367	428	221
13151	Repair, complex, eyelids, nose, ears and/or lips; 1.1 cm to 2.5 cm	22.00	521	608	280
13152	Repair, complex, eyelids, nose, ears and/or lips; 2.6 cm to 7.5 cm	43.00	1018	1188	481
13160	Secondary closure of surgical wound or dehiscence, extensive or complicated	30.00	710	829	519
13300	Repair, unusual, complicated, over 7.5 cm, any area	0.00	0	0	503

14000–15776
Tissue Transfer or Rearrangement, Grafts, Flaps

Coding Insight

Codes 14000–15776 all involve the transplantation of skin or other tissue, such as muscle, from one area of the body to another. The procedure is performed for a variety of reasons, often the result of an injury. This set of codes includes tissue transfers or rearrangement, grafts, and flaps.

Procedures listed in this section can be performed to improve cosmetic appearance as well as functionality of the site. Although all of the codes in this section are not listed with cosmetic warnings, it is important to note that the payer may consider all or part of the procedure as cosmetic. When performing procedures in this section of CPT it is important to obtain prior authorization for the service. If part of the service is considered cosmetic by the payer, be very clear in the operative report when one part of the surgery ends and another begins. The clarity of the report will help the claim reviewer determine what portion of the claim will be paid and what portion will become patient responsibility.

Remember, the patient responsibility does not just extend to the physician's participation in the surgery, but also includes a portion of the hospital stay itself and other ancillary charges. Clarity in the staff notes about the length of stay for each portion of the procedure may significantly affect how much out-of-pocket expense the patient will pay.

Tissue Transfer

Tissue transfer or rearrangement codes (14000–14350) describe moving normal tissue from the donor site to the recipient site. The donor site is adjacent to the affected area, allowing the tissue to remain attached to its original location and blood supply to ensure survival of the graft. These procedures are coded by the location of the placement of the graft, not by the donor site.

Rearrangement of tissue is also coded with this range (14000–14350). Some of the terms seen in operative reports are Z–plasty, W–plasty, and VY–plasty. These terms take their names from the way the tissue is arranged, and the procedures are often performed to release tension created along a scar following a healed laceration or incision closure.

Grafts

Skin grafts (15050–15400) are identified by the size and location of the recipient site and type of graft, ranging from pinch to full thickness. A pinch graft describes a small skin graft used to cover an area up to 2 cm. Split thickness (STSG) and full thickness (FTSG) vary with the depth of the dermis included in the graft. All three of these involve complete removal from the original site before being moved and attached to the recipient location. Closure and/or care of the donor site is included in the skin graft code.

Flaps

Flaps, like tissue transfers, stay attached to the donor site for blood supply. However, they are not "adjacent" and at times are distant from the receiving site. These flaps may be "delayed" or not immediately attached to the new site in order to increase the vascular supply of the flap before the transfer takes place. The region listed in 15570–15738 indicates the donor site when a tube is formed for later transfer and the delayed flap prior to transfer. If these procedures require extensive immobilization with casts or other devices, they are considered to be additional procedures.

Tissue transfer or rearrangement codes are reported when used to repair lacerations developed by the physician for that purpose; however, do not report these codes if the rearrangement or closure is an incidental result of the configuration.

Free skin grafts codes are used when removal of a lesion or planned excision of tissue has created a defect that requires a graft for definitive closure (e.g., when treatment has two components: excision of a lesion and planned skin graft).

Code 15000 is reported in addition to the appropriate code for the skin graft, and the following should be noted:

- Modifier -22 may be added to 15000 when a large, complicated, continuous area is involved. Documentation should accompany the claim
- Code 15000 may be listed more than once when more than one area is excisionally prepared for grafting. The areas should be separate anatomic locations
- Code 15000 is used to report shaving (removal by transverse incision or horizontal slicing without a full-thickness dermal excision) of the skin and subcutaneous tissues (e.g., hypertrophic scars, cicatricial tissue, burns). This procedure is followed by planned grafting, e.g., split or full thickness

Donor site repair is identified separately when a skin graft or local flap is needed to close the defect left with the removal of the tissue for graft.

Cosmetic Warning

This section contains codes which are considered cosmetic 85 percent of the time or more. The codes are 15775–15776.

Subsidiary Codes

Subsidiary codes have relative values that require no further adjustment:

15101 is "in addition" to 15100
15121 is "in addition" to 15120
15201 is "in addition" to 15200
15221 is "in addition" to 15220
15241 is "in addition" to 15240

15261 is "in addition" to 15260
15936 is "in addition" to 15734 and 15738
15937 is "in addition" to 15734 and 15738
15946 is "in addition" to 15734 and 15738
15956 is "in addition" to 15734 and 15738
15958 is "in addition" to 15734 and 15738
20920 is "in addition" to 14000–15776
20922 is "in addition" to 14000–15776
20926 is "in addition" to 14000–15776

Because these are subsidiary or "in addition to" codes, reimbursement reduction and modifier -51 do not apply.

MEDICARE ALERT

Medicare rebundles certain codes in the surgery section when the listed codes are considered a component of a more comprehensive service.

11420–11421, 11440–11441, 11620–11622, 11640–11641 will not be reimbursed when reported with 14040

11440–11441, 11640–11641 will not be reimbursed when reported with 14060

Code	Description	Medicode RVU	50th	75th	Medicare Nat'l Avg
14000	Adjacent tissue transfer or rearrangement, trunk; defect 10 sq cm or less	30.50	732	859	365
14001	Adjacent tissue transfer or rearrangement, trunk; defect 10.1 sq cm to 30.0 sq cm	44.00	1056	1240	526
14020	Adjacent tissue transfer or rearrangement, scalp, arms and/or legs; defect 10 sq cm or less	39.00	936	1099	452
14021	Adjacent tissue transfer or rearrangement, scalp, arms and/or legs; defect 10.1 sq cm to 30.0 sq cm	49.00	1176	1381	651
14040	Adjacent tissue transfer or rearrangement, forehead, cheeks, chin, mouth, neck, axillae, genitalia, hands and/or feet; defect 10 sq cm or less	49.00	1176	1381	572
14041	Adjacent tissue transfer or rearrangement, forehead, cheeks, chin, mouth, neck, axillae, genitalia, hands and/or feet; defect 10.1 sq cm to 30.0 sq cm	62.00	1487	1747	768
14060	Adjacent tissue transfer or rearrangement, eyelids, nose, ears and/or lips; defect 10 sq cm or less	62.00	1487	1747	672
14061	Adjacent tissue transfer or rearrangement, eyelids, nose, ears and/or lips; defect 10.1 sq cm to 30.0 sq cm	88.00	2111	2480	930
14300	Adjacent tissue transfer or rearrangement, more than 30 sq cm, unusual or complicated, any area	0.00	0	0	980
14350	Filleted finger or toe flap, including preparation of recipient site	45.00	1080	1268	638
15000	Excisional preparation or creation of recipient site by excision of essentially intact skin (including subcutaneous tissues), scar, or other lesion prior to repair with free skin graft (list as separate service in addition to skin graft)	0.00	0	0	229
15050	Pinch graft, single or multiple, to cover small ulcer, tip of digit, or other minimal open area (except on face), up to defect size 2 cm diameter	23.00	544	643	225

Code	Description	Medicode RVU	50th	75th	Medicare Nat'l Avg
15100	Split graft, trunk, scalp, arms, legs, hands, and/or feet (except multiple digits); 100 sq cm or less, or each one percent of body area of infants and children (except 15050)	42.00	993	1175	528
15101	Split graft, trunk, scalp, arms, legs, hands, and/or feet (except multiple digits); each additional 100 sq cm, or each one percent of body area of infants and children, or part thereof	21.00	496	587	161
15120	Split graft, face, eyelids, mouth, neck, ears, orbits, genitalia, and/or multiple digits; 100 sq cm or less, or each one percent of body area of infants and children (except 15050)	59.00	1394	1650	656
15121	Split graft, face, eyelids, mouth, neck, ears, orbits, genitalia, and/or multiple digits; each additional 100 sq cm, or each one percent of body area of infants and children, or part thereof	29.50	697	825	245
15200	Full thickness graft, free, including direct closure of donor site, trunk; 20 sq cm or less	31.00	733	867	476
15201	Full thickness graft, free, including direct closure of donor site, trunk; each additional 20 sq cm	15.50	366	434	152
15220	Full thickness graft, free, including direct closure of donor site, scalp, arms, and/or legs; 20 sq cm or less	40.00	945	1119	512
15221	Full thickness graft, free, including direct closure of donor site, scalp, arms, and/or legs; each additional 20 sq cm	20.00	473	559	156
15240	Full thickness graft, free, including direct closure of donor site, forehead, cheeks, chin, mouth, neck, axillae, genitalia, hands, and/or feet; 20 sq cm or less	51.00	1205	1426	612
15241	Full thickness graft, free, including direct closure of donor site, forehead, cheeks, chin, mouth, neck, axillae, genitalia, hands, and/or feet; each additional 20 sq cm	25.50	603	713	216
15260	Full thickness graft, free, including direct closure of donor site, nose, ears, eyelids, and/or lips; 20 sq cm or less	60.00	1418	1678	711
15261	Full thickness graft, free, including direct closure of donor site, nose, ears, eyelids, and/or lips; each additional 20 sq cm	30.00	709	839	254
15350	Application of allograft, skin	0.00	0	0	258
15400	Application of xenograft, skin	0.00	0	0	235
15570	Formation of direct or tubed pedicle, with or without transfer; trunk	55.00	1300	1538	534
15572	Formation of direct or tubed pedicle, with or without transfer; scalp, arms, or legs	54.00	1276	1510	539
15574	Formation of direct or tubed pedicle, with or without transfer; forehead, cheeks, chin, mouth, neck, axillae, genitalia, hands or feet	64.00	1513	1790	573
15576	Formation of direct or tubed pedicle, with or without transfer; eyelids, nose, ears, lips, or intraoral	66.00	1560	1846	489
15580	Cross finger flap, including free graft to donor site	56.00	1324	1566	417
15600	Delay of flap or sectioning of flap (division and inset); at trunk	25.00	591	699	238

Code	Description	Medicode RVU	50th	75th	Medicare Nat'l Avg
15610	Delay of flap or sectioning of flap (division and inset); at scalp, arms, or legs	30.00	709	839	249
15620	Delay of flap or sectioning of flap (division and inset); at forehead, cheeks, chin, neck, axillae, genitalia, hands (except 15625), or feet	35.00	827	979	321
15625	Delay of flap or sectioning of flap (division and inset); section pedicle of cross finger flap	32.00	756	895	230
15630	Delay of flap or sectioning of flap (division and inset); at eyelids, nose, ears, or lips	41.20	974	1152	356
15650	Transfer, intermediate, of any pedicle flap (eg, abdomen to wrist, "Walking" tube), any location	40.10	948	1122	365
15732	Muscle, myocutaneous, or fasciocutaneous flap; head and neck (eg, temporalis, masseter, sternocleidomastoid, levator scapulae)	100.0	2363	2797	1303
15734	Muscle, myocutaneous, or fasciocutaneous flap; trunk	105.0	2482	2937	1591
15736	Muscle, myocutaneous, or fasciocutaneous flap; upper extremity	90.00	2127	2517	1352
15738	Muscle, myocutaneous, or fasciocutaneous flap; lower extremity	90.00	2127	2517	1153
15740	Flap; island pedicle	77.00	1820	2154	854
15750	Flap; neurovascular pedicle	60.00	1418	1678	961
15755	Free flap (microvascular transfer)	270.0	6381	7551	2509
15760	Graft; composite (eg, full thickness of external ear or nasal ala), including primary closure, donor area	50.00	1182	1398	666
15770	Graft; derma-fat-fascia	60.00	1418	1678	621
15775	Punch graft for hair transplant; 1 to 15 punch grafts	5.60	132	157	287
15776	Punch graft for hair transplant; more than 15 punch grafts	0.00	0	0	402

15780–15879
Other Skin and Subcutaneous Tissue Procedures

Cosmetic Warning
This section contains codes which are considered cosmetic 85 percent of the time or more. The codes are 15780–15822, 15824–15839, 15876–15879. Obtain prior authorization when performing procedures in this code range that are considered cosmetic.

Subsidiary Codes
Subsidiary codes have relative values that require no further adjustment:

15787 is "in addition" to 15786
20920 is "in addition" to 15780–15879
20922 is "in addition" to 15780–15879
20926 is "in addition" to 15780–15879

Because these are subsidiary or "in addition to" codes, reimbursement reduction and modifier -51 do not apply.

MEDICARE ALERT

Medicare rebundles certain codes in the surgery section when the listed codes are considered a component of a more comprehensive service.

15822 will not be reimbursed when reported with 15823

Code		Description	Medicode RVU	50th	75th	Medicare Nat'l Avg
15780		Dermabrasion; total face (eg, for acne scarring, fine wrinkling, rhytids, general keratosis)	70.00	1574	1873	339
15781		Dermabrasion; segmental, face	23.00	517	615	342
15782		Dermabrasion; regional, other than face	22.00	495	589	216
15783		Dermabrasion; superficial, any site, (eg, tattoo removal)	22.00	495	589	242
15786	*	Abrasion; single lesion (eg, keratosis, scar)	4.00	90	107	98
15787		Abrasion; each additional four lesions or less	2.00	45	54	23
15788		Chemical peel, facial; epidermal	54.00	1214	1445	151
15789		Chemical peel, facial; dermal	69.00	1552	1846	253
15792		Chemical peel, nonfacial; epidermal	15.00	337	401	96
15793		Chemical peel, nonfacial; dermal	19.00	427	508	160
15810		Salabrasion; 20 sq cm or less	50.00	1124	1338	334
15811		Salabrasion; over 20 sq cm	75.00	1687	2007	373
15819		Cervicoplasty	45.00	1012	1204	690
15820		Blepharoplasty, lower eyelid;	37.00	832	990	458
15821		Blepharoplasty, lower eyelid; with extensive herniated fat pad	42.00	945	1124	512
15822		Blepharoplasty, upper eyelid;	41.00	922	1097	464
15823		Blepharoplasty, upper eyelid; with excessive skin weighting down lid	52.00	1169	1391	613
15824		Rhytidectomy; forehead	70.00	1574	1873	1221
15825		Rhytidectomy; neck with platysmal tightening (platysmal flap, "P-flap")	80.00	1799	2141	–
15826		Rhytidectomy; glabellar frown lines	70.00	1574	1873	–

Code	Description	Medicode RVU	50th	75th	Medicare Nat'l Avg
15828	Rhytidectomy; cheek, chin, and neck	185.0	4160	4950	1567
15829	Rhytidectomy; superficial musculoaponeurotic system (SMAS) flap	205.0	4610	5485	–
15831	Excision, excessive skin and subcutaneous tissue (including lipectomy); abdomen (abdominoplasty)	150.0	3373	4014	940
15832	Excision, excessive skin and subcutaneous tissue (including lipectomy); thigh	70.00	1574	1873	803
15833	Excision, excessive skin and subcutaneous tissue (including lipectomy); leg	70.00	1574	1873	675
15834	Excision, excessive skin and subcutaneous tissue (including lipectomy); hip	70.00	1574	1873	721
15835	Excision, excessive skin and subcutaneous tissue (including lipectomy); buttock	70.00	1574	1873	746
15836	Excision, excessive skin and subcutaneous tissue (including lipectomy); arm	70.00	1574	1873	610
15837	Excision, excessive skin and subcutaneous tissue (including lipectomy); forearm or hand	45.00	1012	1204	579
15838	Excision, excessive skin and subcutaneous tissue (including lipectomy); submental fat pad	40.00	900	1070	520
15839	Excision, excessive skin and subcutaneous tissue (including lipectomy); other area	0.00	0	0	460
15840	Graft for facial nerve paralysis; free fascia graft (including obtaining fascia)	110.0	2474	2943	1207
15841	Graft for facial nerve paralysis; free muscle graft (including obtaining graft)	125.0	2811	3345	1600
15842	Graft for facial nerve paralysis; free muscle graft by microsurgical technique	150.0	3373	4014	2632
15845	Graft for facial nerve paralysis; regional muscle transfer	125.0	2811	3345	1177
15850	Removal of sutures under anesthesia (other than local), same surgeon	2.00	45	54	–
15851	Removal of sutures under anesthesia (other than local), other surgeon	3.40	76	91	39
15852	Dressing change (for other than burns) under anesthesia (other than local)	0.00	0	0	50
15860	Intravenous injection of agent (eg, fluorescein) to test blood flow in flap or graft	10.00	225	268	138
15876	Suction assisted lipectomy; head and neck	0.00	0	0	–
15877	Suction assisted lipectomy; trunk	0.00	0	0	–
15878	Suction assisted lipectomy; upper extremity	0.00	0	0	–
15879	Suction assisted lipectomy; lower extremity	0.00	0	0	–

15920–15999
Decubitus Ulcers

Coding Insight
Muscle or myocutaneous flaps may be billed with a pressure ulcer excision.

Subsidiary Codes
Subsidiary codes have relative values that require no further adjustment:

15936 is "in addition" to 15734, 15738
15937 is "in addition" to 15734, 15738
15946 is "in addition" to 15734, 15738
15956 is "in addition" to 15734, 15738
15958 is "in addition" to 15734, 15738
20920 is "in addition" to 15920–15999
20922 is "in addition" to 15920–15999
20926 is "in addition" to 15920–15999

Because these are subsidiary or "in addition to" codes, reimbursement reduction and modifier -51 do not apply.

Code	Description	Medicode RVU	50th	75th	Medicare Nat'l Avg
15920	Excision, coccygeal pressure ulcer, with coccygectomy; with primary suture	50.00	1099	1270	435
15922	Excision, coccygeal pressure ulcer, with coccygectomy; with flap closure	70.00	1538	1778	636
15931	Excision, sacral pressure ulcer, with primary suture;	50.00	1099	1270	464
15933	Excision, sacral pressure ulcer, with primary suture; with ostectomy	65.00	1428	1651	712
15934	Excision, sacral pressure ulcer, with skin flap closure;	70.00	1538	1778	814
15935	Excision, sacral pressure ulcer, with skin flap closure; with ostectomy	85.00	1868	2158	1071
15936	Excision, sacral pressure ulcer, with muscle or myocutaneous flap closure;	45.00	989	1143	938
15937	Excision, sacral pressure ulcer, with muscle or myocutaneous flap closure; with ostectomy	55.00	1208	1397	1194
15940	Excision, ischial pressure ulcer, with primary suture;	50.00	1099	1270	505
15941	Excision, ischial pressure ulcer, with primary suture; with ostectomy (ischiectomy)	65.00	1428	1651	745
15944	Excision, ischial pressure ulcer, with skin flap closure;	70.00	1538	1778	850
15945	Excision, ischial pressure ulcer, with skin flap closure; with ostectomy	85.00	1868	2158	975
15946	Excision, ischial pressure ulcer, with ostectomy, with muscle or myocutaneous flap closure	55.00	1208	1397	1623
15950	Excision, trochanteric pressure ulcer, with primary suture;	50.00	1099	1270	412

Code	Description	Medicode RVU	50th	75th	Medicare Nat'l Avg
15951	Excision, trochanteric pressure ulcer, with primary suture; with ostectomy	65.00	1428	1651	744
15952	Excision, trochanteric pressure ulcer, with skin flap closure;	70.00	1538	1778	735
15953	Excision, trochanteric pressure ulcer, with skin flap closure; with ostectomy	85.00	1868	2158	883
15956	Excision, trochanteric pressure ulcer, with muscle or myocutaneous flap closure;	45.00	989	1143	1402
15958	Excision, trochanteric pressure ulcer, with muscle or myocutaneous flap closure; with ostectomy	55.00	1208	1397	1480
15999	Unlisted procedure, excision pressure ulcer	0.00	0	0	–

16000–16042
Burns

CODING INSIGHT
Codes in this area are used for local treatment of burns only. Other services provided in addition to the local treatment of the burned surface should be reported according to the procedure(s) performed. This may include surgeries performed on other burned areas, critical care of the patient, initial or subsequent hospital care, or other management services.

Burn management often requires that many different procedures be performed at the same time or at future dates; e.g., skin grafting may be required more than once and to different areas. Be sure to read section guidelines carefully for each code reported. Many procedures performed in conjunction with burns, such as skin grafts, have additional codes that can be reported. Because of the complicated nature of these cases and the unusual combinations of procedures and treatments, coding mistakes are easily made. Be cautious when using modifiers; if additional E/M services are needed on the day of a procedure or other service, append modifier -25.

SUBSIDIARY CODES
Subsidiary codes have relative values that require no further adjustment:

16042 is "in addition" to 16041
20920 is "in addition" to 16000–16042
20922 is "in addition" to 16000–16042
20926 is "in addition" to 16000–16042

Because these are subsidiary or "in addition to" codes, reimbursement reduction and modifier -51 do not apply.

Code	Description	Medicode RVU	50th	75th	Medicare Nat'l Avg
16000	Initial treatment, first degree burn, when no more than local treatment is required	2.75	60	70	41
16010	Dressings and/or debridement, initial or subsequent; under anesthesia, small	8.00	176	203	43

Code		Description	Medicode RVU	50th	75th	Medicare Nat'l Avg
16015		Dressings and/or debridement, initial or subsequent; under anesthesia, medium or large, or with major debridement	20.00	439	508	190
16020	*	Dressings and/or debridement, initial or subsequent; without anesthesia, office or hospital, small	3.00	66	76	39
16025	*	Dressings and/or debridement, initial or subsequent; without anesthesia, medium (eg, whole face or whole extremity)	5.50	121	140	85
16030		Dressings and/or debridement, initial or subsequent; without anesthesia, large (eg, more than one extremity)	10.00	220	254	100
16035		Escharotomy	25.00	549	635	263
16040		Excision burn wound, without skin grafting, employing alloplastic dressing (eg, synthetic mesh), any anatomic site; up to one percent total body surface area	8.00	176	203	184
16041		Excision burn wound, without skin grafting, employing alloplastic dressing (eg, synthetic mesh), any anatomic site; greater than one percent and up to nine percent total body surface area	14.00	308	356	271
16042		Excision burn wound, without skin grafting, employing alloplastic dressing (eg, synthetic mesh), any anatomic site; each additional nine percent total body surface area, or part thereof	12.00	264	305	256

17000–17286
Destruction of Benign, Premalignant, and Malignant Lesions

Coding Insight
Destruction generally is accomplished by means other than excision, such as hot cautery, electrodesiccation, laser, chemical surgery, or cryosurgery. Because these codes include destruction by any method, how the lesions are destroyed is not a consideration in selecting the code. Lesions included are listed in CPT ahead of the destruction codes. Destruction of benign or premalignant lesions includes curettement when it is performed. All destruction codes include the use of local anesthesia.

Note that benign and premalignant lesions are reported per lesion, while malignant destruction codes are listed by size (diameter). Use the correct code and measurement in the destruction of malignant lesions in particular areas — codes for the face and codes for larger-size lesions are more difficult and/or time consuming and thus are reimbursed at higher rates.

Subsidiary Codes
Subsidiary codes have relative values that require no further adjustment:

17001 is "in addition" to 17000
17002 is "in addition" to 17000 and 17001
17101 is "in addition" to 17100
17102 is "in addition" to 17100 and 17101
17201 is "in addition" to 17200
20920 is "in addition" to 17000–17286
20922 is "in addition" to 17000–17286
20926 is "in addition" to 17000–17286

Because these are subsidiary or "in addition to" codes, reimbursement reduction and modifier -51 do not apply.

Code		Description	Medicode RVU	50th	75th	Medicare Nat'l Avg
17000	*	Destruction by any method, including laser, with or without surgical curettement, all benign facial lesions or premalignant lesions in any location, or benign lesions other than cutaneous vascular proliferative lesions, including local anesthesia; one lesion	2.90	63	76	43
17001		Destruction by any method, including laser, with or without surgical curettement, all benign facial lesions or premalignant lesions in any location, or benign lesions other than cutaneous vascular proliferative lesions, including local anesthesia; second and third lesions, each	2.18	47	57	16
17002		Destruction by any method, including laser, with or without surgical curettement, all benign facial lesions or premalignant lesions in any location, or benign lesions other than cutaneous vascular proliferative lesions, including local anesthesia; over three lesions, each additional lesion	1.20	26	32	12
17010		Destruction by any method, including laser, with or without surgical curettement, all benign facial lesions or premalignant lesions in any location, or benign lesions other than cutaneous vascular proliferative lesions, including local anesthesia; complicated lesion(s)	5.20	113	137	64
17100	*	Destruction by any method, including laser, of benign skin lesions other than cutaneous vascular proliferative lesions on any area other than the face, including local anesthesia; one lesion	2.50	56	66	37
17101		Destruction by any method, including laser, of benign skin lesions other than cutaneous vascular proliferative lesions on any area other than the face, including local anesthesia; second lesion	1.50	33	40	13
17102		Destruction by any method, including laser, of benign skin lesions other than cutaneous vascular proliferative lesions on any area other than the face, including local anesthesia; over two lesions, each additional lesion up to 15 lesions	1.25	28	33	8
17104		Destruction by any method, including laser, of benign skin lesions other than cutaneous vascular proliferative lesions on any area other than the face, including local anesthesia; 15 or more lesions	0.00	0	0	79
17105		Destruction by any method, including laser, of benign skin lesions other than cutaneous vascular proliferative lesions on any area other than the face, including local anesthesia; complicated or extensive lesions	10.00	223	264	53
17106		Destruction of cutaneous vascular proliferative lesions (eg, laser technique); less than 10 sq cm	16.00	356	422	261
17107		Destruction of cutaneous vascular proliferative lesions (eg, laser technique); 10.0 - 50.0 sq cm	30.00	668	791	513
17108		Destruction of cutaneous vascular proliferative lesions (eg, laser technique); over 50.0 sq cm	45.00	1001	1187	900
17110	*	Destruction by any method of flat warts or molluscum contagiosum, milia, up to 15 lesions	3.00	67	79	38
17200	*	Electrosurgical destruction of multiple fibrocutaneous tags; up to 15 lesions	3.30	73	87	41

Code		Description	Medicode RVU	50th	75th	Medicare Nat'l Avg
17201		Electrosurgical destruction of multiple fibrocutaneous tags; each additional ten lesions	2.48	55	65	21
17250	*	Chemical cauterization of granulation tissue (proud flesh, sinus or fistula)	2.50	56	66	34
17260	*	Destruction, malignant lesion, any method, trunk, arms or legs; lesion diameter 0.5 cm or less	5.00	111	132	86
17261		Destruction, malignant lesion, any method, trunk, arms or legs; lesion diameter 0.6 to 1.0 cm	6.75	150	178	111
17262		Destruction, malignant lesion, any method, trunk, arms or legs; lesion diameter 1.1 to 2.0 cm	8.25	184	218	145
17263		Destruction, malignant lesion, any method, trunk, arms or legs; lesion diameter 2.1 to 3.0 cm	9.25	206	244	178
17264		Destruction, malignant lesion, any method, trunk, arms or legs; lesion diameter 3.1 to 4.0 cm	10.25	228	270	202
17266		Destruction, malignant lesion, any method, trunk, arms or legs; lesion diameter over 4.0 cm	12.75	284	336	267
17270	*	Destruction, malignant lesion, any method, scalp, neck, hands, feet, genitalia; lesion diameter 0.5 cm or less	6.00	134	158	113
17271		Destruction, malignant lesion, any method, scalp, neck, hands, feet, genitalia; lesion diameter 0.6 to 1.0 cm	7.50	167	198	143
17272		Destruction, malignant lesion, any method, scalp, neck, hands, feet, genitalia; lesion diameter 1.1 to 2.0 cm	9.00	200	237	177
17273		Destruction, malignant lesion, any method, scalp, neck, hands, feet, genitalia; lesion diameter 2.1 to 3.0 cm	10.75	239	283	212
17274		Destruction, malignant lesion, any method, scalp, neck, hands, feet, genitalia; lesion diameter 3.1 to 4.0 cm	11.75	261	310	259
17276		Destruction, malignant lesion, any method, scalp, neck, hands, feet, genitalia; lesion diameter over 4.0 cm	13.25	295	349	308
17280	*	Destruction, malignant lesion, any method, face, ears, eyelids, nose, lips, mucous membrane; lesion diameter 0.5 cm or less	7.25	161	191	128
17281		Destruction, malignant lesion, any method, face, ears, eyelids, nose, lips, mucous membrane; lesion diameter 0.6 to 1.0 cm	8.75	195	231	169
17282		Destruction, malignant lesion, any method, face, ears, eyelids, nose, lips, mucous membrane; lesion diameter 1.1 to 2.0 cm	10.25	228	270	208
17283		Destruction, malignant lesion, any method, face, ears, eyelids, nose, lips, mucous membrane; lesion diameter 2.1 to 3.0 cm	11.75	261	310	249
17284		Destruction, malignant lesion, any method, face, ears, eyelids, nose, lips, mucous membrane; lesion diameter 3.1 to 4.0 cm	13.25	295	349	296
17286		Destruction, malignant lesion, any method, face, ears, eyelids, nose, lips, mucous membrane; lesion diameter over 4.0 cm	14.75	328	389	393

17304–17310
Mohs' Micrographic Surgery

CODING INSIGHT
Mohs' Micrographic surgery is "chemosurgery" used to remove skin cancer. Tumors that would require this type of surgery are often ill-defined (the borders are not well delineated) or they are complex (exacerbated by previous treatments or other complications). The Mohs' microsurgery technique allows three-dimensional tracing of the entire tumor field. Note the following about this technique:

- The tumor is defined and debulked by curettement or excision
- A layer of tissue is excised within narrow margins
- A map of the tissue is drawn to maintain accurate orientation (to pinpoint the location of the remaining tissues)
- The tissue is sectioned and dyed
- Frozen sections are prepared and histologically examined by the surgeon
- The area of remaining tumor, and only this area, is excised and its undersurface examined
- The process is repeated until all of the tumor is removed

In Mohs' micrographic surgery a single physician acts integrally as both surgeon and pathologist. All components of the surgery must be performed and supervised by the surgeon.

The surgeon may not purchase the services of an independent laboratory to provide the technical component (technical preparation of slides) or have a pathologist perform the professional component. If either of the physician's responsibilities, surgery or pathology studies, are delegated to another physician who reports his/her services separately, CPT codes for this procedure are not used.

Complex or reconstructive repair (e.g., adjacent tissue transfer, free skin graft, or flaps) are reported separately. And, it is advisable to verify modifier rules for these codes with payers.

SUBSIDIARY CODES
Subsidiary codes have relative values that require no further adjustment:

17310 is "in addition" to 17304–17307
20920 is "in addition" to 17304–17310
20922 is "in addition" to 17304–17310
20926 is "in addition" to 17304–17310

Because these are subsidiary or "in addition to" codes, reimbursement reduction and modifier -51 do not apply.

MEDICARE ALERT
Medicare rebundles certain codes in the surgery section when the listed codes are considered a component of a more comprehensive service.

88300–88309, 88331–88332 will not be reimbursed when reported with 17304–17310

Code	Description	Medicode RVU	50th	75th	Medicare Nat'l Avg
17304	Chemosurgery (Mohs' micrographic technique), including removal of all gross tumor, surgical excision of tissue specimens, mapping, color coding of specimens, microscopic examination of specimens by the surgeon, and complete histopathologic preparation; first stage, fresh tissue technique, up to 5 specimens	28.50	656	761	468
17305	Chemosurgery (Mohs' micrographic technique), including removal of all gross tumor, surgical excision of tissue specimens, mapping, color coding of specimens, microscopic examination of specimens by the surgeon, and complete histopathologic preparation; second stage, fixed or fresh tissue, up to 5 specimens	17.00	391	454	213
17306	Chemosurgery (Mohs' micrographic technique), including removal of all gross tumor, surgical excision of tissue specimens, mapping, color coding of specimens, microscopic examination of specimens by the surgeon, and complete histopathologic preparation; third stage, fixed or fresh tissue, up to 5 specimens	17.00	391	454	179
17307	Chemosurgery (Mohs' micrographic technique), including removal of all gross tumor, surgical excision of tissue specimens, mapping, color coding of specimens, microscopic examination of specimens by the surgeon, and complete histopathologic preparation; additional stage(s), up to 5 specimens, each stage	17.00	391	454	180
17310	Chemosurgery (Mohs' micrographic technique), including removal of all gross tumor, surgical excision of tissue specimens, mapping, color coding of specimens, microscopic examination of specimens by the surgeon, and complete histopathologic preparation; more than 5 specimens, fixed or fresh tissue, any stage	0.00	0	0	44

17340–17999
Other Procedures

Coding Insight

Cryotherapy is reported per session rather than per lesion. For acne surgery, see 10040. Because 17340 and 17360 are starred procedures, other services such as counseling with issuance of a prescription for isotretinoin, which meets the criteria for an E/M service, is reported in addition to the cryotherapy.

Cosmetic Warning

This section contains codes which are considered cosmetic 85 percent of the time or more. The codes are 17360–17380.

Subsidiary Codes

Subsidiary codes have relative values that require no further adjustment:

20920 is "in addition" to 17340–17999
20922 is "in addition" to 17340–17999
20926 is "in addition" to 17340–17999

Because these are subsidiary or "in addition to" codes, reimbursement reduction and modifier -51 do not apply.

Code		Description	Medicode RVU	50th	75th	Medicare Nat'l Avg
17340	*	Cryotherapy (CO2 slush, liquid N2) for acne	2.20	51	59	38
17360	*	Chemical exfoliation for acne (eg, acne paste, acid)	2.20	51	59	64
17380	*	Electrolysis epilation, each 1/2 hour	3.00	69	80	–
17999		Unlisted procedure, skin, mucous membrane and subcutaneous tissue	0.00	0	0	–

19000–19499
Breast Procedures

Coding Insight

When reporting breast procedure codes use the bilateral modifier as appropriate. Indicate whether the procedure(s) was performed on the left or right breast (-LT or -RT).

Insertion of a mammary implant (19340 or 19342) should not be reported with a capsulotomy or capsulectomy (19370 or 19371). The placement of a new prosthesis is incidental to a capsulotomy or capsulectomy.

If preoperative placement of needle localization wire is performed, see 19290–19291 and 76096 (for radiological supervision and interpretation).

Cosmetic Warning

This section contains codes which are considered cosmetic 85 percent of the time or more. The codes are 19140, 19316, 19324–19325.

Subsidiary Codes

Subsidiary codes have relative values that require no further adjustment:

19001 is "in addition" to 19000
19126 is "in addition" to 19125
19291 is "in addition" to 19290
19340 is "in addition" to 19160–19240, 19316, 19357–19366, 19380
20920 is "in addition" to 19000–19499
20922 is "in addition" to 19000–19499
20926 is "in addition" to 19000–19499

Because these are subsidiary or "in addition to" codes reimbursement reduction and modifier -51 do not apply.

Medicare Alert

Medicare rebundles certain codes in the surgery section when the listed codes are considered a component of a more comprehensive service.

19100–19101 will not be reimbursed when reported with 19120
19100–19101, 19120 will not be reimbursed when reported with 19160
19100–19101, 19120, 19160, 38525, 38745 will not be reimbursed when reported with 19162
19100–19101, 19120, 19160, 19180, 38525, 38745 will not be reimbursed when reported with 19240

Code		Description	Medicode RVU	50th	75th	Medicare Nat'l Avg
19000	*	Puncture aspiration of cyst of breast;	3.70	87	102	49
19001		Puncture aspiration of cyst of breast; each additional cyst	2.78	66	77	27
19020		Mastotomy with exploration or drainage of abscess, deep	16.00	378	441	197
19030		Injection procedure only for mammary ductogram or galactogram	4.50	106	124	70
19100	*	Biopsy of breast; needle core (separate procedure)	6.50	154	179	80
19101		Biopsy of breast; incisional	21.50	508	592	238
19110		Nipple exploration, with or without excision of a solitary lactiferous duct or a papilloma lactiferous duct	23.75	561	654	282
19112		Excision of lactiferous duct fistula	23.50	556	647	243
19120		Excision of cyst, fibroadenoma, or other benign or malignant tumor aberrant breast tissue, duct lesion or nipple lesion (except 19140), male or female, one or more lesions	27.25	644	751	329
19125		Excision of breast lesion identified by pre-operative placement of radiological marker; single lesion	30.00	709	826	361
19126		Excision of breast lesion identified by pre-operative placement of radiological marker; each additional lesion separately identified by a radiological marker	15.00	355	413	215
19140		Mastectomy for gynecomastia	50.00	1172	1349	424
19160		Mastectomy, partial;	40.00	938	1079	463
19162		Mastectomy, partial; with axillary lymphadenectomy	82.00	1923	2213	968
19180		Mastectomy, simple, complete	54.00	1266	1457	596
19182		Mastectomy, subcutaneous	67.00	1571	1808	596
19200		Mastectomy, radical, including pectoral muscles, axillary lymph nodes	76.00	1782	2051	1059
19220		Mastectomy, radical, including pectoral muscles, axillary and internal mammary lymph nodes (Urban type operation)	80.00	1876	2159	1099
19240		Mastectomy, modified radical, including axillary lymph nodes, with or without pectoralis minor muscle, but excluding pectoralis major muscle	90.00	2110	2428	1025
19260		Excision of chest wall tumor including ribs	80.00	1876	2159	781
19271		Excision of chest wall tumor involving ribs, with plastic reconstruction; without mediastinal lymphadenectomy	122.0	2861	3292	1322
19272		Excision of chest wall tumor involving ribs, with plastic reconstruction; with mediastinal lymphadenectomy	132.0	3095	3562	1349

Code	Description	Medicode RVU	50th	75th	Medicare Nat'l Avg
19290	Preoperative placement of needle localization wire, breast;	6.75	157	190	70
19291	Preoperative placement of needle localization wire, breast; each additional lesion	3.37	79	95	37
19316	Mastopexy	85.00	1981	2392	1022
19318	Reduction mammaplasty	127.0	2960	3574	1249
19324	Mammaplasty, augmentation; without prosthetic implant	50.00	1165	1407	373
19325	Mammaplasty, augmentation; with prosthetic implant	65.00	1515	1829	601
19328	Removal of intact mammary implant	29.00	676	816	390
19330	Removal of mammary implant material	40.00	932	1126	463
19340	Immediate insertion of breast prosthesis following mastopexy, mastectomy or in reconstruction	45.00	1049	1266	743
19342	Delayed insertion of breast prosthesis following mastopexy, mastectomy or in reconstruction	88.00	2051	2476	952
19350	Nipple/areola reconstruction	65.00	1515	1829	660
19355	Correction of inverted nipples	21.00	489	591	513
19357	Breast reconstruction, immediate or delayed, with tissue expander, including subsequent expansion	129.0	3006	3630	1213
19361	Breast reconstruction with latissimus dorsi flap, with or without prosthetic implant	208.0	4847	5853	1666
19364	Breast reconstruction with free flap	160.0	3729	4503	1861
19366	Breast reconstruction with other technique	0.00	0	0	1559
19367	Breast reconstruction with transverse rectus abdominis myocutaneous flap (TRAM), single pedicle, including closure of donor site;	270.0	6292	7598	1921
19368	Breast reconstruction with transverse rectus abdominis myocutaneous flap (TRAM), single pedicle, including closure of donor site; with microvascular anastomosis (supercharging)	283.0	6595	7964	2139
19369	Breast reconstruction with transverse rectus abdominis myocutaneous flap (TRAM), double pedicle, including closure of donor site	297.0	6922	8358	2055
19370	Open periprosthetic capsulotomy, breast	70.00	1631	1970	605
19371	Periprosthetic capsulectomy, breast	81.25	1894	2286	739
19380	Revision of reconstructed breast	0.00	0	0	724
19396	Preparation of moulage for custom breast implant	5.00	117	141	157
19499	Unlisted procedure, breast	0.00	0	0	–

Surgery Codes 20000–29909

More than one procedure is frequently performed at the time of surgery on the musculoskeletal system. Although some procedures are performed on a single joint; many are performed on multiple joints and even on several separate anatomical sites. The surgeries may be simple to complex and for varying diagnoses such as arthritis, injury, and trauma. Consequently, coding in this section of CPT can be very difficult.

Differences of opinions exist about what is or is not included in a particular code, making musculoskeletal coding a real challenge on both the payer and provider side. For example, an incision may be made on the lateral side of the knee and a second incision may be made on the medial side, or an arthroscopic procedure may be done laterally and an open procedure done medially.

Payers have formulated guidelines for many different coding scenarios, but not for all. Their guidelines for arthroscopic and joint procedures can sometimes appear to be unbundled even when they are not. For this reason, claims reviewers and auditors look closely at codes from this subsection of CPT when applying payer rules and guidelines. Pay close attention to EOBs to determine how frequently billed payers look at the issues in this subsection.

When reporting codes from this subsection of CPT consider carefully what is included in the code. As an example, look at 27357 *Excision or curettage of bone cyst or benign tumor of femur; with autograft (includes obtaining graft)* and what is included when this procedure is performed:

- Incision
- Biopsies
- Removal of foreign bodies or other small incidental procedures done along the way which do not add significant time
- Debridement
- Casting (as necessary)
- Bone grafts (if included in the description or from the same location)
- Any other procedures included or specified in the code description
- Closure of the operative wound

When more than one procedure is performed in the same operative session, always question whether secondary procedures would be included in the main procedure. If they are not included, list them separately and apply modifier rules as appropriate.

Nota Bene: Internal fixation, when performed, is included in codes in this subsection of CPT. Some payers reimburse for removal of hardware when done at the time of another procedure in the same anatomical area; others do not.

Terms Common to the Musculoskeletal System

Fracture Care

Fracture management codes in this subsection are package services and include same day problem-focused evaluation of the fracture, percutaneous pinning or open or closed treatment of the fracture, application and removal of the initial cast or splint, and normal, uncomplicated follow-up care.

Closed or open treatment and percutaneous skeletal fixation are terms that were carefully chosen for this subsection so that the listed codes would accurately reflect current orthopedic procedures. However, do not confuse the way a bone is fractured (e.g., open, displaced) with the way the fracture is treated. Codes in this subsection are listed by how the fracture is treated.

Closed treatment of a fracture occurs when the fracture site is not surgically opened, and the physician does not repair it directly through an open incision. Closed fracture treatment may, however, be performed with or without manipulation and with or without traction.

Open treatment of a fracture site requires direct visualization through an incision of the fracture. Internal fixation to stabilize the fracture may also be used (e.g., screws, nails, wire).

Percutaneous skeletal fixation is a fracture treatment that is not open or closed. Instead, fixation of the fracture site is accomplished by other methods (e.g., pins), which are placed through the skin and across the fracture site. X-ray imaging is often used to aid in the placement of the fixation device.

Dislocations are reported by the type of manipulation (reduction), and method of stabilization used to relocate the affected joint. Other terms listed in the fracture subsection are:

- *Skeletal traction*: force applied to a limb segment through a wire, pin, screw, or clamp attached to bone
- *Skin traction*: force applied to a limb by using felt or strapping which is directly applied to the skin
- *Manipulation*: of a fracture or joint dislocation is the use of physical force to reduce, i.e., restore, the injured site to its normal alignment

Internal and External Fixation

Two types of fixation — internal and external — are listed in this subsection.

Internal skeletal fixation involves wires, pins, screws, and/or plates placed through or within the fractured area to stabilize and immobilize the injury. This procedure is generally accomplished through an incision over the fracture site. It is commonly described as an open reduction with internal fixation (ORIF). Another way to accomplish internal fixation is with percutaneous pinning. Deep internal devices are usually left in place even after the fracture has healed. If these devices are removed, that procedure may be reported separately. Use modifier -78 *Return to the operating room for a related procedure* or modifier -58 *Staged or related procedure by the same physician during the postoperative period.* Codes describing internal fixation are interspersed throughout the fracture care codes.

External fixation involves skeletal pins that are attached to an external mechanism for treatment of a bony deformity. This type of fixation can be used for acute or chronic conditions. The treatment may be temporary or definitive.

Observe the following general guidelines when coding services for fracture management:

- The code is determined by the anatomical location, type of fracture treatment, and method of reduction and immobilization.
- Fracture care codes are global surgical codes; they include initial cast and same day problem-focused evaluation with normal follow-up care, but exclude certain services such as follow-up x-rays and supplies.
- Postoperative complications requiring additional procedures are reported separately. These procedures may include x-rays, repeat or reapplication of cast, and treatment of complications.

20000–20251
General

Coding Insight
Codes in this section are for incision of soft tissue abscess and biopsies of muscle or bone, by needle and incision. Refer to the listing under biopsies in the introduction to the surgery section for general information about biopsies when they are performed at the time of a second surgery and on the same anatomical area or through the same incision.

Nota Bene: Four new codes (20100–20103) were added to this code range in *CPT '96*. Use them to report "Wound Exploration–Trauma (eg, Penetrating Gunshot, Stab Wound)". Notes preceding the codes describe under what circumstances the codes should be used; read them carefully before selecting a code. New codes are listed with values in Medicodes *Fee & Coding Standard*. The relative values have been established by a committee prior to actual data being collected for the codes. This method of establishing values for new codes has been proven to be extremely accurate in prior years.

Subsidiary Codes
Subsidiary codes have relative values that require no further adjustment:

20690 is "in addition" to 20000–20251
20692 is "in addition" to 20000–20251
20900 is "in addition" to 20000–20251
20902 is "in addition" to 20000–20251
20910 is "in addition" to 20000–20251
20912 is "in addition" to 20000–20251
20920 is "in addition" to 20000–20251
20922 is "in addition" to 20000–20251
20924 is "in addition" to 20000–20251
20926 is "in addition" to 20000–20251

Because these are subsidiary or "in addition to" codes, reimbursement reduction and modifier -51 do not apply.

	Code		Description	Medicode RVU	50th	75th	Medicare Nat'l Avg
	20000	*	Incision of soft tissue abscess (eg, secondary to osteomyelitis); superficial	4.00	91	107	99
	20005		Incision of soft tissue abscess (eg, secondary to osteomyelitis); deep or complicated	20.00	453	536	206
●	20100		Exploration of penetrating wound (separate procedure); neck	60.50	1372	1621	–
●	20101		Exploration of penetrating wound (separate procedure); chest	82.50	1871	2211	–
●	20102		Exploration of penetrating wound (separate procedure); abdomen/flank/back	71.50	1621	1916	–
●	20103		Exploration of penetrating wound (separate procedure); extremity	58.00	1315	1554	–
	20200		Biopsy, muscle; superficial	11.00	249	295	109
	20205		Biopsy, muscle; deep	17.00	385	456	184
	20206	*	Biopsy, muscle, percutaneous needle	7.00	159	188	84

Code	Description	Medicode RVU	50th	75th	Medicare Nat'l Avg
20220	Biopsy, bone, trocar, or needle; superficial (eg, ilium, sternum, spinous process, ribs)	8.00	181	214	93
20225	Biopsy, bone, trocar, or needle; deep (vertebral body, femur)	19.50	442	523	174
20240	Biopsy, excisional; superficial (eg, ilium, sternum, spinous process, ribs, trochanter of femur)	16.50	374	442	203
20245	Biopsy, excisional; deep (eg, humerus, ischium, femur)	28.00	635	750	312
20250	Biopsy, vertebral body, open; thoracic	70.00	1587	1876	431
20251	Biopsy, vertebral body, open; lumbar or cervical	70.00	1587	1876	478

20500–20694
Introduction or Removal

Coding Insight
External fixation (20690–20694) involves hardware passing through bone and held rigid by cross-braces outside the body. External fixation is always removed after the fracture has healed; removal is considered part of the global service. Unless specifically stated as part of the code's description, external fixation may be reported separately.

Arthrocentesis codes (20600–20610) should not be reported with an arthrotomy procedure.

Subsidiary Codes
Subsidiary codes have relative values that require no further adjustment:

20690 is "in addition" to 20500–20694
20692 is "in addition" to 20500–20694
20900 is "in addition" to 20500–20694
20902 is "in addition" to 20500–20694
20910 is "in addition" to 20500–20694
20912 is "in addition" to 20500–20694
20920 is "in addition" to 20500–20694
20922 is "in addition" to 20500–20694
20924 is "in addition" to 20500–20694
20926 is "in addition" to 21920–21935

Because these are subsidiary or "in addition to" codes, reimbursement reduction and modifier -51 do not apply.

Medicare Alert
Medicare rebundles certain codes in the surgery section when the listed codes are considered a component of a more comprehensive service.

10160 will not be reimbursed when reported with 20550, 20600, 20605, 20610

64450 will not be reimbursed when reported with 20550, 20600, 20605

11040, 11041, 11042 will not be reimbursed when reported with 20680

Code		Description	Medicode RVU	50th	75th	Medicare Nat'l Avg
20500	*	Injection of sinus tract; therapeutic (separate procedure)	3.00	68	80	51
20501	*	Injection of sinus tract; diagnostic (sinogram)	4.00	91	107	37
20520	*	Removal of foreign body in muscle or tendon sheath; simple	7.50	170	201	100
20525		Removal of foreign body in muscle or tendon sheath; deep or complicated	22.00	499	590	230
20550	*	Injection, tendon sheath, ligament, trigger points or ganglion cyst	3.00	68	80	42
20600	*	Arthrocentesis, aspiration and/or injection; small joint, bursa or ganglion cyst (eg, fingers, toes)	2.75	62	74	45
20605	*	Arthrocentesis, aspiration and/or injection; intermediate joint, bursa or ganglion cyst (eg, temporomandibular, acromioclavicular, wrist, elbow or ankle, olecranon bursa)	3.00	68	80	45
20610	*	Arthrocentesis, aspiration and/or injection; major joint or bursa (eg, shoulder, hip, knee joint, subacromial bursa)	3.50	79	94	43
20615		Aspiration and injection for treatment of bone cyst	12.00	272	322	91
20650	*	Insertion of wire or pin with application of skeletal traction, including removal (separate procedure)	10.00	227	268	127
20660		Application of cranial tongs, caliper, or stereotactic frame, including removal (separate procedure)	27.00	612	724	175
20661		Application of halo, including removal; cranial	34.50	782	925	353
20662		Application of halo, including removal; pelvic	23.00	521	616	506
20663		Application of halo, including removal; femoral	23.00	521	616	398
20665	*	Removal of tongs or halo applied by another physician	4.00	91	107	73
20670	*	Removal of implant; superficial, (eg, buried wire, pin or rod) (separate procedure)	8.50	193	228	97
20680		Removal of implant; deep (eg, buried wire, pin, screw, metal band, nail, rod or plate)	25.00	567	670	285
20690		Application of a uniplane (pins or wires in one plane), unilateral, external fixation system	34.00	771	911	314
20692		Application of a multiplane (pins or wires in more than one plane), unilateral, external fixation system (eg, Ilizarov, Monticelli type)	47.50	1077	1273	489
20693		Adjustment or revision of external fixation system requiring anesthesia (eg, new pin(s) or wire(s) and/or new ring(s) or bar(s))	25.00	567	670	324
20694		Removal, under anesthesia, of external fixation system	19.00	431	509	264

20802–20838
Replantation

Coding Insight
Wound debridement and irrigation should not be reported in addition to these codes.

Nota Bene: Significant changes to this code range were made in *CPT '96*. Incomplete amputation codes were deleted and the remainder of the undeleted codes were revised (e.g., the semicolon which previously indicated a subordinate code for the incomplete amputation has now been changed to a comma). Instructions for reporting procedures attendent to incomplete amputation are contained in new parenthetical comments in the same code placement order. Review these coding changes carefully.

Subsidiary Codes
Subsidiary codes have relative values that require no further adjustment:

20690 is "in addition" to 20802–20838
20692 is "in addition" to 20802–20838
20900 is "in addition" to 20802–20838
20902 is "in addition" to 20802–20838
20910 is "in addition" to 20802–20838
20912 is "in addition" to 20802–20838
20920 is "in addition" to 20802–20838
20922 is "in addition" to 20802–20838
20924 is "in addition" to 20802–20838
20926 is "in addition" to 20802–20838

Because these are subsidiary or "in addition to" codes, reimbursement reduction and modifier -51 do not apply.

Code	Description	Medicode RVU	50th	75th	Medicare Nat'l Avg
20802	Replantation, arm (includes surgical neck of humerus through elbow joint), complete amputation	0.00	0	0	3239
20805	Replantation, forearm (includes radius and ulna to radial carpal joint), complete amputation	0.00	0	0	3964
20808	Replantation, hand (includes hand through metacarpophalangeal joints), complete amputation	0.00	0	0	4928
20816	Replantation, digit, excluding thumb (includes metacarpophalangeal joint to insertion of flexor sublimis tendon), complete amputation	0.00	0	0	2429
20822	Replantation, digit, excluding thumb (includes distal tip to sublimis tendon insertion), complete amputation	0.00	0	0	2008
20824	Replantation, thumb (includes carpometacarpal joint to MP joint), complete amputation	0.00	0	0	2429
20827	Replantation, thumb (includes distal tip to MP joint), complete amputation	0.00	0	0	2065
20838	Replantation, foot, complete amputation	0.00	0	0	3239

20900–20938
Grafts or Implants

Coding Insight
Throughout this code range there are some important terms you must know:

- Autografts are grafts transferred from one part of the body to another
- Allografts take donor tissue from the same species, e.g., freeze-dried bone, merthiolate-treated bone, and frozen hemopoietic marrow/cancellous bone
- Alloplastic is the use synthetic materials having little or no ability to react with other compositions, e.g., Synthograft® or Calcitite®
- Composite grafts involve combinations of autogenous material and allograft or alloplast

Codes for obtaining autogenous bone grafts through separate incisions should be used only when the graft is not already listed as part of the basic procedure. Codes 20900–20902 should be selected based on the size of the bone harvested rather than the difficulty of the access needed to harvest it. The size of the bone harvested is usually compatible with the base procedure performed. Code 29000 involves harvesting a small piece of bone or bone plug, and code 20902 involves harvesting a significantly larger piece of bone.

Nota Bene: Five new codes (20930–20938) were added to this code range in *CPT '96*. Use them to report bone grafts performed at the time of surgery on the spine. Watch for terms such as autograft and allograft and for the type of graft (e.g., morselized, structural). Only one code should be reported from this code range "per operative session." Also, a new parenthetical phrase listed above code 20900 "(For spinal surgery bone graft(s) see codes 20930–20938)" indicates that codes 20900–20902 should not be used to report bone grafts for spinal surgery.

Subsidiary Codes
Subsidiary codes have relative values that require no further adjustment:

20690 is "in addition" to 20900–20938
20692 is "in addition" to 20900–20938
20900 is "in addition" to 20900–20938
20902 is "in addition" to 20900–20938
20910 is "in addition" to 20900–20938
20912 is "in addition" to 20900–20938
20920 is "in addition" to 20900–20938
20922 is "in addition" to 20900–20938
20924 is "in addition" to 20900–20938
20926 is "in addition" to 20900–20938

Because these are subsidiary or "in addition to" codes, reimbursement reduction and modifier -51 do not apply.

Code	Description	Medicode RVU	50th	75th	Medicare Nat'l Avg
20900	Bone graft, any donor area; minor or small (eg, dowel or button)	19.00	431	509	325
20902	Bone graft, any donor area; major or large	38.00	862	1018	507
20910	Cartilage graft; costochondral	28.00	635	750	242
20912	Cartilage graft; nasal septum	33.00	748	884	444

	Code	Description	Medicode RVU	50th	75th	Medicare Nat'l Avg
	20920	Fascia lata graft; by stripper	22.00	499	590	362
	20922	Fascia lata graft; by incision and area exposure, complex or sheet	30.00	680	804	435
	20924	Tendon graft, from a distance (eg, palmaris, toe extensor, plantaris)	21.00	476	563	480
	20926	Tissue grafts, other (eg, paratenon, fat, dermis)	20.00	453	536	315
●	**20930**	Allograft for spine surgery only; morselized	2.00	45	54	–
●	**20931**	Allograft for spine surgery only; structural	4.00	91	107	–
●	**20936**	Autograft for spine surgery only (includes harvesting the graft); local (eg, ribs, spinous process, or laminar fragments) obtained from same incision	12.50	283	335	–
●	**20937**	Autograft for spine surgery only (includes harvesting the graft); morselized (through separate skin or fascial incision)	38.00	862	1018	–
●	**20938**	Autograft for spine surgery only (includes harvesting the graft); structural, bicortical or tricortical (through separate skin of fascial incision)	38.00	862	1018	–

20950–20999
Other Procedures

Subsidiary Codes

Subsidiary codes have relative values that require no further adjustment:

20690 is "in addition" to 20950–20999
20692 is "in addition" to 20950–20999
20900 is "in addition" to 20950–20999
20902 is "in addition" to 20950–20999
20910 is "in addition" to 20950–20999
20912 is "in addition" to 20950–20999
20920 is "in addition" to 20950–20999
20922 is "in addition" to 20950–20999
20924 is "in addition" to 20950–20999
20926 is "in addition" to 20950–20999

Because these are subsidiary or "in addition to" codes, reimbursement reduction and modifier -51 do not apply.

Code	Description	Medicode RVU	50th	75th	Medicare Nat'l Avg
20950	Monitoring of interstitial fluid pressure (includes insertion of device, eg, wick catheter technique, needle manometer technique) in detection of muscle compartment syndrome	7.00	159	188	99

Code	Description	Medicode RVU	50th	75th	Medicare Nat'l Avg
20955	Bone graft with microvascular anastomosis; fibula	150.0	3401	4020	3077
20960	Bone graft with microvascular anastomosis; rib	150.0	3401	4020	2256
20962	Bone graft with microvascular anastomosis; other bone graft (specify)	175.0	3968	4690	2634
20969	Free osteocutaneous flap with microvascular anastomosis; other than iliac crest, rib, metatarsal, or great toe	200.0	4535	5360	3445
20970	Free osteocutaneous flap with microvascular anastomosis; iliac crest	200.0	4535	5360	3375
20971	Free osteocutaneous flap with microvascular anastomosis; rib	200.0	4535	5360	3498
20972	Free osteocutaneous flap with microvascular anastomosis; metatarsal	200.0	4535	5360	3401
20973	Free osteocutaneous flap with microvascular anastomosis; great toe with web space	213.0	4829	5708	3627
20974	Electrical stimulation to aid bone healing; noninvasive (nonoperative)	25.00	567	670	189
20975	Electrical stimulation to aid bone healing; invasive (operative)	40.00	907	1072	276
20999	Unlisted procedure, musculoskeletal system, general	0.00	0	0	–

21010–21499
Skull, Facial Bones, and Temporomandibular Joint

Coding Insight
Many payers are concerned about the potential overutilization of temporomandibular joint procedures and will not reimburse for them without prior authorization. Be sure to obtain prior authorization and list the prior authorization number on any claims submissions or correspondence.

Subsidiary Codes
Subsidiary codes have relative values that require no further adjustment:

20690 is "in addition" to 21010–21499
20692 is "in addition" to 21010–21499
20900 is "in addition" to 21010–21499
20902 is "in addition" to 21010–21499
20910 is "in addition" to 21010–21499
20912 is "in addition" to 21010–21499
20920 is "in addition" to 21010–21499
20922 is "in addition" to 21010–21499
20924 is "in addition" to 21010–21499
20926 is "in addition" to 21010–21499

Because these are subsidiary or "in addition to" codes, reimbursement reduction and modifier -51 do not apply.

Code	Description	Medicode RVU	50th	75th	Medicare Nat'l Avg
21010	Arthrotomy, temporomandibular joint	105.5	2293	2746	788
21015	Radical resection of tumor (eg, malignant neoplasm), soft tissue of face or scalp	0.00	0	0	480
21025	Excision of bone (eg, for osteomyelitis or bone abscess); mandible	70.00	1521	1822	389
21026	Excision of bone (eg, for osteomyelitis or bone abscess); facial bone(s)	75.00	1630	1952	316
21029	Removal by contouring of benign tumor of facial bone (eg, fibrous dysplasia)	84.00	1825	2186	669
21030	Excision of benign tumor or cyst of facial bone other than mandible	47.00	1021	1223	413
21031	Excision of torus mandibularis	17.55	381	457	240
21032	Excision of maxillary torus palatinus	25.00	543	651	339
21034	Excision of malignant tumor of facial bone other than mandible	83.00	1804	2160	897
21040	Excision of benign cyst or tumor of mandible; simple	23.00	500	599	214
21041	Excision of benign cyst or tumor of mandible; complex	46.00	1000	1197	477
21044	Excision of malignant tumor of mandible;	83.00	1804	2160	845
21045	Excision of malignant tumor of mandible; radical resection	150.0	3260	3904	1196
21050	Condylectomy, temporomandibular joint (separate procedure)	120.0	2608	3123	920
21060	Meniscectomy, partial or complete, temporomandibular joint (separate procedure)	135.0	2934	3514	874
21070	Coronoidectomy (separate procedure)	99.00	2151	2577	594
● 21076	Impression and custom preparation; surgical obturator prosthesis	44.00	956	1145	–
● 21077	Impression and custom preparation; orbital prosthesis	110.5	2401	2876	–
21079	Impression and custom preparation; interim obturator prosthesis	73.25	1592	1906	1028
21080	Impression and custom preparation; definitive obturator prosthesis	82.25	1787	2141	2076
21081	Impression and custom preparation; mandibular resection prosthesis	75.00	1630	1952	2124
21082	Impression and custom preparation; palatal augmentation prosthesis	68.50	1489	1783	1518
21083	Impression and custom preparation; palatal lift prosthesis	63.25	1374	1646	1339
21084	Impression and custom preparation; speech aid prosthesis	73.25	1592	1906	1480

	Code		Description	Medicode RVU	50th	75th	Medicare Nat'l Avg
	21085		Impression and custom preparation; oral surgical splint	29.50	641	768	583
	21086		Impression and custom preparation; auricular prosthesis	81.75	1777	2128	2020
	21087		Impression and custom preparation; nasal prosthesis	81.75	1777	2128	1708
	21088		Impression and custom preparation; facial prosthesis	0.00	0	0	2341
	21089		Unlisted maxillofacial prosthetic procedure	0.00	0	0	–
	21100	*	Application of halo type appliance for maxillofacial fixation, includes removal (separate procedure)	12.75	277	332	206
	21110		Application of interdental fixation device for conditions other than fracture or dislocation, includes removal	30.00	652	781	436
	21116		Injection procedure for temporomandibular joint arthrography	5.70	124	148	63
	21120		Genioplasty; augmentation (autograft, allograft, prosthetic material)	71.00	1543	1848	341
	21121		Genioplasty; sliding osteotomy, single piece	87.00	1891	2264	536
	21122		Genioplasty; sliding osteotomies, two or more osteotomies (eg, wedge excision or bone wedge reversal for asymmetrical chin)	115.0	2499	2993	590
	21123		Genioplasty; sliding, augmentation with interpositional bone grafts (includes obtaining autografts)	128.0	2782	3331	771
	21125		Augmentation, mandibular body or angle; prosthetic material	79.00	1717	2056	447
	21127		Augmentation, mandibular body or angle; with bone graft, onlay or interpositional (includes obtaining autograft)	110.0	2390	2863	749
	21137		Reduction forehead; contouring only	101.0	2195	2629	674
	21138		Reduction forehead; contouring and application of prosthetic material or bone graft (includes obtaining autograft)	126.0	2738	3279	841
	21139		Reduction forehead; contouring and setback of anterior frontal sinus wall	151.0	3281	3930	1009
●	**21141**		Reconstruction midface, LeFort 1; single piece, segment movement in any direction (eg, for Long Face Syndrome), without bone graft	187.5	4075	4880	–
●	**21142**		Reconstruction midface, LeFort 1; two pieces, segment movement in any direction, without bone graft	197.0	4281	5127	–
●	**21143**		Reconstruction midface, LeFort 1; three or more pieces, segment movement in any direction, without bone graft	204.0	4433	5310	–
▲	**21145**		Reconstruction midface, LeFort 1; single piece, segment movement in any direction, requiring bone grafts (includes obtaining autografts)	205.5	4466	5349	1359
▲	**21146**		Reconstruction midface, LeFort 1; two pieces, segment movement in any direction, requiring bone grafts (includes obtaining autografts) (eg, ungrafted unilateral alveolar cleft)	215.0	4672	5596	1406

	Code	Description	Medicode RVU	50th	75th	Medicare Nat'l Avg
▲	21147	Reconstruction midface, LeFort 1; three or more pieces, segment movement in any direction, requiring bone grafts (includes obtaining autografts) (eg, ungrafted bilateral alveolar cleft or multiple osteotomies)	225.0	4889	5856	1459
	21150	Reconstruction midface, LeFort II; anterior intrusion (eg, Treacher-Collins Syndrome)	244.0	5302	6351	1752
	21151	Reconstruction midface, LeFort II; any direction, requiring bone grafts (includes obtaining autografts)	274.0	5954	7131	1962
	21154	Reconstruction midface, LeFort III (extracranial), any type, requiring bone grafts (includes obtaining autografts); without LeFort I	295.0	6411	7678	2101
	21155	Reconstruction midface, LeFort III (extracranial), any type, requiring bone grafts (includes obtaining autografts); with LeFort I	340.0	7389	8849	2382
	21159	Reconstruction midface, LeFort III (extra and intracranial) with forehead advancement (eg, mono bloc), requiring bone grafts (includes obtaining autografts); without LeFort I	415.0	9018	10801	2942
	21160	Reconstruction midface, LeFort III (extra and intracranial) with forehead advancement (eg, mono bloc), requiring bone grafts (includes obtaining autografts); with LeFort I	482.0	10474	12545	3222
	21172	Reconstruction superior-lateral orbital rim and lower forehead, advancement or alteration, with or without grafts (includes obtaining autografts)	184.0	3999	4789	1926
	21175	Reconstruction, bifrontal, superior-lateral orbital rims and lower forehead, advancement or alteration (eg, plagiocephaly, trigonocephaly, brachycephaly), with or without grafts (includes obtaining autografts)	290.0	6302	7548	2311
	21179	Reconstruction, entire or majority of forehead and/or supraorbital rims; with grafts (allograft or prosthetic material)	240.0	5215	6246	1541
	21180	Reconstruction, entire or majority of forehead and/or supraorbital rims; with autograft (includes obtaining grafts)	270.0	5867	7027	1752
	21181	Reconstruction by contouring of benign tumor of cranial bones (eg, fibrous dysplasia), extracranial	95.00	2064	2473	674
	21182	Reconstruction of orbital walls, rims, forehead, nasoethmoid complex following intra- and extracranial excision of benign tumor of cranial bone (eg, fibrous dysplasia), with multiple autografts (includes obtaining grafts); total area of bone grafting less than 40 cm2	294.0	6389	7652	2241
	21183	Reconstruction of orbital walls, rims, forehead, nasoethmoid complex following intra- and extracranial excision of benign tumor of cranial bone (eg, fibrous dysplasia), with multiple autografts (includes obtaining grafts); total area of bone grafting greater than 40 cm2 but less than 80 cm2	322.0	6997	8381	2452
	21184	Reconstruction of orbital walls, rims, forehead, nasoethmoid complex following intra- and extracranial excision of benign tumor of cranial bone (eg, fibrous dysplasia), with multiple autografts (includes obtaining grafts); total area of bone grafting greater than 80 cm2	349.0	7584	9083	2662
	21188	Reconstruction midface, osteotomies (other than LeFort type) and bone grafts (includes obtaining autografts)	232.0	5042	6038	1541
▲	21193	Reconstruction of mandibular rami, horizontal, vertical, "s", or "L" osteotomy; without bone graft	224.5	4879	5843	1166

	Code	Description	Medicode RVU	50th	75th	Medicare Nat'l Avg
▲	**21194**	Reconstruction of mandibular ramus, horizontal, vertical, "s", or "L" osteotomy; with bone graft (includes obtaining graft)	257.8	5601	6708	1351
▲	**21195**	Reconstruction of mandibular rami and/or body, sagittal split; without internal rigid fixation	219.0	4759	5700	1169
▲	**21196**	Reconstruction of mandibular ramus and/or body, sagittal split; with internal rigid fixation	237.3	5156	6175	1289
	21198	Osteotomy, mandible, segmental	110.0	2390	2863	1162
	21206	Osteotomy, maxilla, segmental (eg, Wassmund or Schuchard)	164.0	3564	4268	960
	21208	Osteoplasty, facial bones; augmentation (autograft, allograft, or prosthetic implant)	85.00	1847	2212	862
	21209	Osteoplasty, facial bones; reduction	65.00	1413	1692	455
	21210	Graft, bone; nasal, maxillary or malar areas (includes obtaining graft)	112.0	2434	2915	946
	21215	Graft, bone; mandible (includes obtaining graft)	105.0	2282	2733	1016
	21230	Graft; rib cartilage, autogenous, to face, chin, nose or ear (includes obtaining graft)	114.0	2477	2967	870
	21235	Graft; ear cartilage, autogenous, to nose or ear (includes obtaining graft)	77.00	1673	2004	627
	21240	Arthroplasty, temporomandibular joint, with or without autograft (includes obtaining graft)	170.0	3694	4425	1359
	21242	Arthroplasty, temporomandibular joint, with allograft	170.0	3694	4425	1309
	21243	Arthroplasty, temporomandibular joint, with prosthetic joint replacement	245.0	5324	6377	1368
	21244	Reconstruction of mandible, extraoral, with transosteal bone plate (eg, mandibular staple bone plate)	140.0	3042	3644	1114
	21245	Reconstruction of mandible or maxilla, subperiosteal implant; partial	180.0	3912	4685	933
	21246	Reconstruction of mandible or maxilla, subperiosteal implant; complete	199.0	4324	5179	843
	21247	Reconstruction of mandibular condyle with bone and cartilage autografts (includes obtaining grafts) (eg, for hemifacial microsomia)	195.0	4238	5075	1970
	21248	Reconstruction of mandible or maxilla, endosteal implant (eg, blade, cylinder); partial	155.0	3368	4034	1150
	21249	Reconstruction of mandible or maxilla, endosteal implant (eg, blade, cylinder); complete	200.0	4346	5205	1928
	21255	Reconstruction of zygomatic arch and glenoid fossa with bone and cartilage (includes obtaining autografts)	165.0	3586	4294	1458
	21256	Reconstruction of orbit with osteotomies (extracranial) and with bone grafts (includes obtaining autografts) (eg, micro-ophthalmia)	220.0	4781	5726	1414
	21260	Periorbital osteotomies for orbital hypertelorism, with bone grafts; extracranial approach	224.0	4868	5830	1432

Code		Description	Medicode RVU	50th	75th	Medicare Nat'l Avg
21261		Periorbital osteotomies for orbital hypertelorism, with bone grafts; combined intra- and extracranial approach	280.0	6085	7288	1903
21263		Periorbital osteotomies for orbital hypertelorism, with bone grafts; with forehead advancement	370.0	8040	9630	2464
21267		Orbital repositioning, periorbital osteotomies, unilateral, with bone grafts; extracranial approach	360.0	7823	9370	1339
21268		Orbital repositioning, periorbital osteotomies, unilateral, with bone grafts; combined intra- and extracranial approach	440.0	9562	11452	1606
21270		Malar augmentation, prosthetic material	90.00	1956	2342	902
21275		Secondary revision of orbitocraniofacial reconstruction	220.0	4781	5726	808
21280		Medial canthopexy (separate procedure)	76.00	1652	1978	528
21282		Lateral canthopexy	60.00	1304	1562	394
21295		Reduction of masseter muscle and bone (eg, for treatment of benign masseteric hypertrophy); extraoral approach	121.0	2629	3149	98
21296		Reduction of masseter muscle and bone (eg, for treatment of benign masseteric hypertrophy); intraoral approach	99.00	2151	2577	304
21299		Unlisted craniofacial and maxillofacial procedure	0.00	0	0	–
21300		Closed treatment of skull fracture without operation	16.00	371	441	77
21310		Closed treatment of nasal bone fracture without manipulation	10.00	232	276	54
21315	*	Closed treatment of nasal bone fracture; without stabilization	16.00	371	441	138
21320		Closed treatment of nasal bone fracture; with stabilization	26.00	603	717	191
21325		Open treatment of nasal fracture; uncomplicated	41.00	951	1131	321
21330		Open treatment of nasal fracture; complicated, with internal and/or external skeletal fixation	69.00	1601	1904	497
21335		Open treatment of nasal fracture; with concomitant open treatment of fractured septum	108.0	2506	2979	843
21336		Open treatment of nasal septal fracture, with or without stabilization	44.00	1021	1214	390
21337		Closed treatment of nasal septal fracture, with or without stabilization	28.00	650	772	224
21338		Open treatment of nasoethmoid fracture; without external fixation	70.00	1624	1931	455
21339		Open treatment of nasoethmoid fracture; with external fixation	77.00	1787	2124	598
21340		Percutaneous treatment of nasoethmoid complex fracture, with splint, wire or headcap fixation, including repair of canthal ligaments and/or the nasolacrimal apparatus	101.0	2344	2786	779
21343		Open treatment of depressed frontal sinus fracture	96.00	2228	2648	869

Code		Description	Medicode RVU	50th	75th	Medicare Nat'l Avg
21344		Open treatment of complicated (eg, comminuted or involving posterior wall) frontal sinus fracture, via coronal or multiple approaches	147.0	3411	4055	1117
21345		Closed treatment of nasomaxillary complex fracture (LeFort II type), with interdental wire fixation or fixation of denture or splint	94.00	2181	2593	641
21346		Open treatment of nasomaxillary complex fracture (LeFort II type); with wiring and/or local fixation	120.0	2785	3310	795
21347		Open treatment of nasomaxillary complex fracture (LeFort II type); requiring multiple open approaches	143.0	3319	3945	928
21348		Open treatment of nasomaxillary complex fracture (LeFort II type); with bone grafting (includes obtaining graft)	144.0	3342	3973	1124
21355	*	Percutaneous treatment of fracture of malar area, including zygomatic arch and malar tripod, with manipulation	28.00	650	772	204
21356		Open treatment of depressed zygomatic arch fracture (eg, Gilles approach)	50.00	1160	1379	429
21360		Open treatment of depressed malar fracture, including zygomatic arch and malar tripod	68.00	1578	1876	566
21365		Open treatment of complicated (eg, comminuted or involving cranial nerve foramina) fracture(s) of malar area, including zygomatic arch and malar tripod; with internal fixation and multiple surgical approaches	110.0	2553	3035	1114
21366		Open treatment of complicated (eg, comminuted or involving cranial nerve foramina) fracture(s) of malar area, including zygomatic arch and malar tripod; with bone grafting (includes obtaining graft)	135.0	3133	3724	1214
21385		Open treatment of orbital floor "blowout" fracture; transantral approach (Caldwell-Luc type operation)	68.00	1578	1876	759
21386		Open treatment of orbital floor "blowout" fracture; periorbital approach	84.00	1949	2317	741
21387		Open treatment of orbital floor "blowout" fracture; combined approach	116.0	2692	3200	697
21390		Open treatment of orbital floor "blowout" fracture; periorbital approach, with alloplastic or other implant	96.00	2228	2648	907
21395		Open treatment of orbital floor "blowout" fracture; periorbital approach with bone graft (includes obtaining graft)	118.0	2738	3255	901
21400		Closed treatment of fracture of orbit, except "blowout"; without manipulation	14.00	325	386	111
21401		Closed treatment of fracture of orbit, except "blowout"; with manipulation	24.00	557	662	231
21406		Open treatment of fracture of orbit, except "blowout"; without implant	70.00	1624	1931	491
21407		Open treatment of fracture of orbit, except "blowout"; with implant	88.00	2042	2428	626
21408		Open treatment of fracture of orbit, except "blowout"; with bone grafting (includes obtaining graft)	100.0	2321	2759	822
21421		Closed treatment of palatal or maxillary fracture (LeFort I type), with interdental wire fixation or fixation of denture or splint	60.00	1392	1655	457

Code	Description	Medicode RVU	50th	75th	Medicare Nat'l Avg
21422	Open treatment of palatal or maxillary fracture (LeFort I type);	80.00	1857	2207	734
21423	Open treatment of palatal or maxillary fracture (LeFort I type); complicated (comminuted or involving cranial nerve foramina), multiple approaches	92.00	2135	2538	808
21431	Closed treatment of craniofacial separation (LeFort III type) using interdental wire fixation of denture or splint	66.00	1532	1821	519
21432	Open treatment of craniofacial separation (LeFort III type); with wiring and/or internal fixation	94.00	2181	2593	615
21433	Open treatment of craniofacial separation (LeFort III type); complicated (eg, comminuted or involving cranial nerve foramina), multiple surgical approaches	150.0	3481	4138	1705
21435	Open treatment of craniofacial separation (LeFort III type); complicated, utilizing internal and/or external fixation techniques (eg, head cap, halo device, and/or intermaxillary fixation)	171.0	3968	4717	1223
21436	Open treatment of craniofacial separation (LeFort III type); complicated, multiple surgical approaches, internal fixation, with bone grafting (includes obtaining graft)	200.0	4641	5517	1676
21440	Closed treatment of mandibular or maxillary alveolar ridge fracture (separate procedure)	33.00	766	910	230
21445	Open treatment of mandibular or maxillary alveolar ridge fracture (separate procedure)	39.00	905	1076	455
21450	Closed treatment of mandibular fracture; without manipulation	60.00	1392	1655	232
21451	Closed treatment of mandibular fracture; with manipulation	66.00	1532	1821	453
21452	Percutaneous treatment of mandibular fracture, with external fixation	77.00	1787	2124	133
21453	Closed treatment of mandibular fracture with interdental fixation	66.00	1532	1821	481
21454	Open treatment of mandibular fracture with external fixation	83.00	1926	2290	708
21461	Open treatment of mandibular fracture; without interdental fixation	88.00	2042	2428	762
21462	Open treatment of mandibular fracture; with interdental fixation	104.0	2414	2869	898
21465	Open treatment of mandibular condylar fracture	120.0	2785	3310	802
21470	Open treatment of complicated mandibular fracture by multiple surgical approaches including internal fixation, interdental fixation, and/or wiring of dentures or splints	136.0	3156	3752	1335
21480	Closed treatment of temporomandibular dislocation; initial or subsequent	10.00	232	276	64
21485	Closed treatment of temporomandibular dislocation; complicated (eg, recurrent requiring intermaxillary fixation or splinting), initial or subsequent	22.00	511	607	251
21490	Open treatment of temporomandibular dislocation	88.00	2042	2428	697
21493	Closed treatment of hyoid fracture; without manipulation	8.00	186	221	110

Code	Description	Medicode RVU	50th	75th	Medicare Nat'l Avg
21494	Closed treatment of hyoid fracture; with manipulation	18.00	418	497	545
21495	Open treatment of hyoid fracture	67.00	1555	1848	414
21497	Interdental wiring, for condition other than fracture	24.00	557	662	315
21499	Unlisted musculoskeletal procedure, head	0.00	0	0	–

21501–21899
Neck (Soft Tissues) and Thorax

Subsidiary Codes

20690 is "in addition" to 21501–21899
20692 is "in addition" to 21501–21899
20900 is "in addition" to 21501–21899
20902 is "in addition" to 21501–21899
20910 is "in addition" to 21501–21899
20912 is "in addition" to 21501–21899
20920 is "in addition" to 21501–21899
20922 is "in addition" to 21501–21899
20924 is "in addition" to 21501–21899
20926 is "in addition" to 21501–21899

Code	Description	Medicode RVU	50th	75th	Medicare Nat'l Avg
21501	Incision and drainage, deep abscess or hematoma, soft tissues of neck or thorax;	25.00	583	692	219
21502	Incision and drainage, deep abscess or hematoma, soft tissues of neck or thorax; with partial rib ostectomy	30.00	699	831	444
21510	Incision, deep, with opening of bone cortex (eg, for osteomyelitis or bone abscess), thorax	30.00	699	831	367
21550	Biopsy, soft tissue of neck or thorax	10.00	233	277	121
21555	Excision tumor, soft tissue of neck or thorax; subcutaneous	19.50	454	540	226
21556	Excision tumor, soft tissue of neck or thorax; deep, subfascial, intramuscular	35.00	816	969	394
21557	Radical resection of tumor (eg, malignant neoplasm), soft tissue of neck or thorax	128.0	2983	3544	736
21600	Excision of rib, partial	40.00	932	1108	464
21610	Costotransversectomy (separate procedure)	70.00	1631	1938	562
21615	Excision first and/or cervical rib;	91.00	2121	2520	832
21616	Excision first and/or cervical rib; with sympathectomy	100.0	2331	2769	782

Code	Description	Medicode RVU	50th	75th	Medicare Nat'l Avg
21620	Ostectomy of sternum, partial	81.00	1888	2243	558
21627	Sternal debridement	85.00	1981	2354	484
21630	Radical resection of sternum;	125.0	2913	3461	1220
21632	Radical resection of sternum; with mediastinal lymphadenectomy	185.0	4311	5123	1185
21700	Division of scalenus anticus; without resection of cervical rib	59.00	1375	1634	412
21705	Division of scalenus anticus; with resection of cervical rib	71.00	1655	1966	579
21720	Division of sternocleidomastoid for torticollis, open operation; without cast application	47.50	1107	1315	386
21725	Division of sternocleidomastoid for torticollis, open operation; with cast application	53.50	1247	1481	473
21740	Reconstructive repair of pectus excavatum or carinatum	125.0	2913	3461	1014
21750	Closure of sternotomy separation with or without debridement (separate procedure)	60.00	1398	1661	731
21800	Closed treatment of rib fracture, uncomplicated, each	5.50	128	152	62
21805	Open treatment of rib fracture without fixation, each	50.00	1165	1385	163
21810	Treatment of rib fracture requiring external fixation ("flail chest")	125.0	2913	3461	499
21820	Closed treatment of sternum fracture	12.50	291	346	111
21825	Open treatment of sternum fracture with or without skeletal fixation	50.00	1165	1385	580
21899	Unlisted procedure, neck or thorax	0.00	0	0	–

21920–21935
Back and Flank

Coding Insight
Any skin graft necessary to close a defect created in radical resection 21935 is reported separately.

Subsidiary Codes
Subsidiary codes have relative values that require no further adjustment:

20690 is "in addition" to 21920–21935
20692 is "in addition" to 21920–21935
20900 is "in addition" to 21920–21935
20902 is "in addition" to 21920–21935
20910 is "in addition" to 21920–21935
20912 is "in addition" to 21920–21935

20920 is "in addition" to 21920–21935
20922 is "in addition" to 21920–21935
20924 is "in addition" to 21920–21935
20926 is "in addition" to 21920–21935

Because these are subsidiary or "in addition to" codes, reimbursement reduction and modifier -51 do not apply.

Code	Description	Medicode RVU	50th	75th	Medicare Nat'l Avg
21920	Biopsy, soft tissue of back or flank; superficial	6.75	157	187	113
21925	Biopsy, soft tissue of back or flank; deep	24.00	559	665	255
21930	Excision, tumor, soft tissue of back or flank	38.00	886	1052	379
21935	Radical resection of tumor (eg, malignant neoplasm), soft tissue of back or flank	85.00	1981	2354	970

22100–22899
Spine (Vertebral Column)

CODING INSIGHT
Spinal surgery is easily coded when the operative report is exact and fully documented. Surgeries performed on the spine include excision, osteotomy, fracture/dislocation treatment, arthrodesis, and spinal instrumentation.

Arthrodesis
Codes 22548–22812 are specific to spinal arthrodesis and in the past included a bone allograft or autograft; the only exception was when autograft harvesting was performed through a separate incision and 22820 was used to report the additional service. However, in *CPT '96* 22820 has been deleted and instructions specify that the new code series (20930–20938) should be used to report bone grafts performed for spinal surgery. Modifier -51 should not be appended to the codes since they are "in addition" to the "definitive procedure." Therefore, no reduction should be taken for the code. Note instructions included in the code range (20930–20938) that specify "report only one bone graft code per operative session."

Codes 22544–22558, 22600–22612, and 22630 are for single interspace arthrodesis — two adjacent vertebral segments. When the surgery is performed on more than one interspace, report 22585, 22614, or 22632 for each additional one involved. These codes identify the technique (either anterior/anterolateral, posterior/posterolateral, lateral, transverse, or posterior interbody) used to perform the surgery. These are "in addition to" codes and modifier -51 should not be appended to these codes, nor should they be reduced. Instrumentation codes 22840–22847 are listed separately, in addition to the code for fracture, dislocation, or arthrodesis of the spine.

Arthrodesis is fusion of two bony segments. These segments may be a fracture or a vertebral joint. The fusion itself may be accomplished with bone, internal fixation screws, plates, or rods. Arthrodesis includes placement of pedicle screws and segmental fixation.

The common indications for arthrodesis are nerve root irritation in the cervical and lumbar spines, scoliosis in the lumbar and thoracic spines, and spinal instability or arthritis at any level. The lumbosacral area is the most common for back fusions.

Note the following coding criteria for arthrodesis:

- Identify the surgical approach. Arthrodesis codes are assigned according to the surgical approach used (e.g., posterior spinal fusion, posterolateral fusion, posterior cervical spinal fusion, posterior lumbar spinal fusion). For example, posterior interbody fusion is different from posterolateral fusion and both may be separately reported if performed.
- Identify arthrodesis for spinal deformities with specifically designated CPT codes 22800–22812. The spinal deformity may be congenital or acquired due to disease process. These codes should not be used to report fusion for spinal deformity due to fracture or previous arthrodesis.
- Identify the number of interspaces. One code identifies the first interspace (the space between two adjacent vertebral segments) and a separate code identifies additional interspaces. Specify the number of additional interspaces rather than using modifier -52 for multiple procedures. These codes are subsidiary codes.
- Identify grafting procedures. 22548–22812 no longer include use of allograft or autograft. See 20930–20938 in *CPT '96* for bone grafts that should be reported "in addition to" the "definitive procedure." Bone grafts include contouring or shaping of the graft.
- Identify cosurgery where appropriate. Medicare does not require documentation to support reporting cosurgery services for anterior and posterior arthrodesis. Both surgeons should report the same procedure code with modifier -62 (two surgeons). Payment for cosurgery is 125 percent of the global fee divided equally between the surgeons.

Anterior Spinal Instrumentation

Spinal instrumentation involves insertion of internal fixation devices to connect more than one joint space (across at least two joints).

Segmental fixation is accomplished by using bilateral fixation points at two or more segments with independent fixation systems.

Nonsegmental fixation also uses bilateral fixation points at two or more segments but uses a single rod (e.g., Harrington rod).

Note the following coding criteria for spinal fixation:

- Spinal instrumentation can be used for distraction or compression and can be anterior or posterior, segmental (e.g., Steffe plates and screws), or nonsegmental (Harrington rods).
- Fixation of a single joint space with pedicle screws and plate(s) is an integral part of arthrodesis and does not represent spinal instrumentation.
- Spinal instrumentation should be reported " in addtion" to the "definitive procedure" arthrodesis. Modifier -51 should not be appended to the code and the code should not be reduced.
- Thoracotomy and/or retroperitoneal dissection may not be reimbursed separately by some payers when they are reported with anterior instrumentation codes 22845–22847. They assume that surgical procedure includes the approach, procedure, and closure, and so may deny these codes as the approach component of anterior instrumentation.
- Additionally, 22845–22847 may require documentation to justify the medical necessity for two surgeons (one performing the thoracotomy and one performing the anterior instrumentation) when reported with modifier -62. The same question of medical necessity may also arise if two separate billings are received from two surgeons in different specialties.

Nota Bene: This range of codes has undergone tremendous changes in *CPT '96*. Codes and notes have been added and a number of codes have been deleted or revised. Read notes and codes carefully before using codes in this section.

Subsidiary Codes

Subsidiary codes have relative values that require no further adjustment:

20690 is "in addition" to 22100–22899
20692 is "in addition" to 22100–22899
20900 is "in addition" to 22100–22899
20902 is "in addition" to 22100–22899
20910 is "in addition" to 22100–22899
20912 is "in addition" to 22100–22899
20920 is "in addition" to 22100–22899
20922 is "in addition" to 22100–22899
20924 is "in addition" to 22100–22899
20926 is "in addition" to 22100–22899
20930 is "in addition" to 22548–22847
20931 is "in addition" to 22548–22847
20936 is "in addition" to 22548–22847
20937 is "in addition" to 22548–22847
20938 is "in addition" to 22548–22847
22585 is "in addition" to 22554, 22556, 22558
22614 is "in addition" to 22600–22612
22632 is "in addition" to 22630

Because these are subsidiary or "in addition to" codes, reimbursement reduction and modifier -51 do not apply.

Medicare Alert

Medicare rebundles certain codes in the surgery section when the listed codes are considered a component of a more comprehensive service.

20902 will not be reimbursed when reported with 22554

	Code	Description	Medicode RVU	50th	75th	Medicare Nat'l Avg
▲	22100	Partial excision of posterior vertebral component (eg, spinous process, lamina or facet) for intrinsic bony lesion, single vertebral segment; cervical	45.00	1049	1246	600
▲	22101	Partial resection of vertebral component, spinous processes; thoracic	45.00	1049	1246	620
▲	22102	Partial resection of vertebral component, spinous processes; lumbar	45.00	1049	1246	540
●	22103	Partial excision of posterior vertebral component (eg, spinous process, lamina or facet) for intrinsic bony lesion, single vertebral segment; each additional segment (List separately in addition to code for primary procedure)	13.50	315	374	–
▲	22110	Partial excision of vertebral body for intrinsic bony lesion, without decompression of spinal cord or nerve root(s), single vertebral segment; cervical	60.00	1398	1661	890
▲	22112	Partial excision of vertebrae (eg, for osteomyelitis); thoracic	60.00	1398	1661	898
▲	22114	Partial excision of vertebrae (eg, for osteomyelitis); lumbar	60.00	1398	1661	781

	Code	Description	Medicode RVU	50th	75th	Medicare Nat'l Avg
●	22116	Partial excision of vertebral body for intrinsic bony lesion, without decompression of spinal cord or nerve root(s), single vertebral segment; each additional vertebral segment (List separately in addition to code for primary procedure)	18.00	419	498	–
▲	22210	Osteotomy of spine, posterior or posterolateral approach, one vertebral segment; cervical	177.0	4125	4901	1513
▲	22212	Osteotomy of spine, posterior approach, single segment; thoracic	172.0	4008	4763	1485
▲	22214	Osteotomy of spine, posterior approach, single segment; lumbar	175.0	4078	4846	1406
●	22216	Osteotomy of spine, posterior or posterolateral approach, one vertebral segment; each additional vertebral segment (List separately in addition to primary procedure)	52.50	1224	1454	–
▲	22220	Osteotomy of spine, including diskectomy, anterior approach, single vertebral segment; cervical	187.0	4358	5178	1541
▲	22222	Osteotomy of spine, anterior approach, single segment; thoracic	182.0	4242	5040	1388
▲	22224	Osteotomy of spine, anterior approach, single segment; lumbar	185.0	4311	5123	1457
●	22226	Osteotomy of spine, including diskectomy, anterior approach, single vertebral segment; each additional vertebral segment (List separately in addition to code for primary procedure)	55.50	1293	1537	–
	22305	Closed treatment of vertebral process fracture(s)	13.00	303	360	186
▲	22310	Closed treatment of vertebral body fracture(s), without manipulation, requiring and including casting or bracing	27.50	641	761	266
▲	22315	Closed treatment of vertebral fracture(s) and/or dislocations(s) requiring casting or bracing, with and including casting and/or bracing, with or without anesthesia, by manipulation or traction	40.00	932	1108	582
▲	22325	Open treatment and/or reduction of vertebral fracture(s) and/or dislocation(s); posterior approach, one fractured vertebrae or dislocated segment; lumbar	115.0	2680	3184	1056
▲	22326	Open treatment and/or reduction of vertebral fracture(s) and/or dislocation(s); posterior approach, one fractured vertebrae or dislocated segment; cervical	125.0	2913	3461	1453
▲	22327	Open treatment and/or reduction of vertebral fracture(s) and/or dislocation(s); posterior approach, one fractured vertebrae or dislocated segment; thoracic	120.0	2797	3323	1396
●	22328	Open treatment and/or reduction of vertebral fracture(s) and/or dislocation(s); posterior approach, one fractured vertebrae or dislocated segment; each additional fractured vertebrae or dislocated segment (List separately in addition to code for primary procedure)	36.00	839	997	–
	22505	Manipulation of spine requiring anesthesia, any region	11.50	268	318	111
▲	22548	Arthrodesis, anterior transoral or extraoral technique, clivus-C1-C2 (atlas-axis), with or without excision of odontoid process	152.5	3787	4561	1973

	Code	Description	Medicode RVU	50th	75th	Medicare Nat'l Avg
▲	**22554**	Arthrodesis, anterior interbody technique, including minimal diskectomy to prepare interspace (other than for decompression); cervical below C2	147.5	3662	4412	1673
▲	**22556**	Arthrodesis, anterior interbody technique, including minimal diskectomy to prepare interspace (other than for decompression); thoracic	162.5	4035	4860	1898
▲	**22558**	Arthrodesis, anterior interbody technique, including minimal diskectomy to prepare interspace (other than for decompression); lumbar	147.5	3662	4412	1812
▲	**22585**	Arthrodesis, anterior interbody technique, including minimal diskectomy to prepare interspace (other than for decompression); each additional interspace (List separately in addition to code for primary procedure)	43.00	1068	1286	477
▲	**22590**	Arthrodesis, posterior technique, craniocervical (occiput-C2)	167.5	4159	5010	1741
▲	**22595**	Arthrodesis, posterior technique, atlas-axis (C1-C2)	165.5	4109	4950	1860
▲	**22600**	Arthrodesis, posterior or posterolateral technique, single level; cervical below C2 segment	142.5	3538	4262	1636
▲	**22610**	Arthrodesis, posterior or posterolateral technique, single level; thoracic (with or without lateral transverse technique)	132.5	3290	3963	1416
▲	**22612**	Arthrodesis, posterior or posterolateral technique, single level; lumbar (with or without lateral transverse technique)	129.0	3203	3858	1819
●	**22614**	Arthrodesis, posterior or posterolateral technique, single level; each additional vertebral segment (List separately in addition to code for primary procedure)	43.00	1068	1286	–
▲	**22630**	Arthrodesis, posterior interbody technique, single interspace; lumbar	125.0	3104	3739	1695
●	**22632**	Arthrodesis, posterior interbody technique, single interspace; each additional interspace (List separately in addition to code for primary procedure)	41.50	1030	1241	–
▲	**22800**	Arthrodesis, posterior, for spinal deformity, with or without cast; up to 6 vertebral segments	172.5	4283	5159	1660
▲	**22802**	Arthrodesis, posterior, for spinal deformity, with or without cast; 7 to 12 vertebral segments	207.0	5140	6191	2533
●	**22804**	Arthrodesis, posterior, for spinal deformity, with or without cast; 13 or more vertebral segments	248.5	6170	7433	–
●	**22808**	Arthrodesis, anterior, for spinal deformity, with or without cast; 2 to 3 vertebral segments	166.0	4122	4965	–
▲	**22810**	Arthrodesis, anterior, for spinal deformity, with or without cast; 4 to 7 vertebral segments	200.0	4966	5982	1978
▲	**22812**	Arthrodesis, anterior, for spinal deformity, with or without cast; 8 or more vertebral segments	232.0	5761	6939	2240
	22830	Exploration of spinal fusion	160.0	3973	4786	1031
▲	**22840**	Posterior non-segmental instrumentation (eg, single Harrington rod technique)	92.50	2297	2767	1420
●	**22841**	Internal spinal fixation by wiring of spinous processes	5.00	124	150	–

	Code	Description	Medicode RVU	50th	75th	Medicare Nat'l Avg
▲	22842	Posterior segmental instrumentation (eg, pedicle fixation, dual rods with multiple hooks and sublaminal wires); 3 to 6 vertebral segments	115.0	2855	3440	1666
●	22843	Posterior segmental instrumentation (eg, pedicle fixation, dual rods with multiple hooks and sublaminal wires); 7 to 12 vertebral segments	126.5	3141	3784	–
●	22844	Posterior segmental instrumentation (eg, pedicle fixation, dual rods with multiple hooks and sublaminal wires); 13 or more vertebral segments	139.0	3451	4157	–
▲	22845	Anterior instrumentation; 3 vertebral segments	120.0	2980	3589	1273
●	22846	Anterior instrumentation; 4 to 7 vertebral segments	132.0	3278	3948	–
●	22847	Anterior instrumentation; 8 or more vertebral segments	145.0	3600	4337	–
●	22848	Pelvic fixation (attachment of caudal end of instrumentation to pelvic bony structures) other than sacrum	0.00	0	0	–
	22849	Reinsertion of spinal fixation device	95.00	2359	2841	1036
	22850	Removal of posterior nonsegmental instrumentation (eg, Harrington rod)	65.00	1614	1944	791
●	22851	Application of prosthetic device (eg, metal cages, methylmethacrylate) to vertebral defect or interspace	55.00	1366	1645	–
	22852	Removal of posterior segmental instrumentation	75.00	1862	2243	799
	22855	Removal of anterior instrumentation	125.0	3104	3739	693
	22899	Unlisted procedure, spine	0.00	0	0	–

22900–22999
Abdomen (Musculoskeletal System)

SUBSIDIARY CODES
Subsidiary codes have relative values that require no further adjustment:

20690 is "in addition" to 22900–22999
20692 is "in addition" to 22900–22999
20900 is "in addition" to 22900–22999
20902 is "in addition" to 22900–22999
20910 is "in addition" to 22900–22999
20912 is "in addition" to 22900–22999
20920 is "in addition" to 22900–22999
20922 is "in addition" to 22900–22999
20924 is "in addition" to 22900–22999
20926 is "in addition" to 22900–22999

Because these are subsidiary or "in addition to" codes, reimbursement reduction and CPT modifier -51 do not apply.

Code	Description	Medicode RVU	50th	75th	Medicare Nat'l Avg
22900	Excision, abdominal wall tumor, subfascial (eg, desmoid)	28.00	695	837	413
22999	Unlisted procedure, abdomen, musculoskeletal system	0.00	0	0	–

23000–23929
Shoulder

Coding Insight

Manipulation under anesthesia (23700) should not be reported with an open orthopedic surgical procedure of the shoulder.

A diagnostic arthroscope may be identified separately when performed at the same surgical session as an open shoulder procedure.

Subsidiary Codes

Subsidiary codes have relative values that require no further adjustment:

20690 is "in addition" to 23000–23929
20692 is "in addition" to 23000–23929
20900 is "in addition" to 23000–23929
20902 is "in addition" to 23000–23929
20910 is "in addition" to 23000–23929
20912 is "in addition" to 23000–23929
20920 is "in addition" to 23000–23929
20922 is "in addition" to 23000–23929
20924 is "in addition" to 23000–23929
20926 is "in addition" to 23000–23929

Because these are subsidiary or "in addition to" codes, reimbursement reduction and modifier -51 do not apply.

Medicare Alert

Medicare rebundles certain codes in the surgery section when the listed codes are considered a component of a more comprehensive service.

23412 will not be reimbursed when reported with 23420 and 23472
23130 will not be reimbursed when reported with 23472

Code	Description	Medicode RVU	50th	75th	Medicare Nat'l Avg
23000	Removal of subdeltoid (or intratendinous) calcareous deposits, open method	30.00	685	808	311
23020	Capsular contracture release (Sever type procedure)	60.00	1369	1615	648
23030	Incision and drainage, shoulder area; deep abscess or hematoma	20.00	456	538	226
23031	Incision and drainage, shoulder area; infected bursa	20.00	456	538	125

Code	Description	Medicode RVU	50th	75th	Medicare Nat'l Avg
23035	Incision, deep, with opening of cortex (eg, for osteomyelitis or bone abscess), shoulder area	40.00	913	1077	588
23040	Arthrotomy, glenohumeral joint, for infection, with exploration, drainage or removal of foreign body	57.00	1301	1535	756
23044	Arthrotomy, acromioclavicular, sternoclavicular joint, for infection, with exploration, drainage or removal of foreign body	35.00	799	942	571
23065	Biopsy, soft tissue of shoulder area; superficial	7.00	160	188	115
23066	Biopsy, soft tissue of shoulder area; deep	21.00	479	565	210
23075	Excision, tumor, shoulder area; subcutaneous	17.00	388	458	171
23076	Excision, tumor, shoulder area; deep, subfascial or intramuscular	34.00	776	915	444
23077	Radical resection of tumor (eg, malignant neoplasm), soft tissue of shoulder area	215.0	4906	5788	915
23100	Arthrotomy with biopsy, glenohumeral joint	50.00	1141	1346	553
23101	Arthrotomy with biopsy, or with excision of torn cartilage, acromioclavicular, sternoclavicular joint	53.00	1209	1427	524
23105	Arthrotomy with synovectomy; glenohumeral joint	90.00	2054	2423	781
23106	Arthrotomy with synovectomy; sternoclavicular joint	60.00	1369	1615	443
23107	Arthrotomy, glenohumeral joint, with joint exploration, with or without removal of loose or foreign body	66.00	1506	1777	757
23120	Claviculectomy; partial	50.00	1141	1346	488
23125	Claviculectomy; total	80.00	1825	2154	731
23130	Acromioplasty or acromionectomy, partial	50.00	1141	1346	616
23140	Excision or curettage of bone cyst or benign tumor of clavicle or scapula;	31.00	707	835	444
23145	Excision or curettage of bone cyst or benign tumor of clavicle or scapula; with autograft (includes obtaining graft)	46.50	1061	1252	699
23146	Excision or curettage of bone cyst or benign tumor of clavicle or scapula; with allograft	40.00	913	1077	528
23150	Excision or curettage of bone cyst or benign tumor of proximal humerus;	60.00	1369	1615	605
23155	Excision or curettage of bone cyst or benign tumor of proximal humerus; with autograft (includes obtaining graft)	75.00	1711	2019	767
23156	Excision or curettage of bone cyst or benign tumor of proximal humerus; with allograft	65.00	1483	1750	655
23170	Sequestrectomy (eg, for osteomyelitis or bone abscess), clavicle	45.00	1027	1211	461
23172	Sequestrectomy (eg, for osteomyelitis or bone abscess), scapula	60.00	1369	1615	470

Code	Description	Medicode RVU	50th	75th	Medicare Nat'l Avg
23174	Sequestrectomy (eg, for osteomyelitis or bone abscess), humeral head to surgical neck	100.0	2282	2692	718
23180	Partial excision (craterization, saucerization, or diaphysectomy) of bone (eg, for osteomyelitis), clavicle	41.00	936	1104	499
23182	Partial excision (craterization, saucerization, or diaphysectomy) of bone (eg, for osteomyelitis), scapula	40.00	913	1077	588
23184	Partial excision (craterization, saucerization, or diaphysectomy) of bone (eg, for osteomyelitis), proximal humerus	60.00	1369	1615	739
23190	Ostectomy of scapula, partial (eg, superior medial angle)	32.50	742	875	538
23195	Resection humeral head	80.00	1825	2154	754
23200	Radical resection for tumor; clavicle	60.00	1369	1615	839
23210	Radical resection for tumor; scapula	100.0	2282	2692	861
23220	Radical resection for tumor, proximal humerus;	100.0	2282	2692	1072
23221	Radical resection for tumor, proximal humerus; with autograft (includes obtaining graft)	120.0	2738	3231	1398
23222	Radical resection for tumor, proximal humerus; with prosthetic replacement	120.0	2738	3231	1328
23330	Removal of foreign body, shoulder; subcutaneous	6.00	137	162	93
23331	Removal of foreign body, shoulder; deep (eg, Neer prosthesis removal)	30.00	685	808	378
23332	Removal of foreign body, shoulder; complicated, including "total shoulder"	110.0	2510	2961	859
23350	Injection procedure for shoulder arthrography	5.00	114	135	55
23395	Muscle transfer, any type, shoulder or upper arm; single	100.0	2282	2692	1000
23397	Muscle transfer, any type, shoulder or upper arm; multiple	0.00	0	0	1224
23400	Scapulopexy (eg, Sprengel's deformity or for paralysis)	100.0	2282	2692	952
23405	Tenomyotomy, shoulder area; single	50.00	1141	1346	638
23406	Tenomyotomy, shoulder area; multiple through same incision	65.00	1483	1750	828
23410	Repair of ruptured musculotendinous cuff (eg, rotator cuff); acute	75.50	1723	2033	974
23412	Repair of ruptured musculotendinous cuff (eg, rotator cuff); chronic	90.00	2054	2423	1124
23415	Coracoacromial ligament release, with or without acromioplasty	52.00	1186	1400	632
23420	Repair of complete shoulder (rotator) cuff avulsion, chronic (includes acromioplasty)	115.0	2624	3096	1191

Code	Description	Medicode RVU	50th	75th	Medicare Nat'l Avg
23430	Tenodesis of long tendon of biceps	68.00	1552	1831	714
23440	Resection or transplantation of long tendon of biceps	60.00	1369	1615	722
23450	Capsulorrhaphy, anterior; Putti-Platt procedure or Magnuson type operation	94.00	2145	2531	1084
23455	Capsulorrhaphy, anterior; Bankart type operation with or without stapling	105.0	2396	2827	1245
23460	Capsulorrhaphy, anterior, any type; with bone block	100.0	2282	2692	1208
23462	Capsulorrhaphy, anterior, any type; with coracoid process transfer	100.0	2282	2692	1253
23465	Capsulorrhaphy for recurrent dislocation, posterior, with or without bone block	100.0	2282	2692	1228
23466	Capsulorrhaphy with any type multi-directional instability	122.0	2784	3284	1275
23470	Arthroplasty with proximal humeral implant (eg, Neer type operation)	100.0	2282	2692	1417
23472	Arthroplasty with glenoid and proximal humeral replacement (eg, total shoulder)	180.0	4107	4846	1972
23480	Osteotomy, clavicle, with or without internal fixation;	50.00	1141	1346	707
23485	Osteotomy, clavicle, with or without internal fixation; with bone graft for nonunion or malunion (includes obtaining graft and/or necessary fixation)	70.00	1597	1884	1006
23490	Prophylactic treatment (nailing, pinning, plating or wiring) with or without methylmethacrylate; clavicle	60.00	1369	1615	859
23491	Prophylactic treatment (nailing, pinning, plating or wiring) with or without methylmethacrylate; proximal humerus and humeral head	75.00	1711	2019	1103
23500	Closed treatment of clavicular fracture; without manipulation	10.50	247	290	148
23505	Closed treatment of clavicular fracture; with manipulation	16.50	388	455	252
23515	Open treatment of clavicular fracture, with or without internal or external fixation	50.00	1175	1380	589
23520	Closed treatment of sternoclavicular dislocation; without manipulation	13.00	306	359	140
23525	Closed treatment of sternoclavicular dislocation; with manipulation	17.00	400	469	219
23530	Open treatment of sternoclavicular dislocation, acute or chronic;	50.00	1175	1380	567
23532	Open treatment of sternoclavicular dislocation, acute or chronic; with fascial graft (includes obtaining graft)	60.00	1410	1656	622
23540	Closed treatment of acromioclavicular dislocation; without manipulation	10.00	235	276	150
23545	Closed treatment of acromioclavicular dislocation; with manipulation	15.00	353	414	208
23550	Open treatment of acromioclavicular dislocation, acute or chronic;	66.00	1552	1821	659

Code	Description	Medicode RVU	50th	75th	Medicare Nat'l Avg
23552	Open treatment of acromioclavicular dislocation, acute or chronic; with fascial graft (includes obtaining graft)	86.00	2022	2373	638
23570	Closed treatment of scapular fracture; without manipulation	12.50	294	345	161
23575	Closed treatment of scapular fracture; with manipulation, with or without skeletal traction (with or without shoulder joint involvement)	17.50	411	483	275
23585	Open treatment of scapular fracture (body, glenoid or acromion) with or without internal fixation	70.00	1646	1931	681
23600	Closed treatment of proximal humeral (surgical or anatomical neck) fracture; without manipulation	16.00	376	441	237
23605	Closed treatment of proximal humeral (surgical or anatomical neck) fracture; with manipulation, with or without skeletal traction	26.00	611	717	396
23615	Open treatment of proximal humeral (surgical or anatomical neck) fracture, with or without internal or external fixation, with or without repair of tuberosity(-ies);	70.00	1646	1931	843
23616	Open treatment of proximal humeral (surgical or anatomical neck) fracture, with or without internal or external fixation, with or without repair of tuberosity(-ies); with proximal humeral prosthetic replacement	120.0	2821	3311	1667
23620	Closed treatment of greater tuberosity fracture; without manipulation	15.00	353	414	220
23625	Closed treatment of greater tuberosity fracture; with manipulation	21.00	494	579	318
23630	Open treatment of greater tuberosity fracture, with or without internal or external fixation	53.00	1246	1462	690
23650	Closed treatment of shoulder dislocation, with manipulation; without anesthesia	13.50	317	372	213
23655	Closed treatment of shoulder dislocation, with manipulation; requiring anesthesia	22.00	517	607	290
23660	Open treatment of acute shoulder dislocation	60.00	1410	1656	702
23665	Closed treatment of shoulder dislocation, with fracture of greater tuberosity, with manipulation	20.00	470	552	312
23670	Open treatment of shoulder dislocation, with fracture of greater tuberosity, with or without internal or external fixation	80.00	1881	2207	749
23675	Closed treatment of shoulder dislocation, with surgical or anatomical neck fracture, with manipulation	30.00	705	828	395
23680	Open treatment of shoulder dislocation, with surgical or anatomical neck fracture, with or without internal or external fixation	93.00	2186	2566	938
23700 *	Manipulation under anesthesia, shoulder joint, including application of fixation apparatus (dislocation excluded)	17.50	411	483	190
23800	Arthrodesis, shoulder joint; with or without local bone graft	93.00	2186	2566	1260
23802	Arthrodesis, shoulder joint; with primary autogenous graft (includes obtaining graft)	115.0	2703	3173	1212
23900	Interthoracoscapular amputation (forequarter)	127.0	2986	3504	1308

Code	Description	Medicode RVU	50th	75th	Medicare Nat'l Avg
23920	Disarticulation of shoulder;	95.00	2233	2621	1170
23921	Disarticulation of shoulder; secondary closure or scar revision	30.00	705	828	390
23929	Unlisted procedure, shoulder	0.00	0	0	

23930–24999
Humerus (Upper Arm) and Elbow

Coding Insight
For release of median nerve at the elbow, see 64716

Subsidiary Codes
Subsidiary codes have relative values that require no further adjustment:

20690 is "in addition" to 23930–24999
20692 is "in addition" to 23930–24999
20900 is "in addition" to 23930–24999
20902 is "in addition" to 23930–24999
20910 is "in addition" to 23930–24999
20912 is "in addition" to 23930–24999
20920 is "in addition" to 23930–24999
20922 is "in addition" to 23930–24999
20924 is "in addition" to 23930–24999
20926 is "in addition" to 23930–24999

Because these are subsidiary or "in addition to" codes, reimbursement reduction and modifier -51 do not apply.

Code	Description	Medicode RVU	50th	75th	Medicare Nat'l Avg
23930	Incision and drainage, upper arm or elbow area; deep abscess or hematoma	20.00	472	559	185
23931	Incision and drainage, upper arm or elbow area; infected bursa	20.00	472	559	99
23935	Incision, deep, with opening of bone cortex (eg, for osteomyelitis or bone abscess), humerus or elbow	40.00	944	1118	433
24000	Arthrotomy, elbow, for infection, with exploration, drainage or removal of foreign body	55.00	1298	1538	575
24006	Arthrotomy of the elbow, with capsular excision for capsular release (separate procedure)	55.00	1298	1538	660
24065	Biopsy, soft tissue of upper arm or elbow area; superficial	6.00	142	168	114
24066	Biopsy, soft tissue of upper arm or elbow area; deep	20.00	472	559	311
24075	Excision, tumor, upper arm or elbow area; subcutaneous	17.50	413	489	251

Code	Description	Medicode RVU	50th	75th	Medicare Nat'l Avg
24076	Excision, tumor, upper arm or elbow area; deep, subfascial or intramuscular	32.00	755	895	409
24077	Radical resection of tumor (eg, malignant neoplasm), soft tissue of upper arm or elbow area	100.0	2359	2796	888
24100	Arthrotomy, elbow; with synovial biopsy only	45.00	1062	1258	382
24101	Arthrotomy, elbow; with joint exploration, with or without biopsy, with or without removal of loose or foreign body	55.00	1298	1538	591
24102	Arthrotomy, elbow; with synovectomy	72.00	1699	2013	782
24105	Excision, olecranon bursa	27.00	637	755	317
24110	Excision or curettage of bone cyst or benign tumor, humerus;	60.00	1416	1678	624
24115	Excision or curettage of bone cyst or benign tumor, humerus; with autograft (includes obtaining graft)	75.00	1769	2097	695
24116	Excision or curettage of bone cyst or benign tumor, humerus; with allograft	65.00	1534	1818	868
24120	Excision or curettage of bone cyst or benign tumor of head or neck of radius or olecranon process;	51.00	1203	1426	527
24125	Excision or curettage of bone cyst or benign tumor of head or neck of radius or olecranon process; with autograft (includes obtaining graft)	68.00	1604	1901	537
24126	Excision or curettage of bone cyst or benign tumor of head or neck of radius or olecranon process; with allograft	68.00	1604	1901	635
24130	Excision, radial head	43.00	1015	1202	545
24134	Sequestrectomy (eg, for osteomyelitis or bone abscess), shaft or distal humerus	60.00	1416	1678	732
24136	Sequestrectomy (eg, for osteomyelitis or bone abscess), radial head or neck	60.00	1416	1678	662
24138	Sequestrectomy (eg, for osteomyelitis or bone abscess), olecranon process	60.00	1416	1678	575
24140	Partial excision (craterization, saucerization or diaphysectomy) of bone (eg, for osteomyelitis), humerus	60.00	1416	1678	732
24145	Partial excision (craterization, saucerization or diaphysectomy) of bone (eg, for osteomyelitis), radial head or neck	45.00	1062	1258	568
24147	Partial excision (craterization, saucerization or diaphysectomy) of bone (eg, for osteomyelitis), olecranon process	40.00	944	1118	579
24150	Radical resection for tumor, shaft or distal humerus;	85.00	2005	2377	1123
24151	Radical resection for tumor, shaft or distal humerus; with autograft (includes obtaining graft)	125.0	2949	3495	1188
24152	Radical resection for tumor, radial head or neck;	110.0	2595	3076	686
24153	Radical resection for tumor, radial head or neck; with autograft (includes obtaining graft)	125.0	2949	3495	897

Code	Description	Medicode RVU	50th	75th	Medicare Nat'l Avg
24155	Resection of elbow joint (arthrectomy)	77.00	1817	2153	923
24160	Implant removal; elbow joint	55.00	1298	1538	510
24164	Implant removal; radial head	50.00	1180	1398	474
24200	Removal of foreign body, upper arm or elbow area; subcutaneous	6.00	142	168	81
24201	Removal of foreign body, upper arm or elbow area; deep	20.00	472	559	307
24220	Injection procedure for elbow arthrography	5.25	124	147	64
24301	Muscle or tendon transfer, any type, upper arm or elbow, single (excluding 24320-24331)	70.00	1652	1957	737
24305	Tendon lengthening, upper arm or elbow, single, each	30.00	708	839	413
24310	Tenotomy, open, elbow to shoulder, single, each	25.00	590	699	356
24320	Tenoplasty, with muscle transfer, with or without free graft, elbow to shoulder, single (Seddon-Brookes type procedure)	80.00	1887	2237	800
24330	Flexor-plasty, elbow (eg, Steindler type advancement);	60.00	1416	1678	751
24331	Flexor-plasty, elbow (eg, Steindler type advancement); with extensor advancement	80.00	1887	2237	827
24340	Tenodesis of biceps tendon at elbow (separate procedure)	54.00	1274	1510	614
24342	Reinsertion or repair of ruptured or lacerated biceps or triceps tendon, distal, with or without tendon graft	71.00	1675	1985	871
24350	Fasciotomy, lateral or medial (eg, "tennis elbow" or epicondylitis);	30.00	708	839	389
24351	Fasciotomy, lateral or medial (eg, "tennis elbow" or epicondylitis); with extensor origin detachment	35.00	826	979	429
24352	Fasciotomy, lateral or medial (eg, "tennis elbow" or epicondylitis); with annular ligament resection	40.00	944	1118	495
24354	Fasciotomy, lateral or medial (eg, "tennis elbow" or epicondylitis); with stripping	40.00	944	1118	495
24356	Fasciotomy, lateral or medial (eg, "tennis elbow" or epicondylitis); with partial ostectomy	50.00	1180	1398	580
24360	Arthroplasty, elbow; with membrane	110.0	2595	3076	1151
24361	Arthroplasty, elbow; with distal humeral prosthetic replacement	110.0	2595	3076	1115
24362	Arthroplasty, elbow; with implant and fascia lata ligament reconstruction	110.0	2595	3076	1105
24363	Arthroplasty, elbow; with distal humerus and proximal ulnar prosthetic replacement ("total elbow")	165.0	3893	4614	1785
24365	Arthroplasty, radial head;	45.00	1062	1258	652

Code	Description	Medicode RVU	50th	75th	Medicare Nat'l Avg
24366	Arthroplasty, radial head; with implant	55.00	1298	1538	842
24400	Osteotomy, humerus, with or without internal fixation	68.00	1604	1901	794
24410	Multiple osteotomies with realignment on intramedullary rod, humeral shaft (Sofield type procedure)	80.00	1887	2237	1179
24420	Osteoplasty, humerus (eg, shortening or lengthening) (excluding 64876)	80.00	1887	2237	1058
24430	Repair of nonunion or malunion, humerus; without graft (eg, compression technique)	85.00	2005	2377	1143
24435	Repair of nonunion or malunion, humerus; with iliac or other autograft (includes obtaining graft)	100.0	2359	2796	1243
24470	Hemiepiphyseal arrest (eg, for cubitus varus or valgus, distal humerus)	78.00	1840	2181	681
24495	Decompression fasciotomy, forearm, with brachial artery exploration	60.00	1416	1678	566
24498	Prophylactic treatment (nailing, pinning, plating or wiring), with or without methylmethacrylate, humerus	80.00	1887	2237	909
24500	Closed treatment of humeral shaft fracture; without manipulation	16.00	378	444	234
24505	Closed treatment of humeral shaft fracture; with manipulation, with or without skeletal traction	27.50	649	762	393
24515	Open treatment of humeral shaft fracture with plate/screws, with or without cerclage	66.00	1557	1830	870
24516	Open treatment of humeral shaft fracture, with insertion of intramedullary implant, with or without cerclage and/or locking screws	80.00	1888	2218	870
24530	Closed treatment of supracondylar or transcondylar humeral fracture, with or without intercondylar extension; without manipulation	18.00	425	499	253
24535	Closed treatment of supracondylar or transcondylar humeral fracture, with or without intercondylar extension; with manipulation, with or without skin or skeletal traction	32.00	755	887	474
24538	Percutaneous skeletal fixation of supracondylar or transcondylar humeral fracture, with or without intercondylar extension	55.00	1298	1525	708
24545	Open treatment of humeral supracondylar or transcondylar fracture, with or without internal or external fixation; without intercondylar extension	70.00	1652	1940	834
24546	Open treatment of humeral supracondylar or transcondylar fracture, with or without internal or external fixation; with intercondylar extension	85.00	2006	2356	1015
24560	Closed treatment of humeral epicondylar fracture, medial or lateral; without manipulation	17.50	413	485	200
24565	Closed treatment of humeral epicondylar fracture, medial or lateral; with manipulation	25.50	602	707	358
24566	Percutaneous skeletal fixation of humeral epicondylar fracture, medial or lateral, with manipulation	43.00	1015	1192	553
24575	Open treatment of humeral epicondylar fracture, medial or lateral, with or without internal or external fixation	52.00	1227	1441	736

Code		Description	Medicode RVU	50th	75th	Medicare Nat'l Avg
24576		Closed treatment of humeral condylar fracture, medial or lateral; without manipulation	14.50	342	402	201
24577		Closed treatment of humeral condylar fracture, medial or lateral; with manipulation	24.00	566	665	391
24579		Open treatment of humeral condylar fracture, medial or lateral, with or without internal or external fixation	61.00	1439	1691	804
24582		Percutaneous skeletal fixation of humeral condylar fracture, medial or lateral, with manipulation	41.00	967	1137	609
24586		Open treatment of periarticular fracture and/or dislocation of the elbow (fracture distal humerus and proximal ulna and/or proximal radius);	80.00	1888	2218	1225
24587		Open treatment of periarticular fracture and/or dislocation of the elbow (fracture distal humerus and proximal ulna and/or proximal radius); with implant arthroplasty	110.0	2595	3049	1175
24600		Treatment of closed elbow dislocation; without anesthesia	13.00	307	360	238
24605		Treatment of closed elbow dislocation; requiring anesthesia	18.50	437	513	288
24615		Open treatment of acute or chronic elbow dislocation	57.00	1345	1580	767
24620		Closed treatment of Monteggia type of fracture dislocation at elbow (fracture proximal end of ulna with dislocation of radial head), with manipulation	30.00	708	832	426
24635		Open treatment of Monteggia type of fracture dislocation at elbow (fracture proximal end of ulna with dislocation of radial head), with or without internal or external fixation	73.50	1734	2037	986
24640	*	Closed treatment of radial head subluxation in child, "nursemaid elbow", with manipulation	5.40	127	150	77
24650		Closed treatment of radial head or neck fracture; without manipulation	13.75	324	381	181
24655		Closed treatment of radial head or neck fracture; with manipulation	20.50	484	568	297
24665		Open treatment of radial head or neck fracture, with or without internal fixation or radial head excision;	50.50	1192	1400	627
24666		Open treatment of radial head or neck fracture, with or without internal fixation or radial head excision; with radial head prosthetic replacement	64.50	1522	1788	808
24670		Closed treatment of ulnar fracture, proximal end (olecranon process); without manipulation	13.00	307	360	183
24675		Closed treatment of ulnar fracture, proximal end (olecranon process); with manipulation	23.00	543	638	332
24685		Open treatment of ulnar fracture proximal end (olecranon process), with or without internal or external fixation	54.00	1274	1497	709
24800		Arthrodesis, elbow joint; with or without local autograft or allograft	80.00	1888	2218	891
24802		Arthrodesis, elbow joint; with autograft (includes obtaining graft other than locally obtained)	100.0	2360	2772	1047
24900		Amputation, arm through humerus; with primary closure	50.00	1180	1386	701

Code	Description	Medicode RVU	50th	75th	Medicare Nat'l Avg
24920	Amputation, arm through humerus; open, circular (guillotine)	40.00	944	1109	648
24925	Amputation, arm through humerus; secondary closure or scar revision	20.00	472	554	527
24930	Amputation, arm through humerus; re-amputation	50.00	1180	1386	728
24931	Amputation, arm through humerus; with implant	57.00	1345	1580	959
24935	Stump elongation, upper extremity	75.00	1770	2079	1176
24940	Cineplasty, upper extremity, complete procedure	75.00	1770	2079	1183
24999	Unlisted procedure, humerus or elbow	0.00	0	0	–

25000–25999
Forearm and Wrist

Coding Insight
For release of median nerve at carpal tunnel, see 64721.

Subsidiary Codes
Subsidiary codes have relative values that require no further adjustment:

20690 is "in addition" to 25000–25999
20692 is "in addition" to 25000–25999
20900 is "in addition" to 25000–25999
20902 is "in addition" to 25000–25999
20910 is "in addition" to 25000–25999
20912 is "in addition" to 25000–25999
20920 is "in addition" to 25000–25999
20922 is "in addition" to 25000–25999
20924 is "in addition" to 25000–25999
20926 is "in addition" to 25000–25999

Because these are subsidiary or "in addition to" codes, reimbursement reduction and modifier -51 do not apply.

Medicare Alert
Medicare rebundles certain codes in the surgery section when the listed codes are considered a component of a more comprehensive service.

29125 will not be reimbursed when reported with 25600 and 25605

25600 and 29075 will not be reimbursed when reported with 25605

Code	Description	Medicode RVU	50th	75th	Medicare Nat'l Avg
25000	Tendon sheath incision; at radial styloid (eg, for deQuervain's disease)	29.00	674	795	313
25020	Decompression fasciotomy, forearm and/or wrist; flexor or extensor compartment	35.00	814	959	425
25023	Decompression fasciotomy, forearm and/or wrist; with debridement of nonviable muscle and/or nerve	45.00	1046	1233	707
25028	Incision and drainage, forearm and/or wrist; deep abscess or hematoma	23.00	535	630	281
25031	Incision and drainage, forearm and/or wrist; infected bursa	20.00	465	548	181
25035	Incision, deep, with opening of bone cortex (eg, for osteomyelitis or bone abscess), forearm and/or wrist	40.00	930	1096	547
25040	Arthrotomy, radiocarpal or midcarpal joint, with exploration, drainage, or removal of foreign body	46.00	1070	1261	517
25065	Biopsy, soft tissue of forearm and/or wrist; superficial	8.00	186	219	123
25066	Biopsy, soft tissue of forearm and/or wrist; deep	20.00	465	548	221
25075	Excision, tumor, forearm and/or wrist area; subcutaneous	18.00	419	493	241
25076	Excision, tumor, forearm and/or wrist area; deep, subfascial or intramuscular	30.00	698	822	364
25077	Radical resection of tumor (eg, malignant neoplasm), soft tissue of forearm and/or wrist area	100.0	2325	2741	758
25085	Capsulotomy, wrist (eg, for contracture)	60.00	1395	1645	408
25100	Arthrotomy, wrist joint; with biopsy	40.00	930	1096	361
25101	Arthrotomy, wrist joint; with joint exploration, with or without biopsy, with or without removal of loose or foreign body	52.00	1209	1425	439
25105	Arthrotomy, wrist joint; with synovectomy	55.00	1279	1508	560
25107	Arthrotomy, distal radioulnar joint for repair of triangular cartilage complex	57.00	1325	1562	471
25110	Excision, lesion of tendon sheath, forearm and/or wrist	23.00	535	630	277
25111	Excision of ganglion, wrist (dorsal or volar); primary	30.00	698	822	287
25112	Excision of ganglion, wrist (dorsal or volar); recurrent	32.00	744	877	348
25115	Radical excision of bursa, synovia of wrist, or forearm tendon sheaths (eg, tenosynovitis, fungus, Tbc, or other granulomas, rheumatoid arthritis); flexors	58.00	1349	1590	611
25116	Radical excision of bursa, synovia of wrist, or forearm tendon sheaths (eg, tenosynovitis, fungus, Tbc, or other granulomas, rheumatoid arthritis); extensors, with or without transposition of dorsal retinaculum	58.00	1349	1590	664
25118	Synovectomy, extensor tendon sheath, wrist, single compartment;	45.00	1046	1233	456

Code	Description	Medicode RVU	50th	75th	Medicare Nat'l Avg
25119	Synovectomy, extensor tendon sheath, wrist, single compartment; with resection of distal ulna	50.00	1163	1370	572
25120	Excision or curettage of bone cyst or benign tumor of radius or ulna (excluding head or neck of radius and olecranon process);	50.00	1163	1370	524
25125	Excision or curettage of bone cyst or benign tumor of radius or ulna (excluding head or neck of radius and olecranon process); with autograft (includes obtaining graft)	60.00	1395	1645	583
25126	Excision or curettage of bone cyst or benign tumor of radius or ulna (excluding head or neck of radius and olecranon process); with allograft	60.00	1395	1645	585
25130	Excision or curettage of bone cyst or benign tumor of carpal bones;	50.00	1163	1370	390
25135	Excision or curettage of bone cyst or benign tumor of carpal bones; with autograft (includes obtaining graft)	60.00	1395	1645	507
25136	Excision or curettage of bone cyst or benign tumor of carpal bones; with allograft	60.00	1395	1645	437
25145	Sequestrectomy (eg, for osteomyelitis or bone abscess), forearm and/or wrist	60.00	1395	1645	492
25150	Partial excision (craterization, saucerization or diaphysectomy) of bone (eg, for osteomyelitis); ulna	50.00	1163	1370	558
25151	Partial excision (craterization, saucerization or diaphysectomy) of bone (eg, for osteomyelitis); radius	50.00	1163	1370	531
25170	Radical resection for tumor, radius or ulna	80.00	1860	2193	847
25210	Carpectomy; one bone	40.00	930	1096	443
25215	Carpectomy; all bones of proximal row	70.00	1628	1919	682
25230	Radial styloidectomy (separate procedure)	38.00	884	1042	441
25240	Excision distal ulna partial or complete (eg, Darrach type or matched resection)	40.00	930	1096	451
25246	Injection procedure for wrist arthrography	6.25	145	171	68
25248	Exploration with removal of deep foreign body, forearm or wrist	25.00	581	685	294
25250	Removal of wrist prosthesis; (separate procedure)	25.00	581	685	499
25251	Removal of wrist prosthesis; complicated, including "total wrist"	33.00	767	905	728
25260	Repair, tendon or muscle, flexor, forearm and/or wrist; primary, single, each tendon or muscle	42.00	977	1151	503
25263	Repair, tendon or muscle, flexor, forearm and/or wrist; secondary, single, each tendon or muscle	50.00	1163	1370	550
25265	Repair, tendon or muscle, flexor, forearm and/or wrist; secondary, with free graft (includes obtaining graft), each tendon or muscle	55.00	1279	1508	734

Code	Description	Medicode RVU	50th	75th	Medicare Nat'l Avg
25270	Repair, tendon or muscle, extensor, forearm and/or wrist; primary, single, each tendon or muscle	35.00	814	959	379
25272	Repair, tendon or muscle, extensor, forearm and/or wrist; secondary, single, each tendon or muscle	40.00	930	1096	419
25274	Repair, tendon or muscle, extensor, secondary, with tendon graft (includes obtaining graft), forearm and/or wrist, each tendon or muscle	50.00	1163	1370	630
25280	Lengthening or shortening of flexor or extensor tendon, forearm and/or wrist, single, each tendon	40.00	930	1096	462
25290	Tenotomy, open, flexor or extensor tendon, forearm and/or wrist, single, each tendon	25.00	581	685	311
25295	Tenolysis, flexor or extensor tendon, forearm and/or wrist, single, each tendon	36.00	837	987	388
25300	Tenodesis at wrist; flexors of fingers	70.00	1628	1919	664
25301	Tenodesis at wrist; extensors of fingers	60.00	1395	1645	626
25310	Tendon transplantation or transfer, flexor or extensor, forearm and/or wrist, single; each tendon	65.00	1511	1782	639
25312	Tendon transplantation or transfer, flexor or extensor, forearm and/or wrist, single; with tendon graft(s) (includes obtaining graft), each tendon	70.00	1628	1919	705
25315	Flexor origin slide (eg, for cerebral palsy, Volkmann contracture), forearm and/or wrist;	80.00	1860	2193	735
25316	Flexor origin slide (eg, for cerebral palsy, Volkmann contracture), forearm and/or wrist; with tendon(s) transfer	100.0	2325	2741	926
25320	Capsulorrhaphy or reconstruction, wrist, any method (eg, capsulodesis, ligament repair, tendon transfer or graft) (includes synovectomy, capsulotomy and open reduction) for carpal instability	85.00	1976	2330	786
25330	Arthroplasty, wrist;	60.00	1395	1645	847
25331	Arthroplasty, wrist; with implant	90.00	2093	2467	1166
25332	Arthroplasty, wrist; pseudarthrosis type with internal fixation	90.00	2093	2467	878
25335	Centralization of wrist on ulna (eg, radial club hand)	125.0	2906	3426	975
25337	Reconstruction for stabilization of unstable distal ulna or distal radioulnar joint, secondary by soft tissue stabilization (eg, tendon transfer, tendon graft or weave, or tenodesis) with or without open reduction of distal radioulnar joint	85.00	1976	2330	743
25350	Osteotomy, radius; distal third	55.00	1279	1508	666
25355	Osteotomy, radius; middle or proximal third	70.00	1628	1919	782
25360	Osteotomy; ulna	55.00	1279	1508	597
25365	Osteotomy; radius and ulna	80.00	1860	2193	913

Code	Description	Medicode RVU	50th	75th	Medicare Nat'l Avg
25370	Multiple osteotomies, with realignment on intramedullary rod (Sofield type procedure); radius OR ulna	70.00	1628	1919	1010
25375	Multiple osteotomies, with realignment on intramedullary rod (Sofield type procedure); radius AND ulna	100.0	2325	2741	1032
25390	Osteoplasty, radius OR ulna; shortening	70.00	1628	1919	789
25391	Osteoplasty, radius OR ulna; lengthening with autograft	80.00	1860	2193	1008
25392	Osteoplasty, radius AND ulna; shortening (excluding 64876)	85.00	1976	2330	1070
25393	Osteoplasty, radius AND ulna; lengthening with autograft	90.00	2093	2467	1220
25400	Repair of nonunion or malunion, radius OR ulna; without graft (eg, compression technique)	65.00	1511	1782	888
25405	Repair of nonunion or malunion, radius OR ulna; with iliac or other autograft (includes obtaining graft)	80.00	1860	2193	1097
25415	Repair of nonunion or malunion, radius AND ulna; without graft (eg, compression technique)	80.00	1860	2193	1021
25420	Repair of nonunion or malunion, radius AND ulna; with iliac or other autograft (includes obtaining graft)	95.00	2209	2604	1266
25425	Repair of defect with autograft; radius OR ulna	75.00	1744	2056	1022
25426	Repair of defect with autograft; radius AND ulna	85.00	1976	2330	1118
25440	Repair of nonunion, scaphoid (navicular) bone, with or without radial styloidectomy (includes obtaining graft and necessary fixation)	75.00	1744	2056	804
25441	Arthroplasty with prosthetic replacement; distal radius	85.00	1976	2330	994
25442	Arthroplasty with prosthetic replacement; distal ulna	85.00	1976	2330	728
25443	Arthroplasty with prosthetic replacement; scaphoid (navicular)	85.00	1976	2330	809
25444	Arthroplasty with prosthetic replacement; lunate	95.00	2209	2604	871
25445	Arthroplasty with prosthetic replacement; trapezium	95.00	2209	2604	842
25446	Arthroplasty with prosthetic replacement; distal radius and partial or entire carpus ("total wrist")	130.0	3023	3563	1545
25447	Interposition arthroplasty, intercarpal or carpometacarpal joints	75.00	1744	2056	836
25449	Revision of arthroplasty, including removal of implant, wrist joint	60.00	1395	1645	891
25450	Epiphyseal arrest by epiphysiodesis or stapling; distal radius OR ulna	30.00	698	822	628
25455	Epiphyseal arrest by epiphysiodesis or stapling; distal radius AND ulna	50.00	1163	1370	749
25490	Prophylactic treatment (nailing, pinning, plating or wiring) with or without methylmethacrylate; radius	55.00	1279	1508	746

Code	Description	Medicode RVU	50th	75th	Medicare Nat'l Avg
25491	Prophylactic treatment (nailing, pinning, plating or wiring) with or without methylmethacrylate; ulna	55.00	1279	1508	781
25492	Prophylactic treatment (nailing, pinning, plating or wiring) with or without methylmethacrylate; radius AND ulna	65.00	1511	1782	962
25500	Closed treatment of radial shaft fracture; without manipulation	15.00	349	399	193
25505	Closed treatment of radial shaft fracture; with manipulation	25.50	594	677	352
25515	Open treatment of radial shaft fracture, with or without internal or external fixation	55.50	1292	1474	686
25520	Closed treatment of radial shaft fracture, with dislocation of distal radio-ulnar joint (Galeazzi fracture/dislocation)	25.50	594	677	492
25525	Open treatment of radial shaft fracture, with internal and/or external fixation and closed treatment of dislocation of distal radio-ulnar joint (Galeazzi fracture/dislocation), with or without percutaneous skeletal fixation	65.00	1513	1727	957
25526	Open treatment of radial shaft fracture, with internal and/or external fixation and open treatment, with or without internal or external fixation of distal radio-ulnar joint (Galeazzi fracture/dislocation), includes repair of triangular cartilage	75.00	1746	1993	1018
25530	Closed treatment of ulnar shaft fracture; without manipulation	16.00	373	425	189
25535	Closed treatment of ulnar shaft fracture; with manipulation	24.00	559	638	351
25545	Open treatment of ulnar shaft fracture, with or without internal or external fixation	55.50	1292	1474	670
25560	Closed treatment of radial and ulnar shaft fractures; without manipulation	20.00	466	531	196
25565	Closed treatment of radial and ulnar shaft fractures; with manipulation	38.00	885	1010	417
25574	Open treatment of radial AND ulnar shaft fractures, with internal or external fixation; of radius or ulna	74.00	1723	1966	685
25575	Open treatment of radial AND ulnar shaft fractures, with internal or external fixation; of radius AND ulna	81.00	1886	2152	875
25600	Closed treatment of distal radial fracture (eg, Colles or Smith type) or epiphyseal separation, with or without fracture of ulnar styloid; without manipulation	17.25	402	458	226
25605	Closed treatment of distal radial fracture (eg, Colles or Smith type) or epiphyseal separation, with or without fracture of ulnar styloid; with manipulation	26.50	617	704	392
25611	Percutaneous skeletal fixation of distal radial fracture (eg, Colles or Smith type) or epiphyseal separation, with or without fracture of ulnar styloid, requiring manipulation, with or without external fixation	45.00	1048	1196	550
25620	Open treatment of distal radial fracture (eg, Colles or Smith type) or epiphyseal separation, with or without fracture of ulnar styloid, with or without internal or external fixation	54.00	1257	1435	642
25622	Closed treatment of carpal scaphoid (navicular) fracture; without manipulation	18.50	431	491	199
25624	Closed treatment of carpal scaphoid (navicular) fracture; with manipulation	24.00	559	638	332

Code	Description	Medicode RVU	50th	75th	Medicare Nat'l Avg
25628	Open treatment of carpal scaphoid (navicular) fracture, with or without internal or external fixation	52.00	1211	1381	625
25630	Closed treatment of carpal bone fracture (excluding carpal scaphoid (navicular)); without manipulation, each bone	15.25	355	405	204
25635	Closed treatment of carpal bone fracture (excluding carpal scaphoid (navicular)); with manipulation, each bone	25.00	582	664	311
25645	Open treatment of carpal bone fracture (excluding carpal scaphoid (navicular)), each bone	37.50	873	996	563
25650	Closed treatment of ulnar styloid fracture	22.00	512	584	230
25660	Closed treatment of radiocarpal or intercarpal dislocation, one or more bones, with manipulation	25.00	582	664	255
25670	Open treatment of radiocarpal or intercarpal dislocation, one or more bones	50.00	1164	1328	612
25675	Closed treatment of distal radioulnar dislocation with manipulation	20.00	466	531	273
25676	Open treatment of distal radioulnar dislocation, acute or chronic	40.00	931	1063	621
25680	Closed treatment of trans-scaphoperilunar type of fracture dislocation, with manipulation	35.50	827	943	330
25685	Open treatment of trans-scaphoperilunar type of fracture dislocation	68.00	1583	1807	756
25690	Closed treatment of lunate dislocation, with manipulation	30.00	699	797	418
25695	Open treatment of lunate dislocation	61.00	1420	1621	628
25800	Arthrodesis, wrist joint (including radiocarpal and/or ulnocarpal fusion); without bone graft	62.00	1444	1647	863
25805	Arthrodesis, wrist joint (including radiocarpal and/or ulnocarpal fusion); with sliding graft	75.00	1746	1993	994
25810	Arthrodesis, wrist joint (including radiocarpal and/or ulnocarpal fusion); with iliac or other autograft (includes obtaining graft)	86.00	2002	2285	980
25820	Intercarpal fusion; without bone graft	72.00	1676	1913	687
25825	Intercarpal fusion; with autograft (includes obtaining graft)	98.00	2282	2604	855
25830	Distal radioulnar joint arthrodesis and segmental resection of ulna (eg, Sauve-Kapandji procedure), with or without bone graft	80.00	1863	2125	743
25900	Amputation, forearm, through radius and ulna;	60.00	1397	1594	648
25905	Amputation, forearm, through radius and ulna; open, circular (guillotine)	52.00	1211	1381	647
25907	Amputation, forearm, through radius and ulna; secondary closure or scar revision	23.00	536	611	543
25909	Amputation, forearm, through radius and ulna; re-amputation	60.00	1397	1594	583

Code	Description	Medicode RVU	50th	75th	Medicare Nat'l Avg
25915	Krukenberg procedure	67.00	1560	1780	1359
25920	Disarticulation through wrist;	60.00	1397	1594	634
25922	Disarticulation through wrist; secondary closure or scar revision	20.00	466	531	525
25924	Disarticulation through wrist; re-amputation	60.00	1397	1594	644
25927	Transmetacarpal amputation;	60.00	1397	1594	622
25929	Transmetacarpal amputation; secondary closure or scar revision	20.00	466	531	498
25931	Transmetacarpal amputation; re-amputation	60.00	1397	1594	500
25999	Unlisted procedure, forearm or wrist	0.00	0	0	–

26010–26989
Hand and Fingers

Coding Insight

Payers may restrict the number of procedures that are reimbursed for each hand. They may consider multiple service to be included in the primary surgical procedure. For example, payment may not be made for multiple arthrotomies or capsulotomies involving the same or various fingers on one hand. However, even though payers have their own separate parameters, multiple arthrotomies and capsulectomies that involve joints of totally different body parts (e.g., knee, wrist, elbow) are usually reimbursable.

Be sure to submit operative reports with these claims. Each anatomic location should be clearly identified in the operative report (e.g., little, ring, or middle finger), and also clearly note which limb is involved, such as left or right side, hand.

Be very careful with code selection in this code range. For instance, codes for arthrodesis of the hand, such as 26850, are used once and the number of units are identified; the same code is not repeated on each line for the number involved. Multiply the number of procedures times the cost and list the cost on a single line.

Subsidiary Codes

Subsidiary codes have relative values that require no further adjustment:

20690 is "in addition" to 26010–26989
20692 is "in addition" to 26010–26989
20900 is "in addition" to 26010–26989
20902 is "in addition" to 26010–26989
20910 is "in addition" to 26010–26989
20912 is "in addition" to 26010–26989
20920 is "in addition" to 26010–26989
20922 is "in addition" to 26010–26989
20924 is "in addition" to 26010–26989
20926 is "in addition" to 26010–26989
26125 is "in addition" to 26123

26861 is "in addition" to 26860
26863 is "in addition" to 26862

Because these are subsidiary or "in addition to" codes, reimbursement reduction and modifier -51 do not apply.

MEDICARE ALERT

Medicare rebundles certain codes in the surgery section when the listed codes are considered a component of a more comprehensive service.

29125 will not be reimbursed when reported with 26055

Code		Description	Medicode RVU	50th	75th	Medicare Nat'l Avg
26010	*	Drainage of finger abscess; simple	4.00	94	111	66
26011	*	Drainage of finger abscess; complicated (eg, felon)	15.00	354	416	157
26020		Drainage of tendon sheath, one digit and/or palm	30.00	707	833	332
26025		Drainage of palmar bursa; single, ulnar or radial	30.00	707	833	376
26030		Drainage of palmar bursa; multiple or complicated	70.00	1650	1943	482
26034		Incision, deep, with opening of bone cortex (eg, for osteomyelitis or bone abscess), hand or finger	32.00	754	888	411
26035		Decompression fingers and/or hand, injection injury (eg, grease gun)	70.00	1650	1943	562
26037		Decompressive fasciotomy, hand (excludes 26035)	30.00	707	833	549
26040		Fasciotomy, palmar, for Dupuytren's contracture; closed (subcutaneous)	21.00	495	583	254
26045		Fasciotomy, palmar, for Dupuytren's contracture; open, partial	30.00	707	833	430
26055		Tendon sheath incision (eg, for trigger finger)	26.00	613	722	270
26060		Tenotomy, subcutaneous, single, each digit	13.00	306	361	156
26070		Arthrotomy, for infection, with exploration, drainage or removal of foreign body; carpometacarpal joint	30.00	707	833	265
26075		Arthrotomy, for infection, with exploration, drainage or removal of foreign body; metacarpophalangeal joint	30.00	707	833	312
26080		Arthrotomy, for infection, with exploration, drainage or removal of foreign body; interphalangeal joint, each	24.00	566	666	296
26100		Arthrotomy with synovial biopsy; carpometacarpal joint	30.00	707	833	278
26105		Arthrotomy with synovial biopsy; metacarpophalangeal joint	25.00	589	694	330
26110		Arthrotomy with synovial biopsy; interphalangeal joint, each	21.00	495	583	271
26115		Excision, tumor or vascular malformation, hand or finger; subcutaneous	20.00	471	555	235

Code	Description	Medicode RVU	50th	75th	Medicare Nat'l Avg
26116	Excision, tumor or vascular malformation, hand or finger; deep, subfascial, intramuscular	32.00	754	888	377
26117	Radical resection of tumor (eg, malignant neoplasm), soft tissue of hand or finger	105.0	2475	2914	554
26121	Fasciectomy, palmar only, with or without z-plasty, other local tissue rearrangement, or skin grafting (includes obtaining graft);	65.00	1532	1804	778
26123	Fasciectomy, palmar only, with or without z-plasty, other local tissue rearrangement, or skin grafting (includes obtaining graft); partial palmar excision with release of single digit including proximal interphalangeal joint	75.00	1768	2082	808
26125	Fasciectomy, palmar only, with or without z-plasty, other local tissue rearrangement, or skin grafting (includes obtaining graft); partial excision with release of each additional digit, including proximal interphalangeal joint	25.00	589	694	339
26130	Synovectomy, carpometacarpal joint	45.00	1061	1249	437
26135	Synovectomy, metacarpophalangeal joint including intrinsic release and extensor hood reconstruction, each digit	40.00	943	1110	492
26140	Synovectomy, proximal interphalangeal joint, including extensor reconstruction, each interphalangeal joint	35.00	825	971	436
26145	Synovectomy tendon sheath, radical (tenosynovectomy), flexor, palm or finger, single, each digit	40.00	943	1110	482
26160	Excision of lesion of tendon sheath or capsule (eg, cyst, mucous cyst, or ganglion), hand or finger	23.00	542	638	225
26170	Excision of tendon, palm, flexor, single (separate procedure), each	25.00	589	694	308
26180	Excision of tendon, finger, flexor (separate procedure)	25.00	589	694	377
26200	Excision or curettage of bone cyst or benign tumor of metacarpal;	30.00	707	833	409
26205	Excision or curettage of bone cyst or benign tumor of metacarpal; with autograft (includes obtaining graft)	40.00	943	1110	570
26210	Excision or curettage of bone cyst or benign tumor of proximal, middle or distal phalanx of finger;	27.50	648	763	375
26215	Excision or curettage of bone cyst or benign tumor of proximal, middle or distal phalanx of finger; with autograft (includes obtaining graft)	40.00	943	1110	519
26230	Partial excision (craterization, saucerization, or diaphysectomy) of bone (eg, for osteomyelitis); metacarpal	32.00	754	888	426
26235	Partial excision (craterization, saucerization, or diaphysectomy) of bone (eg, for osteomyelitis); proximal or middle phalanx of finger	30.00	707	833	418
26236	Partial excision (craterization, saucerization, or diaphysectomy) of bone (eg, for osteomyelitis); distal phalanx of finger	28.00	660	777	371
26250	Radical resection (ostectomy) for tumor, metacarpal;	50.00	1179	1388	561
26255	Radical resection (ostectomy) for tumor, metacarpal; with autograft (includes obtaining graft)	70.00	1650	1943	860

Code	Description	Medicode RVU	50th	75th	Medicare Nat'l Avg
26260	Radical resection (ostectomy) for tumor, proximal or middle phalanx of finger;	50.00	1179	1388	532
26261	Radical resection (ostectomy) for tumor, proximal or middle phalanx of finger; with autograft (includes obtaining graft)	60.00	1414	1665	683
26262	Radical resection (ostectomy) for tumor, distal phalanx of finger	50.00	1179	1388	427
26320	Removal of implant from finger or hand	23.00	531	629	314
26350	Flexor tendon repair or advancement, single, not in "no man's land"; primary or secondary without free graft, each tendon	51.00	1178	1395	510
26352	Flexor tendon repair or advancement, single, not in "no man's land"; secondary with free graft (includes obtaining graft), each tendon	70.00	1617	1915	588
26356	Flexor tendon repair or advancement, single, in "no man's land"; primary, each tendon	70.00	1617	1915	617
26357	Flexor tendon repair or advancement, single, in "no man's land"; secondary, each tendon	85.00	1963	2325	621
26358	Flexor tendon repair or advancement, single, in "no man's land"; secondary with free graft (includes obtaining graft), each tendon	95.00	2194	2598	678
26370	Profundus tendon repair or advancement, with intact sublimis; primary	60.00	1386	1641	578
26372	Profundus tendon repair or advancement, with intact sublimis; secondary with free graft (includes obtaining graft)	70.00	1617	1915	617
26373	Profundus tendon repair or advancement, with intact sublimis; secondary without free graft	60.00	1386	1641	607
26390	Flexor tendon excision, implantation of plastic tube or rod for delayed tendon graft, hand or finger	60.00	1386	1641	696
26392	Removal of tube or rod and insertion of flexor tendon graft (includes obtaining graft), hand or finger	70.00	1617	1915	764
26410	Extensor tendon repair, dorsum of hand, single, primary or secondary; without free graft, each tendon	30.00	693	821	324
26412	Extensor tendon repair, dorsum of hand, single, primary or secondary; with free graft (includes obtaining graft), each tendon	42.00	970	1149	503
26415	Extensor tendon excision, implantation of plastic tube or rod for delayed extensor tendon graft, hand or finger	44.00	1016	1203	606
26416	Removal of tube or rod and insertion of extensor tendon graft (includes obtaining graft), hand or finger	47.00	1085	1286	742
26418	Extensor tendon repair, dorsum of finger, single, primary or secondary; without free graft, each tendon	33.00	762	903	327
26420	Extensor tendon repair, dorsum of finger, single, primary or secondary; with free graft (includes obtaining graft) each tendon	45.00	1039	1231	506
26426	Extensor tendon repair, central slip repair, secondary (boutonniere deformity); using local tissues	50.00	1155	1368	529

Code	Description	Medicode RVU	50th	75th	Medicare Nat'l Avg
26428	Extensor tendon repair, central slip repair, secondary (boutonniere deformity); with free graft (includes obtaining graft)	70.00	1617	1915	527
26432	Extensor tendon repair, distal insertion ("mallet finger"), closed, splinting with or without percutaneous pinning	24.00	554	656	293
26433	Extensor tendon repair, distal insertion ("mallet finger"), open, primary or secondary repair; without graft	35.00	808	957	358
26434	Extensor tendon repair, distal insertion ("mallet finger"), open, primary or secondary repair; with free graft (includes obtaining graft)	45.00	1039	1231	451
26437	Extensor tendon realignment, hand	40.00	924	1094	401
26440	Tenolysis, simple, flexor tendon; palm OR finger, single, each tendon	30.00	693	821	354
26442	Tenolysis, simple, flexor tendon; palm AND finger, each tendon	45.00	1039	1231	396
26445	Tenolysis, extensor tendon, dorsum of hand or finger; each tendon	31.00	716	848	315
26449	Tenolysis, complex, extensor tendon, dorsum of hand or finger, including hand and forearm	46.50	1074	1272	505
26450	Tenotomy, flexor, single, palm, open, each	25.00	577	684	242
26455	Tenotomy, flexor, single, finger, open, each	25.00	577	684	223
26460	Tenotomy, extensor, hand or finger, single, open, each	25.00	577	684	210
26471	Tenodesis; for proximal interphalangeal joint stabilization	50.00	1155	1368	408
26474	Tenodesis; for distal joint stabilization	30.00	693	821	409
26476	Tendon lengthening, extensor, hand or finger, single, each	30.00	693	821	319
26477	Tendon shortening, extensor, hand or finger, single, each	30.00	693	821	377
26478	Tendon lengthening, flexor, hand or finger, single, each	40.00	924	1094	414
26479	Tendon shortening, flexor, hand or finger, single, each	40.00	924	1094	455
26480	Tendon transfer or transplant, carpometacarpal area or dorsum of hand, single; without free graft, each	52.00	1201	1422	570
26483	Tendon transfer or transplant, carpometacarpal area or dorsum of hand, single; with free tendon graft (includes obtaining graft), each tendon	64.00	1478	1751	692
26485	Tendon transfer or transplant, palmar, single, each tendon; without free tendon graft	67.00	1547	1833	592
26489	Tendon transfer or transplant, palmar, single, each tendon; with free tendon graft (includes obtaining graft), each tendon	79.00	1825	2161	512
26490	Opponensplasty; sublimis tendon transfer type	60.00	1386	1641	667

Code	Description	Medicode RVU	50th	75th	Medicare Nat'l Avg
26492	Opponensplasty; tendon transfer with graft (includes obtaining graft)	75.00	1732	2051	745
26494	Opponensplasty; hypothenar muscle transfer	80.00	1848	2188	643
26496	Opponensplasty; other methods	80.00	1848	2188	759
26497	Tendon transfer to restore intrinsic function; ring and small finger	70.00	1617	1915	721
26498	Tendon transfer to restore intrinsic function; all four fingers	85.00	1963	2325	1062
26499	Correction claw finger, other methods	0.00	0	0	682
26500	Tendon pulley reconstruction; with local tissues (separate procedure)	35.00	808	957	380
26502	Tendon pulley reconstruction; with tendon or fascial graft (includes obtaining graft) (separate procedure)	47.00	1085	1286	504
26504	Tendon pulley reconstruction; with tendon prosthesis (separate procedure)	57.00	1316	1559	578
26508	Thenar muscle release for thumb contracture	40.00	924	1094	410
26510	Cross intrinsic transfer	85.00	1963	2325	388
26516	Capsulodesis for M-P joint stabilization; single digit	50.00	1155	1368	454
26517	Capsulodesis for M-P joint stabilization; two digits	60.00	1386	1641	648
26518	Capsulodesis for M-P joint stabilization; three or four digits	80.00	1848	2188	634
26520	Capsulectomy or capsulotomy for contracture; metacarpophalangeal joint, single, each	40.00	924	1094	404
26525	Capsulectomy or capsulotomy for contracture; interphalangeal joint, single, each	40.00	924	1094	380
26530	Arthroplasty, metacarpophalangeal joint; single, each	50.00	1155	1368	494
26531	Arthroplasty, metacarpophalangeal joint; with prosthetic implant, single, each	55.00	1270	1504	625
26535	Arthroplasty interphalangeal joint; single, each	42.00	970	1149	415
26536	Arthroplasty interphalangeal joint; with prosthetic implant, single, each	55.00	1270	1504	588
26540	Primary repair of collateral ligament, metacarpophalangeal joint;	50.00	1155	1368	556
26541	Primary repair of collateral ligament, metacarpophalangeal joint; with tendon or fascial graft (includes obtaining graft)	60.00	1386	1641	728
26542	Primary repair of collateral ligament, metacarpophalangeal joint; with local tissue (eg, adductor advancement)	70.00	1617	1915	507
26545	Reconstruction, collateral ligament, interphalangeal joint, single, including graft, each joint	50.00	1155	1368	502

Code	Description	Medicode RVU	50th	75th	Medicare Nat'l Avg
26548	Repair and reconstruction, finger, volar plate, interphalangeal joint	55.00	1270	1504	566
26550	Pollicization of a digit	120.0	2771	3282	1701
26552	Reconstruction thumb with toe	150.0	3464	4103	2059
26555	Positional change of other finger	80.00	1848	2188	1323
26557	Toe to finger transfer; first stage	50.00	1155	1368	2095
26558	Toe to finger transfer; each delay	25.00	577	684	953
26559	Toe to finger transfer; second stage	80.00	1848	2188	989
26560	Repair of syndactyly (web finger) each web space; with skin flaps	50.00	1155	1368	411
26561	Repair of syndactyly (web finger) each web space; with skin flaps and grafts	60.00	1386	1641	813
26562	Repair of syndactyly (web finger) each web space; complex (eg, involving bone, nails)	150.0	3464	4103	818
26565	Osteotomy for correction of deformity; metacarpal	45.00	1039	1231	511
26567	Osteotomy for correction of deformity; phalanx of finger	40.00	924	1094	447
26568	Osteoplasty for lengthening of metacarpal or phalanx	65.00	1501	1778	707
26580	Repair cleft hand	0.00	0	0	1295
26585	Repair bifid digit	0.00	0	0	1112
26587	Reconstruction of supernumerary digit, soft tissue and bone	0.00	0	0	495
26590	Repair macrodactylia	0.00	0	0	1428
26591	Repair, intrinsic muscles of hand (specify)	0.00	0	0	225
26593	Release, intrinsic muscles of hand (specify)	0.00	0	0	379
26596	Excision of constricting ring of finger, with multiple Z-plasties	0.00	0	0	709
26597	Release of scar contracture, flexor or extensor, with skin grafts, rearrangement flaps, or Z-plasties, hand and/or finger	0.00	0	0	730
26600	Closed treatment of metacarpal fracture, single; without manipulation, each bone	11.00	257	304	139
26605	Closed treatment of metacarpal fracture, single; with manipulation, each bone	16.50	386	457	208
26607	Closed treatment of metacarpal fracture, with manipulation, with internal or external fixation, each bone	30.00	701	830	364

Code	Description	Medicode RVU	50th	75th	Medicare Nat'l Avg
26608	Percutaneous skeletal fixation of metacarpal fracture, each bone	35.00	818	969	359
26615	Open treatment of metacarpal fracture, single, with or without internal or external fixation, each bone	38.50	900	1066	435
26641	Closed treatment of carpometacarpal dislocation, thumb, with manipulation	13.50	316	374	192
26645	Closed treatment of carpometacarpal fracture dislocation, thumb (Bennett fracture), with manipulation	18.50	432	512	263
26650	Percutaneous skeletal fixation of carpometacarpal fracture dislocation, thumb (Bennett fracture), with manipulation, with or without external fixation	35.50	830	983	394
26665	Open treatment of carpometacarpal fracture dislocation, thumb (Bennett fracture), with or without internal or external fixation	52.50	1227	1453	573
26670	Closed treatment of carpometacarpal dislocation, other than thumb (Bennett fracture), single, with manipulation; without anesthesia	11.00	257	304	176
26675	Closed treatment of carpometacarpal dislocation, other than thumb (Bennett fracture), single, with manipulation; requiring anesthesia	15.00	351	415	362
26676	Percutaneous skeletal fixation of carpometacarpal dislocation, other than thumb (Bennett fracture), single, with manipulation	26.00	608	720	419
26685	Open treatment of carpometacarpal dislocation, other than thumb (Bennett fracture); single, with or without internal or external fixation	41.00	959	1135	512
26686	Open treatment of carpometacarpal dislocation, other than thumb (Bennett fracture); complex, multiple or delayed reduction	57.00	1333	1578	577
26700	Closed treatment of metacarpophalangeal dislocation, single, with manipulation; without anesthesia	9.00	210	249	167
26705	Closed treatment of metacarpophalangeal dislocation, single, with manipulation; requiring anesthesia	15.00	351	415	232
26706	Percutaneous skeletal fixation of metacarpophalangeal dislocation, single, with manipulation	22.00	514	609	401
26715	Open treatment of metacarpophalangeal dislocation, single, with or without internal or external fixation	37.50	877	1038	401
26720	Closed treatment of phalangeal shaft fracture, proximal or middle phalanx, finger or thumb; without manipulation, each	7.50	175	208	108
26725	Closed treatment of phalangeal shaft fracture, proximal or middle phalanx, finger or thumb; with manipulation, with or without skin or skeletal traction, each	13.00	304	360	189
26727	Percutaneous skeletal fixation of unstable phalangeal shaft fracture, proximal or middle phalanx, finger or thumb, with manipulation, each	24.00	561	664	299
26735	Open treatment of phalangeal shaft fracture, proximal or middle phalanx, finger or thumb, with or without internal or external fixation, each	35.00	818	969	396
26740	Closed treatment of articular fracture, involving metacarpophalangeal or interphalangeal joint; without manipulation, each	11.50	269	318	122

Code	Description	Medicode RVU	50th	75th	Medicare Nat'l Avg
26742	Closed treatment of articular fracture, involving metacarpophalangeal or interphalangeal joint; with manipulation, each	17.00	397	470	232
26746	Open treatment of articular fracture, involving metacarpophalangeal or interphalangeal joint, with or without internal or external fixation, each	46.00	1075	1273	442
26750	Closed treatment of distal phalangeal fracture, finger or thumb; without manipulation, each	6.50	152	180	97
26755	Closed treatment of distal phalangeal fracture, finger or thumb; with manipulation, each	10.00	234	277	160
26756	Percutaneous skeletal fixation of distal phalangeal fracture, finger or thumb, each	20.00	468	554	250
26765	Open treatment of distal phalangeal fracture, finger or thumb, with or without internal or external fixation, each	28.00	655	775	281
26770	Closed treatment of interphalangeal joint dislocation, single, with manipulation; without anesthesia	6.50	152	180	135
26775	Closed treatment of interphalangeal joint dislocation, single, with manipulation; requiring anesthesia	11.00	257	304	180
26776	Percutaneous skeletal fixation of interphalangeal joint dislocation, single, with manipulation	17.00	397	470	272
26785	Open treatment of interphalangeal joint dislocation, with or without internal or external fixation, single	28.00	655	775	295
26820	Fusion in opposition, thumb, with autogenous graft (includes obtaining graft)	60.00	1403	1661	608
26841	Arthrodesis, carpometacarpal joint, thumb, with or without internal fixation;	50.00	1169	1384	554
26842	Arthrodesis, carpometacarpal joint, thumb, with or without internal fixation; with autograft (includes obtaining graft)	60.00	1403	1661	693
26843	Arthrodesis, carpometacarpal joint, digits, other than thumb;	50.00	1169	1384	572
26844	Arthrodesis, carpometacarpal joint, digits, other than thumb; with autograft (includes obtaining graft)	60.00	1403	1661	652
26850	Arthrodesis, metacarpophalangeal joint, with or without internal fixation;	42.00	982	1162	478
26852	Arthrodesis, metacarpophalangeal joint, with or without internal fixation; with autograft (includes obtaining graft)	52.00	1216	1439	577
26860	Arthrodesis, interphalangeal joint, with or without internal fixation;	37.50	877	1038	383
26861	Arthrodesis, interphalangeal joint, with or without internal fixation; each additional interphalangeal joint	18.75	438	519	174
26862	Arthrodesis, interphalangeal joint, with or without internal fixation; with autograft (includes obtaining graft)	47.50	1110	1315	513
26863	Arthrodesis, interphalangeal joint, with or without internal fixation; with autograft (includes obtaining graft), each additional joint	23.00	538	637	304
26910	Amputation, metacarpal, with finger or thumb (ray amputation), single, with or without interosseous transfer	45.00	1052	1245	522
26951	Amputation, finger or thumb, primary or secondary, any joint or phalanx, single, including neurectomies; with direct closure	30.00	701	830	305

Code	Description	Medicode RVU	50th	75th	Medicare Nat'l Avg
26952	Amputation, finger or thumb, primary or secondary, any joint or phalanx, single, including neurectomies; with local advancement flaps (V-Y, hood)	40.00	935	1107	416
26989	Unlisted procedure, hands or fingers	0.00	0	0	–

26990–27299
Pelvis and Hip Joint

Coding Insight
Manipulation under anesthesia (27275) should not be reported with an open orthopedic hip procedure.

Review the operative report to determine if one or more components were replaced in hip arthroplasty, e.g., total, partial, (27125–27130). Conversions of previous hip surgery should be coded to 27132, and removal of total hip prosthesis to 27091. (The ICD•9 code will report a complication of an orthopedic device/implant/graft.) Revisions should be coded to 27134–27138. If closed treatment of post-hip arthroplasty dislocations is performed, see 27265–27266.

Subsidiary Codes
Subsidiary codes have relative values that require no further adjustment:

20690 is "in addition" to 26990–27299
20692 is "in addition" to 26990–27299
20900 is "in addition" to 26990–27299
20902 is "in addition" to 26990–27299
20910 is "in addition" to 26990–27299
20912 is "in addition" to 26990–27299
20920 is "in addition" to 26990–27299
20922 is "in addition" to 26990–27299
20924 is "in addition" to 26990–27299
20926 is "in addition" to 26990–27299

Because these are subsidiary or "in addition to" codes reimbursement reduction and modifier -51 do not apply.

Medicare Alert
Medicare rebundles certain codes in the surgery section when the listed codes are considered a component of a more comprehensive service.

20680 will not be reimbursed when reported with 27134, 27137–27138
27120 will not be reimbursed when reported with 27130, 27132, 27134, 27137
27090 will not be reimbursed when reported with 27091, 27134
27125 will not be reimbursed when reported with 27132, 27134, 27137–27138
27130 will not be reimbursed when reported with 27132
27137 will not be reimbursed when reported with 27134
27235 will not be reimbursed when reported with 27236

Code	Description	Medicode RVU	50th	75th	Medicare Nat'l Avg
26990	Incision and drainage, pelvis or hip joint area; deep abscess or hematoma	24.00	568	652	397
26991	Incision and drainage, pelvis or hip joint area; infected bursa	30.00	709	815	312
26992	Incision, deep, with opening of bone cortex (eg, for osteomyelitis or bone abscess), pelvis and/or hip joint	35.00	828	951	824
27000	Tenotomy, adductor of hip, subcutaneous, closed (separate procedure)	15.00	355	407	283
27001	Tenotomy, adductor of hip, subcutaneous, open	30.00	709	815	403
27003	Tenotomy, adductor, subcutaneous, open, with obturator neurectomy	35.00	828	951	557
27005	Tenotomy, iliopsoas, open (separate procedure)	40.00	946	1087	503
27006	Tenotomy, abductors of hip, open (separate procedure)	40.00	946	1087	581
27025	Fasciotomy, hip or thigh, any type	60.00	1419	1630	673
27030	Arthrotomy, hip, for infection, with drainage	70.00	1655	1901	1002
27033	Arthrotomy, hip, with exploration or removal of loose or foreign body	70.00	1655	1901	1017
27035	Hip joint denervation, intrapelvic or extrapelvic intra-articular branches of sciatic, femoral or obturator nerves	86.00	2034	2336	1157
27040	Biopsy, soft tissue of pelvis and hip area; superficial	6.00	142	163	137
27041	Biopsy, soft tissue of pelvis and hip area; deep	20.00	473	543	468
27047	Excision, tumor, pelvis and hip area; subcutaneous	19.50	461	530	359
27048	Excision, tumor, pelvis and hip area; deep, subfascial, intramuscular	55.00	1301	1494	434
27049	Radical resection of tumor (eg, malignant neoplasm), soft tissue of pelvis and hip area	155.0	3665	4210	959
27050	Arthrotomy, with biopsy; sacroiliac joint	30.00	709	815	370
27052	Arthrotomy, with biopsy; hip joint	70.00	1655	1901	615
27054	Arthrotomy with synovectomy, hip joint	110.0	2601	2988	849
27060	Excision; ischial bursa	30.00	709	815	366
27062	Excision; trochanteric bursa or calcification	31.00	733	842	384
27065	Excision of bone cyst or benign tumor; superficial (wing of ilium, symphysis pubis, or greater trochanter of femur) with or without autograft	40.00	946	1087	452
27066	Excision of bone cyst or benign tumor; deep, with or without autograft	67.00	1584	1820	726

Code		Description	Medicode RVU	50th	75th	Medicare Nat'l Avg
27067		Excision of bone cyst or benign tumor; with autograft requiring separate incision	79.00	1868	2146	1018
27070		Partial excision (craterization, saucerization) (eg, for osteomyelitis); superficial (eg, wing of ilium, symphysis pubis or greater trochanter of femur)	35.00	828	951	705
27071		Partial excision (craterization, saucerization) (eg, for osteomyelitis); deep	65.00	1537	1766	794
27075		Radical resection of tumor or infection; wing of ilium, one pubic or ischial ramus or symphysis pubis	120.0	2838	3260	1276
27076		Radical resection of tumor or infection; ilium, including acetabulum, both pubic rami, or ischium and acetabulum	150.0	3547	4075	1443
27077		Radical resection of tumor or infection; innominate bone, total	200.0	4729	5433	1688
27078		Radical resection of tumor or infection; ischial tuberosity and greater trochanter of femur	60.00	1419	1630	902
27079		Radical resection of tumor or infection; ischial tuberosity and greater trochanter of femur, with skin flaps	90.00	2128	2445	874
27080		Coccygectomy, primary	40.00	946	1087	442
27086	*	Removal of foreign body, pelvis or hip; subcutaneous tissue	6.00	142	163	95
27087		Removal of foreign body, pelvis or hip; deep	30.00	709	815	469
27090		Removal of hip prosthesis; (separate procedure)	59.00	1395	1603	896
27091		Removal of hip prosthesis; complicated, including "total hip" and methylmethacrylate, when applicable	155.0	3665	4210	1749
27093		Injection procedure for hip arthrography; without anesthesia	8.00	189	217	87
27095		Injection procedure for hip arthrography; with anesthesia	15.50	367	421	88
27097		Hamstring recession, proximal	70.00	1655	1901	663
27098		Adductor transfer to ischium	80.00	1892	2173	662
27100		Transfer external oblique muscle to greater trochanter including fascial or tendon extension (graft)	100.0	2365	2716	770
27105		Transfer paraspinal muscle to hip (includes fascial or tendon extension graft)	100.0	2365	2716	721
27110		Transfer iliopsoas; to greater trochanter	125.0	2956	3396	971
27111		Transfer iliopsoas; to femoral neck	80.00	1892	2173	960
27120		Acetabuloplasty; (eg, Whitman, Colonna, Haygroves, or cup type)	120.0	2838	3260	1496
27122		Acetabuloplasty; resection femoral head (Girdlestone procedure)	100.0	2365	2716	1363

Code	Description	Medicode RVU	50th	75th	Medicare Nat'l Avg
27125	Partial hip replacement, prosthesis (eg, femoral stem prosthesis, bipolar arthroplasty)	135.0	3192	3667	1342
27130	Arthroplasty, acetabular and proximal femoral prosthetic replacement (total hip replacement), with or without autograft or allograft	190.0	4493	5161	1979
27132	Conversion of previous hip surgery to total hip replacement, with or without autograft or allograft	225.0	5321	6112	2201
27134	Revision of total hip arthroplasty; both components, with or without autograft or allograft	245.0	5794	6655	2591
27137	Revision of total hip arthroplasty; acetabular component only, with or without autograft or allograft	195.0	4611	5297	2033
27138	Revision of total hip arthroplasty; femoral component only, with or without allograft	195.0	4611	5297	2038
27140	Osteotomy and transfer of greater trochanter (separate procedure)	50.00	1182	1358	942
27146	Osteotomy, iliac, acetabular or innominate bone;	100.0	2365	2716	1020
27147	Osteotomy, iliac, acetabular or innominate bone; with open reduction of hip	130.0	3074	3531	1453
27151	Osteotomy, iliac, acetabular or innominate bone; with femoral osteotomy	130.0	3074	3531	1526
27156	Osteotomy, iliac, acetabular or innominate bone; with femoral osteotomy and with open reduction of hip	145.0	3429	3939	1619
27158	Osteotomy, pelvis, bilateral (eg, for congenital malformation)	150.0	3547	4075	1365
27161	Osteotomy, femoral neck (separate procedure)	95.00	2246	2581	1244
27165	Osteotomy, intertrochanteric or subtrochanteric including internal or external fixation and/or cast	123.0	2909	3341	1405
27170	Bone graft, femoral head, neck, intertrochanteric or subtrochanteric area (includes obtaining bone graft)	120.0	2838	3260	1386
27175	Treatment of slipped femoral epiphysis; by traction, without reduction	70.00	1655	1901	341
27176	Treatment of slipped femoral epiphysis; by single or multiple pinning, in situ	100.0	2365	2716	903
27177	Open treatment of slipped femoral epiphysis; single or multiple pinning or bone graft (includes obtaining graft)	115.0	2719	3124	1105
27178	Open treatment of slipped femoral epiphysis; closed manipulation with single or multiple pinning	120.0	2838	3260	889
27179	Open treatment of slipped femoral epiphysis; osteoplasty of femoral neck (Heyman type procedure)	85.00	2010	2309	960
27181	Open treatment of slipped femoral epiphysis; osteotomy and internal fixation	120.0	2838	3260	1134
27185	Epiphyseal arrest by epiphysiodesis or stapling, greater trochanter	55.00	1301	1494	464
27187	Prophylactic treatment (nailing, pinning, plating or wiring) with or without methylmethacrylate, femoral neck and proximal femur	110.0	2601	2988	1260
27193	Closed treatment of pelvic ring fracture, dislocation, diastasis or subluxation; without manipulation	26.00	623	718	293

Code	Description	Medicode RVU	50th	75th	Medicare Nat'l Avg
27194	Closed treatment of pelvic ring fracture, dislocation, diastasis or subluxation; with manipulation, requiring more than local anesthesia	43.50	1042	1201	512
27200	Closed treatment of coccygeal fracture	11.75	281	325	134
27202	Open treatment of coccygeal fracture	18.00	431	497	526
27215	Open treatment of iliac spine(s), tuberosity avulsion, or iliac wing fracture(s) (eg, pelvic fracture(s) which do not disrupt the pelvic ring), with internal fixation	91.50	2192	2527	946
27216	Percutaneous skeletal fixation of posterior pelvic ring fracture and/or dislocation (includes ilium, sacroiliac joint and/or sacrum)	42.00	1006	1160	700
27217	Open treatment of anterior ring fracture and/or dislocation with internal fixation, (includes pubic symphysis and/or rami)	96.00	2300	2652	1175
27218	Open treatment of posterior ring fracture and/or dislocation with internal fixation (includes ilium, sacroiliac joint and/or sacrum)	105.5	2527	2914	1384
27220	Closed treatment of acetabulum (hip socket) fracture(s); without manipulation	25.00	599	691	398
27222	Closed treatment of acetabulum (hip socket) fracture(s); with manipulation, with or without skeletal traction	55.00	1318	1519	711
27226	Open treatment of posterior or anterior acetabular wall fracture, with internal fixation	83.00	1988	2292	1286
27227	Open treatment of acetabular fracture(s) involving anterior or posterior (one) column, or a fracture running transversely across the acetabulum, with internal fixation	108.0	2587	2983	1500
27228	Open treatment of acetabular fracture(s) involving anterior and posterior (two) columns, includes T-fracture and both column fracture with complete articular detachment, or single column or transverse fracture with associated acetabular wall fracture, with internal fixation	190.0	4552	5248	1604
27230	Closed treatment of femoral fracture, proximal end, neck; without manipulation	26.75	641	739	352
27232	Closed treatment of femoral fracture, proximal end, neck; with manipulation, with or without skeletal traction	55.00	1318	1519	774
27235	Percutaneous skeletal fixation of femoral fracture, proximal end, neck, undisplaced, mildly displaced, or impacted fracture	107.3	2569	2962	1143
27236	Open treatment of femoral fracture, proximal end, neck, internal fixation or prosthetic replacement (direct fracture exposure)	111.0	2659	3066	1351
27238	Closed treatment of intertrochanteric, pertrochanteric, or subtrochanteric femoral fracture; without manipulation	28.00	671	773	435
27240	Closed treatment of intertrochanteric, pertrochanteric, or subtrochanteric femoral fracture; with manipulation, with or without skin or skeletal traction	40.00	958	1105	861
27244	Open treatment of intertrochanteric, pertrochanteric or subtrochanteric femoral fracture; with plate/screw type implant, with or without cerclage	103.5	2480	2859	1322

Code		Description	Medicode RVU	50th	75th	Medicare Nat'l Avg
27245		Open treatment of intertrochanteric, pertrochanteric or subtrochanteric femoral fracture; with intramedullary implant, with or without interlocking screws and/or cerclage	113.5	2719	3135	1476
27246		Closed treatment of greater trochanteric fracture, without manipulation	18.00	431	497	356
27248		Open treatment of greater trochanteric fracture, with or without internal or external fixation	35.00	839	967	956
27250		Closed treatment of hip dislocation, traumatic; without anesthesia	25.00	599	691	384
27252		Closed treatment of hip dislocation, traumatic; requiring anesthesia	32.00	767	884	544
27253		Open treatment of hip dislocation, traumatic, without internal fixation	75.00	1797	2072	1083
27254		Open treatment of hip dislocation, traumatic, with acetabular wall and femoral head fracture, with or without internal or external fixation	100.0	2396	2762	1304
27256	*	Treatment of spontaneous hip dislocation (developmental, including congenital or pathological), by abduction, splint or traction; without anesthesia, without manipulation	41.00	982	1132	233
27257	*	Treatment of spontaneous hip dislocation (developmental, including congenital or pathological), by abduction, splint or traction; with manipulation, requiring anesthesia	50.00	1198	1381	395
27258		Open treatment of spontaneous hip dislocation (developmental, including congenital or pathological), replacement of femoral head in acetabulum (including tenotomy, etc);	94.00	2252	2596	1181
27259		Open treatment of spontaneous hip dislocation (developmental, including congenital or pathological), replacement of femoral head in acetabulum (including tenotomy, etc); with femoral shaft shortening	110.0	2635	3038	1477
27265		Closed treatment of post hip arthroplasty dislocation; without anesthesia	25.00	599	691	371
27266		Closed treatment of post hip arthroplasty dislocation; requiring regional or general anesthesia	30.00	719	829	506
27275	*	Manipulation, hip joint, requiring general anesthesia	21.00	503	580	164
27280		Arthrodesis, sacroiliac joint (including obtaining graft)	92.75	2222	2562	922
27282		Arthrodesis, symphysis pubis (including obtaining graft)	90.00	2156	2486	829
27284		Arthrodesis, hip joint (includes obtaining graft);	125.0	2995	3453	1273
27286		Arthrodesis, hip joint (includes obtaining graft); with subtrochanteric osteotomy	130.0	3114	3591	1292
27290		Interpelviabdominal amputation (hindquarter amputation)	180.0	4312	4972	2018
27295		Disarticulation of hip	150.0	3594	4143	1483
27299		Unlisted procedure, pelvis or hip joint	0.00	0	0	–

27301–27599
Femur (Thigh Region) and Knee Joint

Coding Insight
Manipulation under anesthesia (27570) should not be reported with an open orthopedic knee joint procedure.

Lateral retinacular release (27425) may be reported separately with all arthroscopic knee procedures.

Diagnostic arthroscope is identified separately when performed at the same operative session as an open procedure. See arthroscopic guidelines under 29800–29909 in this subsection.

Reviewing ICD•9 procedure codes can help when you are having difficulty trying to decide which code is the correct one to use; five-in-one, triad, and other repairs listed in the tabular section specify which surgeries are included, and which can help you separately identify and code the CPT procedures.

Subsidiary Codes
Subsidiary codes have relative values that require no further adjustment:

20690 is "in addition" to 27301–27599
20692 is "in addition" to 27301–27599
20900 is "in addition" to 27301–27599
20902 is "in addition" to 27301–27599
20910 is "in addition" to 27301–27599
20912 is "in addition" to 27301–27599
20920 is "in addition" to 27301–27599
20922 is "in addition" to 27301–27599
20924 is "in addition" to 27301–27599
20926 is "in addition" to 27301–27599
27358 is "in addition" to 27355, 27356, 27357

Because these are subsidiary or "in addition to" codes, reimbursement reduction and CPT modifier -51 do not apply.

Medicare Alert
Medicare rebundles certain codes in the surgery section when the listed codes are considered a component of a more comprehensive service.

27425 will not be reimbursed when reported with 27447
27446 will not be reimbursed when reported with 27447
27447 and 27486 will not be reimbursed when reported with 27487
27502 will not be reimbursed when reported with 27506
27596 will not be reimbursed when reported with 27590
37618 will not be reimbursed when reported with 27596

Code	Description	Medicode RVU	50th	75th	Medicare Nat'l Avg
27301	Incision and drainage of deep abscess, infected bursa, or hematoma, thigh or knee region	21.00	494	582	332
27303	Incision, deep, with opening of bone cortex (eg, for osteomyelitis or bone abscess), femur or knee	35.00	824	970	588
27305	Fasciotomy, iliotibial (tenotomy), open	30.00	706	831	387

Code	Description	Medicode RVU	50th	75th	Medicare Nat'l Avg
27306	Tenotomy, subcutaneous, closed, adductor or hamstring, (separate procedure); single	20.00	471	554	256
27307	Tenotomy, subcutaneous, closed, adductor or hamstring, (separate procedure); multiple	30.00	706	831	343
27310	Arthrotomy, knee, for infection, with exploration, drainage or removal of foreign body	60.00	1412	1662	778
27315	Neurectomy, hamstring muscle	50.00	1177	1385	499
27320	Neurectomy, popliteal (gastrocnemius)	50.00	1177	1385	464
27323	Biopsy, soft tissue of thigh or knee area; superficial	6.00	141	166	143
27324	Biopsy, soft tissue of thigh or knee area; deep	25.00	588	693	296
27327	Excision, tumor, thigh or knee area; subcutaneous	17.00	400	471	271
27328	Excision, tumor, thigh or knee area; deep, subfascial, or intramuscular	34.00	800	942	407
27329	Radical resection of tumor (eg, malignant neoplasm), soft tissue of thigh or knee area	145.0	3412	4018	1011
27330	Arthrotomy, knee; with synovial biopsy only	55.00	1294	1524	489
27331	Arthrotomy, knee; with joint exploration, with or without biopsy, with or without removal of loose or foreign bodies	63.00	1483	1746	623
27332	Arthrotomy, knee, with excision of semilunar cartilage (meniscectomy); medial OR lateral	75.00	1765	2078	793
27333	Arthrotomy, knee, with excision of semilunar cartilage (meniscectomy); medial AND lateral	110.0	2589	3048	840
27334	Arthrotomy, knee, with synovectomy; anterior OR posterior	80.00	1883	2217	826
27335	Arthrotomy, knee, with synovectomy; anterior AND posterior including popliteal area	92.00	2165	2549	940
27340	Excision, prepatellar bursa	31.00	730	859	334
27345	Excision of synovial cyst of popliteal space (Baker's cyst)	45.00	1059	1247	501
27350	Patellectomy or hemipatellectomy	67.00	1577	1856	751
27355	Excision or curettage of bone cyst or benign tumor of femur;	55.00	1294	1524	629
27356	Excision or curettage of bone cyst or benign tumor of femur; with allograft	65.00	1530	1801	706
27357	Excision or curettage of bone cyst or benign tumor of femur; with autograft (includes obtaining graft)	75.00	1765	2078	778
27358	Excision or curettage of bone cyst or benign tumor of femur; with internal fixation (list in addition to 27355, 27356, or 27357)	37.50	883	1039	392
27360	Partial excision (craterization, saucerization, or diaphysectomy) of bone (eg, for osteomyelitis), femur, proximal tibia and/or fibula	55.00	1294	1524	760

Code	Description	Medicode RVU	50th	75th	Medicare Nat'l Avg
27365	Radical resection of tumor, bone, femur or knee	145.0	3412	4018	1196
27370	Injection procedure for knee arthrography	5.50	129	152	56
27372	Removal of foreign body, deep, thigh region or knee area	25.00	588	693	354
27380	Suture of infrapatellar tendon; primary	53.00	1246	1422	636
27381	Suture of infrapatellar tendon; secondary reconstruction, including fascial or tendon graft	70.00	1646	1877	890
27385	Suture of quadriceps or hamstring muscle rupture; primary	65.00	1529	1743	707
27386	Suture of quadriceps or hamstring muscle rupture; secondary reconstruction, including fascial or tendon graft	80.00	1881	2146	962
27390	Tenotomy, open, hamstring, knee to hip; single	25.00	588	671	388
27391	Tenotomy, open, hamstring, knee to hip; multiple, one leg	40.00	941	1073	507
27392	Tenotomy, open, hamstring, knee to hip; multiple, bilateral	60.00	1411	1609	683
27393	Lengthening of hamstring tendon; single	30.00	706	805	488
27394	Lengthening of hamstring tendon; multiple, one leg	50.00	1176	1341	570
27395	Lengthening of hamstring tendon; multiple, bilateral	70.00	1646	1877	897
27396	Transplant, hamstring tendon to patella; single	60.00	1411	1609	606
27397	Transplant, hamstring tendon to patella; multiple	70.00	1646	1877	763
27400	Tendon or muscle transfer, hamstrings to femur (Eggers type procedure)	60.00	1411	1609	689
27403	Arthrotomy with open meniscus repair	80.00	1881	2146	707
27405	Repair, primary, torn ligament and/or capsule, knee; collateral	78.50	1846	2105	798
27407	Repair, primary, torn ligament and/or capsule, knee; cruciate	90.00	2117	2414	770
27409	Repair, primary, torn ligament and/or capsule, knee; collateral and cruciate ligaments	105.0	2469	2816	1146
27418	Anterior tibial tubercleplasty (eg, for chondromalacia patellae)	105.0	2469	2816	935
27420	Reconstruction for recurrent dislocating patella; (Hauser type procedure)	83.00	1952	2226	873
27422	Reconstruction for recurrent dislocating patella; with extensor realignment and/or muscle advancement or release (Campbell, Goldwaite type procedure)	86.00	2023	2307	904
27424	Reconstruction for recurrent dislocating patella; with patellectomy	90.00	2117	2414	890

Code	Description	Medicode RVU	50th	75th	Medicare Nat'l Avg
27425	Lateral retinacular release (any method)	75.00	1764	2012	560
27427	Ligamentous reconstruction (augmentation), knee; extra-articular	120.0	2822	3219	892
27428	Ligamentous reconstruction (augmentation), knee; intra-articular (open)	142.0	3340	3809	1064
27429	Ligamentous reconstruction (augmentation), knee; intra-articular (open) and extra-articular	140.0	3293	3755	985
27430	Quadricepsplasty (Bennett or Thompson type)	70.00	1646	1877	790
27435	Capsulotomy, knee, posterior capsular release	60.00	1411	1609	675
27437	Arthroplasty, patella; without prosthesis	70.00	1646	1877	767
27438	Arthroplasty, patella; with prosthesis	80.00	1881	2146	1046
27440	Arthroplasty, knee, tibial plateau;	85.00	1999	2280	921
27441	Arthroplasty, knee, tibial plateau; with debridement and partial synovectomy	100.0	2352	2682	811
27442	Arthroplasty, knee, femoral condyles or tibial plateaus;	90.00	2117	2414	1169
27443	Arthroplasty, knee, femoral condyles or tibial plateaus; with debridement and partial synovectomy	110.0	2587	2950	1133
27445	Arthroplasty, knee, constrained prosthesis (eg, Walldius type)	150.0	3528	4023	1722
27446	Arthroplasty, knee, condyle and plateau; medial OR lateral compartment	146.0	3434	3916	1638
27447	Arthroplasty, knee, condyle and plateau; medial AND lateral compartments with or without patella resurfacing ("total knee replacement")	188.0	4421	5042	2112
27448	Osteotomy, femur, shaft or supracondylar; without fixation	80.00	1881	2146	988
27450	Osteotomy, femur, shaft or supracondylar; with fixation	90.00	2117	2414	1190
27454	Osteotomy, multiple, femoral shaft, with realignment on intramedullary rod (Sofield type procedure)	100.0	2352	2682	1204
27455	Osteotomy, proximal tibia, including fibular excision or osteotomy (includes correction of genu varus (bowleg) or genu valgus (knock-knee)); before epiphyseal closure	80.00	1881	2146	1018
27457	Osteotomy, proximal tibia, including fibular excision or osteotomy (includes correction of genu varus (bowleg) or genu valgus (knock-knee)); after epiphyseal closure	93.00	2187	2494	1105
27465	Osteoplasty, femur; shortening (excluding 64876)	100.0	2352	2682	1058
27466	Osteoplasty, femur; lengthening	140.0	3293	3755	1206
27468	Osteoplasty, femur; combined, lengthening and shortening with femoral segment transfer	180.0	4233	4828	1449

Code	Description	Medicode RVU	50th	75th	Medicare Nat'l Avg
27470	Repair, nonunion or malunion, femur, distal to head and neck; without graft (eg, compression technique)	100.0	2352	2682	1341
27472	Repair, nonunion or malunion, femur, distal to head and neck; with iliac or other autogenous bone graft (includes obtaining graft)	115.0	2705	3084	1576
27475	Epiphyseal arrest by epiphysiodesis or stapling; distal femur	95.00	2234	2548	664
27477	Epiphyseal arrest by epiphysiodesis or stapling; tibia and fibula, proximal	105.0	2469	2816	984
27479	Epiphyseal arrest by epiphysiodesis or stapling; combined distal femur, proximal tibia and fibula	120.0	2822	3219	997
27485	Arrest, hemiepiphyseal, distal femur or proximal leg (eg, for genu varus or valgus)	75.00	1764	2012	680
27486	Revision of total knee arthroplasty, with or without allograft; one component	150.0	3528	4023	1876
27487	Revision of total knee arthroplasty, with or without allograft; all components	220.0	5174	5901	2497
27488	Removal of knee prosthesis, including "total knee," methylmethacrylate and insertion of spacer, when applicable	120.0	2822	3219	1355
27495	Prophylactic treatment (nailing, pinning, plating or wiring) with or without methylmethacrylate, femur	85.00	1999	2280	1371
27496	Decompression fasciotomy, thigh and/or knee, one compartment (flexor or extensor or adductor);	32.00	753	858	389
27497	Decompression fasciotomy, thigh and/or knee, one compartment (flexor or extensor or adductor); with debridement of nonviable muscle and/or nerve	43.00	1011	1153	476
27498	Decompression fasciotomy, thigh and/or knee, multiple compartments;	45.00	1058	1207	543
27499	Decompression fasciotomy, thigh and/or knee, multiple compartments; with debridement of nonviable muscle and/or nerve	56.00	1317	1502	625
27500	Closed treatment of femoral shaft fracture, without manipulation	35.00	834	961	453
27501	Closed treatment of supracondylar or transcondylar femoral fracture with or without intercondylar extension, without manipulation	43.00	1024	1180	453
27502	Closed treatment of femoral shaft fracture, with manipulation, with or without skin or skeletal traction	50.00	1191	1373	715
27503	Closed treatment of supracondylar or transcondylar femoral fracture with or without intercondylar extension, with manipulation, with or without skin or skeletal traction	60.00	1429	1647	715
27506	Open treatment of femoral shaft fracture, with or without external fixation, with insertion of intramedullary implant, with or without cerclage and/or locking screws	115.0	2739	3157	1373
27507	Open treatment of femoral shaft fracture with plate/screws, with or without cerclage	105.0	2501	2882	1269
27508	Closed treatment of femoral fracture, distal end, medial or lateral condyle, without manipulation	30.00	715	824	402

Code	Description	Medicode RVU	50th	75th	Medicare Nat'l Avg
27509	Percutaneous skeletal fixation of femoral fracture, distal end, medial or lateral condyle, or supracondylar or transcondylar, with or without intercondylar extension, or distal femoral epiphyseal separation	61.00	1453	1674	457
27510	Closed treatment of femoral fracture, distal end, medial or lateral condyle, with manipulation	43.00	1024	1180	628
27511	Open treatment of femoral supracondylar or transcondylar fracture without intercondylar extension, with or without internal or external fixation	105.0	2501	2882	1256
27513	Open treatment of femoral supracondylar or transcondylar fracture with intercondylar extension, with or without internal or external fixation	120.0	2858	3294	1401
27514	Open treatment of femoral fracture, distal end, medial or lateral condyle, with or without internal or external fixation	107.0	2549	2937	1354
27516	Closed treatment of distal femoral epiphyseal separation; without manipulation	33.00	786	906	406
27517	Closed treatment of distal femoral epiphyseal separation; with manipulation, with or without skin or skeletal traction	42.00	1000	1153	671
27519	Open treatment of distal femoral epiphyseal separation, with or without internal or external fixation	90.00	2144	2471	1113
27520	Closed treatment of patellar fracture, without manipulation	17.75	423	487	243
27524	Open treatment of patellar fracture, with internal fixation and/or partial or complete patellectomy and soft tissue repair	68.50	1632	1880	851
27530	Closed treatment of tibial fracture, proximal (plateau); without manipulation	23.00	548	631	289
27532	Closed treatment of tibial fracture, proximal (plateau); with or without manipulation, with skeletal traction	31.00	738	851	522
27535	Open treatment of tibial fracture, proximal (plateau); unicondylar, with or without internal or external fixation	76.00	1810	2086	951
27536	Open treatment of tibial fracture, proximal (plateau); bicondylar, with or without internal fixation	84.50	2013	2320	1096
27538	Closed treatment of intercondylar spine(s) and/or tuberosity fracture(s) of knee, with or without manipulation	26.00	619	714	333
27540	Open treatment of intercondylar spine(s) and/or tuberosity fracture(s) of the knee, with or without internal or external fixation	75.00	1787	2059	976
27550	Closed treatment of knee dislocation; without anesthesia	15.00	357	412	327
27552	Closed treatment of knee dislocation; requiring anesthesia	21.00	500	576	438
27556	Open treatment of knee dislocation, with or without internal or external fixation; without primary ligamentous repair or augmentation/reconstruction	84.00	2001	2306	1085
27557	Open treatment of knee dislocation, with or without internal or external fixation; with primary ligamentous repair	123.0	2930	3376	1275
27558	Open treatment of knee dislocation, with or without internal or external fixation; with primary ligamentous repair, with augmentation/reconstruction	144.0	3430	3953	1312

Code		Description	Medicode RVU	50th	75th	Medicare Nat'l Avg
27560		Closed treatment of patellar dislocation; without anesthesia	12.50	298	343	199
27562		Closed treatment of patellar dislocation; requiring anesthesia	18.50	441	508	438
27566		Open treatment of patellar dislocation, with or without partial or total patellectomy	60.00	1429	1647	924
27570	*	Manipulation of knee joint under general anesthesia (includes application of traction or other fixation devices)	17.00	405	467	146
27580		Fusion of knee, any technique	100.0	2382	2745	1233
27590		Amputation, thigh, through femur, any level;	73.00	1739	2004	849
27591		Amputation, thigh, through femur, any level; immediate fitting technique including first cast	75.00	1787	2059	976
27592		Amputation, thigh, through femur, any level; open, circular (guillotine)	90.00	2144	2471	738
27594		Amputation, thigh, through femur, any level; secondary closure or scar revision	30.00	715	824	420
27596		Amputation, thigh, through femur, any level; re-amputation	70.00	1667	1922	755
27598		Disarticulation at knee	80.00	1906	2196	867
27599		Unlisted procedure, femur or knee	0.00	0	0	–

27600–27899
Leg (Tibia and Fibula) and Ankle Joint

CODING INSIGHT
Coding of procedures involving tendons and ligaments can be difficult. Remember, a tendon joins muscle to bone, while a ligament joins bone to bone. One area that is particularly difficult (and is a controversial topic) is the patellar tendon; it is sometimes referred to as the patellar tendon above the knee and the patellar ligament below the knee. The best usage of this term is to refer to both points as either the tendon or the ligament, but not both. Also remember that names of anatomical points change or are referred to depending on what's popular when and where the provider went to school. For example, the medial collateral ligament is also called the tibial collateral ligament or medial check ligament, and the lateral collateral ligament is also called the fibular collateral ligament or lateral check ligament.

SUBSIDIARY CODES
Subsidiary codes have relative values that require no further adjustment:

20690 is "in addition" to 27600–27899
20692 is "in addition" to 27600–27899
20900 is "in addition" to 27600–27899
20902 is "in addition" to 27600–27899
20910 is "in addition" to 27600–27899
20912 is "in addition" to 27600–27899
20920 is "in addition" to 27600–27899
20922 is "in addition" to 27600–27899

20924 is "in addition" to 27600–27899
20926 is "in addition" to 23930–28899
27692 is "in addition" to 27690–27691

Because these are subsidiary or "in addition to" codes, reimbursement reduction and modifier -51 do not apply.

Code		Description	Medicode RVU	50th	75th	Medicare Nat'l Avg
27600		Decompression fasciotomy, leg; anterior and/or lateral compartments only	30.00	727	851	363
27601		Decompression fasciotomy, leg; posterior compartment(s) only	32.00	776	908	355
27602		Decompression fasciotomy, leg; anterior and/or lateral, and posterior compartment(s)	44.00	1067	1249	466
27603		Incision and drainage, leg or ankle; deep abscess or hematoma	24.00	582	681	284
27604		Incision and drainage, leg or ankle; infected bursa	9.00	218	255	207
27605	*	Tenotomy, Achilles tendon, subcutaneous (separate procedure); local anesthesia	13.00	315	369	162
27606		Tenotomy, Achilles tendon, subcutaneous (separate procedure); general anesthesia	20.00	485	568	247
27607		Incision, deep, with opening of bone cortex (eg, for osteomyelitis or bone abscess), leg or ankle	40.00	970	1135	556
27610		Arthrotomy, ankle, for infection, with exploration, drainage or removal of foreign body	51.00	1236	1447	631
27612		Arthrotomy, ankle, posterior capsular release, with or without Achilles tendon lengthening	50.00	1212	1419	612
27613		Biopsy, soft tissue of leg or ankle area; superficial	12.00	291	341	111
27614		Biopsy, soft tissue of leg or ankle area; deep	22.00	533	624	305
27615		Radical resection of tumor (eg, malignant neoplasm), soft tissue of leg or ankle area	112.0	2715	3178	836
27618		Excision, tumor, leg or ankle area; subcutaneous	17.00	412	482	286
27619		Excision, tumor, leg or ankle area; deep, subfascial or intramuscular	34.00	824	965	512
27620		Arthrotomy, ankle, with joint exploration, with or without biopsy, with or without removal of loose or foreign body	54.00	1309	1532	509
27625		Arthrotomy, ankle, with synovectomy;	70.00	1697	1986	704
27626		Arthrotomy, ankle, with synovectomy; including tenosynovectomy	70.00	1697	1986	803
27630		Excision of lesion of tendon sheath or capsule (eg, cyst or ganglion), leg and/or ankle	25.50	618	724	324
27635		Excision or curettage of bone cyst or benign tumor, tibia or fibula;	56.00	1357	1589	657
27637		Excision or curettage of bone cyst or benign tumor, tibia or fibula; with autograft (includes obtaining graft)	75.00	1818	2128	748

Code	Description	Medicode RVU	50th	75th	Medicare Nat'l Avg
27638	Excision or curettage of bone cyst or benign tumor, tibia or fibula; with allograft	70.00	1697	1986	799
27640	Partial excision (craterization, saucerization, or diaphysectomy) of bone (eg, for osteomyelitis or exostosis); tibia	67.00	1624	1901	856
27641	Partial excision (craterization, saucerization, or diaphysectomy) of bone (eg, for osteomyelitis or exostosis); fibula	60.00	1454	1703	660
27645	Radical resection of tumor, bone; tibia	80.00	1939	2270	1049
27646	Radical resection of tumor, bone; fibula	70.00	1697	1986	946
27647	Radical resection of tumor, bone; talus or calcaneus	75.00	1818	2128	874
27648	Injection procedure for ankle arthrography	6.00	145	170	53
27650	Repair, primary, open or percutaneous, ruptured Achilles tendon;	62.00	1503	1759	762
27652	Repair, primary, open or percutaneous, ruptured Achilles tendon; with graft (includes obtaining graft)	74.00	1794	2100	844
27654	Repair, secondary, ruptured Achilles tendon, with or without graft	70.00	1697	1986	868
27656	Repair, fascial defect of leg	30.00	727	851	318
27658	Repair or suture of flexor tendon of leg; primary, without graft, single, each	35.00	848	993	364
27659	Repair or suture of flexor tendon of leg; secondary with or without graft, single tendon, each	45.00	1091	1277	508
27664	Repair or suture of extensor tendon of leg; primary, without graft, single, each	25.00	606	709	322
27665	Repair or suture of extensor tendon of leg; secondary with or without graft, single tendon, each	35.00	848	993	420
27675	Repair for dislocating peroneal tendons; without fibular osteotomy	30.00	727	851	549
27676	Repair for dislocating peroneal tendons; with fibular osteotomy	35.00	848	993	645
27680	Tenolysis, including tibia, fibula and ankle flexor; single	30.00	727	851	395
27681	Tenolysis, including tibia, fibula and ankle flexor; multiple (through same incision), each	40.00	970	1135	512
27685	Lengthening or shortening of tendon, leg or ankle; single (separate procedure)	36.00	873	1022	412
27686	Lengthening or shortening of tendon, leg or ankle; multiple (through same incision), each	40.00	970	1135	562
27687	Gastrocnemius recession (eg, Strayer procedure)	35.00	848	993	469
27690	Transfer or transplant of single tendon (with muscle redirection or rerouting); superficial (eg, anterior tibial extensors into midfoot)	50.00	1212	1419	619

	Code	Description	Medicode RVU	50th	75th	Medicare Nat'l Avg
▲	**27691**	Transfer or transplant of single tendon (with muscle redirection or rerouting; deep (eg, anterior tibial or posterior tibial through interosseous space, flexor digitorum longus, flexor hallicus longus, or peroneal tendon to midfoot or hindfoot)	65.00	1576	1844	720
	27692	Transfer or transplant of single tendon (with muscle redirection or rerouting); each additional tendon	10.00	242	284	164
	27695	Suture, primary, torn, ruptured or severed ligament, ankle; collateral	57.00	1382	1617	617
	27696	Suture, primary, torn, ruptured or severed ligament, ankle; both collateral ligaments	82.00	1988	2327	629
	27698	Suture, secondary repair, torn, ruptured or severed ligament, ankle, collateral (eg, Watson-Jones procedure)	75.00	1818	2128	876
	27700	Arthroplasty, ankle;	100.0	2424	2838	835
	27702	Arthroplasty, ankle; with implant ("total ankle")	170.0	4121	4824	1391
	27703	Arthroplasty, ankle; secondary reconstruction, total ankle	145.0	3515	4114	1190
	27704	Removal of ankle implant	55.00	1333	1561	553
	27705	Osteotomy; tibia	70.00	1697	1986	869
	27707	Osteotomy; fibula	35.00	848	993	367
	27709	Osteotomy; tibia and fibula	80.00	1939	2270	903
	27712	Osteotomy; multiple, with realignment on intramedullary rod (Sofield type procedure)	90.00	2182	2554	952
	27715	Osteoplasty, tibia and fibula, lengthening	120.0	2909	3405	1074
	27720	Repair of nonunion or malunion, tibia; without graft, (eg, compression technique)	90.00	2182	2554	1067
	27722	Repair of nonunion or malunion, tibia; with sliding graft	95.00	2303	2696	909
	27724	Repair of nonunion or malunion, tibia; with iliac or other autograft (includes obtaining graft)	105.0	2545	2979	1248
	27725	Repair of nonunion or malunion, tibia; by synostosis, with fibula, any method	140.0	3393	3973	904
	27727	Repair of congenital pseudarthrosis, tibia	110.0	2666	3121	939
	27730	Epiphyseal arrest by epiphysiodesis or stapling; distal tibia	50.00	1212	1419	440
	27732	Epiphyseal arrest by epiphysiodesis or stapling; distal fibula	40.00	970	1135	415
	27734	Epiphyseal arrest by epiphysiodesis or stapling; distal tibia and fibula	70.00	1697	1986	648
	27740	Epiphyseal arrest by epiphysiodesis or stapling, combined, proximal and distal tibia and fibula;	90.00	2182	2554	717

Code	Description	Medicode RVU	50th	75th	Medicare Nat'l Avg
27742	Epiphyseal arrest by epiphysiodesis or stapling, combined, proximal and distal tibia and fibula; and distal femur	105.0	2545	2979	797
27745	Prophylactic treatment (nailing, pinning, plating or wiring) with or without methylmethacrylate, tibia	85.00	2060	2412	772
27750	Closed treatment of tibial shaft fracture (with or without fibular fracture); without manipulation	22.50	538	621	272
27752	Closed treatment of tibial shaft fracture (with or without fibular fracture); with manipulation, with or without skeletal traction	37.00	884	1022	437
27756	Percutaneous skeletal fixation of tibial shaft fracture (with or without fibular fracture) (eg, pins or screws)	60.00	1434	1657	666
27758	Open treatment of tibial shaft fracture, (with or without fibular fracture) with plate/screws, with or without cerclage	85.00	2031	2347	1043
27759	Open treatment of tibial shaft fracture (with or without fibular fracture) by intramedullary implant, with or without interlocking screws and/or cerclage	91.00	2174	2513	1127
27760	Closed treatment of medial malleolus fracture; without manipulation	16.75	400	463	224
27762	Closed treatment of medial malleolus fracture; with manipulation, with or without skin or skeletal traction	25.00	597	690	335
27766	Open treatment of medial malleolus fracture, with or without internal or external fixation	48.00	1147	1325	663
27780	Closed treatment of proximal fibula or shaft fracture; without manipulation	13.75	329	380	184
27781	Closed treatment of proximal fibula or shaft fracture; with manipulation	18.00	430	497	310
27784	Open treatment of proximal fibula or shaft fracture, with or without internal or external fixation	47.00	1123	1298	504
27786	Closed treatment of distal fibular fracture (lateral malleolus); without manipulation	16.00	382	442	215
27788	Closed treatment of distal fibular fracture (lateral malleolus); with manipulation	22.00	526	607	312
27792	Open treatment of distal fibular fracture (lateral malleolus), with or without internal or external fixation	51.00	1219	1408	624
27808	Closed treatment of bimalleolar ankle fracture, (including Potts); without manipulation	18.50	442	511	232
27810	Closed treatment of bimalleolar ankle fracture, (including Potts); with manipulation	35.00	836	966	424
27814	Open treatment of bimalleolar ankle fracture, with or without internal or external fixation	66.00	1577	1822	845
27816	Closed treatment of trimalleolar ankle fracture; without manipulation	20.50	490	566	275
27818	Closed treatment of trimalleolar ankle fracture; with manipulation	40.00	956	1105	500
27822	Open treatment of trimalleolar ankle fracture, with or without internal or external fixation, medial and/or lateral malleolus; without fixation of posterior lip	77.00	1840	2126	864

Code		Description	Medicode RVU	50th	75th	Medicare Nat'l Avg
27823		Open treatment of trimalleolar ankle fracture, with or without internal or external fixation, medial and/or lateral malleolus; with fixation of posterior lip	91.00	2174	2513	1022
27824		Closed treatment of fracture of weight bearing articular portion of distal tibia (eg, pilon or tibial plafond), with or without anesthesia; without manipulation	20.50	490	566	275
27825		Closed treatment of fracture of weight bearing articular portion of distal tibia (eg, pilon or tibial plafond), with or without anesthesia; with skeletal traction and/or requiring manipulation	40.00	956	1105	500
27826		Open treatment of fracture of weight bearing articular surface/portion of distal tibia (eg, pilon or tibial plafond), with internal or external fixation; of fibula only	80.00	1912	2209	801
27827		Open treatment of fracture of weight bearing articular surface/portion of distal tibia (eg, pilon or tibial plafond), with internal or external fixation; of tibia only	83.00	1983	2292	936
27828		Open treatment of fracture of weight bearing articular surface/portion of distal tibia (eg, pilon or tibial plafond), with internal or external fixation; of both tibia and fibula	95.00	2270	2623	1068
27829		Open treatment of distal tibiofibular joint (syndesmosis) disruption, with or without internal or external fixation	47.50	1135	1312	522
27830		Closed treatment of proximal tibiofibular joint dislocation; without anesthesia	10.00	239	276	281
27831		Closed treatment of proximal tibiofibular joint dislocation; requiring anesthesia	15.00	358	414	343
27832		Open treatment of proximal tibiofibular joint dislocation, with or without internal or external fixation, or with excision of proximal fibula	40.00	956	1105	490
27840		Closed treatment of ankle dislocation; without anesthesia	13.50	323	373	244
27842		Closed treatment of ankle dislocation; requiring anesthesia, with or without percutaneous skeletal fixation	20.00	478	552	318
27846		Open treatment of ankle dislocation, with or without percutaneous skeletal fixation; without repair or internal fixation	60.00	1434	1657	745
27848		Open treatment of ankle dislocation, with or without percutaneous skeletal fixation; with repair or internal or external fixation	70.00	1673	1933	786
27860	*	Manipulation of ankle under general anesthesia (includes application of traction or other fixation apparatus)	13.50	323	373	152
27870		Arthrodesis, ankle, any method	95.00	2270	2623	1056
27871		Arthrodesis, tibiofibular joint, proximal or distal	70.00	1673	1933	698
27880		Amputation, leg, through tibia and fibula;	67.50	1613	1864	816
27881		Amputation, leg, through tibia and fibula; with immediate fitting technique including application of first cast	80.00	1912	2209	942
27882		Amputation, leg, through tibia and fibula; open, circular (guillotine)	55.00	1314	1519	667
27884		Amputation, leg, through tibia and fibula; secondary closure or scar revision	30.00	717	828	444

Code	Description	Medicode RVU	50th	75th	Medicare Nat'l Avg
27886	Amputation, leg, through tibia and fibula; re-amputation	67.00	1601	1850	679
27888	Amputation, ankle, through malleoli of tibia and fibula (Syme, Pirogoff type procedures), with plastic closure and resection of nerves	70.00	1673	1933	795
27889	Ankle disarticulation	70.00	1673	1933	741
27892	Decompression fasciotomy, leg; anterior and/or lateral compartments only, with debridement of nonviable muscle and/or nerve	43.00	1027	1187	399
27893	Decompression fasciotomy, leg; posterior compartment(s) only, with debridement of nonviable muscle and/or nerve	43.00	1027	1187	393
27894	Decompression fasciotomy, leg; anterior and/or lateral, and posterior compartment(s), with debridement of nonviable muscle and/or nerve	56.00	1338	1546	501
27899	Unlisted procedure, leg or ankle	0.00	0	0	–

28001–28899
Foot and Toes

Coding Insight

Even though this information is listed under hand and fingers it bears repeating here.

Payers may restrict the number of procedures that are reimbursed for each foot. They may consider multiple service to be included in the primary surgical procedure. For example, payment may not be made for multiple arthrotomies or capsulotomies involving the same or various toes on one foot. However, even though each payer has separate parameters, multiple arthrotomies and capsulectomies that involve joints of totally different body parts (e.g., knee, wrist, elbow) are usually reimbursable.

Submit operative reports with these claims. Clearly identify each location in the operative report (e.g., little, middle, or great toe), and clearly note which limb is involved (e.g., left or right side, foot).

Be very careful with code selection in this area. For instance, codes for arthrodesis of the foot, such as 28755, are used once and the number of units must be identified. The same code is not repeated on each line for the number involved; rather, multiply the number of procedures times the cost and list the cost on a single line.

A phalangectomy (28150–28160) should not be reported with a hammer toe operation (28285) when it is performed on the same toe. The parenthetical statement in the description of the hammer toe operation includes a phalangectomy.

Subsidiary Codes

Subsidiary codes have relative values that require no further adjustment:

20690 is "in addition" to 28001–28899
20692 is "in addition" to 28001–28899
20900 is "in addition" to 28001–28899
20902 is "in addition" to 28001–28899
20910 is "in addition" to 28001–28899
20912 is "in addition" to 28001–28899

20920 is "in addition" to 28001–28899
20922 is "in addition" to 28001–28899
20924 is "in addition" to 28001–28899
20926 is "in addition" to 28001–28899

Because these are subsidiary or "in addition to" codes reimbursement reduction and modifier -51 do not apply.

Medicare Alert

Medicare rebundles certain codes in the surgery section when the listed codes are considered a component of a more comprehensive service.

28118 will not be reimbursed when reported with 28119
28153, 28160 will not be reimbursed when reported with 28285
28270 will not be reimbursed when reported with 28292, 28296
28288 will not be reimbursed when reported with 28292
28290 will not be reimbursed when reported with 28292, 28296
28292, 28298 will not be reimbursed when reported with 28296

Code		Description	Medicode RVU	50th	75th	Medicare Nat'l Avg
28001	*	Incision and drainage, infected bursa, foot	7.00	167	198	120
28002	*	Deep dissection below fascia, for deep infection of foot, with or without tendon sheath involvement; single bursal space, specify	20.00	476	565	247
28003		Deep dissection below fascia, for deep infection of foot, with or without tendon sheath involvement; multiple areas	30.00	714	847	449
28005		Incision, deep, with opening of bone cortex (eg, for osteomyelitis or bone abscess), foot	32.00	762	904	478
28008		Fasciotomy, foot and/or toe	25.00	595	706	278
28010		Tenotomy, subcutaneous, toe; single	11.00	262	311	251
28011		Tenotomy, subcutaneous, toe; multiple	15.00	357	424	227
28020		Arthrotomy, with exploration, drainage or removal of loose or foreign body; intertarsal or tarsometatarsal joint	33.00	785	932	387
28022		Arthrotomy, with exploration, drainage or removal of loose or foreign body; metatarsophalangeal joint	28.00	666	791	297
28024		Arthrotomy, with exploration, drainage or removal of loose or foreign body; interphalangeal joint	23.00	547	649	264
28030		Neurectomy of intrinsic musculature of foot	35.00	833	988	397
28035		Tarsal tunnel release (posterior tibial nerve decompression)	50.00	1190	1412	488
28043		Excision, tumor, foot; subcutaneous	18.00	428	508	208
28045		Excision, tumor, foot; deep, subfascial, intramuscular	28.00	666	791	353
28046		Radical resection of tumor (eg, malignant neoplasm), soft tissue of foot	140.0	3332	3953	607

Code	Description	Medicode RVU	50th	75th	Medicare Nat'l Avg
28050	Arthrotomy for synovial biopsy; intertarsal or tarsometatarsal joint	30.00	714	847	330
28052	Arthrotomy for synovial biopsy; metatarsophalangeal joint	25.00	595	706	312
28054	Arthrotomy for synovial biopsy; interphalangeal joint	20.00	476	565	223
28060	Fasciectomy, excision of plantar fascia; partial (separate procedure)	34.50	821	974	395
28062	Fasciectomy, excision of plantar fascia; radical (separate procedure)	60.50	1440	1708	563
28070	Synovectomy; intertarsal or tarsometatarsal joint, each	25.00	595	706	384
28072	Synovectomy; metatarsophalangeal joint, each	20.00	476	565	312
28080	Excision of interdigital (Morton) neuroma, single, each	27.00	643	762	314
28086	Synovectomy, tendon sheath, foot; flexor	35.00	833	988	323
28088	Synovectomy, tendon sheath, foot; extensor	35.00	833	988	300
28090	Excision of lesion of tendon or fibrous sheath or capsule (including synovectomy) (cyst or ganglion); foot	24.50	583	692	297
28092	Excision of lesion of tendon or fibrous sheath or capsule (including synovectomy) (cyst or ganglion); toes	17.00	405	480	226
28100	Excision or curettage of bone cyst or benign tumor, talus or calcaneus;	45.00	1071	1271	415
28102	Excision or curettage of bone cyst or benign tumor, talus or calcaneus; with iliac or other autograft (includes obtaining graft)	65.00	1547	1835	585
28103	Excision or curettage of bone cyst or benign tumor, talus or calcaneus; with allograft	50.00	1190	1412	482
28104	Excision or curettage of bone cyst or benign tumor, tarsal or metatarsal bones, except talus or calcaneus;	35.00	833	988	386
28106	Excision or curettage of bone cyst or benign tumor, tarsal or metatarsal bones, except talus or calcaneus; with iliac or other autograft (includes obtaining graft)	50.00	1190	1412	542
28107	Excision or curettage of bone cyst or benign tumor, tarsal or metatarsal bones, except talus or calcaneus; with allograft	50.00	1190	1412	409
28108	Excision or curettage of bone cyst or benign tumor, phalanges of foot	25.00	595	706	343
28110	Ostectomy, partial excision, fifth metatarsal head (bunionette) (separate procedure)	30.00	714	847	307
28111	Ostectomy, complete excision; first metatarsal head	40.00	952	1130	424
28112	Ostectomy, complete excision; other metatarsal head (second, third or fourth)	30.00	714	847	352
28113	Ostectomy, complete excision; fifth metatarsal head	30.00	714	847	359

Code		Description	Medicode RVU	50th	75th	Medicare Nat'l Avg
28114		Ostectomy, complete excision; all metatarsal heads, with partial proximal phalangectomy, excluding first metatarsal (Clayton type procedure)	65.00	1547	1835	744
28116		Ostectomy, excision of tarsal coalition	50.00	1190	1412	479
28118		Ostectomy, calcaneus;	42.00	1000	1186	476
28119		Ostectomy, calcaneus; for spur, with or without plantar fascial release	40.00	952	1130	449
28120		Partial excision (craterization, saucerization, sequestrectomy, or diaphysectomy) of bone (eg, for osteomyelitis or talar bossing), talus or calcaneus	39.00	928	1101	427
28122		Partial excision (craterization, saucerization, or diaphysectomy) of bone (eg, for osteomyelitis or tarsal bossing), tarsal or metatarsal bone, except talus or calcaneus	34.00	809	960	451
28124		Partial excision (craterization, saucerization, or diaphysectomy) of bone (eg, for osteomyelitis or dorsal bossing), phalanx of toe	25.00	595	706	349
28126		Resection, partial or complete, phalangeal base, single toe, each	23.00	547	649	306
28130		Talectomy (astragalectomy)	60.00	1428	1694	596
28140		Metatarsectomy	40.00	952	1130	473
28150		Phalangectomy of toe, single, each	28.00	666	791	295
28153		Resection, head of phalanx, toe	25.00	595	706	310
28160		Hemiphalangectomy or interphalangeal joint excision, toe, single, each	25.00	595	706	318
28171		Radical resection of tumor, bone; tarsal (except talus or calcaneus)	50.00	1190	1412	697
28173		Radical resection of tumor, bone; metatarsal	40.00	952	1130	574
28175		Radical resection of tumor, bone; phalanx of toe	28.00	666	791	453
28190	*	Removal of foreign body, foot; subcutaneous	13.50	321	381	90
28192		Removal of foreign body, foot; deep	23.00	547	649	259
28193		Removal of foreign body, foot; complicated	33.00	785	932	315
28200		Repair or suture of tendon, foot, flexor, single; primary or secondary, without free graft, each tendon	38.00	907	1064	395
28202		Repair or suture of tendon, foot, flexor, single; secondary with free graft, each tendon (includes obtaining graft)	48.00	1145	1344	507
28208		Repair or suture of tendon, foot, extensor, single; primary or secondary, each tendon	19.50	465	546	283

Code	Description	Medicode RVU	50th	75th	Medicare Nat'l Avg
28210	Repair or suture of tendon, foot, extensor, single; secondary with free graft, each tendon (includes obtaining graft)	26.50	632	742	472
28220	Tenolysis, flexor, foot; single	30.00	716	840	336
28222	Tenolysis, flexor, foot; multiple (through same incision)	37.00	883	1036	481
28225	Tenolysis, extensor, foot; single	17.50	418	490	239
28226	Tenolysis, extensor, foot; multiple (through same incision)	23.00	549	644	314
28230	Tenotomy, open, flexor; foot, single or multiple (separate procedure)	18.00	429	504	258
28232	Tenotomy, open, flexor; toe, single (separate procedure)	9.50	227	266	191
28234	Tenotomy, open, extensor, foot or toe	11.50	274	322	186
28238	Advancement of posterior tibial tendon with excision of accessory navicular bone (Kidner type procedure)	45.00	1074	1260	604
28240	Tenotomy, lengthening, or release, abductor hallucis muscle	22.00	525	616	253
28250	Division of plantar fascia and muscle ("Steindler stripping") (separate procedure)	38.00	907	1064	417
28260	Capsulotomy, midfoot; medial release only (separate procedure)	50.00	1193	1400	494
28261	Capsulotomy, midfoot; with tendon lengthening	60.00	1431	1680	600
28262	Capsulotomy, midfoot; extensive, including posterior talotibial capsulotomy and tendon(s) lengthening as for resistant clubfoot deformity	89.50	2135	2506	996
28264	Capsulotomy, midtarsal (Heyman type procedure)	65.00	1551	1820	797
28270	Capsulotomy; metatarsophalangeal joint, with or without tenorrhaphy, single, each joint (separate procedure)	20.00	477	560	289
28272	Capsulotomy; interphalangeal joint, single, each joint (separate procedure)	15.00	358	420	229
28280	Webbing operation (create syndactylism of toes)(Kelikian type procedure)	25.00	596	700	290
28285	Hammertoe operation, one toe (eg, interphalangeal fusion, filleting, phalangectomy)	29.00	692	812	363
28286	Cock-up fifth toe operation with plastic skin closure (Ruiz-Mora type procedure)	30.00	716	840	328
28288	Ostectomy, partial, exostectomy or condylectomy, single, metatarsal head, first through fifth, each metatarsal head	30.00	716	840	315
28290	Hallux valgus (bunion) correction, with or without sesamoidectomy; simple exostectomy (Silver type procedure)	42.00	1002	1176	446
28292	Hallux valgus (bunion) correction, with or without sesamoidectomy; Keller, McBride or Mayo type procedure	54.00	1288	1512	550

Code	Description	Medicode RVU	50th	75th	Medicare Nat'l Avg
28293	Hallux valgus (bunion) correction, with or without sesamoidectomy; resection of joint with implant	61.00	1455	1708	738
28294	Hallux valgus (bunion) correction, with or without sesamoidectomy; with tendon transplants (Joplin type procedure)	55.00	1312	1540	706
28296	Hallux valgus (bunion) correction, with or without sesamoidectomy; with metatarsal osteotomy (eg, Mitchell, Chevron, or concentric type procedures)	68.00	1622	1904	723
28297	Hallux valgus (bunion) correction, with or without sesamoidectomy; Lapidus type procedure	60.00	1431	1680	733
28298	Hallux valgus (bunion) correction, with or without sesamoidectomy; by phalanx osteotomy	51.00	1217	1428	665
28299	Hallux valgus (bunion) correction, with or without sesamoidectomy; by other methods (eg, double osteotomy)	0.00	0	0	771
28300	Osteotomy; calcaneus (Dwyer or Chambers type procedure), with or without internal fixation	53.00	1264	1484	643
28302	Osteotomy; talus	51.50	1229	1442	747
28304	Osteotomy, midtarsal bones, other than calcaneus or talus;	46.00	1097	1288	616
28305	Osteotomy, midtarsal bones, other than calcaneus or talus; with autograft (includes obtaining graft) (Fowler type)	50.00	1193	1400	810
28306	Osteotomy, metatarsal, base or shaft, single, with or without lengthening, for shortening or angular correction; first metatarsal	43.00	1026	1204	439
28307	Osteotomy, metatarsal, base or shaft, single, with or without lengthening, for shortening or angular correction; first metatarsal with autograft	48.50	1157	1358	494
28308	Osteotomy, metatarsal, base or shaft, single, with or without lengthening, for shortening or angular correction; other than first metatarsal	33.00	787	924	453
28309	Osteotomy, metatarsals, multiple, for cavus foot (Swanson type procedure)	41.00	978	1148	650
28310	Osteotomy for shortening, angular or rotational correction; proximal phalanx, first toe (separate procedure)	29.00	692	812	382
28312	Osteotomy for shortening, angular or rotational correction; other phalanges, any toe	24.00	573	672	360
28313	Reconstruction, angular deformity of toe (overlapping second toe, fifth toe, curly toes), soft tissue procedures only	20.00	477	560	297
28315	Sesamoidectomy, first toe (separate procedure)	27.00	644	756	366
28320	Repair of nonunion or malunion; tarsal bones (eg, calcaneus, talus)	40.00	954	1120	719
28322	Repair of nonunion or malunion; metatarsal, with or without bone graft (includes obtaining graft)	36.00	859	1008	517
28340	Reconstruction, toe, macrodactyly; soft tissue resection	0.00	0	0	537

Code	Description	Medicode RVU	50th	75th	Medicare Nat'l Avg
28341	Reconstruction, toe, macrodactyly; requiring bone resection	0.00	0	0	639
28344	Reconstruction, toe(s); polydactyly	0.00	0	0	318
28345	Reconstruction, toe(s); syndactyly, with or without skin graft(s), each web	0.00	0	0	450
28360	Reconstruction, cleft foot	0.00	0	0	1023
28400	Closed treatment of calcaneal fracture; without manipulation	16.00	384	448	201
28405	Closed treatment of calcaneal fracture; with manipulation	26.00	624	728	343
28406	Percutaneous skeletal fixation of calcaneal fracture, with manipulation	35.00	840	980	501
28415	Open treatment of calcaneal fracture, with or without internal or external fixation;	64.00	1536	1792	919
28420	Open treatment of calcaneal fracture, with or without internal or external fixation; with primary iliac or other autogenous bone graft (includes obtaining graft)	78.00	1872	2184	1103
28430	Closed treatment of talus fracture; without manipulation	16.25	390	455	190
28435	Closed treatment of talus fracture; with manipulation	22.00	528	616	278
28436	Percutaneous skeletal fixation of talus fracture, with manipulation	32.00	768	896	360
28445	Open treatment of talus fracture, with or without internal or external fixation	64.00	1536	1792	742
28450	Treatment of tarsal bone fracture (except talus and calcaneus); without manipulation, each	14.75	354	413	155
28455	Treatment of tarsal bone fracture (except talus and calcaneus); with manipulation, each	20.00	480	560	227
28456	Percutaneous skeletal fixation of tarsal bone fracture (except talus and calcaneus), with manipulation, each	30.00	720	840	195
28465	Open treatment of tarsal bone fracture (except talus and calcaneus), with or without internal or external fixation, each	43.50	1044	1218	503
28470	Closed treatment of metatarsal fracture; without manipulation, each	12.00	288	336	148
28475	Closed treatment of metatarsal fracture; with manipulation, each	16.50	396	462	209
28476	Percutaneous skeletal fixation of metatarsal fracture, with manipulation, each	30.00	720	840	271
28485	Open treatment of metatarsal fracture, with or without internal or external fixation, each	39.00	936	1092	420
28490	Closed treatment of fracture great toe, phalanx or phalanges; without manipulation	6.75	162	189	78
28495	Closed treatment of fracture great toe, phalanx or phalanges; with manipulation	11.00	264	308	106

Code		Description	Medicode RVU	50th	75th	Medicare Nat'l Avg
28496		Percutaneous skeletal fixation of fracture great toe, phalanx or phalanges, with manipulation	16.00	384	448	177
28505		Open treatment of fracture great toe, phalanx or phalanges, with or without internal or external fixation	25.75	618	721	273
28510		Closed treatment of fracture, phalanx or phalanges, other than great toe; without manipulation, each	5.50	132	154	76
28515		Closed treatment of fracture, phalanx or phalanges, other than great toe; with manipulation, each	8.25	198	231	100
28525		Open treatment of fracture, phalanx or phalanges, other than great toe, with or without internal or external fixation, each	21.00	504	588	219
28530		Closed treatment of sesamoid fracture	10.00	240	280	82
28531		Open treatment of sesamoid fracture, with or without internal fixation	20.00	480	560	165
28540		Closed treatment of tarsal bone dislocation, other than talotarsal; without anesthesia	9.00	216	252	101
28545		Closed treatment of tarsal bone dislocation, other than talotarsal; requiring anesthesia	15.00	360	420	142
28546		Percutaneous skeletal fixation of tarsal bone dislocation, other than talotarsal, with manipulation	18.00	432	504	236
28555		Open treatment of tarsal bone dislocation, with or without internal or external fixation	38.50	924	1078	474
28570		Closed treatment of talotarsal joint dislocation; without anesthesia	12.00	288	336	130
28575		Closed treatment of talotarsal joint dislocation; requiring anesthesia	18.00	432	504	237
28576		Percutaneous skeletal fixation of talotarsal joint dislocation, with manipulation	24.00	576	672	270
28585		Open treatment of talotarsal joint dislocation, with or without internal or external fixation	50.00	1200	1400	518
28600		Closed treatment of tarsometatarsal joint dislocation; without anesthesia	11.50	276	322	99
28605		Closed treatment of tarsometatarsal joint dislocation; requiring anesthesia	17.50	420	490	195
28606		Percutaneous skeletal fixation of tarsometatarsal joint dislocation, with manipulation	26.50	636	742	331
28615		Open treatment of tarsometatarsal joint dislocation, with or without internal or external fixation	47.00	1128	1316	425
28630	*	Closed treatment of metatarsophalangeal joint dislocation; without anesthesia	7.75	186	217	109
28635	*	Closed treatment of metatarsophalangeal joint dislocation; requiring anesthesia	12.25	294	343	136
28636		Percutaneous skeletal fixation of metatarsophalangeal joint dislocation, with manipulation	16.00	384	448	219
28645		Open treatment of metatarsophalangeal joint dislocation, with or without internal or external fixation	25.00	600	700	298

Code		Description	Medicode RVU	50th	75th	Medicare Nat'l Avg
28660	*	Closed treatment of interphalangeal joint dislocation; without anesthesia	5.00	120	140	72
28665	*	Closed treatment of interphalangeal joint dislocation; requiring anesthesia	9.00	216	252	114
28666		Percutaneous skeletal fixation of interphalangeal joint dislocation, with manipulation	9.00	216	252	210
28675		Open treatment of interphalangeal joint dislocation, with or without internal or external fixation	19.00	456	532	238
28705		Pantalar arthrodesis	100.0	2400	2800	1237
28715		Triple arthrodesis	91.00	2184	2548	1048
28725		Subtalar arthrodesis	73.00	1752	2044	853
28730		Arthrodesis, midtarsal or tarsometatarsal, multiple or transverse;	62.00	1488	1736	801
28735		Arthrodesis, midtarsal or tarsometatarsal, multiple or transverse; with osteotomy as for flatfoot correction	70.00	1680	1960	832
28737		Arthrodesis, midtarsal navicular-cuneiform, with tendon lengthening and advancement (Miller type procedure)	60.00	1440	1680	736
28740		Arthrodesis, midtarsal or tarsometatarsal, single joint	48.00	1152	1344	482
28750		Arthrodesis, great toe; metatarsophalangeal joint	44.00	1056	1232	444
28755		Arthrodesis, great toe; interphalangeal joint	31.00	744	868	346
28760		Arthrodesis, great toe, interphalangeal joint, with extensor hallucis longus transfer to first metatarsal neck (Jones type procedure)	39.50	948	1106	460
28800		Amputation, foot; midtarsal (Chopart type procedure)	50.00	1200	1400	617
28805		Amputation, foot; transmetatarsal	50.00	1200	1400	617
28810		Amputation, metatarsal, with toe, single	35.00	840	980	410
28820		Amputation, toe; metatarsophalangeal joint	26.00	624	728	261
28825		Amputation, toe; interphalangeal joint	23.00	552	644	239
28899		Unlisted procedure, foot or toes	0.00	0	0	

29000–29799
Application of Casts and Strapping

Coding Insight
Casts are applied to immobilize a body part for treatment following a fracture or many orthopedic surgical procedures. A cast may be made of plaster, fiberglass, or synthetic material.

A splint is a flexible or rigid device used to immobilize, protect, and support a part of the body. Splints are available in many different designs and materials and may be made from wood, cloth, metal, or plastic.

Strapping consists of the application of overlapping strips of adhesive tape to a body part to exert pressure on it and hold a structure in place. Strapping is used to treat strains, sprains, dislocations, and some fractures.

Codes found in the application of casts and strapping section (29000–29799) do not identify initial procedures. The codes within this section are used only for replacement procedures.

When a cast is applied for a sprain and no surgery is performed, an appropriate level of E/M service is reported; cast codes are not reported. Supplies are reported with 99070 or with HCPCS Level II codes.
Nota Bene: Many additions and revisions have been made to the notes listed for application of casts and strapping in *CPT '96*. Read the notes carefully before making your code selection.

Subsidiary Codes
Subsidiary codes have relative values that require no further adjustment:

20690 is "in addition" to 29000–29799
20692 is "in addition" to 29000–29799
20900 is "in addition" to 29000–29799
20902 is "in addition" to 29000–29799
20910 is "in addition" to 29000–29799
20912 is "in addition" to 29000–29799
20920 is "in addition" to 29000–29799
20922 is "in addition" to 29000–29799
20924 is "in addition" to 29000–29799
20926 is "in addition" to 29000–29799

Because these are subsidiary or "in addition to" codes, reimbursement reduction and modifier -51 do not apply.

Medicare Alert
Medicare rebundles certain codes in the surgery section when the listed codes are considered a component of a more comprehensive service.

29345 will not be reimbursed when reported with 29355
29405 will not be reimbursed when reported with 29425
64450 will not be reimbursed when reported with 29580

Code	Description	Medicode RVU	50th	75th	Medicare Nat'l Avg
29000	Application of halo type body cast (see 20661-20663 for insertion)	25.00	577	687	176
29010	Application of Risser jacket, localizer, body; only	20.00	462	550	185

Code	Description	Medicode RVU	50th	75th	Medicare Nat'l Avg
29015	Application of Risser jacket, localizer, body; including head	25.00	577	687	199
29020	Application of turnbuckle jacket, body; only	20.00	462	550	162
29025	Application of turnbuckle jacket, body; including head	25.00	577	687	132
29035	Application of body cast, shoulder to hips;	10.00	231	275	158
29040	Application of body cast, shoulder to hips; including head, Minerva type	15.00	346	412	176
29044	Application of body cast, shoulder to hips; including one thigh	12.00	277	330	177
29046	Application of body cast, shoulder to hips; including both thighs	14.00	323	385	194
29049	Application; plaster figure-of-eight	5.00	115	137	53
29055	Application; shoulder spica	10.00	231	275	123
29058	Application; plaster Velpeau	6.00	138	165	80
29065	Application; shoulder to hand (long arm)	5.50	127	151	72
29075	Application; elbow to finger (short arm)	4.25	98	117	58
29085	Application; hand and lower forearm (gauntlet)	4.00	92	110	56
29105	Application of long arm splint (shoulder to hand)	3.50	81	96	56
29125	Application of short arm splint (forearm to hand); static	3.00	69	82	39
29126	Application of short arm splint (forearm to hand); dynamic	4.00	92	110	48
29130	Application of finger splint; static	2.00	46	55	26
29131	Application of finger splint; dynamic	3.50	81	96	39
29200	Strapping; thorax	2.00	46	55	32
29220	Strapping; low back	3.00	69	82	41
29240	Strapping; shoulder (eg, Velpeau)	2.00	46	55	38
29260	Strapping; elbow or wrist	1.75	40	48	30
29280	Strapping; hand or finger	1.50	35	41	28
29305	Application of hip spica cast; one leg	14.00	323	385	167

Code	Description	Medicode RVU	50th	75th	Medicare Nat'l Avg
29325	Application of hip spica cast; one and one-half spica or both legs	17.00	392	467	178
29345	Application of long leg cast (thigh to toes);	7.25	167	199	101
29355	Application of long leg cast (thigh to toes); walker or ambulatory type	8.00	185	220	113
29358	Application of long leg cast brace	14.00	323	385	153
29365	Application of cylinder cast (thigh to ankle)	6.50	150	179	85
29405	Application of short leg cast (below knee to toes);	6.00	138	165	70
29425	Application of short leg cast (below knee to toes); walking or ambulatory type	7.00	162	192	84
29435	Application of patellar tendon bearing (PTB) cast	9.00	208	247	101
29440	Adding walker to previously applied cast	2.00	46	55	32
29450	Application of clubfoot cast with molding or manipulation, long or short leg	4.20	97	115	56
29505	Application of long leg splint (thigh to ankle or toes)	5.00	115	137	52
29515	Application of short leg splint (calf to foot)	3.25	75	89	49
29520	Strapping; hip	3.00	69	82	36
29530	Strapping; knee	2.30	53	63	37
29540	Strapping; ankle	2.00	46	55	32
29550	Strapping; toes	1.25	29	34	29
29580	Strapping; Unna boot	2.80	65	77	50
29590	Denis-Browne splint strapping	3.00	69	82	42
29700	Removal or bivalving; gauntlet, boot or body cast	2.00	46	55	46
29705	Removal or bivalving; full arm or full leg cast	2.30	53	63	55
29710	Removal or bivalving; shoulder or hip spica, Minerva, or Risser jacket, etc.	4.00	92	110	72
29715	Removal or bivalving; turnbuckle jacket	5.00	115	137	75
29720	Repair of spica, body cast or jacket	1.50	35	41	36
29730	Windowing of cast	1.80	42	49	39

Code	Description	Medicode RVU	50th	75th	Medicare Nat'l Avg
29740	Wedging of cast (except clubfoot casts)	2.70	62	74	58
29750	Wedging of clubfoot cast	2.30	53	63	70
29799	Unlisted procedure, casting or strapping	0.00	0	0	–

29800–29909
Arthroscopy

CODING INSIGHT

Surgical arthroscopy always includes a diagnostic arthroscopy, and when arthroscopy is performed in conjunction with arthrotomy, add modifier -51. Do not combine the secondary and primary procedures and report them as a single code. Instead, identify the codes by descending value, designating the service with the highest value as the primary procedure. List the secondary procedures (performed during the same operative session) as subsequent line items with their assigned fees and use modifier -51 to indicate a multiple procedure.

When an arthroscopy procedure is described as a separate procedure, do not report it in addition to the primary arthroscopic procedure.

Lateral retinacular release (27425) may be reported separately with all arthroscopic knee procedures.

Arthroscopy and Unbundling Guidelines

Determining which procedures are considered unbundled with a given code can be difficult. Although CPT is very specific with some guidelines, it is vague with others. Payers either assimilate guidelines into computer systems or establish written guidelines to determine what to pay. When there is no guideline or the guideline is vague, each payer will make its own determination about which codes will or will not be paid and how they will be paid. That includes rules on modifiers, "in-addition codes," unbundling, and other coding issues.

Some payers rely on claims edit computer systems for internal guidelines and documentation to make their decisions. Hence, although many of the coding rules may be the same, there is a great disparity among —and often within — payer policies.

Usual, customary, and reasonable (UCR) also comes into the equation with many vendors of claims edit software. Payers scan thousands of claims to ascertain how the majority of providers report a code. This then becomes the norm for all claims submitted with the code within a given region.

The best way for you to determine if you are unbundling may be to:

- Keep in mind that an "unbundle" includes every codeable component of a procedure that is intrinsic to that procedure
- Track EOBs to determine what you are and are not being paid. How many of the carriers are denying the same code or issues? If it is more than one you should review why or how you are using the code. Contact payers directly for particularly problematic instances
- Medicare publishes a list of unbundle/fragmentation codes. Look under the terms Medicare Alert throughout this book to see if the code you are reporting goes against Medicare guidelines. Remember, the Medicare list presented here is partial, and this book is only one resource; many payers pay for services that Medicare denies

- Always appeal denied claims if you disagree with a decision and/or the logic used by a payer for the denial. If you win an appeal on a coding issue, you and all providers who report the code will have helped to clarify policy for future claims submissions

Knee Arthroscopy

A diagnostic arthroscopy should not be reported with a surgical arthroscopy of the same joint. Surgical arthroscopy always includes diagnostic arthroscopy.

When an open procedure (arthrotomy) is reported with a comparable arthroscopic procedure of the same joint, the open procedure code may be allowed and the surgical arthroscopy code may be transferred to a diagnostic arthroscope, depending upon payer policy. It may be assumed the arthroscopic procedure was unsuccessful, necessitating the open procedure. Exceptions may be made when there is no diagnostic arthroscopic code available, as is the case with ankle arthroscopy.

When a minor open procedure such as a biopsy or limited synovectomy is reported with a major athroscopic procedure such as a chondroplasty or meniscectomy of the same joint, it may be assumed that the minor open procedure was actually arthroscopic in nature. The arthroscopic procedure would be allowed and the minor open procedure would be denied as incidental to the major arthroscopic procedure.

A major arthroscopic procedure (e.g., chondroplasty, meniscectomy) and a major open procedure (e.g., ligament repair, meniscectomy, lateral retinacular release) of the same joint may be reported together.

Manipulation of a joint under general anesthesia should not be reported with an arthroscopic procedure of the same joint.

Chondroplasty

A chondroplasty involves plastic surgery on cartilage by repair of lacerated, displaced, or diseased articular cartilage. This procedure involves identifying lesions of the articular surface with the use of an arthroscope and probe. A motorized suction catheter is used to debride unstable hyaline cartilage or partially fragmented cartilage. This procedure smoothes the articular surface to remove irregularities or roughened or damaged cartilage.

Use 29877 to identify arthroscopically performed chondroplasty of the knee. The following apply to 29877:

- It is identified once per knee per operative session, regardless of the articular surface operated on (i.e., posterior patellae, medial and lateral femoral condyles, medial and lateral tibial plateaus)
- It may be separately identified when it involves significant physician effort, the procedure is performed in a different area above and beyond the preparation of the joint for another procedure (i.e., meniscectomy), or both
- Notchplasty, which involves increasing the indentation or groove in the femoral condyle, is usually performed to create more space to accommodate the intra-articular ligaments. Notchplasty may be separately identified by using an unlisted code (e.g., 29909) or a modifier -22
- Diagnostic arthroscopy, intra-operative photos(s), video imaging (video recording), and other imaging techniques are included in the code
- Manipulation of the knee joint under general anesthesia (includes application of traction or other fixation devices) is incidental to arthroscopically performed chondroplasty
- It may be separately identified with another procedure (i.e., major synovectomy) when it involves significant physician effort

Subsidiary Codes

Subsidiary codes have relative values that require no further adjustment:

20690 is "in addition" to 29800–29909
20692 is "in addition" to 29800–29909
20900 is "in addition" to 29800–29909
20902 is "in addition" to 29800–29909
20910 is "in addition" to 29800–29909
20912 is "in addition" to 29800–29909
20920 is "in addition" to 29800–29909
20922 is "in addition" to 29800–29909
20924 is "in addition" to 29800–29909
20926 is "in addition" to 29800–29909

Because these are subsidiary or "in addition to" codes, reimbursement reduction and modifier -51 do not apply.

Medicare Alert

Medicare rebundles certain codes in the surgery section when the listed codes are considered a component of a more comprehensive service.

20610 will not be reimbursed when reported with 29874, 29875, 29876, 29877, 29879, 29880, 29881
29870 will not be reimbursed when reported with 29874, 29875, 29876, 29877, 29879, 29880, 29881
29874 will not be reimbursed when reported with 29876, 29877, 29879, 29880 or 29881
29875 will not be reimbursed when reported with 29876, 29877, 29879, 29880, or 29881
29877 will not be reimbursed when reported with 29879
29881 will not be reimbursed when reported with 29880

Code	Description	Medicode RVU	50th	75th	Medicare Nat'l Avg
29800	Arthroscopy, temporomandibular joint, diagnostic, with or without synovial biopsy (separate procedure)	55.00	1300	1492	380
29804	Arthroscopy, temporomandibular joint, surgical	94.00	2222	2551	822
29815	Arthroscopy, shoulder, diagnostic, with or without synovial biopsy (separate procedure)	40.00	945	1085	450
29819	Arthroscopy, shoulder, surgical; with removal of loose body or foreign body	66.00	1560	1791	737
29820	Arthroscopy, shoulder, surgical; synovectomy, partial	70.00	1654	1899	688
29821	Arthroscopy, shoulder, surgical; synovectomy, complete	85.00	2009	2306	791
29822	Arthroscopy, shoulder, surgical; debridement, limited	76.00	1796	2062	742
29823	Arthroscopy, shoulder, surgical; debridement, extensive	104.5	2470	2836	885
29825	Arthroscopy, shoulder, surgical; with lysis and resection of adhesions, with or without manipulation	80.00	1891	2171	782
29826	Arthroscopy, shoulder, surgical; decompression of subacromial space with partial acromioplasty, with or without coracoacromial release	104.5	2470	2836	935

Code	Description	Medicode RVU	50th	75th	Medicare Nat'l Avg
29830	Arthroscopy, elbow, diagnostic, with or without synovial biopsy (separate procedure)	40.00	945	1085	456
29834	Arthroscopy, elbow, surgical; with removal of loose body or foreign body	73.00	1725	1981	510
29835	Arthroscopy, elbow, surgical; synovectomy, partial	80.00	1891	2171	524
29836	Arthroscopy, elbow, surgical; synovectomy, complete	95.00	2245	2578	609
29837	Arthroscopy, elbow, surgical; debridement, limited	73.00	1725	1981	553
29838	Arthroscopy, elbow, surgical; debridement, extensive	93.00	2198	2524	616
29840	Arthroscopy, wrist, diagnostic, with or without synovial biopsy (separate procedure)	44.00	1040	1194	360
29843	Arthroscopy, wrist, surgical; for infection, lavage and drainage	50.00	1182	1357	481
29844	Arthroscopy, wrist, surgical; synovectomy, partial	70.00	1654	1899	502
29845	Arthroscopy, wrist, surgical; synovectomy, complete	80.00	1891	2171	609
29846	Arthroscopy, wrist, surgical; excision and/or repair of triangular fibrocartilage and/or joint debridement	75.00	1772	2035	711
29847	Arthroscopy, wrist, surgical; internal fixation for fracture or instability	90.00	2127	2442	576
29848	Arthroscopy, wrist, surgical; with release of transverse carpal ligament	56.00	1323	1520	330
29850	Arthroscopically aided treatment of intercondylar spine(s) and/or tuberosity fracture(s) of the knee, with or without manipulation; without internal or external fixation (includes arthroscopy)	71.00	1678	1927	778
29851	Arthroscopically aided treatment of intercondylar spine(s) and/or tuberosity fracture(s) of the knee, with or without manipulation; with internal or external fixation (includes arthroscopy)	78.00	1843	2117	976
29855	Arthroscopically aided treatment of tibial fracture, proximal (plateau); unicondylar, with or without internal or external fixation (includes arthroscopy)	76.00	1796	2062	921
29856	Arthroscopically aided treatment of tibial fracture, proximal (plateau); bicondylar, with or without internal or external fixation (includes arthroscopy)	84.50	1997	2293	1055
29870	Arthroscopy, knee, diagnostic, with or without synovial biopsy (separate procedure)	37.50	886	1018	382
29871	Arthroscopy, knee, surgical; for infection, lavage and drainage	60.00	1418	1628	569
29874	Arthroscopy, knee, surgical; for removal of loose body or foreign body (eg, osteochondritis dissecans fragmentation, chondral fragmentation)	76.00	1796	2062	706
29875	Arthroscopy, knee, surgical; synovectomy, limited (eg, plica or shelf resection) (separate procedure)	75.00	1772	2035	687
29876	Arthroscopy, knee, surgical; synovectomy, major, two or more compartments (eg, medial or lateral)	89.50	2115	2429	827

Code	Description	Medicode RVU	50th	75th	Medicare Nat'l Avg
29877	Arthroscopy, knee, surgical; debridement/shaving of articular cartilage (chondroplasty)	80.00	1891	2171	779
29879	Arthroscopy, knee, surgical; abrasion arthroplasty (includes chondroplasty where necessary) or multiple drilling	92.00	2174	2496	866
29880	Arthroscopy, knee, surgical; with meniscectomy (medial AND lateral, including any meniscal shaving)	110.0	2600	2985	923
29881	Arthroscopy, knee, surgical; with meniscectomy (medial OR lateral, including any meniscal shaving)	91.00	2151	2469	788
29882	Arthroscopy, knee, surgical; with meniscus repair (medial OR lateral)	98.50	2328	2673	834
29883	Arthroscopy, knee, surgical; with meniscus repair (medial AND lateral)	128.0	3025	3473	1006
29884	Arthroscopy, knee, surgical; with lysis of adhesions, with or without manipulation (separate procedure)	75.00	1772	2035	697
29885	Arthroscopy, knee, surgical; drilling for osteochondritis dissecans with bone grafting, with or without internal fixation (including debridement of base of lesion)	110.0	2600	2985	713
29886	Arthroscopy, knee, surgical; drilling for intact osteochondritis dissecans lesion	88.00	2080	2388	589
29887	Arthroscopy, knee, surgical; drilling for intact osteochondritis dissecans lesion with internal fixation	105.0	2481	2849	812
29888	Arthroscopically aided anterior cruciate ligament repair/augmentation or reconstruction	161.0	3805	4369	1312
29889	Arthroscopically aided posterior cruciate ligament repair/augmentation or reconstruction	161.0	3805	4369	882
29894	Arthroscopy, ankle (tibiotalar and fibulotalar joints), surgical; with removal of loose body or foreign body	77.00	1820	2089	686
29895	Arthroscopy, ankle (tibiotalar and fibulotalar joints), surgical; synovectomy, partial	77.00	1820	2089	667
29897	Arthroscopy, ankle (tibiotalar and fibulotalar joints), surgical; debridement, limited	72.00	1702	1954	690
29898	Arthroscopy, ankle (tibiotalar and fibulotalar joints), surgical; debridement, extensive	101.0	2387	2741	806
29909	Unlisted procedure, arthroscopy	0.00	0	0	–

Surgery Codes 30000–39599

30000–30999
Nose

CODING INSIGHT

Lysis of intra-nasal synechia may be considered inherent to a septoplasty and should not be reported in addition to the septoplasty code.

Intra-nasal biopsy(s) should not be reported with another incisional or excisional nasal procedure.

COSMETIC WARNING

Codes 30120, 30400, 30410, 30430, 30435, 30450 are considered cosmetic 85 percent of the time or more.

SUBSIDIARY CODES

Subsidiary codes have relative values that require no further adjustment:

20900 is "in addition" to 30000–30999
20902 is "in addition" to 30000–30999
20910 is "in addition" to 30000–30999
20912 is "in addition" to 30000–30999
20920 is "in addition" to 30000–30999
20922 is "in addition" to 30000–30999
20926 is "in addition" to 30000–30999
38746 is "in addition" to 30000–30999
49905 is "in addition" to 30000–30999

Because these are subsidiary or "in addition to" codes, reimbursement reduction and modifier -51 do not apply.

Code		Description	Medicode RVU	50th	75th	Medicare Nat'l Avg
30000	*	Drainage abscess or hematoma, nasal, internal approach	5.00	116	139	79
30020	*	Drainage abscess or hematoma, nasal septum	7.00	162	194	81
30100		Biopsy, intranasal	6.00	139	167	67
30110		Excision, nasal polyp(s), simple	11.00	255	305	117
30115		Excision, nasal polyp(s), extensive	26.00	602	722	288

Code		Description	Medicode RVU	50th	75th	Medicare Nat'l Avg
30117		Excision or destruction, any method (including laser), intranasal lesion; internal approach	20.00	463	555	255
30118		Excision or destruction, any method (including laser), intranasal lesion; external approach (lateral rhinotomy)	50.00	1157	1389	728
30120		Excision or surgical planing of skin of nose for rhinophyma	60.00	1389	1666	524
30124		Excision dermoid cyst, nose; simple, skin, subcutaneous	20.00	463	555	177
30125		Excision dermoid cyst, nose; complex, under bone or cartilage	75.00	1736	2083	511
30130		Excision turbinate, partial or complete	26.00	602	722	200
30140		Submucous resection turbinate, partial or complete	37.00	856	1028	287
30150		Rhinectomy; partial	30.00	694	833	696
30160		Rhinectomy; total	50.00	1157	1389	863
30200	*	Injection into turbinate(s), therapeutic	2.75	64	76	45
30210	*	Displacement therapy (Proetz type)	1.50	35	42	49
30220		Insertion, nasal septal prosthesis (button)	15.50	359	430	130
30300	*	Removal foreign body, intranasal; office type procedure	4.00	93	111	57
30310		Removal foreign body, intranasal; requiring general anesthesia	18.50	428	514	145
30320		Removal foreign body, intranasal; by lateral rhinotomy	40.00	926	1111	354
30400		Rhinoplasty, primary; lateral and alar cartilages and/or elevation of nasal tip	80.00	1876	2216	798
30410		Rhinoplasty, primary; complete, external parts including bony pyramid, lateral and alar cartilages, and/or elevation of nasal tip	104.0	2438	2880	1123
30420		Rhinoplasty, primary; including major septal repair	138.0	3236	3822	1374
30430		Rhinoplasty, secondary; minor revision (small amount of nasal tip work)	40.00	938	1108	524
30435		Rhinoplasty, secondary; intermediate revision (bony work with osteotomies)	65.00	1524	1800	875
30450		Rhinoplasty, secondary; major revision (nasal tip work and osteotomies)	104.0	2438	2880	1177
30460		Rhinoplasty for nasal deformity secondary to congenital cleft lip and/or palate, including columellar lengthening; tip only	55.00	1290	1523	738
30462		Rhinoplasty for nasal deformity secondary to congenital cleft lip and/or palate, including columellar lengthening; tip, septum, osteotomies	146.5	3435	4058	1478

Code		Description	Medicode RVU	50th	75th	Medicare Nat'l Avg
30520		Septoplasty or submucous resection, with or without cartilage scoring, contouring or replacement with graft	75.00	1758	2077	604
30540		Repair choanal atresia; intranasal	60.00	1407	1662	578
30545		Repair choanal atresia; transpalatine	90.00	2110	2493	882
30560	*	Lysis intranasal synechia	8.00	188	222	71
30580		Repair fistula; oromaxillary (combine with 31030 if antrotomy is included)	50.00	1172	1385	534
30600		Repair fistula; oronasal	50.00	1172	1385	396
30620		Septal or other intranasal dermatoplasty (does not include obtaining graft)	85.00	1993	2354	602
30630		Repair nasal septal perforations	61.50	1442	1703	545
30801	*	Cauterization and/or ablation, mucosa of turbinates, unilateral or bilateral, any method, (separate procedure); superficial	9.00	211	249	61
30802		Cauterization and/or ablation, mucosa of turbinates, unilateral or bilateral, any method, (separate procedure); intramural	17.00	399	471	118
30901	*	Control nasal hemorrhage, anterior, simple (limited cautery and/or packing) any method	5.00	117	138	69
30903	*	Control nasal hemorrhage, anterior, complex (extensive cautery and/or packing) any method	8.00	188	222	94
30905	*	Control nasal hemorrhage, posterior, with posterior nasal packs and/or cauterization, any method; initial	15.50	363	429	157
30906	*	Control nasal hemorrhage, posterior, with posterior nasal packs and/or cauterization, any method; subsequent	14.50	340	402	137
30915		Ligation arteries; ethmoidal	55.00	1290	1523	491
30920		Ligation arteries; internal maxillary artery, transantral	85.00	1993	2354	810
30930		Fracture nasal turbinate(s), therapeutic	10.00	234	277	85
30999		Unlisted procedure, nose	0.00	0	0	–

31000–31299
Accessory Sinuses, Nasal and Sinus Endoscopy

Coding Insight

CPT '95 deleted 18 codes that had been added in 1994 to describe combination sinus endoscopy services. Concurrent sinus endoscopy procedures reported in 1994 with a single code are now reported with multiple codes that describe individual components of the total service.

Some payers will consider each nasal passage and each set of sinuses as unilateral structures (in which case modifier -50 should be appended), but they may exclude the septum. Others may have guidelines specifying the nasal passage as unilateral, but that second and subsequent procedures on the same side should be reduced using modifier -51.

When reporting sinus endoscopy codes remember that payers generally have definite but very different guidelines. If you report a major/open procedure code with a nasal/sinus endoscopy procedure code, make sure the nasal/sinus endoscopy code does not contain any of the procedures listed in the open code, such as 31020 *Sinusotomy, maxillary (antrotomy); intranasal* with 31256 *Nasal/sinus endoscopy, surgical, with maxillary antrostomy*.

Sinus endoscopy always includes a sinusotomy and diagnostic endoscopy. Codes 31231–31294 report unilateral procedures unless otherwise specified.

Codes 31231–31235 report nasal/sinus endoscope and include diagnostic evaluation and inspection of the interior nasal cavity, middle and superior meatus, turbinates, and sphenoethmoid recess.

Track EOBs to determine payer billing preferences and to track payments. Carefully consider codes before using them to avoid the appearance of unbundling. Cut secondary codes and append modifiers as appropriate. Contract for the way you feel these codes should be paid and the rationale behind your billing.

SUBSIDIARY CODES

Subsidiary codes have relative values that require no further adjustment:

33350 is "in addition" to 31000–31299
38746 is "in addition" to 31000–31299
20900 is "in addition" to 31000–31299
20902 is "in addition" to 31000–31299
20910 is "in addition" to 31000–31299
20912 is "in addition" to 31000–31299
20920 is "in addition" to 31000–31299
20922 is "in addition" to 31000–31299
20926 is "in addition" to 31000–31299
49905 is "in addition" to 31000–31299

Because these are subsidiary or "in addition to" codes, reimbursement reduction and modifier -51 do not apply.

Code		Description	Medicode RVU	50th	75th	Medicare Nat'l Avg
31000	*	Lavage by cannulation; maxillary sinus (antrum puncture or natural ostium)	5.00	116	137	58
31002	*	Lavage by cannulation; sphenoid sinus	10.00	231	275	91
31020		Sinusotomy, maxillary (antrotomy); intranasal	29.00	671	796	230
31030		Sinusotomy, maxillary (antrotomy); radical (Caldwell-Luc) without removal of antrochoanal polyps	65.00	1504	1785	570
31032		Sinusotomy, maxillary (antrotomy); radical (Caldwell-Luc) with removal of antrochoanal polyps	75.00	1735	2059	625
31040		Pterygomaxillary fossa surgery, any approach	140.0	3238	3844	693

Code	Description	Medicode RVU	50th	75th	Medicare Nat'l Avg
31050	Sinusotomy, sphenoid, with or without biopsy;	100.0	2313	2746	484
31051	Sinusotomy, sphenoid, with or without biopsy; with mucosal stripping or removal of polyp(s)	105.0	2429	2883	625
31070	Sinusotomy frontal; external, simple (trephine operation)	50.00	1157	1373	370
31075	Sinusotomy frontal; transorbital, unilateral (for mucocele or osteoma, Lynch type)	85.00	1966	2334	803
31080	Sinusotomy frontal; obliterative without osteoplastic flap, brow incision (includes ablation)	100.0	2313	2746	827
31081	Sinusotomy frontal; obliterative, without osteoplastic flap, coronal incision (includes ablation)	100.0	2313	2746	918
31084	Sinusotomy frontal; obliterative, with osteoplastic flap, brow incision	120.0	2776	3295	1146
31085	Sinusotomy frontal; obliterative, with osteoplastic flap, coronal incision	120.0	2776	3295	1212
31086	Sinusotomy frontal; nonobliterative, with osteoplastic flap, brow incision	120.0	2776	3295	937
31087	Sinusotomy frontal; nonobliterative, with osteoplastic flap, coronal incision	120.0	2776	3295	929
31090	Sinusotomy combined, three or more sinuses	150.0	3470	4118	1117
31200	Ethmoidectomy; intranasal, anterior	52.50	1214	1441	395
31201	Ethmoidectomy; intranasal, total	70.00	1619	1922	624
31205	Ethmoidectomy; extranasal, total	78.00	1804	2142	745
31225	Maxillectomy; without orbital exenteration	155.0	3585	4256	1507
31230	Maxillectomy; with orbital exenteration (en bloc)	182.0	4210	4997	1773
31231	Nasal endoscopy, diagnostic, unilateral or bilateral (separate procedure)	25.00	552	677	104
31233	Nasal/sinus endoscopy, diagnostic with maxillary sinusoscopy (via inferior meatus or canine fossa puncture)	32.00	707	866	220
31235	Nasal/sinus endoscopy, diagnostic with sphenoid sinusoscopy (via puncture of sphenoidal face or cannulation of ostium)	65.00	1436	1759	207
31237	Nasal/sinus endoscopy, surgical; with biopsy, polypectomy or debridement (separate procedure)	54.00	1193	1461	273
31238	Nasal/sinus endoscopy, surgical; with control of epistaxis	35.00	773	947	256
31239	Nasal/sinus endoscopy, surgical; with dacryocystorhinostomy	80.00	1768	2165	878
31240	Nasal/sinus endoscopy, surgical; with concha bullosa resection	40.00	884	1082	276
31254	Nasal/sinus endoscopy, surgical; with ethmoidectomy, partial (anterior)	71.00	1569	1921	476

Code	Description	Medicode RVU	50th	75th	Medicare Nat'l Avg
31255	Nasal/sinus endoscopy, surgical; with ethmoidectomy, total (anterior and posterior)	97.00	2143	2625	719
31256	Nasal/sinus endoscopy, surgical, with maxillary antrostomy;	56.00	1237	1515	318
31267	Nasal/sinus endoscopy, surgical, with maxillary antrostomy; with removal of tissue from maxillary sinus	84.00	1856	2273	473
31276	Nasal/sinus endoscopy, surgical with frontal sinus exploration, with or without removal of tissue from frontal sinus	84.00	1856	2273	578
31287	Nasal/sinus endoscopy, surgical, with sphenoidotomy;	70.00	1547	1894	407
31288	Nasal/sinus endoscopy, surgical, with sphenoidotomy; with removal of tissue from the sphenoid sinus	77.00	1701	2084	464
31290	Nasal/sinus endoscopy, surgical, with repair of cerebrospinal fluid leak; ethmoid region	90.00	1989	2435	1307
31291	Nasal/sinus endoscopy, surgical, with repair of cerebrospinal fluid leak; sphenoid region	90.00	1989	2435	1363
31292	Nasal/sinus endoscopy, surgical; with medial or inferior orbital wall decompression	80.00	1768	2165	1054
31293	Nasal/sinus endoscopy, surgical; with medial orbital wall and inferior orbital wall decompression	90.00	1989	2435	1153
31294	Nasal/sinus endoscopy, surgical; with optic nerve decompression	0.00	0	0	1317
31299	Unlisted procedure, accessory sinuses	0.00	0	0	–

31300–31599
Larynx

CODING INSIGHT
Direct laryngoscopy allows the physician to see the larynx through a scope in the throat, as if looking through a tunnel. Indirect laryngoscopy, on the other hand, uses mirrors, and the physician does not directly see the larynx.

Surgical endoscopy includes a diagnostic endoscopy; however diagnostic endoscopy can be identified separately when performed at the same surgical session as an open procedure. Append modifier -51 to the diagnostic endoscope code.

SUBSIDIARY CODES
Subsidiary codes have relative values that require no further adjustment:

20900 is "in addition" to 31300–31599
20902 is "in addition" to 31300–31599
20910 is "in addition" to 31300–31599
20912 is "in addition" to 31300–31599
20920 is "in addition" to 31300–31599
20922 is "in addition" to 31300–31599
20926 is "in addition" to 31300–31599
38746 is "in addition" to 31300–31599
49905 is "in addition" to 31300–31599

Because these are subsidiary or "in addition to" codes, reimbursement reduction and modifier -51 do not apply.

MEDICARE ALERT

Medicare rebundles certain codes in the surgery section when the listed codes are considered a component of a more comprehensive service.

31535 will not be reimbursed when reported with 31536

31525 and 31540 will not be reimbursed when reported with 31541

Code	Description	Medicode RVU	50th	75th	Medicare Nat'l Avg
31300	Laryngotomy (thyrotomy, laryngofissure); with removal of tumor or laryngocele, cordectomy	100.0	2381	2797	1024
31320	Laryngotomy (thyrotomy, laryngofissure); diagnostic	45.00	1072	1259	348
31360	Laryngectomy; total, without radical neck dissection	135.0	3215	3776	1492
31365	Laryngectomy; total, with radical neck dissection	200.0	4762	5595	2099
31367	Laryngectomy; subtotal supraglottic, without radical neck dissection	135.0	3215	3776	1496
31368	Laryngectomy; subtotal supraglottic, with radical neck dissection	200.0	4762	5595	2103
31370	Partial laryngectomy (hemilaryngectomy); horizontal	135.0	3215	3776	1491
31375	Partial laryngectomy (hemilaryngectomy); laterovertical	110.0	2619	3077	1367
31380	Partial laryngectomy (hemilaryngectomy); anterovertical	110.0	2619	3077	1466
31382	Partial laryngectomy (hemilaryngectomy); antero-latero-vertical	110.0	2619	3077	1421
31390	Pharyngolaryngectomy, with radical neck dissection; without reconstruction	175.0	4167	4895	2101
31395	Pharyngolaryngectomy, with radical neck dissection; with reconstruction	230.0	5477	6434	2526
31400	Arytenoidectomy or arytenoidopexy, external approach	90.00	2143	2518	713
31420	Epiglottidectomy	75.00	1786	2098	705
31500	Intubation, endotracheal, emergency procedure	10.00	238	280	119
31502	Tracheotomy tube change prior to establishment of fistula tract	8.50	202	238	52
31505	Laryngoscopy, indirect (separate procedure); diagnostic	8.00	193	224	45
31510	Laryngoscopy, indirect (separate procedure); with biopsy	22.00	531	615	103
31511	Laryngoscopy, indirect (separate procedure); with removal of foreign body	25.00	603	699	129

Code	Description	Medicode RVU	50th	75th	Medicare Nat'l Avg
31512	Laryngoscopy, indirect (separate procedure); with removal of lesion	30.00	724	839	164
31513	Laryngoscopy, indirect (separate procedure); with vocal cord injection	40.00	966	1119	209
31515	Laryngoscopy direct, with or without tracheoscopy; for aspiration	15.00	362	419	122
31520	Laryngoscopy direct, with or without tracheoscopy; diagnostic, newborn	13.00	314	364	171
31525	Laryngoscopy direct, with or without tracheoscopy; diagnostic, except newborn	22.00	531	615	208
31526	Laryngoscopy direct, with or without tracheoscopy; diagnostic, with operating microscope	34.00	821	951	266
31527	Laryngoscopy direct, with or without tracheoscopy; with insertion of obturator	50.00	1207	1398	257
31528	Laryngoscopy direct, with or without tracheoscopy; with dilatation, initial	30.00	724	839	212
31529	Laryngoscopy direct, with or without tracheoscopy; with dilatation, subsequent	25.00	603	699	211
31530	Laryngoscopy, direct, operative, with foreign body removal;	34.00	821	951	308
31531	Laryngoscopy, direct, operative, with foreign body removal; with operating microscope	41.00	990	1147	369
31535	Laryngoscopy, direct, operative, with biopsy;	30.00	724	839	314
31536	Laryngoscopy, direct, operative, with biopsy; with operating microscope	43.00	1038	1202	364
31540	Laryngoscopy, direct, operative, with excision of tumor and/or stripping of vocal cords or epiglottis;	39.00	941	1091	409
31541	Laryngoscopy, direct, operative, with excision of tumor and/or stripping of vocal cords or epiglottis; with operating microscope	51.00	1231	1426	437
31560	Laryngoscopy, direct, operative, with arytenoidectomy;	30.00	724	839	443
31561	Laryngoscopy, direct, operative, with arytenoidectomy; with operating microscope	80.00	1931	2237	557
31570	Laryngoscopy, direct, with injection into vocal cord(s), therapeutic;	39.00	941	1091	392
31571	Laryngoscopy, direct, with injection into vocal cord(s), therapeutic; with operating microscope	48.00	1159	1342	390
31575	Laryngoscopy, flexible fiberoptic; diagnostic	10.50	253	294	117
31576	Laryngoscopy, flexible fiberoptic; with biopsy	23.00	555	643	201
31577	Laryngoscopy, flexible fiberoptic; with removal of foreign body	35.00	845	979	243
31578	Laryngoscopy, flexible fiberoptic; with removal of lesion	40.00	966	1119	281
▲ 31579	Laryngoscopy, flexible or rigid fiberoptic, with stroboscopy	27.00	652	755	192

Code	Description	Medicode RVU	50th	75th	Medicare Nat'l Avg
31580	Laryngoplasty; for laryngeal web, two stage, with keel insertion and removal	100.0	2414	2796	1051
31582	Laryngoplasty; for laryngeal stenosis, with graft or core mold, including tracheotomy	90.00	2173	2517	1537
31584	Laryngoplasty; with open reduction of fracture	95.00	2293	2657	1268
31585	Treatment of closed laryngeal fracture; without manipulation	15.00	362	419	335
31586	Treatment of closed laryngeal fracture; with closed manipulative reduction	25.00	603	699	567
31587	Laryngoplasty, cricoid split	90.00	2173	2517	621
31588	Laryngoplasty, not otherwise specified (eg, for burns, reconstruction after partial laryngectomy)	0.00	0	0	921
31590	Laryngeal reinnervation by neuromuscular pedicle	110.0	2655	3076	495
31595	Section recurrent laryngeal nerve, therapeutic (separate procedure), unilateral	50.00	1207	1398	592
31599	Unlisted procedure, larynx	0.00	0	0	–

31600–31899
Trachea and Bronchi

CODING INSIGHT
Surgical endoscopy includes a diagnostic endoscopy; however, diagnostic endoscopy can be identified separately when performed at the same surgical session as an open procedure. Append modifier -51 to the diagnostic endoscope code.

Payers may treat the bronchial tree as one structure and not accept a bilateral modifier. However, procedures performed on the larynx, pharynx, and bronchus will usually be paid as separate anatomical sites.

SUBSIDIARY CODES
Subsidiary codes have relative values that require no further adjustment:

20900 is "in addition" to 31600–31899
20902 is "in addition" to 31600–31899
20910 is "in addition" to 31600–31899
20912 is "in addition" to 31600–31899
20920 is "in addition" to 31600–31899
20922 is "in addition" to 31600–31899
20926 is "in addition" to 31600–31899
38746 is "in addition" to 31600–31899
49905 is "in addition" to 31600–31899

Because these are subsidiary or "in addition to" codes, reimbursement reduction and modifier -51 do not apply.

Medicare Alert

Medicare rebundles certain codes in the surgery section when the listed codes are considered a component of a more comprehensive service.

31622 will not be reimbursed when reported with 31625, 31628, and 31645

31625 will not be reimbursed when reported with 31628

Code	Description	Medicode RVU	50th	75th	Medicare Nat'l Avg
31600	Tracheostomy, planned (separate procedure);	35.00	808	920	332
31601	Tracheostomy, planned (separate procedure); under two years	40.00	923	1051	395
31603	Tracheostomy, emergency procedure; transtracheal	40.00	923	1051	364
31605	Tracheostomy, emergency procedure; cricothyroid membrane	35.00	808	920	328
31610	Tracheostomy, fenestration procedure with skin flaps	60.00	1385	1577	604
31611	Construction of tracheoesophageal fistula and subsequent insertion of an alaryngeal speech prosthesis (eg, voice button, Blom-Singer prosthesis)	65.00	1500	1708	539
31612	Tracheal puncture, percutaneous with transtracheal aspiration and/or injection	8.00	185	210	88
31613	Tracheostoma revision; simple, without flap rotation	30.00	692	788	270
31614	Tracheostoma revision; complex, with flap rotation	60.00	1385	1577	541
31615	Tracheobronchoscopy through established tracheostomy incision	20.00	462	526	175
31622	Bronchoscopy; diagnostic, (flexible or rigid), with or without cell washing or brushing	25.25	583	664	242
31625	Bronchoscopy; with biopsy	27.00	623	710	268
31628	Bronchoscopy; with transbronchial lung biopsy, with or without fluoroscopic guidance	30.00	692	788	331
31629	Bronchoscopy; with transbronchial needle aspiration biopsy	35.00	808	920	286
31630	Bronchoscopy; with tracheal or bronchial dilation or closed reduction of fracture	32.00	739	841	320
31631	Bronchoscopy; with tracheal dilation and placement of tracheal stent	40.00	923	1051	304
31635	Bronchoscopy; with removal of foreign body	50.00	1154	1314	359
31640	Bronchoscopy; with excision of tumor	50.00	1154	1314	423
31641	Bronchoscopy; with destruction of tumor or relief of stenosis by any method other than excision (eg, laser)	65.00	1500	1708	475
31645	Bronchoscopy; with therapeutic aspiration of tracheobronchial tree, initial (eg, drainage of lung abscess)	27.00	623	710	251

Code	Description	Medicode RVU	50th	75th	Medicare Nat'l Avg
31646	Bronchoscopy; with therapeutic aspiration of tracheobronchial tree, subsequent	27.00	623	710	212
31656	Bronchoscopy; with injection of contrast material for segmental bronchography (fiberscope only)	23.00	531	604	190
31700	Catheterization, transglottic (separate procedure)	15.00	346	394	105
31708	Instillation of contrast material for laryngography or bronchography, without catheterization	5.00	115	131	78
31710	Catheterization for bronchography, with or without instillation of contrast material	7.00	162	184	79
31715	Transtracheal injection for bronchography	6.50	150	171	56
31717	Catheterization with bronchial brush biopsy	5.00	115	131	100
31720	Catheter aspiration (separate procedure); nasotracheal	5.00	115	131	65
31725	Catheter aspiration (separate procedure); tracheobronchial with fiberscope, bedside	10.00	231	263	122
31730	Transtracheal (percutaneous) introduction of needle wire dilator/stent or indwelling tube for oxygen therapy	10.00	231	263	194
31750	Tracheoplasty; cervical	100.0	2308	2628	771
31755	Tracheoplasty; tracheopharyngeal fistulization, each stage	120.0	2770	3153	1144
31760	Tracheoplasty; intrathoracic	120.0	2770	3153	1338
31766	Carinal reconstruction	133.0	3070	3495	1884
31770	Bronchoplasty; graft repair	133.0	3070	3495	1490
31775	Bronchoplasty; excision stenosis and anastomosis	133.0	3070	3495	1572
31780	Excision tracheal stenosis and anastomosis; cervical	125.0	2885	3285	1399
31781	Excision tracheal stenosis and anastomosis; cervicothoracic	140.0	3231	3679	1603
31785	Excision of tracheal tumor or carcinoma; cervical	115.0	2654	3022	1030
31786	Excision of tracheal tumor or carcinoma; thoracic	135.0	3116	3548	1489
31800	Suture of tracheal wound or injury; cervical	65.00	1500	1708	495
31805	Suture of tracheal wound or injury; intrathoracic	90.00	2077	2365	925
31820	Surgical closure tracheostomy or fistula; without plastic repair	30.00	692	788	323
31825	Surgical closure tracheostomy or fistula; with plastic repair	40.00	923	1051	465

Code	Description	Medicode RVU	50th	75th	Medicare Nat'l Avg
31830	Revision of tracheostomy scar	30.00	692	788	329
31899	Unlisted procedure, trachea, bronchi	0.00	0	0	–

32000–32999
Lungs and Pleura

Coding Insight
Surgical thoracoscopy includes diagnostic throacoscopy, and for endoscopic procedures, code the appropriate endoscopy of each anatomical site examined.

A diagnostic thoracoscopy is identified separately when performed with a major/open procedure.

Subsidiary Codes
Subsidiary codes have relative values that require no further adjustment:

20900 is "in addition" to 32000–32999
20902 is "in addition" to 32000–32999
20910 is "in addition" to 32000–32999
20912 is "in addition" to 32000–32999
20920 is "in addition" to 32000–32999
20922 is "in addition" to 32000–32999
20926 is "in addition" to 32000–32999
32501 is "in addition" to 32480, 32482, and 32484
38746 is "in addition" to 32000–32999
49905 is "in addition" to 32000–32999

Because these are subsidiary or "in addition to" codes, reimbursement reduction and modifier -51 do not apply.

Medicare Alert
Medicare rebundles certain codes in the surgery section when the listed codes are considered a component of a more comprehensive service.

32020 will not be reimbursed when reported with 32100, 32480, 32500

32100 will not be reimbursed when reported with 32480, 32500

Code		Description	Medicode RVU	50th	75th	Medicare Nat'l Avg
32000	*	Thoracentesis, puncture of pleural cavity for aspiration, initial or subsequent	8.00	187	221	84
32002		Thoracentesis with insertion of tube with or without water seal (eg, for pneumothorax) (separate procedure)	15.00	351	414	139
32005		Chemical pleurodesis (eg, for recurrent or persistent pneumothorax)	10.00	234	276	133
32020		Tube thoracostomy with or without water seal (eg, for abscess, hemothorax, empyema) (separate procedure)	25.00	585	690	269

Code		Description	Medicode RVU	50th	75th	Medicare Nat'l Avg
32035		Thoracostomy; with rib resection for empyema	65.00	1522	1794	581
32036		Thoracostomy; with open flap drainage for empyema	75.00	1756	2070	640
32095		Thoracotomy, limited, for biopsy of lung or pleura	75.00	1756	2070	700
32100		Thoracotomy, major; with exploration and biopsy	80.00	1873	2208	969
32110		Thoracotomy, major; with control of traumatic hemorrhage and/or repair of lung tear	92.00	2154	2540	1016
32120		Thoracotomy, major; for postoperative complications	100.0	2341	2761	851
32124		Thoracotomy, major; with open intrapleural pneumonolysis	80.00	1873	2208	951
32140		Thoracotomy, major; with cyst(s) removal, with or without a pleural procedure	100.0	2341	2761	1057
32141		Thoracotomy, major; with excision-plication of bullae, with or without any pleural procedure	100.0	2341	2761	1140
32150		Thoracotomy, major; with removal of intrapleural foreign body or fibrin deposit	95.00	2224	2623	970
32151		Thoracotomy, major; with removal of intrapulmonary foreign body	95.00	2224	2623	898
32160		Thoracotomy, major; with cardiac massage	100.0	2341	2761	713
32200		Pneumonostomy, with open drainage of abscess or cyst	65.00	1522	1794	815
32215		Pleural scarification for repeat pneumothorax	88.00	2060	2429	746
32220		Decortication, pulmonary, (separate procedure); total	100.0	2341	2761	1461
32225		Decortication, pulmonary, (separate procedure); partial	75.00	1756	2070	1041
32310		Pleurectomy, parietal (separate procedure)	95.00	2224	2623	1021
32320		Decortication and parietal pleurectomy	120.0	2809	3313	1632
32400	*	Biopsy, pleura; percutaneous needle	11.00	258	304	122
32402		Biopsy, pleura; open	50.00	1171	1380	621
32405		Biopsy, lung or mediastinum, percutaneous needle	17.00	398	469	156
32420	*	Pneumonocentesis, puncture of lung for aspiration	10.00	234	276	141
32440		Removal of lung, total pneumonectomy;	130.0	3044	3589	1677
32442		Removal of lung, total pneumonectomy; with resection of segment of trachea followed by broncho-tracheal anastomosis (sleeve pneumonectomy)	167.0	3910	4610	1791

Code	Description	Medicode RVU	50th	75th	Medicare Nat'l Avg
32445	Removal of lung, total pneumonectomy; extrapleural	150.0	3512	4141	1868
32480	Removal of lung, other than total pneumonectomy; single lobe (lobectomy)	120.0	2809	3313	1515
32482	Removal of lung, other than total pneumonectomy; two lobes (bilobectomy)	125.0	2927	3451	1563
32484	Removal of lung, other than total pneumonectomy; single segment (segmentectomy)	120.0	2809	3313	1590
32486	Removal of lung, other than total pneumonectomy; with circumferential resection of segment of bronchus followed by broncho-bronchial anastomosis (sleeve lobectomy)	155.0	3629	4279	1651
32488	Removal of lung, other than total pneumonectomy; all remaining lung following previous removal of a portion of lung (completion pneumonectomy)	162.0	3793	4472	1771
32500	Removal of lung, other than total pneumonectomy; wedge resection, single or multiple	100.0	2341	2761	1188
● 32501	Resection and repair of portion of bronchus (bronchoplasty) when performed at time of lobectomy or segmentectomy (List separately in addition to code for primary procedure)	30.00	702	828	–
32520	Resection of lung; with resection of chest wall	150.0	3512	4141	1770
32522	Resection of lung; with reconstruction of chest wall, without prosthesis	170.0	3980	4693	1878
32525	Resection of lung; with major reconstruction of chest wall, with prosthesis	180.0	4214	4969	2046
32540	Extrapleural enucleation of empyema (empyemectomy)	100.0	2341	2761	1081
32601	Thoracoscopy, diagnostic (separate procedure); lungs and pleural space, without biopsy	30.00	702	828	373
32602	Thoracoscopy, diagnostic (separate procedure); lungs and pleural space, with biopsy	35.00	819	966	411
32603	Thoracoscopy, diagnostic (separate procedure); pericardial sac, without biopsy	40.00	936	1104	459
32604	Thoracoscopy, diagnostic (separate procedure); pericardial sac, with biopsy	45.00	1054	1242	510
32605	Thoracoscopy, diagnostic (separate procedure); mediastinal space, without biopsy	35.00	819	966	427
32606	Thoracoscopy, diagnostic (separate procedure); mediastinal space, with biopsy	40.00	936	1104	497
32650	Thoracoscopy, surgical; with pleurodesis, any method	82.00	1920	2264	746
32651	Thoracoscopy, surgical; with partial pulmonary decortication	85.00	1990	2347	1041
32652	Thoracoscopy, surgical; with total pulmonary decortication, including intrapleural pneumonolysis	88.00	2060	2429	1461
32653	Thoracoscopy, surgical; with removal of intrapleural foreign body or fibrin deposit	85.00	1990	2347	970
32654	Thoracoscopy, surgical; with control of traumatic hemorrhage	90.00	2107	2485	1016

Code	Description	Medicode RVU	50th	75th	Medicare Nat'l Avg
32655	Thoracoscopy, surgical; with excision-plication of bullae, including any pleural procedure	95.00	2224	2623	1149
32656	Thoracoscopy, surgical; with parietal pleurectomy	90.00	2107	2485	1108
32657	Thoracoscopy, surgical; with wedge resection of lung, single or multiple	100.0	2341	2761	1188
32658	Thoracoscopy, surgical; with removal of clot or foreign body from pericardial sac	107.0	2505	2954	1091
32659	Thoracoscopy, surgical; with creation of pericardial window or partial resection of pericardial sac for drainage	105.0	2458	2899	1152
32660	Thoracoscopy, surgical; with total pericardiectomy	133.0	3114	3672	1648
32661	Thoracoscopy, surgical; with excision of pericardial cyst, tumor, or mass	120.0	2809	3313	927
32662	Thoracoscopy, surgical; with excision of mediastinal cyst, tumor, or mass	115.0	2692	3175	1324
32663	Thoracoscopy, surgical; with lobectomy, total or segmental	130.0	3044	3589	1531
32664	Thoracoscopy, surgical; with thoracic sympathectomy	105.0	2458	2899	1034
32665	Thoracoscopy, surgical; with esophagomyotomy (Heller type)	96.00	2248	2650	1241
32800	Repair lung hernia through chest wall	80.00	1873	2208	856
32810	Closure of chest wall following open flap drainage for empyema (Clagett type procedure)	40.00	936	1104	755
32815	Open closure of major bronchial fistula	140.0	3278	3865	1527
32820	Major reconstruction, chest wall (post-traumatic)	125.0	2927	3451	1631
32850	Donor pneumonectomy(ies) with preparation and maintenance of allograft (cadaver)	0.00	0	0	–
32851	Lung transplant, single; without cardiopulmonary bypass	0.00	0	0	3629
32852	Lung transplant, single; with cardiopulmonary bypass	0.00	0	0	3779
32853	Lung transplant, double (bilateral sequential or en bloc); without cardiopulmonary bypass	0.00	0	0	4256
32854	Lung transplant, double (bilateral sequential or en bloc); with cardiopulmonary bypass	0.00	0	0	4480
32900	Resection of ribs, extrapleural, all stages	70.00	1639	1932	1102
32905	Thoracoplasty, Schede type or extrapleural (all stages);	90.00	2107	2485	1346
32906	Thoracoplasty, Schede type or extrapleural (all stages); with closure of bronchopleural fistula	140.0	3278	3865	1691
32940	Pneumonolysis, extraperiosteal, including filling or packing procedures	60.00	1405	1656	1216

Code		Description	Medicode RVU	50th	75th	Medicare Nat'l Avg
32960	*	Pneumothorax, therapeutic, intrapleural injection of air	7.50	176	207	99
32999		Unlisted procedure, lungs and pleura	0.00	0	0	–

33010–33130
Heart and Pericardium

Coding Insight
Thoracotomy/mediastinotomy will usually not be reimbursed by payers when reported with intra-thoracic cardiovascular procedures. Most claims systems assume the thoracotomy/mediastinotomy is inherent to the procedure (i.e., the incision necessary to perform the procedure).

Subsidiary Codes
Subsidiary codes have relative values that require no further adjustment:

20926 is "in addition" to 33010–33130
38746 is "in addition" to 33010–33130
49905 is "in addition" to 33010–33130

Because these are subsidiary or "in addition to" codes, reimbursement reduction and modifier -51 do not apply.

Code		Description	Medicode RVU	50th	75th	Medicare Nat'l Avg
33010	*	Pericardiocentesis; initial	13.50	301	360	136
33011	*	Pericardiocentesis; subsequent	8.25	184	220	118
33015		Tube pericardiostomy	18.00	401	479	420
33020		Pericardiotomy for removal of clot or foreign body (primary procedure)	90.00	2005	2397	1091
33025		Creation of pericardial window or partial resection for drainage	92.00	2049	2450	1152
33030		Pericardiectomy, subtotal or complete; without cardiopulmonary bypass	105.0	2339	2797	1691
33031		Pericardiectomy, subtotal or complete; with cardiopulmonary bypass	190.0	4232	5061	1411
33050		Excision of pericardial cyst or tumor	100.0	2228	2664	927
33120		Excision of intracardiac tumor, resection with cardiopulmonary bypass	225.0	5012	5993	2286
33130		Resection of external cardiac tumor	150.0	3341	3995	1372

33200–33261
Pacemaker or Defibrillator

CODING INSIGHT
Pacemaker or defibrillator codes 33200–33261 include repositioning or replacement in the first 14 days.

Temporary pacemaker insertion codes (33210–33211) may not be reimbursed when reported with an intra-thoracic (intrapleural/extrapleural) cardiovascular procedure. Electronic pacemaker analysis code 93734 should not be reported with a pacemaker insertion/replacement code.

Nota Bene: Instructional notes have been added to the pacemaker or defibrillator code range in *CPT '96*. The notes identify what is included in a pacemaker system (single and dual chamber) and what is included in a defibrillator system. The notes state "When a battery is changed, it is actually the pulse generator that is changed" and that two codes are required to report a pulse generator change; one for removal and one for insertion. Further instructions specify modifiers -76 and -77 should not be reported 14 days after the initial insertion or replacement of either device because after that time period it would be considered a new procedure. Be sure to read the new notes before making a code selection.

Code 33253 *Operative incisions and reconstruction of atria for treatment of atrial fibrillation or atrial flutter (eg, maze procedure)* has been added to *CPT '96*. Code 33261 has been revised with the word "ventricular" added and the words "or pathway" deleted, and 33260 has been deleted.

SUBSIDIARY CODES
Subsidiary codes have relative values that require no further adjustment:

20926 is "in addition" to 33200–33261
38746 is "in addition" to 33200–33261
49905 is "in addition" to 33200–33261

Because these are subsidiary or "in addition to" codes, reimbursement reduction and modifier -51 do not apply.

MEDICARE ALERT
Medicare rebundles certain codes in the surgery section when the listed codes are considered a component of a more comprehensive service.

33206 will not be reimbursed when reported with 33207, 33208

33207 will not be reimbursed when reported with 33208

Code	Description	Medicode RVU	50th	75th	Medicare Nat'l Avg
33200	Insertion of permanent pacemaker with epicardial electrode(s); by thoracotomy	105.0	2339	2797	1050
33201	Insertion of permanent pacemaker with epicardial electrode(s); by xiphoid approach	85.00	1893	2264	899
33206	Insertion or replacement of permanent pacemaker with transvenous electrode(s); atrial	80.00	1782	2131	663
33207	Insertion or replacement of permanent pacemaker with transvenous electrode(s); ventricular	85.00	1893	2264	735
33208	Insertion or replacement of permanent pacemaker with transvenous electrode(s); atrial and ventricular	90.00	2005	2397	726

Code	Description	Medicode RVU	50th	75th	Medicare Nat'l Avg
33210	Insertion or replacement of temporary transvenous single chamber cardiac electrode or pacemaker catheter (separate procedure)	37.00	824	986	244
33211	Insertion or replacement of temporary transvenous dual chamber pacing electrodes (separate procedure)	42.00	936	1119	247
33212	Insertion or replacement of pacemaker pulse generator only; single chamber, atrial or ventricular	43.00	958	1145	463
33213	Insertion or replacement of pacemaker pulse generator only; dual chamber	46.00	1025	1225	441
33214	Upgrade of implanted pacemaker system, conversion of single chamber system to dual chamber system (includes removal of previously placed pulse generator, testing of existing lead, insertion of new lead, insertion of new pulse generator)	85.00	1893	2264	473
33216	Insertion, replacement or repositioning of permanent transvenous electrode(s) only (15 days or more after initial insertion); single chamber, atrial or ventricular	50.00	1114	1332	395
33217	Insertion, replacement or repositioning of permanent transvenous electrode(s) only (15 days or more after initial insertion); dual chamber	55.00	1225	1465	405
33218	Repair of pacemaker electrode(s) only; single chamber, atrial or ventricular	30.00	668	799	406
33220	Repair of pacemaker electrode(s) only; dual chamber	35.00	780	932	363
33222	Revision or relocation of skin pocket for pacemaker	40.00	891	1065	464
33223	Revision or relocation of skin pocket for implantable cardioverter-defibrillator	30.00	668	799	516
33233	Removal of permanent pacemaker pulse generator;	30.00	668	799	245
33234	Removal of permanent pacemaker pulse generator; with transvenous electrode(s), single lead system, atrial or ventricular	31.00	691	826	503
33235	Removal of permanent pacemaker pulse generator; with transvenous electrode(s), dual lead system	31.00	691	826	501
33236	Removal of permanent epicardial pacemaker and electrodes by thoracotomy; single lead system, atrial or ventricular	115.0	2562	3063	636
33237	Removal of permanent epicardial pacemaker and electrodes by thoracotomy; dual lead system	115.0	2562	3063	911
33238	Removal of permanent transvenous electrode(s) by thoracotomy	120.0	2673	3196	1027
33240	Insertion or replacement of implantable cardioverter-defibrillator pulse generator only	49.50	1103	1318	529
33241	Removal of implantable cardioverter-defibrillator pulse generator only	43.00	958	1145	216
33242	Repair of implantable cardioverter-defibrillator pulse generator and/or leads	35.00	780	932	626
33243	Removal of implantable cardioverter-defibrillator pulse generator and/or lead system; by thoracotomy	115.0	2562	3063	1248

	Code	Description	Medicode RVU	50th	75th	Medicare Nat'l Avg
	33244	Removal of implantable cardioverter-defibrillator pulse generator and/or lead system; by other than thoracotomy	115.0	2562	3063	770
	33245	Implantation or replacement of implantable cardioverter-defibrillator pads by thoracotomy, with or without sensing electrodes;	175.0	3898	4661	1298
	33246	Implantation or replacement of implantable cardioverter-defibrillator pads by thoracotomy, with or without sensing electrodes; with insertion of implantable cardioverter-defibrillator pulse generator	197.0	4388	5247	1753
	33247	Insertion or replacement of implantable cardioverter-defibrillator lead(s), by other than thoracotomy;	175.0	3898	4661	992
	33249	Insertion or replacement of implantable cardioverter-defibrillator lead(s), by other than thoracotomy; with insertion of cardio-defibrillator pulse generator	197.0	4388	5247	1395
	33250	Operative ablation of supraventricular arrhythmogenic focus or pathway (eg, Wolff-Parkinson-White, A-V node re-entry), tract(s) and/or focus (foci); without cardiopulmonary bypass	116.0	2584	3090	1251
	33251	Operative ablation of supraventricular arrhythmogenic focus or pathway (eg, Wolff-Parkinson-White, A-V node re-entry), tract(s) and/or focus (foci); with cardiopulmonary bypass	153.0	3408	4075	1655
●	**33253**	Operative incisions and reconstruction of atria for treatment of atrial fibrillation or atrial flutter (eg, maze procedure)	0.00	0	0	–
▲	**33261**	Operative ablation of ventricular arrhythmogenic focus with cardiopulmonary bypass	143.0	3185	3809	1550

33300–33478
Wounds of the Heart, Great Vessels, and Cardiac Valves

Coding Insight
When coding more than one valve procedure (33400–33478), list each valve separately and append modifier -51 to the second and subsequent codes. Indicate the separate corresponding ICD•9 code next to the appropriate CPT code.

Code 92960 should not be reported with a cardiovascular procedure code that includes the phrase "with cardiopulmonary bypass." Payers may consider the intra-operative electric shock part of the procedure.

Endomyocardial biopsy code 93505 should not be reported with an open heart procedure code.

Subsidiary Codes
Subsidiary codes have relative values that require no further adjustment:

20926 is "in addition" to 33300–33478
33530 is "in addition" to 33300–33478
33924 is "in addition" to 33470–33475
38746 is "in addition" to 33300–33478
49905 is "in addition" to 33300–33478

Because these are subsidiary or "in addition to" codes, reimbursement reduction and modifier -51 do not apply.

Code	Description	Medicode RVU	50th	75th	Medicare Nat'l Avg
33300	Repair of cardiac wound; without bypass	110.0	2450	2930	1313
33305	Repair of cardiac wound; with cardiopulmonary bypass	165.0	3675	4395	1559
33310	Cardiotomy, exploratory (includes removal of foreign body); without bypass	120.0	2673	3196	1192
33315	Cardiotomy, exploratory (includes removal of foreign body); with cardiopulmonary bypass	200.0	4455	5327	1475
33320	Suture repair of aorta or great vessels; without shunt or cardiopulmonary bypass	113.0	2517	3010	1260
33321	Suture repair of aorta or great vessels; with shunt bypass	138.0	3074	3676	1724
33322	Suture repair of aorta or great vessels; with cardiopulmonary bypass	154.0	3430	4102	1711
33330	Insertion of graft, aorta or great vessels; without shunt, or cardiopulmonary bypass	165.0	3675	4395	1328
33332	Insertion of graft, aorta or great vessels; with shunt bypass	184.0	4099	4901	1599
33335	Insertion of graft, aorta or great vessels; with cardiopulmonary bypass	204.0	4544	5434	1792
33400	Valvuloplasty, aortic valve; open, with cardiopulmonary bypass	200.0	4679	5473	2103
33401	Valvuloplasty, aortic valve; open, with inflow occlusion	180.0	4211	4926	2000
33403	Valvuloplasty, aortic valve; using transventricular dilation, with cardiopulmonary bypass	191.0	4468	5227	2038
33404	Construction of apical-aortic conduit	250.0	5849	6842	2462
33405	Replacement, aortic valve, with cardiopulmonary bypass; with prosthetic valve other than homograft	235.0	5498	6431	2617
33406	Replacement, aortic valve, with cardiopulmonary bypass; with homograft valve (freehand)	235.0	5498	6431	2995
33411	Replacement, aortic valve; with aortic annulus enlargement, noncoronary cusp	250.0	5849	6842	2977
33412	Replacement, aortic valve; with transventricular aortic annulus enlargement (Konno procedure)	250.0	5849	6842	3031
33413	Replacement, aortic valve; by translocation of autologous pulmonary valve with homograft replacement of pulmonary valve (Ross procedure)	312.5	7311	8552	3197
33414	Repair of left ventricular outflow tract obstruction by patch enlargement of the outflow tract	245.0	5732	6705	2918
33415	Resection or incision of subvalvular tissue for discrete subvalvular aortic stenosis	200.0	4679	5473	2354
33416	Ventriculomyotomy (-myectomy) for idiopathic hypertrophic subaortic stenosis (eg, asymmetric septal hypertrophy)	225.0	5264	6157	2383

Code	Description	Medicode RVU	50th	75th	Medicare Nat'l Avg
33417	Aortoplasty (gusset) for supravalvular stenosis	225.0	5264	6157	2643
33420	Valvotomy, mitral valve; closed heart	160.0	3743	4379	1702
33422	Valvotomy, mitral valve; open heart, with cardiopulmonary bypass	220.0	5147	6021	2406
33425	Valvuloplasty, mitral valve, with cardiopulmonary bypass;	208.0	4866	5692	2550
33426	Valvuloplasty, mitral valve, with cardiopulmonary bypass; with prosthetic ring	228.0	5334	6239	2523
33427	Valvuloplasty, mitral valve, with cardiopulmonary bypass; radical reconstruction, with or without ring	0.00	0	0	2864
33430	Replacement, mitral valve, with cardiopulmonary bypass	225.0	5264	6157	2936
33460	Valvectomy, tricuspid valve, with cardiopulmonary bypass	200.0	4679	5473	2104
33463	Valvuloplasty, tricuspid valve; without ring insertion	228.0	5334	6239	2430
33464	Valvuloplasty, tricuspid valve; with ring insertion	234.0	5474	6404	2497
33465	Replacement, tricuspid valve, with cardiopulmonary bypass	215.0	5030	5884	2571
33468	Tricuspid valve repositioning and plication for Ebstein anomaly	270.0	6317	7389	2686
33470	Valvotomy, pulmonary valve, closed heart; transventricular	160.0	3743	4379	1623
33471	Valvotomy, pulmonary valve, closed heart; via pulmonary artery	160.0	3743	4379	1948
33472	Valvotomy, pulmonary valve, open heart; with inflow occlusion	160.0	3743	4379	2111
33474	Valvotomy, pulmonary valve, open heart; with cardiopulmonary bypass	225.0	5264	6157	2111
33475	Replacement, pulmonary valve	248.0	5802	6787	2646
33476	Right ventricular resection for infundibular stenosis, with or without commissurotomy	220.0	5147	6021	2230
33478	Outflow tract augmentation (gusset), with or without commissurotomy or infundibular resection	240.0	5615	6568	2405

33500–33572
Coronary Artery Anomalies, Coronary Artery Bypass Grafting (CABG)

Coding Insight
Coronary artery bypass codes 33510–33545 are differentiated by the type of graft performed (e.g., venous, arterial, or combined arterial-venous). The surgeon should clearly specify in the operative report the number and type of grafts performed.

For this range of codes, carefully review your contracts with payers and their payment policy for the procedures, especially if the physician's fee schedule is incorporated into the payer's claims system.

If the fee schedule indicates a fee for a service such as assembly and operation of pump with oxygenator or heat exchanger (with or without ECG and/or pressure monitoring); each hour, and the physician generally reports two hours for the service, the fee schedule should indicate the per hour charge and that the number of units reported is indicated in the correct box on the HCFA-1500 claim form. Otherwise, the service may not be reimbursed correctly. For example, the fee schedule may have been incorporated with the two-hour price, and two units are indicated, when there is really only one two-hour unit of time. Or, the fee schedule may have been incorporated with the one-hour price and you are so accustomed to reporting the two-hour price that you only indicate one unit.

Claims adjudication requires the code and the number or units for the code. The system then searches the fee schedule and finds the contracted price to reimburse, based on a provider number or tax identification number. Check all EOBs carefully; with the number of contracts each payer incorporates and administers, some mistakes will be made. Make sure the mistake is not made in your contract.

When checking EOBs, any underpayments should be immediately requested, and any overpayments to the amount negotiated in the contract (i.e., you repay anything over $25) should be made promptly. Large overpayments that are not repaid immediately can target all future claims for audit.

Nota Bene: Providers of services in this CPT code range frequently use a team assembled and trained to perform certain procedures. The team may include nurses, physician assistants, or other nonphysician team members. While most payers will compensate for these services to varying degrees, it is important to understand what the reimbursement will be. Stipulate in the contract the percentage allocated to these team members and use modifier -81 when reporting these services. Compensation is typically 10 percent to 15 percent of the surgeon's fee. In contract talks, negotiate for the higher rate by showing how the team cuts down on the amount of time (and the amount of complications) it takes to perform the procedure. Stress the difficulties involved in working with different residents or hospital employees versus the advantages of team members who perform the procedure over and over again.

Some payers consider the ventilation assist and management code 94656 as incidental to the postoperative care when reported with a primary cardiovascular procedure.

Subsidiary Codes

Subsidiary codes have relative values that require no further adjustment:

20926 is "in addition" to 33533–33545
33517 is "in addition" to 33533–33536
33518 is "in addition" to 33533–33536
33519 is "in addition" to 33533–33536
33521 is "in addition" to 33533–33536
33522 is "in addition" to 33533–33536
33523 is "in addition" to 33533–33536
33530 is "in addition" to 33510–33536
33572 is "in addition" to 33510–33516, 33533–33536
38746 is "in addition" to 33500–33545
49905 is "in addition" to 33533–33545

Because these are subsidiary or "in addition to" codes, reimbursement reduction and modifier -51 do not apply.

MEDICARE ALERT

Medicare rebundles certain codes in the surgery section when the listed codes are considered a component of a more comprehensive service.

32020, 32100, 33210, 37720, 37730 will not be reimbursed when reported with 33510, 33511 33512, 33513, 33514, 33516
33510 will not be reimbursed when reported with 33511, 33512, 33513, 33514, 33516
33511 will not be reimbursed when reported with 33512, 33513, 33514, 33516
33512 will not be reimbursed when reported with 33513, 33514, 33516
33513 will not be reimbursed when reported with 33514, 33516
33514 will not be reimbursed when reported with 33516

Code	Description	Medicode RVU	50th	75th	Medicare Nat'l Avg
33500	Repair of coronary arteriovenous or arteriocardiac chamber fistula; with cardiopulmonary bypass	213.0	4983	5829	2275
33501	Repair of coronary arteriovenous or arteriocardiac chamber fistula; without cardiopulmonary bypass	142.0	3322	3886	1287
33502	Repair of anomalous coronary artery; by ligation	110.0	2573	3010	1429
33503	Repair of anomalous coronary artery; by graft, without cardiopulmonary bypass	150.0	3509	4105	2116
33504	Repair of anomalous coronary artery; by graft, with cardiopulmonary bypass	220.0	5147	6021	2244
33505	Repair of anomalous coronary artery; with construction of intrapulmonary artery tunnel (Takeuchi procedure)	239.0	5591	6540	2543
33506	Repair of anomalous coronary artery; by translocation from pulmonary artery to aorta	239.0	5591	6540	2543
33510	Coronary artery bypass, vein only; single coronary venous graft	196.0	4585	5364	2351
33511	Coronary artery bypass, vein only; two coronary venous grafts	220.0	5147	6021	2622
33512	Coronary artery bypass, vein only; three coronary venous grafts	245.0	5732	6705	2853
33513	Coronary artery bypass, vein only; four coronary venous grafts	259.0	6059	7088	3069
33514	Coronary artery bypass, vein only; five coronary venous grafts	275.0	6434	7526	3256
33516	Coronary artery bypass, vein only; six or more coronary venous grafts	0.00	0	0	3425
33517	Coronary artery bypass, using venous graft(s) and arterial graft(s); single vein graft (list separately in addition to code for arterial graft)	23.00	538	629	241
33518	Coronary artery bypass, using venous graft(s) and arterial graft(s); two venous grafts (list separately in addition to code for arterial graft)	46.00	1076	1259	469
33519	Coronary artery bypass, using venous graft(s) and arterial graft(s); three venous grafts (list separately in addition to code for arterial graft)	69.00	1614	1888	663
33521	Coronary artery bypass, using venous graft(s) and arterial graft(s); four venous grafts (list separately in addition to code for arterial graft)	85.00	1989	2326	840

Code	Description	Medicode RVU	50th	75th	Medicare Nat'l Avg
33522	Coronary artery bypass, using venous graft(s) and arterial graft(s); five venous grafts (list separately in addition to code for arterial graft)	101.0	2363	2764	1030
33523	Coronary artery bypass, using venous graft(s) and arterial graft(s); six or more venous grafts (list separately in addition to code for arterial graft)	120.0	2807	3284	1183
33530	Reoperation, coronary artery bypass procedure or valve procedure, more than one month after original operation (list separately in addition to code for primary procedure)	0.00	0	0	672
33533	Coronary artery bypass, using arterial graft(s); single arterial graft	214.5	5018	5870	2448
33534	Coronary artery bypass, using arterial graft(s); two coronary arterial grafts	240.0	5615	6568	2731
33535	Coronary artery bypass, using arterial graft(s); three coronary arterial grafts	267.0	6246	7307	3005
33536	Coronary artery bypass, using arterial graft(s); four or more coronary arterial grafts	0.00	0	0	3272
33542	Myocardial resection (eg, ventricular aneurysmectomy)	190.0	4445	5200	2575
33545	Repair of postinfarction ventricular septal defect, with or without myocardial resection	260.0	6083	7115	3027
33572	Coronary endarterectomy, open, any method, of left anterior descending, circumflex, or right coronary artery performed in conjunction with coronary artery bypass graft procedure, each vessel (list separately in addition to primary procedure)	108.5	2538	2969	323

33600–33999
Other Cardiac Procedures

Coding Insight
Procedures in this code range are often very complicated and may, in certain circumstances, require that the physician improvise to solve unforeseen problems on the spot. Submitting an operative report is very important with this type of claim. If significant additional time is required because of the unusual nature of the surgery, append modifier -22 and submit a cover letter explaining the unique aspects of the case and any unusual time or measures taken to correct the problem.

Subsidiary Codes
Subsidiary codes have relative values that require no further adjustment:

20926 is "in addition" to 33542–33999
33924 is "in addition" to 33600–33616, 33684–33688, 33692–33697, 33735–33767, 33770, 33781, 33786, and 33918–33922
33961 is "in addition" to 33960
38746 is "in addition" to 33542–33999
49905 is "in addition" to 33542–33999

Because these are subsidiary or "in addition to" codes, reimbursement reduction and modifier -51 do not apply.

Code	Description	Medicode RVU	50th	75th	Medicare Nat'l Avg
33600	Closure of atrioventricular valve (mitral or tricuspid) by suture or patch	228.0	5334	6239	2684
33602	Closure of semilunar valve (aortic or pulmonary) by suture or patch	228.0	5334	6239	2448
33606	Anastomosis of pulmonary artery to aorta (Damus-Kaye-Stansel procedure)	140.0	3275	3831	2918
33608	Repair of complex cardiac anomaly other than pulmonary atresia with ventricular septal defect by construction or replacement of conduit from right or left ventricle to pulmonary artery	277.0	6480	7580	2947
33610	Repair of complex cardiac anomalies (eg, single ventricle with subaortic obstruction) by surgical enlargement of interventricular septal defect	274.0	6410	7498	2918
33611	Repair of double outlet right ventricle with intraventricular tunnel repair;	289.0	6761	7909	2995
33612	Repair of double outlet right ventricle with intraventricular tunnel repair; with repair of right ventricular outflow tract obstruction	284.0	6644	7772	3027
33615	Repair of complex cardiac anomalies (eg, tricuspid atresia) by closure of atrial septal defect and anastomosis of atria or vena cava to pulmonary artery (simple Fontan procedure)	279.0	6527	7635	2966
33617	Repair of complex cardiac anomalies (eg, single ventricle) by modified Fontan procedure	285.0	6668	7799	3033
33619	Repair of single ventricle with aortic outflow obstruction and aortic arch hypoplasia (hypoplastic left heart syndrome) (eg, Norwood procedure)	319.0	7463	8730	3399
33641	Repair atrial septal defect, secundum, with cardiopulmonary bypass, with or without patch	160.0	3743	4379	1949
33645	Direct or patch closure, sinus venosus, with or without anomalous pulmonary venous drainage	190.0	4445	5200	2138
33647	Repair of atrial septal defect and ventricular septal defect, with direct or patch closure	250.0	5849	6842	2659
33660	Repair of incomplete or partial atrioventricular canal (ostium primum atrial septal defect), with or without atrioventricular valve repair	215.0	5030	5884	2367
33665	Repair of intermediate or transitional atrioventricular canal, with or without atrioventricular valve repair	230.0	5381	6294	2482
33670	Repair of complete atrioventricular canal, with or without prosthetic valve	270.0	6317	7389	2995
33681	Closure of ventricular septal defect, with or without patch	228.0	5334	6239	2617
33684	Closure of ventricular septal defect, with or without patch with pulmonary valvotomy or infundibular resection (acyanotic)	230.0	5381	6294	2693

Code	Description	Medicode RVU	50th	75th	Medicare Nat'l Avg
33688	Closure of ventricular septal defect, with or without patch with removal of pulmonary artery band, with or without gusset	230.0	5381	6294	2731
33690	Banding of pulmonary artery	95.00	2223	2600	1731
33692	Complete repair tetralogy of Fallot without pulmonary atresia;	220.0	5147	6021	2918
33694	Complete repair tetralogy of Fallot without pulmonary atresia; with transannular patch	245.0	5732	6705	2957
33697	Complete repair tetralogy of Fallot with pulmonary atresia including construction of conduit from right ventricle to pulmonary artery and closure of ventricular septal defect	256.0	5989	7006	3033
33702	Repair sinus of Valsalva fistula, with cardiopulmonary bypass;	200.0	4679	5473	2371
33710	Repair sinus of Valsalva fistula, with cardiopulmonary bypass; with repair of ventricular septal defect	260.0	6083	7115	2695
33720	Repair sinus of Valsalva aneurysm, with cardiopulmonary bypass	235.0	5498	6431	2371
33722	Closure of aortico-left ventricular tunnel	230.0	5381	6294	2448
33730	Complete repair of anomalous venous return (supracardiac, intracardiac, or infracardiac types)	235.0	5498	6431	2942
33732	Repair of cor triatriatum or supravalvular mitral ring by resection of left atrial membrane	232.0	5428	6349	2472
33735	Atrial septectomy or septostomy; closed heart (Blalock-Hanlon type operation)	150.0	3509	4105	1957
33736	Atrial septectomy or septostomy; open heart with cardiopulmonary bypass	189.0	4422	5172	2054
33737	Atrial septectomy or septostomy; open heart, with inflow occlusion	170.0	3977	4652	1978
33750	Shunt; subclavian to pulmonary artery (Blalock-Taussig type operation)	125.0	2924	3421	1803
33755	Shunt; ascending aorta to pulmonary artery (Waterston type operation)	140.0	3275	3831	1817
33762	Shunt; descending aorta to pulmonary artery (Potts-Smith type operation)	125.0	2924	3421	1817
33764	Shunt; central, with prosthetic graft	150.0	3509	4105	1817
33766	Shunt; superior vena cava to pulmonary artery for flow to one lung (classical Glenn procedure)	116.0	2714	3174	1855
33767	Shunt; superior vena cava to pulmonary artery for flow to both lungs (bidirectional Glenn procedure)	147.0	3439	4023	2092
33770	Repair of transposition of the great arteries with ventricular septal defect and subpulmonary stenosis; without surgical enlargement of ventricular septal defect	284.0	6644	7772	3024
33771	Repair of transposition of the great arteries with ventricular septal defect and subpulmonary stenosis; with surgical enlargement of ventricular septal defect	288.0	6738	7881	3072

Code	Description	Medicode RVU	50th	75th	Medicare Nat'l Avg
33774	Repair of transposition of the great arteries, atrial baffle procedure (eg, Mustard or Senning type) with cardiopulmonary bypass;	250.0	5849	6842	2558
33775	Repair of transposition of the great arteries, atrial baffle procedure (eg, Mustard or Senning type) with cardiopulmonary bypass; with removal of pulmonary band	290.0	6785	7936	2606
33776	Repair of transposition of the great arteries, atrial baffle procedure (eg, Mustard or Senning type) with cardiopulmonary bypass; with closure of ventricular septal defect	300.0	7019	8210	2846
33777	Repair of transposition of the great arteries, atrial baffle procedure (eg, Mustard or Senning type) with cardiopulmonary bypass; with repair of subpulmonic obstruction	300.0	7019	8210	2654
33778	Repair of transposition of the great arteries, aortic pulmonary artery reconstruction (eg, Jatene type);	300.0	7019	8210	3230
33779	Repair of transposition of the great arteries, aortic pulmonary artery reconstruction (eg, Jatene type); with removal of pulmonary band	310.0	7252	8483	3240
33780	Repair of transposition of the great arteries, aortic pulmonary artery reconstruction (eg, Jatene type); with closure of ventricular septal defect	360.0	8422	9852	3268
33781	Repair of transposition of the great arteries, aortic pulmonary artery reconstruction (eg, Jatene type); with repair of subpulmonic obstruction	360.0	8422	9852	3249
33786	Total repair, truncus arteriosus (Rastelli type operation)	273.0	6387	7471	3072
33788	Reimplantation of an anomalous pulmonary artery	165.0	3860	4515	2331
33800	Aortic suspension (aortopexy) for tracheal decompression (eg, for tracheomalacia) (separate procedure)	116.0	2714	3174	1234
33802	Division of aberrant vessel (vascular ring);	110.0	2573	3010	1664
33803	Division of aberrant vessel (vascular ring); with reanastomosis	140.0	3275	3831	1740
33813	Obliteration of aortopulmonary septal defect; without cardiopulmonary bypass	167.0	3907	4570	1779
33814	Obliteration of aortopulmonary septal defect; with cardiopulmonary bypass	219.0	5124	5993	2333
33820	Repair of patent ductus arteriosus; by ligation	100.0	2340	2737	1626
33822	Repair of patent ductus arteriosus; by division, under 18 years	120.0	2807	3284	1664
33824	Repair of patent ductus arteriosus; by division, 18 years and older	140.0	3275	3831	1740
33840	Excision of coarctation of aorta, with or without associated patent ductus arteriosus; with direct anastomosis	140.0	3275	3831	2181
33845	Excision of coarctation of aorta, with or without associated patent ductus arteriosus; with graft	200.0	4679	5473	2239

Code	Description	Medicode RVU	50th	75th	Medicare Nat'l Avg
33851	Excision of coarctation of aorta, with or without associated patent ductus arteriosus; repair using either left subclavian artery or prosthetic material as gusset for enlargement	220.0	5147	6021	2200
33852	Repair of hypoplastic or interrupted aortic arch using autogenous or prosthetic material; without cardiopulmonary bypass	185.0	4328	5063	2296
33853	Repair of hypoplastic or interrupted aortic arch using autogenous or prosthetic material; with cardiopulmonary bypass	246.0	5755	6732	2957
33860	Ascending aorta graft, with cardiopulmonary bypass, with or without valve suspension;	225.0	5264	6157	2967
33861	Ascending aorta graft, with cardiopulmonary bypass, with or without valve suspension; with coronary reconstruction	250.0	5849	6842	3032
33863	Ascending aorta graft, with cardiopulmonary bypass, with or without valve suspension; with aortic root replacement using composite prosthesis and coronary reconstruction	275.0	6434	7526	3097
33870	Transverse arch graft, with cardiopulmonary bypass	370.0	8656	10125	3575
33875	Descending thoracic aorta graft, with or without bypass	200.0	4679	5473	2609
33877	Repair of thoracoabdominal aortic aneurysm with graft, with or without cardiopulmonary bypass	0.00	0	0	3659
33910	Pulmonary artery embolectomy; with cardiopulmonary bypass	180.0	4211	4926	1569
33915	Pulmonary artery embolectomy; without cardiopulmonary bypass	135.0	3158	3694	1294
33916	Pulmonary endarterectomy, with or without embolectomy, with cardiopulmonary bypass	180.0	4211	4926	1754
33917	Repair of pulmonary artery stenosis by reconstruction with patch or graft	225.0	5264	6157	2494
33918	Repair of pulmonary atresia with ventricular septal defect, by unifocalization of pulmonary arteries; without cardiopulmonary bypass	219.0	5124	5993	2331
33919	Repair of pulmonary atresia with ventricular septal defect, by unifocalization of pulmonary arteries; with cardiopulmonary bypass	281.0	6574	7690	2990
33920	Repair of pulmonary atresia with ventricular septal defect, by construction or replacement of conduit from right or left ventricle to pulmonary artery	140.0	3275	3831	2976
33922	Transection of pulmonary artery with cardiopulmonary bypass	150.0	3509	4105	2000
● **33924**	Ligation and takedown of a systemic-to-pulmonary artery shunt, performed in conjunction with a congenital heart procedure (List separately in addition to code for primary procedure)	25.00	585	684	–
33930	Donor cardiectomy-pneumonectomy, with preparation and maintenance of allograft	0.00	0	0	–
33935	Heart-lung transplant with recipient cardiectomy-pneumonectomy	0.00	0	0	5503
33940	Donor cardiectomy, with preparation and maintenance of allograft	0.00	0	0	–

Code	Description	Medicode RVU	50th	75th	Medicare Nat'l Avg
33945	Heart transplant, with or without recipient cardiectomy	0.00	0	0	5188
33960	Prolonged extracorporeal circulation for cardiopulmonary insufficiency; initial 24 hours	84.00	1965	2299	1065
33961	Prolonged extracorporeal circulation for cardiopulmonary insufficiency; each additional 24 hours	84.00	1965	2299	735
33970	Insertion of intra-aortic balloon assist device through the femoral artery, open approach	65.00	1521	1779	707
33971	Removal of intra-aortic balloon assist device including repair of femoral artery, with or without graft	75.00	1755	2052	450
33973	Insertion of intra-aortic balloon assist device through the ascending aorta	66.50	1556	1820	760
33974	Removal of intra-aortic balloon assist device from the ascending aorta, including repair of the ascending aorta, with or without graft	70.00	1638	1916	762
33975	Implantation of ventricular assist device; single ventricle support	132.0	3088	3612	1417
33976	Implantation of ventricular assist device; biventricular support	158.5	3708	4338	1930
33977	Removal of ventricular assist device; single ventricle support	116.0	2714	3174	1239
33978	Removal of ventricular assist device; biventricular support	139.0	3252	3804	1417
33999	Unlisted procedure, cardiac surgery	0.00	0	0	–

34001–35390
Arteries and Veins

CODING INSIGHT

Codes listed in 35001–35162 were affected in 1995 by changes in either the code description or the descriptive notes in CPT. In the past, the notes or codes have specified these codes could be reported for direct repair of an aneurysm or excision and graft insertion for aneurysm, false aneurysm, ruptured aneurysm, or occlusive disease. The revised notes or codes now specify that they can be used for direct repair of aneurysm or excision and graft insertion for aneurysm, false aneurysm, ruptured aneurysm, and associated occlusive disease.

The notes/code changes may have affected the way you have used these codes in the past. If they were used for occlusive disease, they can now only be used when the occlusive disease is associated with the repair and graft insertions associated with aneurysm. CPT guides you to codes 35201–35286 for direct repair associated with occlusive disease only.

Embolectomy/Thrombectomy

Notes in CPT aid the coder in what is included in an embolectomy/thrombectomy. The main heading states Arteries and Veins, but the verbiage also includes that portion of the operative arteriogram performed by the surgeon. Remember, venograms are also included as part of the procedure because the main heading includes them.

Inflow/outflow procedure(s) that should not be reported with an open vascular procedure code include embolectomy, thrombectomy, balloon angioplasty, and intravascular stent placement.

Subsidiary Codes

Subsidiary codes have relative values that require no further adjustment:

20926 is "in addition" to 34001–35390
35390 is "in addition" to 35301
38746 is "in addition" to 34001–35390
49905 is "in addition" to 34001–35390

Because these are subsidiary or "in addition to" codes, reimbursement reduction and CPT modifier -51 do not apply.

Medicare Alert

Medicare rebundles certain codes in the surgery section when the listed codes are considered a component of a more comprehensive service.

37720 will not be reimbursed when reported with 35301, 35371, 35381
37730 will not be reimbursed when reported with 35301, 35371, 35381
36000 and 36140 will not be reimbursed when reported with 34201
44005, 49000 will not be reimbursed when reported with 35081, 35082, 35102
35371, 35372, 35381 will not be reimbursed when reported with 35141
35456 will not be reimbursed when reported with 35371, 35381

Code	Description	Medicode RVU	50th	75th	Medicare Nat'l Avg
34001	Embolectomy or thrombectomy, with or without catheter; carotid, subclavian or innominate artery, by neck incision	70.00	1556	1811	921
34051	Embolectomy or thrombectomy, with or without catheter; innominate, subclavian artery, by thoracic incision	80.00	1779	2070	937
34101	Embolectomy or thrombectomy, with or without catheter; axillary, brachial, innominate, subclavian artery, by arm incision	60.00	1334	1552	780
34111	Embolectomy or thrombectomy, with or without catheter; radial or ulnar artery, by arm incision	120.0	2668	3105	668
34151	Embolectomy or thrombectomy, with or without catheter; renal, celiac, mesentery, aortoiliac artery, by abdominal incision	120.0	2668	3105	1198
34201	Embolectomy or thrombectomy, with or without catheter; femoropopliteal, aortoiliac artery, by leg incision	100.0	2223	2587	795
34203	Embolectomy or thrombectomy, with or without catheter; popliteal-tibio-peroneal artery, by leg incision	90.00	2001	2328	878
34401	Thrombectomy, direct or with catheter; vena cava, iliac vein, by abdominal incision	90.00	2001	2328	848
34421	Thrombectomy, direct or with catheter; vena cava, iliac, femoropopliteal vein, by leg incision	68.00	1512	1759	712
34451	Thrombectomy, direct or with catheter; vena cava, iliac, femoropopliteal vein, by abdominal and leg incision	115.0	2557	2975	1031
34471	Thrombectomy, direct or with catheter; subclavian vein, by neck incision	70.00	1556	1811	524
34490	Thrombectomy, direct or with catheter; axillary and subclavian vein, by arm incision	70.00	1556	1811	624

Code	Description	Medicode RVU	50th	75th	Medicare Nat'l Avg
34501	Valvuloplasty, femoral vein	65.00	1445	1682	697
34502	Reconstruction of vena cava, any method	174.0	3869	4502	1862
34510	Venous valve transposition, any vein donor	79.00	1756	2044	843
34520	Cross-over vein graft to venous system	83.00	1845	2147	885
34530	Saphenopopliteal vein anastomosis	80.00	1779	2070	1172
35001	Direct repair of aneurysm, false aneurysm, or excision (partial or total) and graft insertion, with or without patch graft; for aneurysm and associated occlusive disease, carotid, subclavian artery, by neck incision	135.0	3002	3493	1497
35002	Direct repair of aneurysm, false aneurysm, or excision (partial or total) and graft insertion, with or without patch graft; for ruptured aneurysm, carotid, subclavian artery, by neck incision	135.0	3002	3493	1363
35005	Direct repair of aneurysm, false aneurysm, or excision (partial or total) and graft insertion, with or without patch graft; for aneurysm, false aneurysm, and associated occlusive disease, vertebral artery	135.0	3002	3493	1139
35011	Direct repair of aneurysm, false aneurysm, or excision (partial or total) and graft insertion, with or without patch graft; for aneurysm and associated occlusive disease, axillary-brachial artery, by arm incision	104.0	2312	2691	1101
35013	Direct repair of aneurysm, false aneurysm, or excision (partial or total) and graft insertion, with or without patch graft; for ruptured aneurysm, axillary-brachial artery, by arm incision	110.0	2446	2846	1333
35021	Direct repair of aneurysm, false aneurysm, or excision (partial or total) and graft insertion, with or without patch graft; for aneurysm, false aneurysm, and associated occlusive disease, innominate, subclavian artery, by thoracic incision	140.0	3113	3622	1542
35022	Direct repair of aneurysm, false aneurysm, or excision (partial or total) and graft insertion, with or without patch graft; for ruptured aneurysm, innominate, subclavian artery, by thoracic incision	125.0	2779	3234	1518
35045	Direct repair of aneurysm, false aneurysm, or excision (partial or total) and graft insertion, with or without patch graft; for aneurysm, false aneurysm, and associated occlusive disease, radial or ulnar artery	90.00	2001	2328	1044
35081	Direct repair of aneurysm, false aneurysm, or excision (partial or total) and graft insertion, with or without patch graft; for aneurysm, false aneurysm, and associated occlusive disease, abdominal aorta	160.0	3557	4139	1950
35082	Direct repair of aneurysm, false aneurysm, or excision (partial or total) and graft insertion, with or without patch graft; for ruptured aneurysm, abdominal aorta	165.0	3669	4269	2271
35091	Direct repair of aneurysm, false aneurysm, or excision (partial or total) and graft insertion, with or without patch graft; for aneurysm, false aneurysm, and associated occlusive disease, abdominal aorta involving visceral vessels (mesenteric, celiac, renal)	184.0	4091	4760	2181

Code	Description	Medicode RVU	50th	75th	Medicare Nat'l Avg
35092	Direct repair of aneurysm, false aneurysm, or excision (partial or total) and graft insertion, with or without patch graft; for ruptured aneurysm, abdominal aorta involving visceral vessels (mesenteric, celiac, renal)	200.0	4447	5174	2677
35102	Direct repair of aneurysm, false aneurysm, or excision (partial or total) and graft insertion, with or without patch graft; for aneurysm, false aneurysm, and associated occlusive disease, abdominal aorta involving iliac vessels (common, hypogastric, external)	170.0	3780	4398	2039
35103	Direct repair of aneurysm, false aneurysm, or excision (partial or total) and graft insertion, with or without patch graft; for ruptured aneurysm, abdominal aorta involving iliac vessels (common, hypogastric, external)	165.0	3669	4269	2529
35111	Direct repair of aneurysm, false aneurysm, or excision (partial or total) and graft insertion, with or without patch graft; for aneurysm, false aneurysm, and associated occlusive disease, splenic artery	112.0	2490	2898	1428
35112	Direct repair of aneurysm, false aneurysm, or excision (partial or total) and graft insertion, with or without patch graft; for ruptured aneurysm, splenic artery	115.0	2557	2975	1174
35121	Direct repair of aneurysm, false aneurysm, or excision (partial or total) and graft insertion, with or without patch graft; for aneurysm, false aneurysm, and associated occlusive disease, hepatic, celiac, renal, or mesenteric artery	144.0	3202	3725	1885
35122	Direct repair of aneurysm, false aneurysm, or excision (partial or total) and graft insertion, with or without patch graft; for ruptured aneurysm, hepatic, celiac, renal, or mesenteric artery	135.0	3002	3493	2114
35131	Direct repair of aneurysm, false aneurysm, or excision (partial or total) and graft insertion, with or without patch graft; for aneurysm, false aneurysm, and associated occlusive disease, iliac artery (common, hypogastric, external)	135.0	3002	3493	1518
35132	Direct repair of aneurysm, false aneurysm, or excision (partial or total) and graft insertion, with or without patch graft; for ruptured aneurysm, iliac artery (common, hypogastric, external)	140.0	3113	3622	1699
35141	Direct repair of aneurysm, false aneurysm, or excision (partial or total) and graft insertion, with or without patch graft; for aneurysm, false aneurysm, and associated occlusive disease, common femoral artery (profunda femoris, superficial femoral)	115.0	2557	2975	1297
35142	Direct repair of aneurysm, false aneurysm, or excision (partial or total) and graft insertion, with or without patch graft; for ruptured aneurysm, common femoral artery (profunda femoris, superficial femoral)	115.0	2557	2975	1392
35151	Direct repair of aneurysm, false aneurysm, or excision (partial or total) and graft insertion, with or without patch graft; for aneurysm, false aneurysm, and associated occlusive disease, popliteal artery	115.0	2557	2975	1404
35152	Direct repair of aneurysm, false aneurysm, or excision (partial or total) and graft insertion, with or without patch graft; for ruptured aneurysm, popliteal artery	115.0	2557	2975	1072

Code	Description	Medicode RVU	50th	75th	Medicare Nat'l Avg
35161	Direct repair of aneurysm, false aneurysm, or excision (partial or total) and graft insertion, with or without patch graft; for aneurysm, false aneurysm, and associated occlusive disease, other arteries	0.00	0	0	1415
35162	Direct repair of aneurysm, false aneurysm, or excision (partial or total) and graft insertion, with or without patch graft; for ruptured aneurysm, other arteries	100.0	2223	2587	1578
35180	Repair, congenital arteriovenous fistula; head and neck	120.0	2668	3105	834
35182	Repair, congenital arteriovenous fistula; thorax and abdomen	110.0	2446	2846	1120
35184	Repair, congenital arteriovenous fistula; extremities	120.0	2668	3105	898
35188	Repair, acquired or traumatic arteriovenous fistula; head and neck	120.0	2668	3105	898
35189	Repair, acquired or traumatic arteriovenous fistula; thorax and abdomen	110.0	2446	2846	1217
35190	Repair, acquired or traumatic arteriovenous fistula; extremities	120.0	2668	3105	990
35201	Repair blood vessel, direct; neck	120.0	2668	3105	860
35206	Repair blood vessel, direct; upper extremity	97.00	2157	2509	853
35207	Repair blood vessel, direct; hand, finger	103.0	2290	2665	859
35211	Repair blood vessel, direct; intrathoracic, with bypass	165.0	3669	4269	1413
35216	Repair blood vessel, direct; intrathoracic, without bypass	140.0	3113	3622	1188
35221	Repair blood vessel, direct; intra-abdominal	140.0	3113	3622	1177
35226	Repair blood vessel, direct; lower extremity	92.00	2046	2380	899
35231	Repair blood vessel with vein graft; neck	130.0	2890	3363	1096
35236	Repair blood vessel with vein graft; upper extremity	130.0	2890	3363	1041
35241	Repair blood vessel with vein graft; intrathoracic, with bypass	185.0	4113	4786	1454
35246	Repair blood vessel with vein graft; intrathoracic, without bypass	135.0	3002	3493	1449
35251	Repair blood vessel with vein graft; intra-abdominal	135.0	3002	3493	1110
35256	Repair blood vessel with vein graft; lower extremity	130.0	2890	3363	1074
35261	Repair blood vessel with graft other than vein; neck	130.0	2890	3363	1039
35266	Repair blood vessel with graft other than vein; upper extremity	130.0	2890	3363	976

Code	Description	Medicode RVU	50th	75th	Medicare Nat'l Avg
35271	Repair blood vessel with graft other than vein; intrathoracic, with bypass	185.0	4113	4786	1374
35276	Repair blood vessel with graft other than vein; intrathoracic, without bypass	135.0	3002	3493	1181
35281	Repair blood vessel with graft other than vein; intra-abdominal	135.0	3002	3493	1423
35286	Repair blood vessel with graft other than vein; lower extremity	130.0	2890	3363	1074
35301	Thromboendarterectomy, with or without patch graft; carotid, vertebral, subclavian, by neck incision	130.0	2890	3363	1344
35311	Thromboendarterectomy, with or without patch graft; subclavian, innominate, by thoracic incision	130.0	2890	3363	1920
35321	Thromboendarterectomy, with or without patch graft; axillary-brachial	130.0	2890	3363	1127
35331	Thromboendarterectomy, with or without patch graft; abdominal aorta	145.0	3224	3751	1571
35341	Thromboendarterectomy, with or without patch graft; mesenteric, celiac, or renal	120.0	2668	3105	1781
35351	Thromboendarterectomy, with or without patch graft; iliac	120.0	2668	3105	1523
35355	Thromboendarterectomy, with or without patch graft; iliofemoral	130.0	2890	3363	1361
35361	Thromboendarterectomy, with or without patch graft; combined aortoiliac	145.0	3224	3751	1835
35363	Thromboendarterectomy, with or without patch graft; combined aortoiliofemoral	160.0	3557	4139	1963
35371	Thromboendarterectomy, with or without patch graft; common femoral	100.0	2223	2587	1102
35372	Thromboendarterectomy, with or without patch graft; deep (profunda) femoral	100.0	2223	2587	1100
35381	Thromboendarterectomy, with or without patch graft; femoral and/or popliteal, and/or tibioperoneal	100.0	2223	2587	1303
35390	Reoperation, carotid, thromboendarterectomy, more than one month after original operation (List separately in addition to code for primary procedure) (Use 35390 only with 35301)	0.00	0	0	204

35450–35495
Transluminal Angioplasty and Atherectomy

Coding Insight
Transluminal angioplasty and atherectomy are sometimes performed prior to or as part of another procedure, in which case modifier -51 is appended. Unforeseen complications may also arise (e.g., more widespread disease of the artery than anticipated, accidental puncture of the artery necessitating an open procedure), in which case a reduction in the procedure cost should be made and modifier -52 appended.

If the physician supervises and interprets fluoroscopy during the procedure it is separately identified.

Nota Bene: When balloon angioplasty and atherectomy are performed at the same session in the same anatomic region, both should be separately identified. However, inflation of a positioning balloon during atherectomy should not be coded as a balloon angioplasty in addition to the atherectomy.

When balloon angioplasty and intra-vascular stent placement are performed at the same session in the same anatomic region, both should be separately identified. However, angioplasty performed as the method of stent deployment is not a separately coded service.

Subsidiary Codes

Subsidiary codes have relative values that require no further adjustment:

20926 is "in addition" to 35450–35495
38746 is "in addition" to 35450–35495
49905 is "in addition" to 35450–35495

Because these are subsidiary or "in addition to" codes, reimbursement reduction and modifier -51 do not apply.

Code	Description	Medicode RVU	50th	75th	Medicare Nat'l Avg
35450	Transluminal balloon angioplasty, open; renal or other visceral artery	89.00	1979	2303	839
35452	Transluminal balloon angioplasty, open; aortic	100.0	2223	2587	480
35454	Transluminal balloon angioplasty, open; iliac	80.00	1779	2070	663
35456	Transluminal balloon angioplasty, open; femoral-popliteal	82.00	1823	2121	808
35458	Transluminal balloon angioplasty, open; brachiocephalic trunk or branches, each vessel	80.00	1779	2070	852
35459	Transluminal balloon angioplasty, open; tibioperoneal trunk and branches	75.00	1668	1940	803
35460	Transluminal balloon angioplasty, open; venous	0.00	0	0	386
35470	Transluminal balloon angioplasty, percutaneous; tibioperoneal trunk or branches, each vessel	68.00	1512	1759	705
35471	Transluminal balloon angioplasty, percutaneous; renal or visceral artery	80.00	1779	2070	839
35472	Transluminal balloon angioplasty, percutaneous; aortic	90.00	2001	2328	405
35473	Transluminal balloon angioplasty, percutaneous; iliac	72.00	1601	1863	584
35474	Transluminal balloon angioplasty, percutaneous; femoral-popliteal	74.00	1645	1914	709
35475	Transluminal balloon angioplasty, percutaneous; brachiocephalic trunk or branches, each vessel	72.00	1601	1863	746
35476	Transluminal balloon angioplasty, percutaneous; venous	0.00	0	0	339
35480	Transluminal peripheral atherectomy, open; renal or other visceral artery	98.00	2179	2535	1015
35481	Transluminal peripheral atherectomy, open; aortic	110.0	2446	2846	507

Code	Description	Medicode RVU	50th	75th	Medicare Nat'l Avg
35482	Transluminal peripheral atherectomy, open; iliac	88.00	1957	2277	709
35483	Transluminal peripheral atherectomy, open; femoral-popliteal	90.00	2001	2328	864
35484	Transluminal peripheral atherectomy, open; brachiocephalic trunk or branches, each vessel	88.00	1957	2277	888
35485	Transluminal peripheral atherectomy, open; tibioperoneal trunk and branches	83.00	1845	2147	586
35490	Transluminal peripheral atherectomy, percutaneous; renal or other visceral artery	88.00	1957	2277	891
35491	Transluminal peripheral atherectomy, percutaneous; aortic	99.00	2201	2561	445
35492	Transluminal peripheral atherectomy, percutaneous; iliac	79.00	1756	2044	623
35493	Transluminal peripheral atherectomy, percutaneous; femoral-popliteal	81.00	1801	2096	759
35494	Transluminal peripheral atherectomy, percutaneous; brachiocephalic trunk or branches, each vessel	79.00	1756	2044	780
35495	Transluminal peripheral atherectomy, percutaneous; tibioperoneal trunk and branches	75.00	1668	1940	514

35501–35907
Bypass Graft

Coding Insight
Postoperative complications of a bypass graft (such as a clot) necessitating a return trip to the operating room for a related or unrelated procedure should be listed with modifiers -78 or -79 appended to the code. Unrelated or separately identifiable E/M services should be listed with modifier -24 or -25 appended. Using correct modifiers helps explain the circumstance for additional charges and will speed up the payer's claims processing time.

Subsidiary Codes
Subsidiary codes have relative values that require no further adjustment:

20926 is "in addition" to 35501–35907
35681 is "in addition" to 35501–35671
35700 is "in addition" to 35556, 35566, 35571, 35583, 35585, 35587, 35656, 35666, 35671.
38746 is "in addition" to 35501–35907
49905 is "in addition" to 35501–35907

Because these are subsidiary or "in addition to" codes, reimbursement reduction and modifier -51 do not apply.

Medicare Alert
Medicare rebundles certain codes in the surgery section when the listed codes are considered a component of a more comprehensive service.

37720, 37730 will not be reimbursed when reported with reported 35556, 35583, 35585

Code	Description	Medicode RVU	50th	75th	Medicare Nat'l Avg
35501	Bypass graft, with vein; carotid	120.0	2703	3161	1622
35506	Bypass graft, with vein; carotid-subclavian	120.0	2703	3161	1640
35507	Bypass graft, with vein; subclavian-carotid	120.0	2703	3161	1560
35508	Bypass graft, with vein; carotid-vertebral	135.0	3040	3556	1512
35509	Bypass graft, with vein; carotid-carotid	120.0	2703	3161	1557
35511	Bypass graft, with vein; subclavian-subclavian	120.0	2703	3161	1107
35515	Bypass graft, with vein; subclavian-vertebral	135.0	3040	3556	1193
35516	Bypass graft, with vein; subclavian-axillary	120.0	2703	3161	1418
35518	Bypass graft, with vein; axillary-axillary	140.0	3153	3687	1372
35521	Bypass graft, with vein; axillary-femoral	120.0	2703	3161	1457
35526	Bypass graft, with vein; aortosubclavian or carotid	133.0	2995	3503	1335
35531	Bypass graft, with vein; aortoceliac or aortomesenteric	138.0	3108	3635	1943
35533	Bypass graft, with vein; axillary-femoral-femoral	175.0	3941	4609	1756
35536	Bypass graft, with vein; splenorenal	133.0	2995	3503	1845
35541	Bypass graft, with vein; aortoiliac or bi-iliac	133.0	2995	3503	1902
35546	Bypass graft, with vein; aortofemoral or bifemoral	150.0	3378	3951	2030
35548	Bypass graft, with vein; aortoiliofemoral, unilateral	135.0	3040	3556	1680
35549	Bypass graft, with vein; aortoiliofemoral, bilateral	180.0	4054	4741	1844
35551	Bypass graft, with vein; aortofemoral-popliteal	154.0	3468	4056	1901
35556	Bypass graft, with vein; femoral-popliteal	130.0	2928	3424	1591
35558	Bypass graft, with vein; femoral-femoral	120.0	2703	3161	1380
35560	Bypass graft, with vein; aortorenal	150.0	3378	3951	1869
35563	Bypass graft, with vein; ilioiliac	125.0	2815	3292	946
35565	Bypass graft, with vein; iliofemoral	125.0	2815	3292	1425

Code	Description	Medicode RVU	50th	75th	Medicare Nat'l Avg
35566	Bypass graft, with vein; femoral-anterior tibial, posterior tibial, peroneal artery or other distal vessels	150.0	3378	3951	1851
35571	Bypass graft, with vein; popliteal-tibial, -peroneal artery or other distal vessels	150.0	3378	3951	1689
35582	In-situ vein bypass; aortofemoral-popliteal (only femoral-popliteal portion in-situ)	127.0	2860	3345	2135
35583	In-situ vein bypass; femoral-popliteal	137.0	3086	3608	1712
35585	In-situ vein bypass; femoral-anterior tibial, posterior tibial, or peroneal artery	157.0	3536	4135	1948
35587	In-situ vein bypass; popliteal-tibial, peroneal	125.0	2815	3292	1750
35601	Bypass graft, with other than vein; carotid	115.0	2590	3029	1522
35606	Bypass graft, with other than vein; carotid-subclavian	115.0	2590	3029	1561
35612	Bypass graft, with other than vein; subclavian-subclavian	115.0	2590	3029	1359
35616	Bypass graft, with other than vein; subclavian-axillary	115.0	2590	3029	1381
35621	Bypass graft, with other than vein; axillary-femoral	120.0	2703	3161	1470
35623	Bypass graft, with other than vein; axillary-popliteal or -tibial	156.0	3513	4109	986
35626	Bypass graft, with other than vein; aortosubclavian or carotid	123.0	2770	3240	1844
35631	Bypass graft, with other than vein; aortoceliac, aortomesenteric, aortorenal	128.0	2883	3371	1805
35636	Bypass graft, with other than vein; splenorenal (splenic to renal arterial anastomosis)	123.0	2770	3240	1466
35641	Bypass graft, with other than vein; aortoiliac or bi-iliac	151.0	3401	3977	1932
35642	Bypass graft, with other than vein; carotid-vertebral	125.0	2815	3292	1143
35645	Bypass graft, with other than vein; subclavian-vertebral	125.0	2815	3292	1153
35646	Bypass graft, with other than vein; aortofemoral or bifemoral	165.0	3716	4346	2205
35650	Bypass graft, with other than vein; axillary-axillary	125.0	2815	3292	1344
35651	Bypass graft, with other than vein; aortofemoral-popliteal	144.0	3243	3793	2090
35654	Bypass graft, with other than vein; axillary-femoral-femoral	175.0	3941	4609	1870
35656	Bypass graft, with other than vein; femoral-popliteal	125.0	2815	3292	1477
35661	Bypass graft, with other than vein; femoral-femoral	120.0	2703	3161	1328

Code	Description	Medicode RVU	50th	75th	Medicare Nat'l Avg
35663	Bypass graft, with other than vein; ilioiliac	127.0	2860	3345	1308
35665	Bypass graft, with other than vein; iliofemoral	125.0	2815	3292	1500
35666	Bypass graft, with other than vein; femoral-anterior tibial, posterior tibial, or peroneal artery	125.0	2815	3292	1631
35671	Bypass graft, with other than vein; popliteal-tibial or - peroneal artery	150.0	3378	3951	1366
35681	Bypass graft, composite	0.00	0	0	944
35691	Transposition and/or reimplantation; vertebral to carotid artery	120.0	2703	3161	1567
35693	Transposition and/or reimplantation; vertebral to subclavian artery	120.0	2703	3161	986
35694	Transposition and/or reimplantation; subclavian to carotid artery	120.0	2703	3161	1139
35695	Transposition and/or reimplantation; carotid to subclavian artery	120.0	2703	3161	1139
35700	Reoperation, femoral-popliteal or femoral (popliteal) - anterior tibial, posterior tibial, peroneal artery or other distal vessels, more than one month after original operation (List separately in addition to code for primary procedure)	0.00	0	0	197
35701	Exploration (not followed by surgical repair), with or without lysis of artery; carotid artery	57.00	1284	1501	496
35721	Exploration (not followed by surgical repair), with or without lysis of artery; femoral artery	45.00	1013	1185	483
35741	Exploration (not followed by surgical repair), with or without lysis of artery; popliteal artery	45.00	1013	1185	480
35761	Exploration (not followed by surgical repair), with or without lysis of artery; other vessels	50.00	1126	1317	490
35800	Exploration for postoperative hemorrhage, thrombosis or infection; neck	55.00	1239	1449	508
35820	Exploration for postoperative hemorrhage, thrombosis or infection; chest	75.00	1689	1975	840
35840	Exploration for postoperative hemorrhage, thrombosis or infection; abdomen	65.00	1464	1712	701
35860	Exploration for postoperative hemorrhage, thrombosis or infection; extremity	53.00	1194	1396	502
35870	Repair of graft-enteric fistula	180.0	4054	4741	1300
35875	Thrombectomy of arterial or venous graft;	63.50	1430	1672	784
35876	Thrombectomy of arterial or venous graft; with revision of arterial or venous graft	75.00	1689	1975	906
35901	Excision of infected graft; neck	60.00	1351	1580	705
35903	Excision of infected graft; extremity	60.00	1351	1580	748

Code	Description	Medicode RVU	50th	75th	Medicare Nat'l Avg
35905	Excision of infected graft; thorax	75.00	1689	1975	1003
35907	Excision of infected graft; abdomen	72.00	1622	1896	1027

36000–36680
Vascular Injection Procedures — Intra-osseous

Coding Insight
Codes 36011–36012 describe selective catheter placement, with the first order branch from the vena cava (36011) being any initial vessel draining directly into the vena cava (e.g., renal or jugular vein), and the second order branch of the vena cava (36012) being any vein draining into a first order branch (e.g., left adrenal, petrosal sinus). Catheters, drugs, and contrast media are reported in addition to the service. For injection procedures in conjunction with cardiac catheterization, see 93541–93545, for chemotherapy of malignant disease, see 96400–96549."

Nota Bene: Read new notes listed in this code range under vascular injection procedures, and note that the parenthetical phrase describing the deletion of code 36230 has been revised.

Know the difference between port, catheter, and pump, associated with codes 36488–36491 and 36533.

Port
A port is a device situated at the end of a catheter. Part of the port (bottom and sides) may be made of a metal like steel or titanium and/or a combination of these, depending on the manufacturer. The upper part of a port looks similar to a small diaphragm and is called the septum. The septum is usually made of a rubbery material like plastic. The material allows the septum to close off (contract) after a blood withdrawal or injection of medication or other fluid has been performed. A catheter may have one or more ports, which allows multiple injections or withdrawals to be made. Some catheters are inserted so that the port ends up flush with the skin, others are more closed system and are inserted into a central or peripheral vein and the port end is buried in the subcutaneous tissue (e.g., Port-A-Cath®). Some catheters not only have ports but also subcutaneous reservoirs with small pumps that are implanted in subcutaneous tissues (e.g., Infuse-A-Port®) where medication is stored and slowly released by a pump into a vein through the tip of the catheter.

Catheter
A catheter is a hollow tube made of rubber, elastic, plastic, or a combination of materials. The type of catheter depends partially on the construction of the tip. Some tips are rounded and have an eye, while others have a tip that is cut off flush or at an angle. Catheters are inserted into body cavities or into veins or arteries within the body.

Venous catheters are used for infusion of fluids, withdrawal of blood for sampling, and for monitoring. They may be used for short term therapy (IV) or be placed for long term therapy (central venous line). The tip of the catheter may have one or more lumens (openings inside of the catheter with separate compartments that run the length of the catheter) or may even have one or more actual catheters and tips that can be routed into different veins. Catheter ends can have one or more exits, and may end outside the body or be placed with the port end inside the body in a subcutaneous pocket. Intra-venous therapy catheters can have other tubing that can be connected to the outside of the catheter or be part of the catheter itself, including Y-type connectors, pigtails, and extension sets. The connectors and pigtails allow other IV tubing and extensions to be connected, or they serve as a site to inject and/or infuse one or more medications. Extra tubing, connectors, and extensions can be used with central venous lines, where a needle is inserted into the port, tubing, etc., and attached to the end of the needle.

Catheter insertion allows the performance of multiple procedures without repeatedly performing a venipuncture, and is a good method for delivering constant or periodic infusions. Veins are spared and frequent IV insertions become unnecessary when central venous lines are inserted.

Pump

A pump is a device used to deliver a specific amount of fluid, doses of medications, or parenteral feeding needs.

One type has an IV line placed through a small box containing a pumping device, and the box is attached to a stand. The IV line enters and exits through the box, and the pump works by exerting pressure on the IV line at specified intervals. Cassettes are used to program the pump to deliver a certain amount of fluid in a given amount of time and at different intervals. If more than one medication is being delivered at a time and if they are at different rates, more than one cassette or pump will be used. Remember, IV lines and central venous lines can have more than one hub and/or port on the end, so that more than one fluid/medication can be delivered at one time.

Another type of pump is part of a peritoneal, epidural, or a closed central venous line system, in which the catheter, port, pump, and reservoir are all implanted within the body. The pump may be electronic or driven by bellows and freon.

Codes 36488–36491 all refer to the placement of a central venous line. Codes 36488–36489 are used for placement of a central venous catheter when it is a percutaneous insertion and the patient is more than two years of age. The catheter can be inserted into the subclavian, jugular, or other vein, and once inserted it could be used for recording central venous pressure, hyperalimentation, hemodialysis, chemotherapy, and so forth. The tip of the catheter allows for infusion, monitoring, or blood sampling. Use of codes 36488–36489 is determined by the age of the patient.

An example of a percutaneous placement of a central venous catheter follows. A needle is inserted into the skin overlying the subclavian, jugular, or other vein and into the vein itself. (A wire may then be inserted through the needle into the vein and the needle removed.) The physician threads a catheter along the wire into the vessel and removes the wire. The catheter tip is advanced into the superior or inferior vena cava. The catheter may be passed through a subcutaneous tunnel and brought out at a point distant from the entry into the vein. A suture is placed through the skin to hold the catheter (line) in place.

In 36490 and 36491 an incision is made through the skin over the vein, and the physician isolates and dissects the vein for placement of the catheter. The vein is nicked (cutdown) and the catheter is inserted and the tip advanced into the vena cava. The incision is sutured closed and the catheter is left in the vein until treatment is completed. Use of 36490 or 36491 is determined by the age of the patient.

Code 36533 is used when an implantable venous access port is inserted. The code also specifies that the port may or may not have a subcutaneous reservoir. This procedure installs a type of closed system wherein the catheter, port, and even the reservoir is implanted; it may include a pump. The catheter is inserted into a vein, but the port, reservoir, and pump are implanted in subcutaneous tissue. Be sure to code separately for other services performed beyond placement of the catheter (e.g., review of prescription or fluids for long-term or permanent hyperalimentation).

Codes 36415 and 36600 should only be reported one time for each blood draw, not for each laboratory test ordered. Generally, blood from a single draw is used to perform different laboratory tests.

When determining physician charges for hospital visits, the correct E/M visit, when performed, may be identified separately. A physician may not only insert a catheter, but also concurrently or on separate dates manage other problems associated with the care of a patient. Too often, staff notes or physician coding are the only resources used to determine the correct E/M code. Keep in mind that hospital regulations frequently require a physician to rewrite orders for treatments or medications every 24–48 hours, and that the extra time required to complete these tasks takes significant time and can change the E/M code that is used. In the event of an audit, all of these factors are taken into account. You could be reporting a lower level E/M service than is being performed, which would result in a coding error.

A physician may manage a patient's sepsis and at the same time be managing TPN, blood transfusion, or ventilator management. Or, he/she may discuss the sepsis and orders for blood in the staff notes but may not mention other orders that were rewritten (such as TPN and ventilator management), which generally must be written on a separate physician order form. Coders should encourage the physician to document in the staff notes all of the services performed, and then check all documents for uniformity.

Medicare and Venous Access Devices

Medicare does not seem to have a clear national policy regarding venous access devices, and, consequently, different state Medicare payers have a wide array of policies in this regard. They range from very little to total reimbursement for approved uses. Contact your local carrier to obtain its policy for venous access devices.

Use HCPCS code G0001 to report routine venipuncture to Medicare. Code 36415 should only be used when the specimen is obtained by a routine capillary stick (e.g., finger/heel/ear stick).

Cosmetic Warning

This section contains codes that are considered cosmetic 85 percent of the time or more. The codes are 36468 and 36469.

Subsidiary Codes

Subsidiary codes have relative values that require no further adjustment:

20926 is "in addition" to 36000–36680
36218 is "in addition" to 36216–36217
36248 is "in addition" to 36246–36247
38746 is "in addition" to 36000–36680
49905 is "in addition" to 36000–36680

Because these are subsidiary or "in addition to" codes, reimbursement reduction and modifier -51 do not apply.

Code		Description	Medicode RVU	50th	75th	Medicare Nat'l Avg
36000	*	Introduction of needle or intracatheter, vein	3.55	84	99	24
36005		Injection procedure for contrast venography (including introduction of needle or intracatheter)	7.00	166	195	49
36010		Introduction of catheter, superior or inferior vena cava	18.00	427	501	176

Code	Description	Medicode RVU	50th	75th	Medicare Nat'l Avg
36011	Selective catheter placement, venous system; first order branch (eg, renal vein, jugular vein)	20.00	474	556	180
36012	Selective catheter placement, venous system; second order, or more selective, branch (eg, left adrenal vein, petrosal sinus)	24.00	569	668	222
36013	Introduction of catheter, right heart or main pulmonary artery	20.00	474	556	178
36014	Selective catheter placement, left or right pulmonary artery	24.00	569	668	190
36015	Selective catheter placement, segmental or subsegmental pulmonary artery	28.00	663	779	222
36100	Introduction of needle or intracatheter, carotid or vertebral artery	22.00	521	612	206
36120	Introduction of needle or intracatheter; retrograde brachial artery	20.00	474	556	168
36140	Introduction of needle or intracatheter; extremity artery	15.00	355	417	133
36145	Introduction of needle or intracatheter; arteriovenous shunt created for dialysis (cannula, fistula, or graft)	17.50	415	487	219
36160	Introduction of needle or intracatheter, aortic, translumbar	25.00	592	696	208
36200	Introduction of catheter, aorta	22.50	533	626	213
36215	Selective catheter placement, arterial system; each first order thoracic or brachiocephalic branch, within a vascular family	24.00	569	668	257
36216	Selective catheter placement, arterial system; initial second order thoracic or brachiocephalic branch, within a vascular family	31.00	735	863	302
36217	Selective catheter placement, arterial system; initial third order or more selective thoracic or brachiocephalic branch, within a vascular family	36.34	861	1011	360
36218	Selective catheter placement, arterial system; additional second order, third order, and beyond, thoracic or brachiocephalic branch, within a vascular family (use in addition to 36216 or 36217 as appropriate)	8.00	190	223	58
36245	Selective catheter placement, arterial system; each first order abdominal, pelvic, or lower extremity artery branch, within a vascular family	25.00	592	696	287
36246	Selective catheter placement, arterial system; initial second order abdominal, pelvic, or lower extremity artery branch, within a vascular family	28.00	663	779	302
36247	Selective catheter placement, arterial system; initial third order or more selective abdominal, pelvic, or lower extremity artery branch, within a vascular family	35.00	829	974	360
36248	Selective catheter placement, arterial system; additional second order, third order, and beyond, abdominal, pelvic, or lower extremity artery branch, within a vascular family (use in addition to 36246 or 36247 as appropriate)	6.50	154	181	58
36260	Insertion of implantable intra-arterial infusion pump (eg, for chemotherapy of liver)	60.00	1422	1669	722

Code		Description	Medicode RVU	50th	75th	Medicare Nat'l Avg
36261		Revision of implanted intra-arterial infusion pump	30.00	711	835	305
36262		Removal of implanted intra-arterial infusion pump	25.00	592	696	242
36299		Unlisted procedure, vascular injection	0.00	0	0	–
36400		Venipuncture, under age 3 years; femoral, jugular or sagittal sinus	2.50	57	67	10
36405	*	Venipuncture, under age 3 years; scalp vein	3.75	85	101	23
36406		Venipuncture, under age 3 years; other vein	2.75	62	74	14
36410	*	Venipuncture, child over age 3 years or adult, necessitating physician's skill (separate procedure), for diagnostic or therapeutic purposes. Not to be used for routine venipuncture.	2.00	45	54	16
36415	*	Routine venipuncture or finger/heel/ear stick for collection of specimen(s)	0.41	9	11	–
36420		Venipuncture, cutdown; under age 1 year	5.25	121	147	55
36425		Venipuncture, cutdown; age 1 or over	4.50	104	126	31
36430		Transfusion, blood or blood components	4.00	92	112	35
36440	*	Push transfusion, blood, 2 years or under	7.00	162	197	79
36450		Exchange transfusion, blood; newborn	25.00	578	702	149
36455		Exchange transfusion, blood; other than newborn	25.00	578	702	175
36460		Transfusion, intrauterine, fetal	50.00	1156	1405	422
36468		Single or multiple injections of sclerosing solutions, spider veins (telangiectasia); limb or trunk	0.00	0	0	–
36469		Single or multiple injections of sclerosing solutions, spider veins (telangiectasia); face	0.00	0	0	–
36470	*	Injection of sclerosing solution; single vein	4.00	92	112	49
36471	*	Injection of sclerosing solution; multiple veins, same leg	9.00	208	253	71
36481		Percutaneous portal vein catheterization by any method	44.00	1017	1236	502
36488	*	Placement of central venous catheter (subclavian, jugular, or other vein) (eg, for central venous pressure, hyperalimentation, hemodialysis, or chemotherapy); percutaneous, age 2 years or under	11.50	266	323	86
36489	*	Placement of central venous catheter (subclavian, jugular, or other vein) (eg, for central venous pressure, hyperalimentation, hemodialysis, or chemotherapy); percutaneous, over age 2	11.50	266	323	91

Code		Description	Medicode RVU	50th	75th	Medicare Nat'l Avg
36490	*	Placement of central venous catheter (subclavian, jugular, or other vein) (eg, for central venous pressure, hyperalimentation, hemodialysis, or chemotherapy); cutdown, age 2 years or under	26.00	601	730	118
36491	*	Placement of central venous catheter (subclavian, jugular, or other vein) (eg, for central venous pressure, hyperalimentation, hemodialysis, or chemotherapy); cutdown, over age 2	22.00	509	618	128
36493		Repositioning of previously placed central venous catheter under fluoroscopic guidance	5.50	127	155	68
36500		Venous catheterization for selective organ blood sampling	16.00	370	450	123
36510	*	Catheterization of umbilical vein for diagnosis or therapy, newborn	7.50	173	211	50
36520		Therapeutic apheresis (plasma and/or cell exchange)	17.00	393	478	137
36522		Photopheresis, extracorporeal	19.00	439	534	213
36530		Insertion of implantable intravenous infusion pump	41.00	948	1152	413
36531		Revision of implantable intravenous infusion pump	35.00	809	983	367
36532		Removal of implantable intravenous infusion pump	23.00	532	646	209
36533		Insertion of implantable venous access port, with or without subcutaneous reservoir	41.00	948	1152	404
36534		Revision of implantable venous access port and/or subcutaneous reservoir	33.00	763	927	298
36535		Removal of implantable venous access port and/or subcutaneous reservoir	23.00	532	646	182
36600	*	Arterial puncture, withdrawal of blood for diagnosis	2.50	55	68	21
36620		Arterial catheterization or cannulation for sampling, monitoring or transfusion (separate procedure); percutaneous	8.50	187	232	71
36625		Arterial catheterization or cannulation for sampling, monitoring or transfusion (separate procedure); cutdown	8.50	187	232	110
36640		Arterial catheterization for prolonged infusion therapy (chemotherapy), cutdown	15.00	331	409	172
36660	*	Catheterization, umbilical artery, newborn, for diagnosis or therapy	10.00	220	273	67
36680		Placement of needle for intraosseous infusion	0.00	0	0	88

36800–36861
Intervascular Cannulization or Shunt

Coding Insight
Because the anastomosis created in codes 36821 and 36825–36830 must mature before use, an external cannulization for hemodialysis (36488*–36489*) is often performed in the same operative session. The external cannulization is reported separately, and modifier -51 is appended to the cannulization code.

Complications of a shunt (declotting) procedure should be listed separately. Append the correct modifier if performed in the postoperative period.

Treatment of underlying conditions such as diabetes should be reported separately. Append the correct E/M modifier if performed in the postoperative period.

Subsidiary Codes
Subsidiary codes have relative values that require no further adjustment:

20926 is "in addition" to 36800–36861
38746 is "in addition" to 36800–36861
49905 is "in addition" to 36800–36861

Because these are subsidiary or "in addition to" codes, reimbursement reduction and modifier -51 do not apply.

Code	Description	Medicode RVU	50th	75th	Medicare Nat'l Avg
36800	Insertion of cannula for hemodialysis, other purpose (separate procedure); vein to vein	17.00	404	477	176
36810	Insertion of cannula for hemodialysis, other purpose (separate procedure); arteriovenous, external (Scribner type)	40.00	951	1122	409
36815	Insertion of cannula for hemodialysis, other purpose (separate procedure); arteriovenous, external revision, or closure	28.00	665	786	292
36821	Arteriovenous anastomosis, direct, any site (eg, Cimino type) (separate procedure)	62.00	1473	1740	700
36822	Insertion of cannula(s) for prolonged extracorporeal circulation for cardiopulmonary insufficiency (ECMO) (separate procedure)	45.00	1069	1263	460
36825	Creation of arteriovenous fistula by other than direct arteriovenous anastomosis (separate procedure); autogenous graft	80.00	1901	2245	959
36830	Creation of arteriovenous fistula by other than direct arteriovenous anastomosis (separate procedure); nonautogenous graft	80.50	1913	2259	889
36832	Revision of an arteriovenous fistula, with or without thrombectomy, autogenous or non-autogenous graft (separate procedure)	70.50	1676	1978	724
36834	Plastic repair of arteriovenous aneurysm (separate procedure)	80.00	1901	2245	794
36835	Insertion of Thomas shunt (separate procedure)	100.0	2377	2806	418

Code	Description	Medicode RVU	50th	75th	Medicare Nat'l Avg
36860	Cannula declotting (separate procedure); without balloon catheter	15.00	356	421	181
36861	Cannula declotting (separate procedure); with balloon catheter	23.00	547	645	316

37140–37181
Portal Decompression Procedures

Coding Insight
Treatment of an underlying condition is reported separately. Append modifier -24 or -25 if done during the postoperative period.

Subsidiary Codes
Subsidiary codes have relative values that require no further adjustment:

20926 is "in addition" to 37140–37181
38746 is "in addition" to 37140–37181
49905 is "in addition" to 37140–37181

Because these are subsidiary or "in addition to" codes, reimbursement reduction and modifier -51 do not apply.

Code	Description	Medicode RVU	50th	75th	Medicare Nat'l Avg
37140	Venous anastomosis; portocaval	155.0	3684	4349	169
37145	Venous anastomosis; renoportal	155.0	3684	4349	164
37160	Venous anastomosis; caval-mesenteric	155.0	3684	4349	165
37180	Venous anastomosis; splenorenal, proximal	155.0	3684	4349	158
37181	Venous anastomosis; splenorenal, distal (selective decompression of esophagogastric varices, any technique)	155.0	3684	4349	177

37200–37209
Transcatheter Therapy and Biopsy

Coding Insight
Radiology supervision and interpretation and treatment of any underlying condition/disease is identified separately.

Nota Bene: Open and percutaneous procedure codes for transcatheter placement of an intravascular stent(s) that relate to the same vessel should not be reported together.

SUBSIDIARY CODES

Subsidiary codes have relative values that require no further adjustment:

20926 is "in addition" to 37200–37209
37206 is "in addition" to 37205
37208 is "in addition" to 37207
38746 is "in addition" to 37200–37209
49905 is "in addition" to 37200–37209

Because these are subsidiary or "in addition to" codes, reimbursement reduction and modifier -51 do not apply.

Code	Description	Medicode RVU	50th	75th	Medicare Nat'l Avg
37200	Transcatheter biopsy	36.00	856	1010	215
37201	Transcatheter therapy, infusion for thrombolysis other than coronary	39.00	927	1094	457
37202	Transcatheter therapy, infusion other than for thrombolysis, any type (eg, spasmolytic, vasoconstrictive)	32.00	761	898	358
37203	Transcatheter retrieval, percutaneous, of intravascular foreign body (eg, fractured venous or arterial catheter)	29.00	689	814	317
37204	Transcatheter occlusion or embolization (eg, for tumor destruction, to achieve hemostasis, to occlude a vascular malformation), percutaneous, any method, non-central nervous system, non-head or neck	95.00	2258	2665	1144
37205	Transcatheter placement of an intravascular stent(s), (non-coronary vessel), percutaneous; initial vessel	64.00	1521	1796	540
37206	Transcatheter placement of an intravascular stent(s), (non-coronary vessel), percutaneous; each additional vessel	32.00	761	898	270
37207	Transcatheter placement of an intravascular stent(s), (non-coronary vessel), open; initial vessel	64.00	1521	1796	540
37208	Transcatheter placement of an intravascular stent(s), (non-coronary vessel), open; each additional vessel	32.00	761	898	270
37209	Exchange of a previously placed arterial catheter during thrombolytic therapy	14.00	333	393	85

37565–37799
Ligation and Other Procedures

SUBSIDIARY CODES

Subsidiary codes have relative values that require no further adjustment:

20926 is "in addition" to 37565–37799
38746 is "in addition" to 37565–37799
49905 is "in addition" to 37565–37799

Because these are subsidiary or "in addition to" codes, reimbursement reduction and modifier -51 do not apply.

Code	Description	Medicode RVU	50th	75th	Medicare Nat'l Avg
37565	Ligation, internal jugular vein	50.00	1188	1403	339
37600	Ligation; external carotid artery	45.00	1069	1263	399
37605	Ligation; internal or common carotid artery	45.00	1069	1263	449
37606	Ligation; internal or common carotid artery, with gradual occlusion, as with Selverstone or Crutchfield clamp	50.00	1188	1403	448
37607	Ligation or banding of angioaccess arteriovenous fistula	20.00	475	561	373
37609	Ligation or biopsy, temporal artery	20.00	475	561	207
37615	Ligation, major artery (eg, post-traumatic, rupture); neck	40.00	951	1122	442
37616	Ligation, major artery (eg, post-traumatic, rupture); chest	75.00	1782	2104	775
37617	Ligation, major artery (eg, post-traumatic, rupture); abdomen	60.00	1426	1683	957
37618	Ligation, major artery (eg, post-traumatic, rupture); extremity	50.00	1188	1403	446
37620	Interruption, partial or complete, of inferior vena cava by suture, ligation, plication, clip, extravascular, intravascular (umbrella device)	75.00	1782	2104	821
37650	Ligation of femoral vein	30.00	713	842	356
37660	Ligation of common iliac vein	30.00	713	842	642
37700	Ligation and division of long saphenous vein at saphenofemoral junction, or distal interruptions	39.00	927	1094	319
37720	Ligation and division and complete stripping of long or short saphenous veins	46.00	1093	1291	469
37730	Ligation and division and complete stripping of long and short saphenous veins	57.00	1355	1599	607
37735	Ligation and division and complete stripping of long or short saphenous veins with radical excision of ulcer and skin graft and/or interruption of communicating veins of lower leg, with excision of deep fascia	87.50	2080	2455	789
37760	Ligation of perforators, subfascial, radical (Linton type), with or without skin graft	61.00	1450	1711	757
37780	Ligation and division of short saphenous vein at saphenopopliteal junction (separate procedure)	10.00	238	281	225
37785	Ligation, division, and/or excision of recurrent or secondary varicose veins (clusters), one leg	27.00	642	758	178
37788	Penile revascularization, artery, with or without vein graft	138.0	3280	3872	1477
37790	Penile venous occlusive procedure	52.00	1236	1459	555
37799	Unlisted procedure, vascular surgery	0.00	0	0	–

38100–38999
Hemic and Lymphatic Systems

Coding Insight

Treatment of an underlying disease (e.g., idiopathic thrombocytopenia purpura) during a splenectomy is reported separately. Use the appropriate modifier to describe the circumstances of the E/M service.

Physicians frequently are not reimbursed for 38100 *Splenectomy; total (separate procedure)*, because 38100 is a separate procedure.

Each payer interprets what constitutes a separate procedure independently of other payers. While some payers strictly interpret CPT, others may be more lenient in interpreting separate procedure guidelines. Separate procedures can be interpreted as a procedure performed alone and for a specific purpose, meaning it would not be performed with any other procedure. Or, it can be interpreted as performed with another procedure as long as it is not an integral part of the other procedure.

To ensure reimbursement for a splenectomy for extensive disease when it is performed with another surgical procedure, use 38102 *Splenectomy; total, en bloc for extensive disease, in conjunction with other procedure (Report in addition to code for primary procedure)* instead of 38100.

Code 38102 addresses splenectomy when it is reported for extensive disease with another primary procedure. However, 38102 does not address reporting for a splenectomy due to trauma.

If a splenectomy is reported with another procedure (not due to extensive disease) and you feel a charge is warranted you may have to append modifier -22 to the primary code. Submit documentation and a letter explaining the significant additional time and effort necessary to complete the splenectomy. Or, if you feel a splenectomy should be allowed separately due to the increased chance of bleeding, infection, and the issue of malpractice and risk due to patient lifetime immunosupression, you may have to use the unlisted code 38999. Again, be sure to submit documentation.

If a claim for a splenectomy is denied and has not been reviewed, appeal the decision when you feel the charge has merit.

Nota Bene: It is important that bone marrow procedures receive prior authorization. Medicare and other payers have very definite guidelines to determine if the procedure is a covered benefit and under what circumstances.

Subsidiary Codes

Subsidiary codes have relative values that require no further adjustment:

20926 is "in addition" to 38100–38999
38746 is "in addition" to 38100–38999
49905 is "in addition" to 38100–38999

Because these are subsidiary or "in addition to" codes, reimbursement reduction and modifier -51 do not apply.

	Code		Description	Medicode RVU	50th	75th	Medicare Nat'l Avg
	38100		Splenectomy; total (separate procedure)	90.00	2060	2451	912
	38101		Splenectomy; partial (separate procedure)	90.00	2060	2451	827
	38102		Splenectomy; total, en bloc for extensive disease, in conjunction with other procedure (Report in addition to code for primary procedure)	45.00	1030	1226	307
	38115		Repair of ruptured spleen (splenorrhaphy) with or without partial splenectomy	85.00	1945	2315	864
	38200		Injection procedure for splenoportography	17.00	389	463	176
	38230		Bone marrow harvesting for transplantation	74.00	1694	2015	220
●	**38231**		blood-derived peripheral stem cell harvesting for transplantation, per collection	74.00	1694	2015	–
▲	**38240**		Bone marrow or blood-derived peripheral stem cell transplantation; allogenic	78.00	1785	2124	153
▲	**38241**		Bone marrow transplantation; autologous	78.00	1785	2124	151
	38300	*	Drainage of lymph node abscess or lymphadenitis; simple	5.00	114	136	83
	38305		Drainage of lymph node abscess or lymphadenitis; extensive	10.00	229	272	254
	38308		Lymphangiotomy or other operations on lymphatic channels	20.00	458	545	326
	38380		Suture and/or ligation of thoracic duct; cervical approach	50.00	1144	1362	464
	38381		Suture and/or ligation of thoracic duct; thoracic approach	100.0	2289	2724	829
	38382		Suture and/or ligation of thoracic duct; abdominal approach	85.00	1945	2315	593
	38500		Biopsy or excision of lymph node(s); superficial (separate procedure)	18.00	412	490	188
	38505		Biopsy or excision of lymph node(s); by needle, superficial (eg, cervical, inguinal, axillary)	10.00	229	272	101
	38510		Biopsy or excision of lymph node(s); deep cervical node(s)	30.00	687	817	272
	38520		Biopsy or excision of lymph node(s); deep cervical node(s) with excision scalene fat pad	25.00	572	681	334
	38525		Biopsy or excision of lymph node(s); deep axillary node(s)	30.00	687	817	300
	38530		Biopsy or excision of lymph node(s); internal mammary node(s) (separate procedure)	35.00	801	953	377
	38542		Dissection, deep jugular node(s)	38.00	870	1035	407
	38550		Excision of cystic hygroma, axillary or cervical; without deep neurovascular dissection	30.00	687	817	407

Code	Description	Medicode RVU	50th	75th	Medicare Nat'l Avg
38555	Excision of cystic hygroma, axillary or cervical; with deep neurovascular dissection	80.00	1831	2179	872
38562	Limited lymphadenectomy for staging (separate procedure); pelvic and para-aortic	75.00	1716	2043	722
38564	Limited lymphadenectomy for staging (separate procedure); retroperitoneal (aortic and/or splenic)	85.00	1945	2315	765
38700	Suprahyoid lymphadenectomy	60.00	1373	1634	750
38720	Cervical lymphadenectomy (complete)	115.0	2632	3132	1241
38724	Cervical lymphadenectomy (modified radical neck dissection)	120.0	2746	3268	1222
38740	Axillary lymphadenectomy; superficial	40.00	915	1089	492
38745	Axillary lymphadenectomy; complete	85.00	1945	2315	753
38746	Thoracic lymphadenectomy, regional, including mediastinal and peritracheal nodes (Report in addition to code for primary procedure)	25.50	584	695	280
38747	Abdominal lymphadenectomy, regional, including celiac, para-aortic and vena caval nodes (Report in addition to code for primary procedure)	28.50	652	776	312
38760	Inguinofemoral lymphadenectomy, superficial, including Cloquet's node (separate procedure)	50.00	1144	1362	654
38765	Inguinofemoral lymphadenectomy, superficial, in continuity with pelvic lymphadenectomy, including external iliac, hypogastric, and obturator nodes (separate procedure)	105.0	2403	2860	1206
38770	Pelvic lymphadenectomy, including external iliac, hypogastric, and obturator nodes (separate procedure)	91.00	2083	2478	1205
38780	Retroperitoneal transabdominal lymphadenectomy, extensive, including pelvic, aortic, and renal nodes (separate procedure)	150.0	3433	4085	1411
38790	Injection procedure for lymphangiography	17.00	389	463	117
38794	Cannulation, thoracic duct	15.00	343	409	284
38999	Unlisted procedure, hemic or lymphatic system	0.00	0	0	–

39000–39599
Mediastinum and Diaphragm

CODING INSIGHT

Other procedures performed at the time of repair of a lacerated diaphragm should be reported separately. Append the appropriate modifier.

Subsidiary Codes

Subsidiary codes have relative values that require no further adjustment:

20926 is "in addition" to 39000–39599
38746 is "in addition" to 39000–39599
49905 is "in addition" to 39000–39599

Because these are subsidiary or "in addition to" codes, reimbursement reduction and modifier -51 do not apply.

Code	Description	Medicode RVU	50th	75th	Medicare Nat'l Avg
39000	Mediastinotomy with exploration, drainage, removal of foreign body, or biopsy; cervical approach	43.00	984	1171	491
39010	Mediastinotomy with exploration, drainage, removal of foreign body, or biopsy; transthoracic approach, including either transthoracic or median sternotomy	89.00	2037	2424	998
39200	Excision of mediastinal cyst	100.0	2289	2724	1029
39220	Excision of mediastinal tumor	110.0	2517	2996	1361
39400	Mediastinoscopy, with or without biopsy	40.00	915	1089	455
39499	Unlisted procedure, mediastinum	0.00	0	0	–
39501	Repair, laceration of diaphragm, any approach	90.00	2060	2451	988
39502	Repair, paraesophageal hiatus hernia, transabdominal, with or without fundoplasty, vagotomy, and/or pyloroplasty, except neonatal	90.00	2060	2451	1200
39503	Repair, neonatal diaphragmatic hernia, with or without chest tube insertion and with or without creation of ventral hernia	110.0	2517	2996	2386
39520	Repair, diaphragmatic hernia (esophageal hiatal); transthoracic	86.00	1968	2342	1194
39530	Repair, diaphragmatic hernia (esophageal hiatal); combined, thoracoabdominal	95.00	2174	2587	1209
39531	Repair, diaphragmatic hernia (esophageal hiatal); combined, thoracoabdominal, with dilation of stricture (with or without gastroplasty)	110.0	2517	2996	1059
39540	Repair, diaphragmatic hernia (other than neonatal), traumatic; acute	114.0	2609	3105	1062
39541	Repair, diaphragmatic hernia (other than neonatal), traumatic; chronic	86.00	1968	2342	1094
39545	Imbrication of diaphragm for eventration, transthoracic or transabdominal, paralytic or nonparalytic	110.0	2517	2996	842
39599	Unlisted procedure, diaphragm	0.00	0	0	–

Surgery Codes 40490–49999

A major portion of CPT digestive system codes involves endoscopies. When reporting endoscopy procedures keep in mind that the codes are based on the type of endoscope used and the anatomy involved. They may also be distinguished as diagnostic or therapeutic.

Generally, a procedure is diagnostic when the endoscope is placed only for visualization to determine abnormality or the extent of a disease, and therapeutic when the endoscope is placed for visualization and treatment of an abnormality or disease process.

Diagnostic endoscopy is always included in surgical (therapeutic) endoscopy of the same code family. It is performed independently of and not immediately related to other services and is the only procedure performed on the date of service.

Diagnostic procedures may include:

- Diagnostic endoscopy
- Biopsy same lesion, same area
- Collection of specimens by brushing or washing

Minor therapeutic procedures may include:

- Dilation
- Biopsy different lesion, different area
- Removal of foreign body
- Removal of stent

Major therapeutic procedures may include:

- Control of bleeding
- Removal of tumor(s), polyp(s), or other lesion(s) by hot biopsy forceps or bipolar cautery
- Removal of tumor(s), polyp(s), or other lesion(s) by snare technique
- Ablation of tumor(s), polyp(s), or other lesion(s) not amenable to removal by hot biopsy forceps, bipolar cautery, or snare technique

Parent codes for endoscopic procedures include collection of specimens and are designated as separate procedures. A separate procedure indicates that the endoscopic procedure, with or without collection of specimen(s), was performed alone and for a specific purpose.

Coding Issues for Gastrointestinal Endoscopy
An endoscopic procedure should never be identified with a CPT code specific to an open procedure. Use an appropriate unlisted code to identify endoscopic procedures without a specific CPT code.

Although endoscopic procedures include minor related functions, payers determine what is included in a particular endoscopic code. Some payers consider the following procedures included in endoscopies and, therefore, they should not be reported separately:

- IV sedation: components of performing sedation include 36000 *Introduction of needle or intracatheter, vein*, 90782 *Therapeutic or diagnostic injection; subcutaneous or intramuscular*, and 90784 *Therapeutic or diagnostic injection (specify material injected), intravenous*
- Placement of the endoscope
- Diagnostic evaluation
- Videotaping/monitoring
- Irrigation and suction
- Control of minor bleeding

Modifiers that are commonly associated with and/or used incorrectly with digestive system endoscopy codes may, depending upon the payer, include the following:

- Modifier -20 for operative microscope is usually not used with endoscopy procedures
- Modifier -22 is added only when unusual circumstances (e.g., congenital anomaly, significant time and/or effort) are encountered. Substantiating documentation is required
- Modifier -50 for bilateral procedures is not used with digestive system endoscopy because the procedures involve a single, midline structure
- Modifier -51 is used to identify secondary, additional, or lesser procedure(s) or service(s) when two distinct procedures are performed at the same operative session and there is no single inclusive code available. Modifier -51 should not be used to identify a diagnostic endoscopy followed by minor or significant therapeutic procedures through the same endoscope. The procedure code with the highest value within a code family is identified
- Modifier -51 may be used when:
  - One procedure is endoscopic and is followed by open surgery
  - Multiple minor and significant procedures are done through the same endoscope
  - Multiple minor and significant procedures are done through different endoscopes
  - Upper with lower GI procedure is done (two upper GI or two lower GI procedures)

Modifier -52 for reduced procedures is used to identify incomplete or aborted procedures when the endoscopic procedure or a portion of the procedure is not completed.

Modifier -62 for cosurgery is used when two or more surgeons, usually with different skills, are required to perform a single or multiple procedures to manage a specific surgical problem.

Modifier -78 for return to operating room for a related procedure is used when the patient has a postoperative complication that requires an operative procedure during postoperative care.

Multiple Endoscopic Procedures

Payer policies vary widely, so when coding multiple procedures through the same endoscope, you may encounter some of the following guidelines:

- A single procedure code should be used when a diagnostic procedure is performed with any therapeutic procedure (minor or major) through the same endoscope (e.g., anoscopy, sigmoidoscopy, colonoscopy)
- Multiple procedure codes are used when multiple therapeutic (minor or major) procedures are performed through the same endoscope (e.g., anoscopy, sigmoidoscopy, colonoscopy)
- Multiple procedure codes are used when biopsy, single or multiple, of a lesion is performed with removal or destruction of a lesion in another area (same code family) during the same operative session

- A single procedure code is used when biopsy, single or multiple, of a lesion is followed by removal or destruction of the same lesion during the same operative session. The biopsy is incidental and should not be separately identified
- A single procedure code is used when multiple tumors, polyps, or other lesions are removed by hot biopsy forceps, bipolar cautery, or snare technique (e.g., laser) through a proctosigmoidoscope or anoscope
- A single code is used when a foreign body is removed with any other procedure (diagnostic, minor or major) through the same endoscope at the same session
- Removal of stent may be considered incidental to a placement of a stent of the same location and endoscope (e.g., ERCP) by some payers. The procedure code for the placement of the stent is used rather than the code for removal of the stent

When coding multiple procedures through different endoscopes you may encounter some of the following guidelines:

- A single procedure code is used when a diagnostic procedure through a less invasive endoscope (e.g., anoscopy) is performed with any procedure (diagnostic, minor therapeutic, or significant therapeutic) through a more invasive endoscope (e.g., sigmoidoscopy)
- Multiple codes are used when a therapeutic procedure (minor or major) through a less invasive endoscope (e.g., anoscopy) is performed with any procedure (diagnostic, minor therapeutic, or major therapeutic) through a more invasive endoscope (e.g., sigmoidoscopy)
- Diagnostic anoscopy and anoscopy with dilation are incidental to all lower gastrointestinal endoscopic procedures

When coding an endoscopic procedure with an open procedure, you may encounter some of the following guidelines:

- Multiple codes are used when endoscopic procedures (e.g., diagnostic, minor therapeutic, or significant therapeutic) are performed prior to open procedures (e.g., laparotomy)
- The endoscopic procedure is not identified separately when it is performed during the open procedure to check the open work
- Diagnostic anoscopy and minor therapeutic procedures performed though an anoscope are incidental to all anal reconstructive procedures

MEDICARE AND ENDOSCOPIES

Special payment rules apply when multiple endoscopy procedures are rendered at the same session. HCFA has identified "families" of related endoscopies and has developed a "base" endoscopy procedure for each family. The rules apply to services performed after December 31, 1994.

Multiple Endoscopy Groupings

HCFA provides a list of base endoscopic codes and related procedure codes. The digestive system endoscopies are included here, but Medicare reviews all endoscopic procedure codes. For a complete listing see the Surgery Introduction in this book under Medicare Revised Multiple Endoscoy Groupings.

Payment for multiple related endoscopies is determined as follows: 100 percent for the primary endoscopy plus the difference between the Medicare Fee Schedule amount for the next highest procedure and the base endoscopy amount. No payment is made for a secondary procedure if the base procedure has a higher value. This payment adjustment applies only when the related multiple procedures are performed through the same orifice. Medicare will not pay for any portion of the diagnostic procedure when reimbursing other secondary surgical procedures performed through the same orifice and at the same time.

Base Code	*Related Procedure Codes*
43200	43202, 43204–43205, 43215–43217, 43219–43220, 43226–43228
43235	43239, 43241, 43243–42347, 42349–42351, 43255, 43258–43259
43260	43261–43265, 43267–43269, 43271–43272
44360	44361, 44363–44366, 44369, 44372–44373
44376	44377–44378
44388	44389–44394
45300	45303, 45305, 45307–45309, 45315, 45317, 45320–45321
45330	45331–45334, 45337–45339
45378	45379–45380, 45382–45385
46600	46604, 46606, 46608, 46610–46612, 46614–46615
47522	47553–47556

Special reimbursement rules apply to multiple endoscopic procedures. The payment for multiple procedures depends upon the endoscopic procedures performed on one day.

"Stand alone" endoscopy procedures (procedures that do not have a base code) and single endoscopy procedures from several different code families are reimbursed under the multiple surgery guidelines at 100 percent for the first endoscopy procedure, 50 percent for the second through fifth procedures. Subsequent procedures are "by report."

Multiple endoscopy procedures from a single code family are reimbursed at 100 percent for the major endoscopy, plus the difference between the Medicare Fee Schedule (MFS) value for the next highest procedure and the MFS value for the base endoscopy. The base procedure, when reported with a more extensive procedure within the same endoscopic family of procedure codes, is not separately reimbursable (refer to the Medicare November 1993 Rebundle Edit List for more specific unbundling information).

An example of Medicare's payment rules is as follows:

In the course of performing a fiberoptic colonoscopy (45378), a physician performs a biopsy on a lesion (45380) and removes a polyp (45385) from a different part of the colon. The physician reports 45380 and 45385. Codes 45380 and 45385 both have the value of the diagnostic colonoscopy (45378) built in. Rather than paying 100 percent for the highest valued procedure (45385) and 50 percent for the next (45380), the full value of the higher valued endoscopy (45385) is paid, plus the difference between the next highest endoscopy (45380) and the base endoscopy (45378).

Assume the following fee schedule amounts for these codes:

45385 = $374.56 (Not on base list, pay at full value)

45378 = $255.40
45380 = $285.98

(On base list, pay difference between 45378 and 45380 = $30.58)

Total payment = $405.14 (Full value for 45385 plus difference between 45378 and 45380)

40490–42699
Lips, Mouth, Tongue, Dentoalveolar Structures, Salivary Glands

CODING INSIGHT
Although technically there are no cosmetic warnings in this code`range, payers consider some procedures in this subsection cosmetic or for pre-existing conditions. With the different types of healthcaree coverage available today and the number of times a person changes jobs, issues frequently arise about coverage for these procedures. Codes in this range may be especially vulnerable because they describe procedures that can be performed for injuries, malignancies, or a desire to change appearance.

Pre-existing Conditions
Pre-existing condition clauses are included in many plans, and the conditions may be covered at any range from no coverage to full coverage. Examples are:

- When a patient suffers an injury on one plan and the repair of the injury results in an unfavorable cosmetic appearance. The patient then changes plans and desires a more favorable repair
- When a patient has joined a new plan and is found to have a malignancy (e.g., lip, tongue) that must be removed
- When a congenital anomaly is present and requires repair/reconstruction

This combination of conditions that can result in a cosmetic ruling creates a situation where it is imperative that the provider obtain prior authorization for many procedures. Make sure to request prior authorization for services in this area that may fit into one of these categories. Prior authorization informs you as to the amount the patient must pay and advises the patient about payment issues that may arise before the procedure is performed.

Patient Liability
When a procedure is reimbursable, in full or in part, remember that a provider usually can charge only up to the negotiated contracted amount (when a contract is in place), not the fee-for-service amount. For example, if a condition is pre-existing and the patient has a 50 percent benefit, the provider can only charge 50 percent of the contracted rate. This should be a consideration when negotiating a contract, especially if a provider intends to allow patients to make installment payments. Negotiate a clause that will allow a reasonable increase in the contracted fee for handling the account. If the patient's condition is 100 percent pre-existing the provider must make arrangements with the patient for the fee, in which case a discount may not be an option.

Traumatic Procedures
Another consideration in this code range is coordination of benefits (COB), if the condition is a result of an accident or injury/trauma that may be covered by another third-party insurer. In this situation bill the third-party insurer first and the primary payer second. If the amount of the third party's payment is equal to or greater than the contracted rate with the primary payer, additional payment will probably not be made. However, third party insurers often will reimburse more than a primary payer because they do not normally contract with providers.

A disadvantage of third-party payments is the long waiting period before being reimbursed (frequently due to litigation accompanying accidental injuries). Consider a contract clause that stipulates payment will be made by the primary insurer after a specified period of time. Once the third-party payer has settled the account, be sure to submit a claim to the primary insurer, along with all EOBs. Also include any prior authorization numbers obtained from the primary insurer at the time of the accident.

Subsidiary Codes

Subsidiary codes have relative values that require no further adjustment:

20900 is "in addition" to 40490–42699
20902 is "in addition" to 40490–42699
20910 is "in addition" to 40490–42699
20912 is "in addition" to 40490–42699
20920 is "in addition" to 40490–42699
20922 is "in addition" to 40490–42699
20926 is "in addition" to 40490–42699
38102 is "in addition" to 40490–42699
38747 is "in addition" to 40490–42699
41114 is "in addition" to 41112, 41113
44015 is "in addition" to 40490–42699
44955 is "in addition" to 40490–42699
47001 is "in addition" to 40490–42699
49905 is "in addition" to 40490–42699

Because these are subsidiary or "in addition to" codes, reimbursement reduction and CPT modifier -51 do not apply.

Code	Description	Medicode RVU	50th	75th	Medicare Nat'l Avg
40490	Biopsy of lip	5.50	123	145	79
40500	Vermilionectomy (lip shave), with mucosal advancement	48.50	1084	1283	471
40510	Excision of lip; transverse wedge excision with primary closure	50.00	1118	1323	480
40520	Excision of lip; V-excision with primary direct linear closure	40.00	894	1058	400
40525	Excision of lip; full thickness, reconstruction with local flap (eg, Estlander or fan)	80.00	1789	2116	730
40527	Excision of lip; full thickness, reconstruction with cross lip flap (Abbe-Estlander)	94.00	2102	2486	850
40530	Resection of lip, more than one-fourth, without reconstruction	40.00	894	1058	437
40650	Repair lip, full thickness; vermilion only	25.00	559	661	352
40652	Repair lip, full thickness; up to half vertical height	33.00	738	873	404
40654	Repair lip, full thickness; over one-half vertical height, or complex	47.00	1051	1243	508
40700	Plastic repair of cleft lip/nasal deformity; primary, partial or complete, unilateral	110.0	2459	2910	850
40701	Plastic repair of cleft lip/nasal deformity; primary bilateral, one stage procedure	126.5	2828	3346	1401
40702	Plastic repair of cleft lip/nasal deformity; primary bilateral, one of two stages	110.0	2459	2910	887
40720	Plastic repair of cleft lip/nasal deformity; secondary, by recreation of defect and reclosure	93.50	2090	2473	946

Code		Description	Medicode RVU	50th	75th	Medicare Nat'l Avg
40761		Plastic repair of cleft lip/nasal deformity; with cross lip pedicle flap (Abbe-Estlander type), including sectioning and inserting of pedicle	132.0	2951	3492	1043
40799		Unlisted procedure, lips	0.00	0	0	–
40800	*	Drainage of abscess, cyst, hematoma, vestibule of mouth; simple	5.25	117	139	74
40801		Drainage of abscess, cyst, hematoma, vestibule of mouth; complicated	27.00	604	714	170
40804	*	Removal of embedded foreign body, vestibule of mouth; simple	8.00	179	212	70
40805		Removal of embedded foreign body, vestibule of mouth; complicated	24.00	537	635	211
40806		Incision of labial frenum (frenotomy)	12.00	268	317	28
40808		Biopsy, vestibule of mouth	8.00	179	212	68
40810		Excision of lesion of mucosa and submucosa, vestibule of mouth; without repair	10.00	224	265	99
40812		Excision of lesion of mucosa and submucosa, vestibule of mouth; with simple repair	12.50	279	331	147
40814		Excision of lesion of mucosa and submucosa, vestibule of mouth; with complex repair	30.00	671	794	275
40816		Excision of lesion of mucosa and submucosa, vestibule of mouth; complex, with excision of underlying muscle	39.00	872	1032	279
40818		Excision of mucosa of vestibule of mouth as donor graft	16.50	369	436	185
40819		Excision of frenum, labial or buccal (frenumectomy, frenulectomy, frenectomy)	14.00	313	370	141
40820		Destruction of lesion or scar of vestibule of mouth by physical methods (eg, laser, thermal, cryo, chemical)	12.00	268	317	75
40830		Closure of laceration, vestibule of mouth; 2.5 cm or less	8.00	179	212	95
40831		Closure of laceration, vestibule of mouth; over 2.5 cm or complex	20.00	447	529	179
40840		Vestibuloplasty; anterior	40.00	894	1058	596
40842		Vestibuloplasty; posterior, unilateral	31.00	693	820	596
40843		Vestibuloplasty; posterior, bilateral	44.00	984	1164	835
40844		Vestibuloplasty; entire arch	70.00	1565	1852	1103
40845		Vestibuloplasty; complex (including ridge extension, muscle repositioning)	85.00	1900	2248	1704
40899		Unlisted procedure, vestibule of mouth	0.00	0	0	–
41000	*	Intraoral incision and drainage of abscess, cyst, or hematoma of tongue or floor of mouth; lingual	8.00	182	215	80

Code		Description	Medicode RVU	50th	75th	Medicare Nat'l Avg
41005	*	Intraoral incision and drainage of abscess, cyst, or hematoma of tongue or floor of mouth; sublingual, superficial	9.00	204	242	74
41006		Intraoral incision and drainage of abscess, cyst, or hematoma of tongue or floor of mouth; sublingual, deep, supramylohyoid	25.00	567	672	161
41007		Intraoral incision and drainage of abscess, cyst, or hematoma of tongue or floor of mouth; submental space	25.00	567	672	236
41008		Intraoral incision and drainage of abscess, cyst, or hematoma of tongue or floor of mouth; submandibular space	25.00	567	672	168
41009		Intraoral incision and drainage of abscess, cyst, or hematoma of tongue or floor of mouth; masticator space	25.00	567	672	270
41010		Incision of lingual frenum (frenotomy)	12.00	272	323	63
41015		Extraoral incision and drainage of abscess, cyst, or hematoma of floor of mouth; sublingual	26.00	590	699	182
41016		Extraoral incision and drainage of abscess, cyst, or hematoma of floor of mouth; submental	20.00	454	538	300
41017		Extraoral incision and drainage of abscess, cyst, or hematoma of floor of mouth; submandibular	26.00	590	699	204
41018		Extraoral incision and drainage of abscess, cyst, or hematoma of floor of mouth; masticator space	26.00	590	699	351
41100		Biopsy of tongue; anterior two-thirds	8.00	182	215	93
41105		Biopsy of tongue; posterior one-third	10.00	227	269	100
41108		Biopsy of floor of mouth	7.00	159	188	76
41110		Excision of lesion of tongue without closure	9.00	204	242	119
41112		Excision of lesion of tongue with closure; anterior two-thirds	22.00	499	591	213
41113		Excision of lesion of tongue with closure; posterior one-third	26.00	590	699	277
41114		Excision of lesion of tongue with closure; with local tongue flap	24.00	544	645	584
41115		Excision of lingual frenum (frenectomy)	16.00	363	430	142
41116		Excision, lesion of floor of mouth	30.00	681	806	217
41120		Glossectomy; less than one-half tongue	54.00	1225	1452	672
41130		Glossectomy; hemiglossectomy	84.00	1906	2258	810
41135		Glossectomy; partial, with unilateral radical neck dissection	150.0	3403	4032	1439
41140		Glossectomy; complete or total, with or without tracheostomy, without radical neck dissection	98.00	2223	2634	1739

Code		Description	Medicode RVU	50th	75th	Medicare Nat'l Avg
41145		Glossectomy; complete or total, with or without tracheostomy, with unilateral radical neck dissection	170.0	3857	4570	2084
41150		Glossectomy; composite procedure with resection floor of mouth and mandibular resection, without radical neck dissection	155.0	3516	4167	1633
41153		Glossectomy; composite procedure with resection floor of mouth, with suprahyoid neck dissection	170.0	3857	4570	1943
41155		Glossectomy; composite procedure with resection floor of mouth, mandibular resection, and radical neck dissection (Commando type)	205.0	4651	5511	2347
41250	*	Repair of laceration 2.5 cm or less; floor of mouth and/or anterior two-thirds of tongue	9.00	204	242	118
41251	*	Repair of laceration 2.5 cm or less; posterior one-third of tongue	8.00	182	215	173
41252	*	Repair of laceration of tongue, floor of mouth, over 2.6 cm or complex	36.00	817	968	220
41500		Fixation of tongue, mechanical, other than suture (eg, K-wire)	20.00	454	538	275
41510		Suture of tongue to lip for micrognathia (Douglas type procedure)	36.00	817	968	246
41520		Frenoplasty (surgical revision of frenum, eg, with Z-plasty)	24.00	544	645	226
41599		Unlisted procedure, tongue, floor of mouth	0.00	0	0	–
41800	*	Drainage of abscess, cyst, hematoma from dentoalveolar structures	8.00	182	215	72
41805		Removal of embedded foreign body from dentoalveolar structures; soft tissues	9.00	204	242	83
41806		Removal of embedded foreign body from dentoalveolar structures; bone	10.00	227	269	173
41820		Gingivectomy, excision gingiva, each quadrant	20.00	454	538	–
41821		Operculectomy, excision pericoronal tissues	4.50	102	121	–
41822		Excision of fibrous tuberosities, dentoalveolar structures	10.00	227	269	215
41823		Excision of osseous tuberosities, dentoalveolar structures	23.00	522	618	299
41825		Excision of lesion or tumor (except listed above), dentoalveolar structures; without repair	10.00	227	269	118
41826		Excision of lesion or tumor (except listed above), dentoalveolar structures; with simple repair	17.50	397	470	188
41827		Excision of lesion or tumor (except listed above), dentoalveolar structures; with complex repair	27.50	624	739	300
41828		Excision of hyperplastic alveolar mucosa, each quadrant (specify)	29.00	658	780	120
41830		Alveolectomy, including curettage of osteitis or sequestrectomy	24.00	544	645	106

Code		Description	Medicode RVU	50th	75th	Medicare Nat'l Avg
41850		Destruction of lesion (except excision), dentoalveolar structures	10.00	227	269	–
41870		Periodontal mucosal grafting	25.00	567	672	–
41872		Gingivoplasty, each quadrant (specify)	30.00	681	806	232
41874		Alveoloplasty, each quadrant (specify)	21.00	476	565	279
41899		Unlisted procedure, dentoalveolar structures	0.00	0	0	–
42000	*	Drainage of abscess of palate, uvula	9.00	204	242	72
42100		Biopsy of palate, uvula	10.00	227	269	82
42104		Excision, lesion of palate, uvula; without closure	14.50	329	390	145
42106		Excision, lesion of palate, uvula; with simple primary closure	18.50	420	497	219
42107		Excision, lesion of palate, uvula; with local flap closure	33.00	749	887	381
42120		Resection of palate or extensive resection of lesion	53.00	1202	1425	580
42140		Uvulectomy, excision of uvula	21.00	476	565	123
42145		Palatopharyngoplasty (eg, uvulopalatopharyngoplasty, uvulopharyngoplasty)	90.50	2053	2433	787
42160		Destruction of lesion, palate or uvula (thermal, cryo or chemical)	6.00	136	161	133
42180		Repair, laceration of palate; up to 2 cm	11.00	250	296	192
42182		Repair, laceration of palate; over 2 cm or complex	27.00	613	726	296
42200		Palatoplasty for cleft palate, soft and/or hard palate only	117.0	2654	3145	691
42205		Palatoplasty for cleft palate, with closure of alveolar ridge; soft tissue only	123.0	2791	3306	800
42210		Palatoplasty for cleft palate, with closure of alveolar ridge; with bone graft to alveolar ridge (includes obtaining graft)	155.0	3516	4167	913
42215		Palatoplasty for cleft palate; major revision	150.0	3403	4032	664
42220		Palatoplasty for cleft palate; secondary lengthening procedure	115.0	2609	3091	501
42225		Palatoplasty for cleft palate; attachment pharyngeal flap	100.0	2269	2688	667
42226		Lengthening of palate, and pharyngeal flap	125.0	2836	3360	708
42227		Lengthening of palate, with island flap	125.0	2836	3360	650

Code		Description	Medicode RVU	50th	75th	Medicare Nat'l Avg
42235		Repair of anterior palate, including vomer flap	91.00	2065	2446	549
42260		Repair of nasolabial fistula	50.00	1134	1344	334
42280		Maxillary impression for palatal prosthesis	9.00	204	242	141
42281		Insertion of pin-retained palatal prosthesis	18.00	408	484	133
42299		Unlisted procedure, palate, uvula	0.00	0	0	–
42300	*	Drainage of abscess; parotid, simple	7.00	159	188	115
42305		Drainage of abscess; parotid, complicated	15.00	340	403	311
42310	*	Drainage of abscess; submaxillary or sublingual, intraoral	9.00	204	242	104
42320	*	Drainage of abscess; submaxillary, external	10.00	227	269	170
42325		Fistulization of sublingual salivary cyst (ranula);	13.00	295	349	195
42326		Fistulization of sublingual salivary cyst (ranula); with prosthesis	21.00	476	565	323
42330		Sialolithotomy; submandibular (submaxillary), sublingual or parotid, uncomplicated, intraoral	15.00	340	403	129
42335		Sialolithotomy; submandibular (submaxillary), complicated, intraoral	33.00	749	887	233
42340		Sialolithotomy; parotid, extraoral or complicated intraoral	50.00	1134	1344	360
42400	*	Biopsy of salivary gland; needle	6.00	136	161	67
42405		Biopsy of salivary gland; incisional	12.50	284	336	191
42408		Excision of sublingual salivary cyst (ranula)	25.00	567	672	316
42409		Marsupialization of sublingual salivary cyst (ranula)	25.00	567	672	230
42410		Excision of parotid tumor or parotid gland; lateral lobe, without nerve dissection	41.00	930	1102	621
42415		Excision of parotid tumor or parotid gland; lateral lobe, with dissection and preservation of facial nerve	95.00	2155	2554	1206
42420		Excision of parotid tumor or parotid gland; total, with dissection and preservation of facial nerve	105.0	2382	2823	1387
42425		Excision of parotid tumor or parotid gland; total, en bloc removal with sacrifice of facial nerve	70.00	1588	1882	980
42426		Excision of parotid tumor or parotid gland; total, with unilateral radical neck dissection	155.0	3516	4167	1896
42440		Excision of submandibular (submaxillary) gland	76.50	1736	2056	643

Code		Description	Medicode RVU	50th	75th	Medicare Nat'l Avg
42450		Excision of sublingual gland	35.00	794	941	327
42500		Plastic repair of salivary duct, sialodochoplasty; primary or simple	40.00	907	1075	366
42505		Plastic repair of salivary duct, sialodochoplasty; secondary or complicated	60.00	1361	1613	552
42507		Parotid duct diversion, bilateral (Wilke type procedure);	65.00	1475	1747	442
42508		Parotid duct diversion, bilateral (Wilke type procedure); with excision of one submandibular gland	84.50	1917	2272	672
42509		Parotid duct diversion, bilateral (Wilke type procedure); with excision of both submandibular glands	95.00	2155	2554	765
42510		Parotid duct diversion, bilateral (Wilke type procedure); with ligation of both submandibular (Wharton's) ducts	80.00	1815	2151	633
42550		Injection procedure for sialography	4.25	96	114	57
42600		Closure salivary fistula	50.00	1134	1344	352
42650	*	Dilation salivary duct	3.00	68	81	46
42660	*	Dilation and catheterization of salivary duct, with or without injection	4.50	102	121	66
42665		Ligation salivary duct, intraoral	6.00	136	161	185
42699		Unlisted procedure, salivary glands or ducts	0.00	0	0	–

42700–42999
Pharynx, Adenoids, and Tonsils

Coding Insight

Most unbundling software used by payers considers tonsillectomy and adenoidectomy codes in this range to be bilateral. It is advisable to request prior authorization for these procedures. Payers generally have specific criteria for tonsillectomy and adenoidectomy. Laboratory results that report repeated strep infections or other payer requisites typically must be met before prior authorization will be issued.

Subsidiary Codes

Subsidiary codes have relative values that require no further adjustment:

20900 is "in addition" to 42700–42999
20902 is "in addition" to 42700–42999
20910 is "in addition" to 42700–42999
20912 is "in addition" to 42700–42999
20920 is "in addition" to 42700–42999
20922 is "in addition" to 42700–42999
20926 is "in addition" to 42700–42999
38102 is "in addition" to 42700–42999
38747 is "in addition" to 42700–42999

44015 is "in addition" to 42700–42999
44955 is "in addition" to 42700–42999
47001 is "in addition" to 42700–42999
49905 is "in addition" to 42700–42999

Because these are subsidiary or "in addition to" codes reimbursement reduction and modifier -51 do not apply.

Code		Description	Medicode RVU	50th	75th	Medicare Nat'l Avg
42700	*	Incision and drainage abscess; peritonsillar	10.50	249	280	97
42720		Incision and drainage abscess; retropharyngeal or parapharyngeal, intraoral approach	17.00	402	453	186
42725		Incision and drainage abscess; retropharyngeal or parapharyngeal, external approach	30.00	710	800	489
42800		Biopsy; oropharynx	7.00	166	187	83
42802		Biopsy; hypopharynx	8.00	189	213	107
42804		Biopsy; nasopharynx, visible lesion, simple	7.00	166	187	103
42806		Biopsy; nasopharynx, survey for unknown primary lesion	14.00	331	373	126
42808		Excision or destruction of lesion of pharynx, any method	18.00	426	480	205
42809		Removal of foreign body from pharynx	10.00	237	267	106
42810		Excision branchial cleft cyst or vestige, confined to skin and subcutaneous tissues	23.00	544	613	269
42815		Excision branchial cleft cyst, vestige, or fistula, extending beneath subcutaneous tissues and/or into pharynx	57.00	1349	1519	653
42820		Tonsillectomy and adenoidectomy; under age 12	29.00	686	773	275
42821		Tonsillectomy and adenoidectomy; age 12 or over	31.00	734	826	333
42825		Tonsillectomy, primary or secondary; under age 12	28.00	663	746	241
42826		Tonsillectomy, primary or secondary; age 12 or over	29.50	698	786	305
42830		Adenoidectomy, primary; under age 12	21.00	497	560	180
42831		Adenoidectomy, primary; age 12 or over	22.00	521	586	203
42835		Adenoidectomy, secondary; under age 12	17.75	420	473	163
42836		Adenoidectomy, secondary; age 12 or over	21.00	497	560	241
42842		Radical resection of tonsil, tonsillar pillars, and/or retromolar trigone; without closure	135.0	3195	3598	620

Code	Description	Medicode RVU	50th	75th	Medicare Nat'l Avg
42844	Radical resection of tonsil, tonsillar pillars, and/or retromolar trigone; closure with local flap (eg, tongue, buccal)	180.0	4260	4798	969
42845	Radical resection of tonsil, tonsillar pillars, and/or retromolar trigone; closure with other flap	180.0	4260	4798	1657
42860	Excision of tonsil tags	18.00	426	480	168
42870	Excision or destruction lingual tonsil, any method (separate procedure)	30.00	710	800	301
42880	Excision nasopharyngeal lesion (eg, fibroma)	45.00	1065	1199	452
42890	Limited pharyngectomy	70.00	1657	1866	866
42892	Resection of lateral pharyngeal wall or pyriform sinus, direct closure by advancement of lateral and posterior pharyngeal walls	87.00	2059	2319	1025
42894	Resection of pharyngeal wall requiring closure with myocutaneous flap	160.0	3787	4264	1509
42900	Suture pharynx for wound or injury	28.00	663	746	379
42950	Pharyngoplasty (plastic or reconstructive operation on pharynx)	70.00	1657	1866	734
42953	Pharyngoesophageal repair	88.00	2083	2345	607
42955	Pharyngostomy (fistulization of pharynx, external for feeding)	23.00	544	613	403
42960	Control oropharyngeal hemorrhage, primary or secondary (eg, posttonsillectomy); simple	11.00	260	293	135
42961	Control oropharyngeal hemorrhage, primary or secondary (eg, posttonsillectomy); complicated, requiring hospitalization	17.50	414	466	276
42962	Control oropharyngeal hemorrhage, primary or secondary (eg, posttonsillectomy); with secondary surgical intervention	21.00	497	560	513
42970	Control of nasopharyngeal hemorrhage, primary or secondary (eg, postadenoidectomy); simple, with posterior nasal packs, with or without anterior packs and/or cauterization	15.00	355	400	197
42971	Control of nasopharyngeal hemorrhage, primary or secondary (eg, postadenoidectomy); complicated, requiring hospitalization	19.50	462	520	342
42972	Control of nasopharyngeal hemorrhage, primary or secondary (eg, postadenoidectomy); with secondary surgical intervention	22.00	521	586	460
42999	Unlisted procedure, pharynx, adenoids, or tonsils	0.00	0	0	–

43020–43499
Esophagus/Endoscopy

Coding Insight
CPT's esophageal excision code section was extensively revised in 1995. Two codes were changed, seven codes were deleted, and 11 new codes were added to describe current surgical techniques. The new codes detail specific surgical approaches, major procedural components, and reconstructive methods.

You may find that these code changes may have affected payer claims software unbundle edits. For example, if a single resection of the small intestine with anastomosis (44120) is reported with a partial/total esophagectomy with colon interpostition or small bowel reconstruction (43108, 43113, 43118 or 43123), the small bowel resection code (44120) will be considered inherent to the esophagectomy by most payers, and payment for the service will not be made separately.

Remember, indented codes within a code family are subordinate to the semicolon.

Some terms which may be helpful in this code range are:

- *Esophagoscopy*: examination is limited to the esophagus
- *Esophagogastroscopy*: examination of esophagus, the endoscope passes the diaphragm to the stomach
- *Esophagogastroduodenoscopy* (EGD): the pyloric channel is transversed. Upper gastrointestinal endoscopy includes the esophagus, stomach, and either the duodenum and/or jejunum
- *Endoscopic retrograde cholangiopancreatography* (ERCP): endoscopy to identify and cannulate the ampulla of Vater in the second portion of the duodenum with injection of contrast material into the biliary and pancreatic ducts

Upper GI Endoscopy with Percutaneous Placement of PEG Tube
Note that when reporting percutaneous endoscopic gastrostomy (PEG), many payers will consider the following to be basic elements of the procedure:

- Placement of the endoscope into the stomach
- Gastric insufflation to bring the stomach into apposition to the abdominal wall
- Passage of a suture or guidewire into the stomach
- Placement of the gastrostomy tube
- Endoscopic verification of the proper position

The procedures that are considered inherent may restrict the codes that can be used when reporting this procedure. Payers may not reimburse the following codes when they are reported together: 43750 should not be reported on the same date of service with 43226, and 43453 should not be reported on the same date of service with 43226.

When percutaneous placement of a gastrostomy tube (PEG) is performed by two physicians it will generally be considered single-shared cosurgery by payers, with the following considerations:

- A gastroenterologist places the endoscope into the stomach
- A general surgeon places the percutaneous gastrostomy tube

The procedure should be coded as if performed by one physician with modifier -62 added. In other words, the gastroenterologist and the surgeon would both code 43246-62 *Upper gastrointestinal endoscopy including esophagus, stomach, and either duodenum and/or jejunum as appropriate; with directed placement of percutaneous gastrostomy tube.*

Physicians should discuss, in advance of reporting, the coordination of codes with charges, any additional percentage increase based on the complexity of the procedure performed, and how the reimbursement should be divided between the physicians.

Subsidiary Codes

Subsidiary codes have relative values that require no further adjustment:

20926 is "in addition" to 43020–43499
38102 is "in addition" to 43020–43499
38747 is "in addition" to 43020–43499
44015 is "in addition" to 43020–43499
44955 is "in addition" to 43020–43499
45355 is "in addition" to 43020–43499
47001 is "in addition" to 43020–43499
49905 is "in addition" to 43020–43499

Because these are subsidiary or "in addition to" codes, reimbursement reduction and modifier -51 do not apply.

Medicare Alert

Some Medicare carriers have developed their own guidelines for percutaneous placement of a gastrostomy tube, so it is good policy to verify such with with your local carrier.

Some carriers have instructions for claims for percutaneous placement of a gastrostomy tube (PEG), when the procedure is performed by two physicians, as follows:

- The physician who performs the upper gastrointestinal (UGI) portion of the procedure should report 43246 only (no modifier -62 required)
- The physician who performs the placement of the gastrostomy tube (PEG) should report 43750 only (no modifier -62 required)
- The allowable for each physician is 100 percent of the fee schedule

If both procedures are performed by the same physician, the physician should report 43246 only. The allowable is 100 percent of the fee schedule. Code 43750 is not separately reportable.

Medicare rebundles certain codes in the surgery section when the listed codes are considered a component of a more comprehensive service.

43200, 43234 will not be reimbursed when reported with 43235, 43239, 43246, 43247, 43255, 43260, 43262, 43264, 43268
43202 will not be reimbursed when reported with 43239, 43246, 43247, 43255
43204 will not be reimbursed when reported with 43255
43215 will not be reimbursed when reported with 43247, 43264
43235 will not be reimbursed when reported with 43239, 43246, 43247, 43255, 43260, 43262 43264, 43268
43241 will not be reimbursed when reported with 43246
43260 will not be reimbursed when reported with 43262, 43264, 43268
43750, 43760 will not be reimbursed when reported with 43246

Code	Description	Medicode RVU	50th	75th	Medicare Nat'l Avg
43020	Esophagotomy, cervical approach, with removal of foreign body	70.00	1626	1820	591
43030	Cricopharyngeal myotomy	70.00	1626	1820	745
43045	Cricopharyngeal myotomy Esophagotomy, thoracic approach, with removal of foreign body	98.00	2277	2549	1307
43100	Excision of lesion, esophagus, with primary repair; cervical approach	95.00	2207	2471	640
43101	Excision of lesion, esophagus, with primary repair; thoracic or abdominal approach	120.0	2788	3121	1045
43107	Total or near total esophagectomy, without thoracotomy; with pharyngogastrostomy or cervical esophagogastrostomy, with or without pyloroplasty (transhiatal)	100.0	2323	2601	2123
43108	Total or near total esophagectomy, without thoracotomy; with colon interposition or small bowel reconstruction, including bowel mobilization, preparation and anastomosis(es)	137.0	3183	3563	2466
43112	Total or near total esophagectomy, with thoracotomy; with pharyngogastrostomy or cervical esophagogastrostomy, with or without pyloroplasty	137.0	3183	3563	2191
43113	Total or near total esophagectomy, with thoracotomy; with colon interposition or small bowel reconstruction, including bowel mobilization, preparation, and anastomosis(es)	140.0	3252	3641	2502
43116	Partial esophagectomy, cervical, with free intestinal graft, including microvascular anastomosis, obtaining the graft and intestinal reconstruction	240.0	5575	6241	2358
43117	Partial esophagectomy, distal two-thirds, with thoracotomy and separate abdominal incision, with or without proximal gastrectomy; with thoracic esophagogastrostomy, with or without pyloroplasty (Ivor Lewis)	174.0	4042	4525	2314
43118	Partial esophagectomy, distal two-thirds, with thoracotomy and separate abdominal incision, with or without proximal gastrectomy; with colon interposition or small bowel reconstruction, including bowel mobilization, preparation, and anastomosis(es)	240.0	5575	6241	2430
43121	Partial esophagectomy, distal two-thirds, with thoracotomy only, with or without proximal gastrectomy, with thoracic esophagogastrostomy, with or without pyloroplasty	160.0	3717	4161	2115
43122	Partial esophagectomy, thoracoabdominal or abdominal approach, with or without proximal gastrectomy; with esophagogastrostomy, with or without pyloroplasty	174.0	4042	4525	2115
43123	Partial esophagectomy, thoracoabdominal or abdominal approach, with or without proximal gastrectomy; with colon interposition or small bowel reconstruction, including bowel mobilization, preparation, and anastomosis(es)	214.0	4971	5565	2430
43124	Total or partial esophagectomy, without reconstruction (any approach), with cervical esophagostomy	75.00	1742	1950	2034
43130	Diverticulectomy of hypopharynx or esophagus, with or without myotomy; cervical approach	70.00	1626	1820	931
43135	Diverticulectomy of hypopharynx or esophagus, with or without myotomy; thoracic approach	100.0	2323	2601	1147

Code	Description	Medicode RVU	50th	75th	Medicare Nat'l Avg
43200	Esophagoscopy, rigid or flexible; diagnostic, with or without collection of specimen(s) by brushing or washing (separate procedure)	22.00	511	572	185
43202	Esophagoscopy, rigid or flexible; with biopsy, single or multiple	24.00	558	624	191
43204	Esophagoscopy, rigid or flexible; with injection sclerosis of esophageal varices	33.00	767	858	343
43205	Esophagoscopy, rigid or flexible; with band ligation of esophageal varices	33.00	767	858	228
43215	Esophagoscopy, rigid or flexible; with removal of foreign body	32.00	743	832	263
43216	Esophagoscopy, rigid or flexible; with removal of tumor(s), polyp(s), or other lesion(s) by hot biopsy forceps or bipolar cautery	35.00	813	910	233
43217	Esophagoscopy, rigid or flexible; with removal of tumor(s), polyp(s), or other lesion(s) by snare technique	35.00	813	910	248
43219	Esophagoscopy, rigid or flexible; with insertion of plastic tube or stent	30.00	697	780	254
43220	Esophagoscopy, rigid or flexible; with balloon dilation (less than 30 mm diameter)	27.00	627	702	198
43226	Esophagoscopy, rigid or flexible; with insertion of guide wire followed by dilation over guide wire	24.00	558	624	225
43227	Esophagoscopy, rigid or flexible; with control of bleeding, any method	33.00	767	858	307
43228	Esophagoscopy, rigid or flexible; with ablation of tumor(s), polyp(s), or other lesion(s), not amenable to removal by hot biopsy forceps, bipolar cautery or snare technique	30.00	697	780	314
43234	Upper gastrointestinal endoscopy, simple primary examination (eg, with small diameter flexible endoscope) (separate procedure)	20.00	465	520	188
43235	Upper gastrointestinal endoscopy including esophagus, stomach, and either the duodenum and/or jejunum as appropriate; diagnostic, with or without collection of specimen(s) by brushing or washing (separate procedure)	22.00	511	572	223
43239	Upper gastrointestinal endoscopy including esophagus, stomach, and either the duodenum and/or jejunum as appropriate; with biopsy, single or multiple	25.50	592	663	251
43241	Upper gastrointestinal endoscopy including esophagus, stomach, and either the duodenum and/or jejunum as appropriate; with transendoscopic tube or catheter placement	28.00	650	728	263
43243	Upper gastrointestinal endoscopy including esophagus, stomach, and either the duodenum and/or jejunum as appropriate; with injection sclerosis of esophageal and/or gastric varices	36.00	836	936	383
43244	Upper gastrointestinal endoscopy including esophagus, stomach, and either the duodenum and/or jejunum as appropriate; with band ligation of esophageal and/or gastric varices	34.00	790	884	289
43245	Upper gastrointestinal endoscopy including esophagus, stomach, and either the duodenum and/or jejunum as appropriate; with dilation of gastric outlet for obstruction, any method	30.00	697	780	310

Code	Description	Medicode RVU	50th	75th	Medicare Nat'l Avg
43246	Upper gastrointestinal endoscopy including esophagus, stomach, and either the duodenum and/or jejunum as appropriate; with directed placement of percutaneous gastrostomy tube	44.00	1022	1144	398
43247	Upper gastrointestinal endoscopy including esophagus, stomach, and either the duodenum and/or jejunum as appropriate; with removal of foreign body	30.00	697	780	307
43248	Upper gastrointestinal endoscopy including esophagus, stomach, and either the duodenum and/or jejunum as appropriate; with insertion of guide wire followed by dilation of esophagus over guide wire	26.50	616	689	257
43249	Upper gastrointestinal endoscopy including esophagus, stomach, and either the duodenum and/or jejunum as appropriate; with balloon dilation of esophagus (less than 30 mm diameter)	29.00	674	754	257
43250	Upper gastrointestinal endoscopy including esophagus, stomach, and either the duodenum and/or jejunum as appropriate; with removal of tumor(s), polyp(s), or other lesion(s) by hot biopsy forceps or bipolar cautery	33.00	767	858	323
43251	Upper gastrointestinal endoscopy including esophagus, stomach, and either the duodenum and/or jejunum as appropriate; with removal of tumor(s), polyp(s), or other lesion(s) by snare technique	33.00	767	858	333
43255	Upper gastrointestinal endoscopy including esophagus, stomach, and either the duodenum and/or jejunum as appropriate; with control of bleeding, any method	35.00	813	910	381
43258	Upper gastrointestinal endoscopy including esophagus, stomach, and either the duodenum and/or jejunum as appropriate; with ablation of tumor(s), polyp(s), or other lesion(s) not amenable to removal by hot biopsy forceps, bipolar cautery or snare technique	36.50	848	949	373
43259	Upper gastrointestinal endoscopy including esophagus, stomach, and either the duodenum and/or jejunum as appropriate; with endoscopic ultrasound examination	26.50	616	689	316
43260	Endoscopic retrograde cholangiopancreatography (ERCP); diagnostic, with or without collection of specimen(s) by brushing or washing (separate procedure)	37.00	860	962	437
43261	Endoscopic retrograde cholangiopancreatography (ERCP); with biopsy, single or multiple	41.50	964	1079	446
43262	Endoscopic retrograde cholangiopancreatography (ERCP); with sphincterotomy/papillotomy	58.00	1347	1508	625
43263	Endoscopic retrograde cholangiopancreatography (ERCP); with pressure measurement of sphincter of Oddi (pancreatic duct or common bile duct)	50.00	1162	1300	432
43264	Endoscopic retrograde cholangiopancreatography (ERCP); with endoscopic retrograde removal of stone(s) from biliary and/or pancreatic ducts	63.00	1463	1638	666
43265	Endoscopic retrograde cholangiopancreatography (ERCP); with endoscopic retrograde destruction, lithotripsy of stone(s), any method	59.00	1371	1534	562
43267	Endoscopic retrograde cholangiopancreatography (ERCP); with endoscopic retrograde insertion of nasobiliary or nasopancreatic drainage tube	55.00	1278	1430	537

Code	Description	Medicode RVU	50th	75th	Medicare Nat'l Avg
43268	Endoscopic retrograde cholangiopancreatography (ERCP); with endoscopic retrograde insertion of tube or stent into bile or pancreatic duct	56.00	1301	1456	600
43269	Endoscopic retrograde cholangiopancreatography (ERCP); with endoscopic retrograde removal of foreign body and/or change of tube or stent	49.00	1138	1274	496
43271	Endoscopic retrograde cholangiopancreatography (ERCP); with endoscopic retrograde balloon dilation of ampulla, biliary and/or pancreatic duct(s)	54.00	1254	1404	545
43272	Endoscopic retrograde cholangiopancreatography (ERCP); with ablation of tumor(s), polyp(s), or other lesion(s) not amenable to removal by hot biopsy forceps, bipolar cautery or snare technique	42.00	976	1092	459
43300	Esophagoplasty, (plastic repair or reconstruction), cervical approach; without repair of tracheoesophageal fistula	75.00	1709	2001	857
43305	Esophagoplasty, (plastic repair or reconstruction), cervical approach; with repair of tracheoesophageal fistula	110.0	2506	2934	1246
43310	Esophagoplasty, (plastic repair or reconstruction), thoracic approach; without repair of tracheoesophageal fistula	125.0	2848	3335	1743
43312	Esophagoplasty, (plastic repair or reconstruction), thoracic approach; with repair of tracheoesophageal fistula	142.0	3236	3788	1688
43320	Esophagogastrostomy (cardioplasty), with or without vagotomy and pyloroplasty, transabdominal or transthoracic approach	100.0	2279	2668	1134
43324	Esophagogastric fundoplasty (eg, Nissen, Belsey IV, Hill procedures)	99.00	2256	2641	1209
43325	Esophagogastric fundoplasty; with fundic patch (Thal-Nissen procedure)	115.0	2620	3068	1135
43326	Esophagogastric fundoplasty; with gastroplasty (eg, Collis)	130.0	2962	3468	920
43330	Esophagomyotomy (Heller type); abdominal approach	87.50	1994	2334	1102
43331	Esophagomyotomy (Heller type); thoracic approach	95.00	2165	2534	1241
43340	Esophagojejunostomy (without total gastrectomy); abdominal approach	115.0	2620	3068	1144
43341	Esophagojejunostomy (without total gastrectomy); thoracic approach	130.0	2962	3468	1048
43350	Esophagostomy, fistulization of esophagus, external; abdominal approach	70.00	1595	1867	796
43351	Esophagostomy, fistulization of esophagus, external; thoracic approach	80.00	1823	2134	923
43352	Esophagostomy, fistulization of esophagus, external; cervical approach	60.00	1367	1601	834
43360	Gastrointestinal reconstruction for previous esophagectomy, for obstructing esophageal lesion or fistula, or for previous esophageal exclusion; with stomach, with or without pyloroplasty	163.0	3714	4348	2067

Code		Description	Medicode RVU	50th	75th	Medicare Nat'l Avg
43361		Gastrointestinal reconstruction for previous esophagectomy, for obstructing esophageal lesion or fistula, or for previous esophageal exclusion; with colon interposition or small bowel reconstruction, including bowel mobilization, preparation, and anastomosis(es)	203.0	4626	5415	2358
43400		Ligation, direct, esophageal varices	100.0	2279	2668	1100
43401		Transection of esophagus with repair, for esophageal varices	55.00	1253	1467	1095
43405		Ligation or stapling at gastroesophageal junction for pre-existing esophageal perforation	55.00	1253	1467	1245
43410		Suture of esophageal wound or injury; cervical approach	58.00	1322	1547	792
43415		Suture of esophageal wound or injury; transthoracic or transabdominal approach	96.00	2187	2561	1233
43420		Closure of esophagostomy or fistula; cervical approach	60.00	1367	1601	660
43425		Closure of esophagostomy or fistula; transthoracic or transabdominal approach	81.00	1846	2161	1063
43450	*	Dilation of esophagus, by unguided sound or bougie, single or multiple passes	7.00	160	187	72
43453		Dilation of esophagus, over guide wire	13.00	296	347	119
43456		Dilation of esophagus, by balloon or dilator, retrograde	20.00	456	534	214
43458		Dilation of esophagus with balloon (30 mm diameter or larger) for achalasia	29.00	661	774	196
43460		Esophagogastric tamponade, with balloon (Sengstaaken type)	21.00	479	560	192
43499		Unlisted procedure, esophagus	0.00	0	0	–

43500–43999
Stomach

CODING INSIGHT

Certain procedures in this section for gastric bypass for morbid obesity are considered experimental or investigational, and as such are not covered by most payers.

Any treatment, procedure, facility, equipment, drug, device, or supply may be considered experimental or investigational by a payer, of unproved value, redundant in connection with other services, or not accepted practice. In addition, "experimental" and "investigative" includes any treatment, procedure, facility, equipment, drug, device, or supply that requires the approval of a regulatory agency, in which approval was not granted for the treatment of the specified condition or illness at the time services were rendered or requested.

Medicare Experimental or Investigational Procedures

Medicare criteria for experimental or investigational procedures are as follows:

1. The technology must have final approval from the appropriate government regulatory bodies.

2. A device, drug, or biological product must have Food and Drug Administration approval to market for those specific indications and methods of use.
3. Approval to market refers to permission for commercial distribution. Any other approval that is granted as an interim step in the FDA regulatory process (e.g., an Investigational Device Exemption, is not sufficient).
4. The scientific evidence must permit conclusions concerning the effect of the technology on health outcomes.
5. The evidence should consist of well-designed and well-conducted investigations published in peer-reviewed journals. The quality of the body of studies and the consistency of the results are considered in evaluating the evidence.
6. The evidence should demonstrate that the technology can measure or alter the physiological changes related to a disease, injury, illness, or condition. In addition, there should also be evidence or a convincing argument based on established medical facts that such measurement or alteration affects the health outcomes.
7. Opinions and evaluations by national medical associations, consensus panels, or other technology evaluation bodies are evaluated according to the scientific quality of the supporting evidence and rationale.
8. The technology must improve the net health outcome.
9. The technology's beneficial effects on health outcomes should outweigh any harmful effects on health outcomes.
10. The technology must be as beneficial as any established alternatives.
11. The technology should improve the net health outcome as much or more than established alternatives.
12. The improvement must be attainable outside the investigational settings.
13. When used under the usual conditions of medical practice, the technology should be reasonably expected to satisfy criteria #3 and #4.
14. Experimental and investigative procedures are usually excluded from coverage.

Subsidiary Codes

Subsidiary codes have relative values that require no further adjustment:

20926 is "in addition" to 43500–43999
38102 is "in addition" to 43500–43999
38747 is "in addition" to 43500–43999
43635 is "in addition" to 43631–43634
44015 is "in addition" to 43500–43999
44955 is "in addition" to 43500–43999
45355 is "in addition" to 43500–43999
47001 is "in addition" to 43500–43999
49905 is "in addition" to 43500–43999
58611 is "in addition" to 43605–43641, 43800–43825, 43832–43999

Because these are subsidiary or "in addition to" codes, reimbursement reduction and modifier -51 do not apply.

Medicare Alert

Medicare rebundles certain codes in the surgery section when the listed codes are considered a component of a more comprehensive service.

38100 will not be reimbursed when reported with 43630, 43635, 43640

38500 will not be reimbursed when reported with reported with 43630, 43635, 43832, 43840
43610 will not be reimbursed when reported with 43630 and 43635
43640 will not be reimbursed when reported with 43635
43750 will not be reimbursed when reported with 43630, 43635, 43640, 43830, 43832, 43840
43760 will not be reimbursed when reported with 43630, 43635, 43640, 43750, 43830, 43832, 43840
43825 will not be reimbursed when reported with 43630, 43635, 43640
43830 will not be reimbursed when reported with 43630, 43635, 43640, 43832
43840 will not be reimbursed when reported with 43630, 43635, 43640
43860 will not be reimbursed when reported with 43630 and 43635
44005 will not be reimbursed when reported with 43630, 43635, 43640, 43832, 43840
44600 will not be reimbursed when reported with 43630, 43635, 43840
44950, 49000 and 49255 will not be reimbursed when reported with 43630, 43635, 43640, 43840
43630 will not be reimbursed when reported with 43635
43832 will not be reimbursed when reported with 43635, 43640
44300 will not be reimbursed when reported with 43640, 43832
43234 will not be reimbursed when reported with 43750
49010 will not be reimbursed with reported with 43840

Code	Description	Medicode RVU	50th	75th	Medicare Nat'l Avg
43500	Gastrotomy; with exploration or foreign body removal	60.00	1356	1580	621
43501	Gastrotomy; with suture repair of bleeding ulcer	83.00	1876	2186	978
43502	Gastrotomy; with suture repair of pre-existing esophagogastric laceration (eg, Mallory-Weiss)	83.00	1876	2186	1034
43510	Gastrotomy; with esophageal dilation and insertion of permanent intraluminal tube (eg, Celestin or Mousseaux-Barbin)	53.00	1198	1396	641
43520	Pyloromyotomy, cutting of pyloric muscle (Fredet-Ramstedt type operation)	60.00	1356	1580	487
43600	Biopsy of stomach; by capsule, tube, peroral (one or more specimens)	10.00	226	263	86
43605	Biopsy of stomach; by laparotomy	70.00	1582	1844	626
43610	Excision, local; ulcer or benign tumor of stomach	77.00	1741	2028	830
43611	Excision, local; malignant tumor of stomach	88.50	2001	2331	899
43620	Gastrectomy, total; with esophagoenterostomy	140.0	3165	3687	1616
43621	Gastrectomy, total; with Roux-en-Y reconstruction	185.0	4182	4872	1630
43622	Gastrectomy, total; with formation of intestinal pouch, any type	202.5	4578	5333	1673
43631	Gastrectomy, partial, distal; with gastroduodenostomy	100.0	2261	2634	1319
43632	Gastrectomy, partial, distal; with gastrojejunostomy	100.0	2261	2634	1319

Code		Description	Medicode RVU	50th	75th	Medicare Nat'l Avg
43633		Gastrectomy, partial, distal; with Roux-en-Y reconstruction	132.0	2984	3476	1333
43634		Gastrectomy, partial, distal; with formation of intestinal pouch	162.5	3673	4280	1808
43635		Vagotomy with partial distal gastrectomy (List separately in addition to code(s) for primary procedure) (Use 43635 only with 43631, 43632, 43633, 43634)	37.50	848	988	132
43638		Gastrectomy, partial, proximal, thoracic or abdominal approach including esophagogastrostomy, with vagotomy;	125.0	2826	3292	1441
43639		Gastrectomy, partial, proximal, thoracic or abdominal approach including esophagogastrostomy, with vagotomy; with pyloroplasty or pyloromyotomy	160.0	3617	4214	1458
43640		Vagotomy including pyloroplasty, with or without gastrostomy; truncal or selective	96.50	2181	2542	1048
43641		Vagotomy including pyloroplasty, with or without gastrostomy; parietal cell (highly selective)	115.0	2600	3029	1011
43750		Percutaneous placement of gastrostomy tube	41.00	927	1080	394
43760	*	Change of gastrostomy tube	6.00	136	158	66
43761		Repositioning of the gastric feeding tube through the duodenum for enteric nutrition	10.00	226	263	113
43800		Pyloroplasty	70.00	1582	1844	731
43810		Gastroduodenostomy	75.00	1695	1975	766
43820		Gastrojejunostomy; without vagotomy	75.50	1707	1988	840
43825		Gastrojejunostomy; with vagotomy, any type	90.00	2034	2370	1091
43830		Gastrostomy, temporary (tube, rubber or plastic) (separate procedure);	61.00	1379	1607	549
43831		Gastrostomy, temporary (tube, rubber or plastic) (separate procedure); neonatal, for feeding	61.00	1379	1607	493
43832		Gastrostomy, permanent, with construction of gastric tube	70.00	1582	1844	819
43840		Gastrorrhaphy, suture of perforated duodenal or gastric ulcer, wound, or injury	75.00	1695	1975	813
43842		Gastric restrictive procedure, without gastric bypass, for morbid obesity; vertical-banded gastroplasty	138.0	3119	3635	1189
43843		Gastric restrictive procedure, without gastric bypass, for morbid obesity; other than vertical-banded gastroplasty	155.0	3504	4082	1188
43846		Gastric restrictive procedure, with gastric bypass for morbid obesity; with short limb (less than 100 cm) Roux-en-Y gastroenterostomy	174.0	3933	4583	1399
43847		Gastric restrictive procedure, with gastric bypass for morbid obesity; with small bowel reconstruction to limit absorption	174.0	3933	4583	1199
43848		Revision of gastric restrictive procedure for morbid obesity (separate procedure)	0.00	0	0	1554

Code	Description	Medicode RVU	50th	75th	Medicare Nat'l Avg
43850	Revision of gastroduodenal anastomosis (gastroduodenostomy) with reconstruction; without vagotomy	100.0	2261	2634	1261
43855	Revision of gastroduodenal anastomosis (gastroduodenostomy) with reconstruction; with vagotomy	115.0	2600	3029	1241
43860	Revision of gastrojejunal anastomosis (gastrojejunostomy) with reconstruction, with or without partial gastrectomy or bowel resection; without vagotomy	100.0	2261	2634	1290
43865	Revision of gastrojejunal anastomosis (gastrojejunostomy) with reconstruction, with or without partial gastrectomy or bowel resection; with vagotomy	115.0	2600	3029	1391
43870	Closure of gastrostomy, surgical	50.00	1130	1317	558
43880	Closure of gastrocolic fistula	75.00	1695	1975	1108
43999	Unlisted procedure, stomach	0.00	0	0	–

44005–44799
Intestines (Except Rectum) Endoscope, Small Bowel, and Stomach

Coding Insight
Terms which may be helpful in this code range are:

- *Small intestinal endoscopy*: (1) enteroscopy beyond second portion of duodenum, not including the ileum (2) enteroscopy beyond the second portion of duodenum, including ileum
- *Ileoscopy*: through stoma: endoscopic examination of the ileum through an artificial opening (stoma)
- *Endoscopic evaluation*: of small intestinal (abdominal or pelvic) pouch

Refer to *CPT '96* guidelines at the begining of the 40000 codes for information about endoscopic codes.

Subsidiary Codes
Subsidiary codes have relative values that require no further adjustment:

38102 is "in addition" to 44005–44799
38747 is "in addition" to 44005–44799
44015 is "in addition" to 44005–44799
44121 is "in addition" to 44120
44139 is "in addition" to 44140–44147
44955 is "in addition" to 44005–44799
45355 is "in addition" to 44005–44799
47001 is "in addition" to 44005–44799
49905 is "in addition" to 44005–44799
58611 is "in addition" to 44005–44055, 44110–44346, 44602–44799

Because these are subsidiary or "in addition to" codes, reimbursement reduction and CPT modifier -51 do not apply.

MEDICARE ALERT

Medicare rebundles certain codes in the surgery section when the listed codes are considered a component of a more comprehensive service.

38500 will not be reimbursed when reported with 44005, 44120, 44140, 44141, 44143, 44144, 44145, 44150, 44160, 44320
44950 will not be reimbursed when reported with 44005, 44120, 44130, 44140, 44141, 44143, 44144, 44145, 44150, 44160, 44320
49000 will not be reimbursed when reported with 44005, 44120, 44130, 44140, 44141, 44143, 41444, 44145, 4415044160, 44320, 44625
49255 will not be reimbursed when reported with 44005, 44120, 44130, 44140, 44141, 44143, 44144, 44145, 44150, 44160, 44320
44005 will not be reimbursed when reported with 44120, 44130, 44140, 44141, 44143, 44144, 44145, 44150, 44160, 44320, 44625
44130 will not be reimbursed when reported with 44120, 44140, 44150
44600 will not be reimbursed when reported with 44120, 44130, 44140, 44141, 44143, 44144, 44145, 44150, 44160
44020 will not be reimbursed when reported with 44120
49010 will not be reimbursed when reported with 44140, 49141, 44143, 49144, 44145, 44150, 44160
44320 will not be reimbursed when reported with 44141 and 44144
44140 will not be reimbursed when reported with 44141, 44145, 44150, 44160
44141 will not be reimbursed when reported with 44144, 44150, 44160
44144 will not be reimbursed when reported with 44150 and 44160
44300 will not be reimbursed when reported with 44320
44620 will not be reimbursed when reported with 44625

Code	Description	Medicode RVU	50th	75th	Medicare Nat'l Avg
44005	Enterolysis (freeing of intestinal adhesion) (separate procedure)	75.00	1764	2005	914
44010	Duodenotomy, for exploration, biopsy(s), or foreign body removal	75.00	1764	2005	724
44015	Tube or needle catheter jejunostomy for enteral alimentation, intraoperative, any method (List separately in addition to primary procedure)	34.50	811	922	298
44020	Enterotomy, small bowel, other than duodenum; for exploration, biopsy(s), or foreign body removal	75.00	1764	2005	828
44021	Enterotomy, small bowel, other than duodenum; for decompression (eg, Baker tube)	65.00	1528	1738	780
44025	Colotomy, for exploration, biopsy(s), or foreign body removal	75.00	1764	2005	846
44050	Reduction of volvulus, intussusception, internal hernia, by laparotomy	65.00	1528	1738	816
44055	Correction of malrotation by lysis of duodenal bands and/or reduction of midgut volvulus (eg, Ladd procedure)	88.00	2069	2353	841
44100	Biopsy of intestine by capsule, tube, peroral (one or more specimens)	11.00	259	294	125
44110	Excision of one or more lesions of small or large bowel not requiring anastomosis, exteriorization, or fistulization; single enterotomy	66.00	1552	1765	781

Code	Description	Medicode RVU	50th	75th	Medicare Nat'l Avg
44111	Excision of one or more lesions of small or large bowel not requiring anastomosis, exteriorization, or fistulization; multiple enterotomies	100.0	2352	2674	918
44120	Enterectomy, resection of small intestine; single resection and anastomosis	92.00	2163	2460	990
44121	Enterectomy, resection of small intestine; each additional resection and anastomosis	46.00	1082	1230	284
44125	Enterectomy, resection of small intestine; with enterostomy	97.00	2281	2593	1050
44130	Enteroenterostomy, anastomosis of intestine, with or without cutaneous enterostomy (separate procedure)	88.00	2069	2353	885
44139	Mobilization (take-down) of splenic flexure performed in conjunction with partial colectomy (List separately in addition to primary procedure)	6.50	153	174	143
44140	Colectomy, partial; with anastomosis	100.0	2352	2674	1213
44141	Colectomy, partial; with skin level cecostomy or colostomy	105.0	2469	2807	1259
44143	Colectomy, partial; with end colostomy and closure of distal segment (Hartmann type procedure)	105.0	2469	2807	1211
44144	Colectomy, partial; with resection, with colostomy or ileostomy and creation of mucofistula	110.0	2587	2941	1201
44145	Colectomy, partial; with coloproctostomy (low pelvic anastomosis)	110.0	2587	2941	1470
44146	Colectomy, partial; with coloproctostomy (low pelvic anastomosis), with colostomy	125.0	2939	3342	1614
44147	Colectomy, partial; abdominal and transanal approach	145.0	3410	3877	1397
44150	Colectomy, total, abdominal, without proctectomy; with ileostomy or ileoproctostomy	125.0	2939	3342	1489
44151	Colectomy, total, abdominal, without proctectomy; with continent ileostomy	175.0	4115	4679	1198
44152	Colectomy, total, abdominal, without proctectomy; with rectal mucosectomy, ileoanal anastomosis, with or without loop ileostomy	175.0	4115	4679	1636
44153	Colectomy, total, abdominal, without proctectomy; with rectal mucosectomy, ileoanal anastomosis, creation of ileal reservoir (S or J), with or without loop ileostomy	195.0	4585	5214	1857
44155	Colectomy, total, abdominal, with proctectomy; with ileostomy	160.0	3762	4278	1702
44156	Colectomy, total, abdominal, with proctectomy; with continent ileostomy	220.0	5173	5882	1349
44160	Colectomy with removal of terminal ileum and ileocolostomy	110.0	2587	2941	1210
44300	Enterostomy or cecostomy, tube (eg, for decompression or feeding) (separate procedure)	58.00	1328	1544	628
44310	Ileostomy or jejunostomy, non-tube (separate procedure)	75.00	1717	1996	812
44312	Revision of ileostomy; simple (release of superficial scar) (separate procedure)	26.00	595	692	350

Code	Description	Medicode RVU	50th	75th	Medicare Nat'l Avg
44314	Revision of ileostomy; complicated (reconstruction in-depth) (separate procedure)	80.00	1832	2129	722
44316	Continent ileostomy (Kock procedure) (separate procedure)	125.0	2862	3327	966
44320	Colostomy or skin level cecostomy; (separate procedure)	58.00	1328	1544	815
44322	Colostomy or skin level cecostomy; with multiple biopsies (eg, for Hirschsprung disease) (separate procedure)	68.00	1557	1810	834
44340	Revision of colostomy; simple (release of superficial scar) (separate procedure)	25.50	584	679	266
44345	Revision of colostomy; complicated (reconstruction in-depth) (separate procedure)	58.00	1328	1544	623
44346	Revision of colostomy; with repair of paracolostomy hernia (separate procedure)	68.00	1557	1810	766
44360	Small intestinal endoscopy, enteroscopy beyond second portion of duodenum, not including ileum; diagnostic, with or without collection of specimen(s) by brushing or washing (separate procedure)	28.00	641	745	256
44361	Small intestinal endoscopy, enteroscopy beyond second portion of duodenum, not including ileum; with biopsy, single or multiple	30.00	687	798	279
44363	Small intestinal endoscopy, enteroscopy beyond second portion of duodenum, not including ileum; with removal of foreign body	30.00	687	798	252
44364	Small intestinal endoscopy, enteroscopy beyond second portion of duodenum, not including ileum; with removal of tumor(s), polyp(s), or other lesion(s) by snare technique	34.00	778	905	334
44365	Small intestinal endoscopy, enteroscopy beyond second portion of duodenum, not including ileum; with removal of tumor(s), polyp(s), or other lesion(s) by hot biopsy forceps or bipolar cautery	34.00	778	905	319
44366	Small intestinal endoscopy, enteroscopy beyond second portion of duodenum, not including ileum; with control of bleeding, any method	40.00	916	1065	389
44369	Small intestinal endoscopy, enteroscopy beyond second portion of duodenum, not including ileum; with ablation of tumor(s), polyp(s), or other lesion(s) not amenable to removal by hot biopsy forceps, bipolar cautery or snare technique	34.00	778	905	414
44372	Small intestinal endoscopy, enteroscopy beyond second portion of duodenum, not including ileum; with placement of percutaneous jejunostomy tube	28.00	641	745	401
44373	Small intestinal endoscopy, enteroscopy beyond second portion of duodenum, not including ileum; with conversion of percutaneous gastrostomy tube to percutaneous jejunostomy tube	28.00	641	745	336
44376	Small intestinal endoscopy, enteroscopy beyond second portion of duodenum, including ileum; diagnostic, with or without collection of specimen(s) by brushing or washing (separate procedure)	31.00	710	825	342
44377	Small intestinal endoscopy, enteroscopy beyond second portion of duodenum, including ileum; with biopsy, single or multiple	34.00	778	905	360

Code	Description	Medicode RVU	50th	75th	Medicare Nat'l Avg
44378	Small intestinal endoscopy, enteroscopy beyond second portion of duodenum, including ileum; with control of bleeding, any method	47.00	1076	1251	456
44380	Ileoscopy, through stoma; diagnostic, with or without collection of specimen(s) by brushing or washing (separate procedure)	22.00	504	585	141
44382	Ileoscopy, through stoma; with biopsy, single or multiple	29.00	664	772	171
44385	Endoscopic evaluation of small intestinal (abdominal or pelvic) pouch; diagnostic, with or without collection of specimen(s) by brushing or washing (separate procedure)	26.50	607	705	185
44386	Endoscopic evaluation of small intestinal (abdominal or pelvic) pouch; with biopsy, single or multiple	31.00	710	825	134
44388	Colonoscopy through stoma; diagnostic, with or without collection of specimen(s) by brushing or washing (separate procedure)	30.00	687	798	296
44389	Colonoscopy through stoma; with biopsy, single or multiple	35.00	801	931	275
44390	Colonoscopy through stoma; with removal of foreign body	35.00	801	931	232
44391	Colonoscopy through stoma; with control of bleeding, any method	48.00	1099	1277	349
44392	Colonoscopy through stoma; with removal of tumor(s), polyp(s), or other lesion(s) by hot biopsy forceps or bipolar cautery	41.00	939	1091	356
44393	Colonoscopy through stoma; with ablation of tumor(s), polyp(s), or other lesion(s) not amenable to removal by hot biopsy forceps, bipolar cautery or snare technique	41.00	939	1091	379
44394	Colonoscopy through stoma; with removal of tumor(s), polyp(s), or other lesion(s) by snare technique	41.00	939	1091	371
44500	Introduction of long gastrointestinal tube (eg, Miller-Abbott) (separate procedure)	4.20	96	112	30
44602	Suture of small intestine (enterorrhaphy) for perforated ulcer, diverticulum, wound, injury or rupture; single perforation	75.00	1717	1996	794
44603	Suture of small intestine (enterorrhaphy) for perforated ulcer, diverticulum, wound, injury or rupture; multiple perforations	87.50	2003	2329	1000
44604	Suture of large intestine (colorrhaphy) for perforated ulcer, diverticulum, wound, injury or rupture (single or multiple perforations); without colostomy	75.00	1717	1996	905
44605	Suture of large intestine (colorrhaphy) for perforated ulcer, diverticulum, wound, injury or rupture (single or multiple perforations); with colostomy	85.00	1946	2262	1029
44615	Intestinal stricturoplasty (enterotomy and enterorrhaphy) with or without dilation, for intestinal obstruction	90.00	2061	2395	824
44620	Closure of enterostomy, large or small intestine;	55.00	1259	1464	672
44625	Closure of enterostomy, large or small intestine; with resection and anastomosis	82.00	1877	2182	969

Code	Description	Medicode RVU	50th	75th	Medicare Nat'l Avg
44640	Closure of intestinal cutaneous fistula	58.00	1328	1544	861
44650	Closure of enteroenteric or enterocolic fistula	70.00	1603	1863	893
44660	Closure of enterovesical fistula; without intestinal or bladder resection	70.00	1603	1863	899
44661	Closure of enterovesical fistula; with bowel and/or bladder resection	110.0	2518	2927	1291
44680	Intestinal plication (separate procedure)	90.00	2061	2395	963
44799	Unlisted procedure, intestine	0.00	0	0	–

44800–44899
Meckel's Diverticulum and the Mesentery

Subsidiary Codes
Subsidiary codes have relative values that require no further adjustment:

20926 is "in addition" to 44800–44899
38102 is "in addition" to 44800–44899
38747 is "in addition" to 44800–44899
44015 is "in addition" to 44800–44899
44955 is "in addition" to 44800–44899
45355 is "in addition" to 44800–44899
47001 is "in addition" to 44800–44899
49905 is "in addition" to 44800–44899
58611 is "in addition" to 44800–44899

Because these are subsidiary or "in addition to" codes, reimbursement reduction and modifier -51 do not apply.

Code	Description	Medicode RVU	50th	75th	Medicare Nat'l Avg
44800	Excision of Meckel's diverticulum (diverticulectomy) or omphalomesenteric duct	60.00	1374	1597	659
44820	Excision of lesion of mesentery (separate procedure)	50.00	1145	1331	646
44850	Suture of mesentery (separate procedure)	60.00	1374	1597	607
44899	Unlisted procedure, Meckel's diverticulum and the mesentery	0.00	0	0	–

44900–44960
Appendix

Coding Insight
Incidental appendectomy at the time of another surgery is not separately reported.

Subsidiary Codes

Subsidiary codes have relative values that require no further adjustment:

20926 is "in addition" to 44900–44960
38102 is "in addition" to 44900–44960
38747 is "in addition" to 44900–44960
44015 is "in addition" to 44900–44960
44955 is "in addition" to 44900–44960
45355 is "in addition" to 44900–44960
47001 is "in addition" to 44900–44960
49905 is "in addition" to 44900–44960
58611 is "in addition" to 44900–44960

Because these are subsidiary or "in addition to" codes, reimbursement reduction and modifier -51 do not apply.

Medicare Alert

Medicare rebundles certain codes in the surgery section when the listed codes are considered a component of a more comprehensive service.

44950 will not be reimbursed when reported with 44955, 44960

Code	Description	Medicode RVU	50th	75th	Medicare Nat'l Avg
44900	Incision and drainage of appendiceal abscess, transabdominal	42.00	977	1110	513
44950	Appendectomy;	48.00	111	1268	485
44955	Appendectomy; when done for indicated purpose at time of other major procedure (not as separate procedure)	26.00	605	687	205
44960	Appendectomy; for ruptured appendix with abscess or generalized peritonitis	60.00	139	1586	665

45000–46999
Rectum/Anus

Coding Insight

Some terms which may be helpful in this code range are:

- *Proctosigmoidoscopy*: endoscopic examination of the rectum and sigmoid colon
- *Sigmoidoscopy*: endoscopic examination of entire rectum, sigmoid colon, and may include examination of a portion of the descending colon
- *Colonoscopy (through stoma)*: endoscope placed through existing artificially created opening (stoma); includes examination of any existing colon, from the rectum to the cecum, and may include examination of the terminal ilium
- *Colonoscopy*: endoscopic examination of the entire colon, from the rectum to the cecum, and may include examination of the terminal ilium
- *Anoscopy*: endoscopic examination of the anus; inherent to invasive anal procedures

Refer to CPT guidelines at the begining of the 40000 codes for information about endoscopic procedures.

Medicare Colonoscopy Issues

HCFA mandates that when a colonoscopy fails, the physician should be paid for the procedure that was actually performed and not the procedure that was intended. HCFA further specifies:

- A colonoscopy is defined as the ability to extend beyond the splenic flexure. When the procedure performed does not meet the criteria for a colonoscopy, a sigmoidoscopy (45330) should be reported instead
- Use modifier -22 only when supporting documentation indicates that significantly more time and effort was involved than in the typical sigmoidoscopy. The fact that a particular sigmoidoscopy was intended to be a colonoscopy does not in itself automatically justify the use of modifier -22
- The site-of-service reduction will apply when the sigmoidoscopy/failed colonoscopy is done in a hospital setting

Subsidiary Codes

Subsidiary codes have relative values that require no further adjustment:

20926 is "in addition" to 45000–46999
38102 is "in addition" to 45000–46999
38747 is "in addition" to 45000–46999
44015 is "in addition" to 45000–46999
44955 is "in addition" to 45000–46999
45355 is "in addition" to 45000–46999
47001 is "in addition" to 45000–46999
49905 is "in addition" to 45000–46999
58611 is "in addition" to 45000–45020, 45110–45121

Because these are subsidiary or "in addition to" codes, reimbursement reduction and modifier -51 do not apply.

Medicare Alert

Medicare rebundles certain codes in the surgery section when the listed codes are considered a component of a more comprehensive service.

38500, 44005, 44141, 44143, 44144, 44145, 44146, 44150, 44155, 44160, 44320, 44345, 44600, 44620, 44625, 44950, 45170, 45180, 49000, 49010, 44255 will not be reimbursed when reported with 45110
46600 will not be reimbursed when reported with 45300, 45330, 45380, 45383, 46260
45300 will not be reimbursed when reported with 45330 45331, 45378, 45380, 45383, 45385
45305 will not be reimbursed when reported with 45331 and 45380
45330 will not be reimbursed when reported with 45331, 45378, 45380, 45383, 45385
45331 will not be reimbursed when reported with 45380, 45383
45378 will not be reimbursed when reported with 45380, 45383, 45385
45302, 45310, 45320, 45336, 45355 will not be reimbursed when reported with 45383
45333 will not be reimbursed when reported with 45383, 45385
46221, 46255, 46934 will not be reimbursed when reported with 46260

Code	Description	Medicode RVU	50th	75th	Medicare Nat'l Avg
45000	Transrectal drainage of pelvic abscess	17.50	401	467	241
45005	Incision and drainage of submucosal abscess, rectum	14.00	321	373	144

Code	Description	Medicode RVU	50th	75th	Medicare Nat'l Avg
45020	Incision and drainage of deep supralevator, pelvirectal, or retrorectal abscess	22.50	516	600	302
45100	Biopsy of anorectal wall, anal approach (eg, congenital megacolon)	20.00	458	533	226
45108	Anorectal myomectomy	50.00	1146	1333	294
45110	Proctectomy; complete, combined abdominoperineal, with colostomy	130.0	2980	3466	1669
45111	Proctectomy; partial resection of rectum, transabdominal approach	105.0	2407	2800	1166
45112	Proctectomy, combined abdominoperineal, pull-through procedure (eg, colo-anal anastomosis)	130.0	2980	3466	1708
45113	Proctectomy, partial, with rectal mucosectomy, ileoanal anastomosis, creation of ileal reservoir (S or J), with or without loop ileostomy	160.0	3668	4266	1731
45114	Proctectomy, partial, with anastomosis; abdominal and transsacral approach	150.0	3438	4000	1557
45116	Proctectomy, partial, with anastomosis; transacral approach only (Kraske type)	105.0	2407	2800	1260
45120	Proctectomy, complete (for congenital megacolon), abdominal and perineal approach; with pull-through procedure and anastomosis (eg, Swenson, Duhamel, or Soave type operation)	150.0	3438	4000	1668
45121	Proctectomy, complete (for congenital megacolon), abdominal and perineal approach; with subtotal or total colectomy, with multiple biopsies	130.0	2980	3466	1476
45123	Proctectomy, partial, without anastomosis, perineal approach	85.00	1948	2266	1109
45130	Excision of rectal procidentia, with anastomosis; perineal approach	83.00	1903	2213	940
45135	Excision of rectal procidentia, with anastomosis; abdominal and perineal approach	140.0	3209	3733	1386
45150	Division of stricture of rectum	35.00	802	933	367
45160	Excision of rectal tumor by proctotomy, transacral or transcoccygeal approach	90.00	2063	2400	855
45170	Excision of rectal tumor, transanal approach	40.00	917	1067	559
45190	Destruction of rectal tumor, any method (eg, electrodesiccation) transanal approach	20.00	458	533	561
45300	Proctosigmoidoscopy, rigid; diagnostic, with or without collection of specimen(s) by brushing or washing (separate procedure)	4.25	99	114	52
45303	Proctosigmoidoscopy, rigid; with dilation, any method	5.50	128	148	54
45305	Proctosigmoidoscopy, rigid; with biopsy, single or multiple	7.00	163	188	80
45307	Proctosigmoidoscopy, rigid; with removal of foreign body	10.00	233	268	125

Code	Description	Medicode RVU	50th	75th	Medicare Nat'l Avg
45308	Proctosigmoidoscopy, rigid; with removal of single tumor, polyp, or other lesion by hot biopsy forceps or bipolar cautery	10.00	233	268	113
45309	Proctosigmoidoscopy, rigid; with removal of single tumor, polyp, or other lesion by snare technique	10.00	233	268	130
45315	Proctosigmoidoscopy, rigid; with removal of multiple tumors, polyps, or other lesions by hot biopsy forceps, bipolar cautery or snare technique	16.00	372	429	152
45317	Proctosigmoidoscopy, rigid; with control of bleeding, any method	15.00	349	402	164
45320	Proctosigmoidoscopy, rigid; with ablation of tumor(s), polyp(s), or other lesion(s) not amenable to removal by hot biopsy forceps, bipolar cautery or snare technique (eg, laser)	16.00	372	429	214
45321	Proctosigmoidoscopy, rigid; with decompression of volvulus	13.00	302	349	160
45330	Sigmoidoscopy, flexible; diagnostic, with or without collection of specimen(s) by brushing or washing (separate procedure)	8.25	191	220	85
45331	Sigmoidoscopy, flexible; with biopsy, single or multiple	12.00	279	319	113
45332	Sigmoidoscopy, flexible; with removal of foreign body	15.00	348	399	139
45333	Sigmoidoscopy, flexible; with removal of tumor(s), polyp(s), or other lesion(s) by hot biopsy forceps or bipolar cautery	26.00	603	692	169
45334	Sigmoidoscopy, flexible; with control of bleeding, any method	22.50	522	599	217
45337	Sigmoidoscopy, flexible; with decompression of volvulus, any method	21.00	487	559	222
45338	Sigmoidoscopy, flexible; with removal of tumor(s), polyp(s), or other lesion(s) by snare technique	26.00	603	692	182
45339	Sigmoidoscopy, flexible; with ablation of tumor(s), polyp(s), or other lesion(s) not amenable to removal by hot biopsy forceps, bipolar cautery or snare technique	26.00	603	692	243
45355	Colonoscopy, rigid or flexible, transabdominal via colotomy, single or multiple	16.00	371	426	169
45378	Colonoscopy, flexible, proximal to splenic flexure; diagnostic, with or without collection of specimen(s) by brushing or washing, with or without colon decompression (separate procedure)	30.00	704	795	292
45379	Colonoscopy, flexible, proximal to splenic flexure; with removal of foreign body	35.00	821	927	369
45380	Colonoscopy, flexible, proximal to splenic flexure; with biopsy, single or multiple	33.00	774	874	330
45382	Colonoscopy, flexible, proximal to splenic flexure; with control of bleeding, any method	40.00	939	1060	423
45383	Colonoscopy, flexible, proximal to splenic flexure; with ablation of tumor(s), polyp(s), or other lesion(s) not amenable to removal by hot biopsy forceps, bipolar cautery or snare technique	42.50	997	1126	432

Code		Description	Medicode RVU	50th	75th	Medicare Nat'l Avg
45384		Colonoscopy, flexible, proximal to splenic flexure; with removal of tumor(s), polyp(s), or other lesion(s) by hot biopsy forceps or bipolar cautery	42.50	997	1126	445
45385		Colonoscopy, flexible, proximal to splenic flexure; with removal of tumor(s), polyp(s), or other lesion(s) by snare technique	42.50	997	1126	455
45500		Proctoplasty; for stenosis	55.00	1235	1472	548
45505		Proctoplasty; for prolapse of mucous membrane	55.00	1235	1472	548
45520		Perirectal injection of sclerosing solution for prolapse	4.00	90	107	45
45540		Proctopexy for prolapse; abdominal approach	90.00	2020	2408	980
45541		Proctopexy for prolapse; perineal approach	90.00	2020	2408	879
45550		Proctopexy combined with sigmoid resection, abdominal approach	105.0	2357	2810	1144
45560		Repair of rectocele (separate procedure)	34.00	763	910	525
45562		Exploration, repair, and presacral drainage for rectal injury;	95.00	2132	2542	808
45563		Exploration, repair, and presacral drainage for rectal injury; with colostomy	105.0	2357	2810	1274
45800		Closure of rectovesical fistula;	95.00	2132	2542	953
45805		Closure of rectovesical fistula; with colostomy	105.0	2357	2810	1171
45820		Closure of rectourethral fistula;	95.00	2132	2542	921
45825		Closure of rectourethral fistula; with colostomy	105.0	2357	2810	1054
45900	*	Reduction of procidentia (separate procedure) under anesthesia	6.00	135	161	90
45905	*	Dilation of anal sphincter (separate procedure) under anesthesia other than local	9.00	202	241	93
45910		Dilation of rectal stricture (separate procedure) under anesthesia other than local	17.00	382	455	113
45915	*	Removal of fecal impaction or foreign body (separate procedure) under anesthesia	17.00	382	455	98
45999		Unlisted procedure, rectum	0.00	0	0	–
46030	*	Removal of anal seton, other marker	5.00	112	134	66
46040		Incision and drainage of ischiorectal and/or perirectal abscess (separate procedure)	19.00	427	510	264
46045		Incision and drainage of intramural, intramuscular or submucosal abscess, transanal, under anesthesia	21.25	477	570	240

Code		Description	Medicode RVU	50th	75th	Medicare Nat'l Avg
46050	*	Incision and drainage, perianal abscess, superficial	8.00	180	215	72
46060		Incision and drainage of ischiorectal or intramural abscess, with fistulectomy or fistulotomy, submuscular, with or without placement of seton	48.00	1078	1287	487
46070		Incision, anal septum (infant)	8.00	180	215	168
46080	*	Sphincterotomy, anal, division of sphincter (separate procedure)	21.00	471	563	199
46083		Incision of thrombosed hemorrhoid, external	5.75	129	154	69
46200		Fissurectomy, with or without sphincterotomy	31.00	728	845	295
46210		Cryptectomy; single	10.00	235	273	133
46211		Cryptectomy; multiple (separate procedure)	36.00	845	982	254
46220		Papillectomy or excision of single tag, anus (separate procedure)	6.00	141	164	88
46221		Hemorrhoidectomy, by simple ligature (eg, rubber band)	9.00	211	245	85
46230		Excision of external hemorrhoid tags and/or multiple papillae	7.50	176	205	130
46250		Hemorrhoidectomy, external, complete	30.00	704	818	310
46255		Hemorrhoidectomy, internal and external, simple;	40.00	939	1091	436
46257		Hemorrhoidectomy, internal and external, simple; with fissurectomy	42.50	998	1159	489
46258		Hemorrhoidectomy, internal and external, simple; with fistulectomy, with or without fissurectomy	45.00	1057	1227	534
46260		Hemorrhoidectomy, internal and external, complex or extensive;	50.00	1174	1364	571
46261		Hemorrhoidectomy, internal and external, complex or extensive; with fissurectomy	52.50	1233	1432	595
46262		Hemorrhoidectomy, internal and external, complex or extensive; with fistulectomy, with or without fissurectomy	55.00	1291	1500	608
46270		Surgical treatment of anal fistula (fistulectomy/fistulotomy); subcutaneous	30.00	704	818	225
46275		Surgical treatment of anal fistula (fistulectomy/fistulotomy); submuscular	44.00	1033	1200	467
46280		Surgical treatment of anal fistula (fistulectomy/fistulotomy); complex or multiple, with or without placement of seton	51.00	1198	1391	538
46285		Surgical treatment of anal fistula (fistulectomy/fistulotomy); second stage	16.00	376	436	258
46288		Closure of anal fistula with rectal advancement flap	50.00	1174	1364	436
46320	*	Enucleation or excision of external thrombotic hemorrhoid	7.50	176	205	91

Code		Description	Medicode RVU	50th	75th	Medicare Nat'l Avg
46500	*	Injection of sclerosing solution, hemorrhoids	2.75	65	75	70
46600		Anoscopy; diagnostic, with or without collection of specimen(s) by brushing or washing (separate procedure)	2.30	55	63	27
46604		Anoscopy; with dilation, any method	4.50	108	124	65
46606		Anoscopy; with biopsy, single or multiple	4.50	108	124	47
46608		Anoscopy; with removal of foreign body	4.50	108	124	92
46610		Anoscopy; with removal of single tumor, polyp, or other lesion by hot biopsy forceps or bipolar cautery	9.00	215	248	97
46611		Anoscopy; with removal of single tumor, polyp, or other lesion by snare technique	9.00	215	248	112
46612		Anoscopy; with removal of multiple tumors, polyps, or other lesions by hot biopsy forceps, bipolar cautery or snare technique	10.50	251	289	152
46614		Anoscopy; with control of bleeding, any method	10.00	239	276	148
46615		Anoscopy; with ablation of tumor(s), polyp(s), or other lesion(s) not amenable to removal by hot biopsy forceps, bipolar cautery or snare technique	10.50	251	289	170
46700		Anoplasty, plastic operation for stricture; adult	41.00	944	1092	563
46705		Anoplasty, plastic operation for stricture; infant	46.00	1059	1225	423
46715		Repair of low imperforate anus; with anoperineal fistula ("cut-back" procedure)	40.00	921	1065	431
46716		Repair of low imperforate anus; with transposition of anoperineal or anovestibular fistula	50.00	1151	1332	741
46730		Repair of high imperforate anus without fistula; perineal or sacroperineal approach	100.0	2302	2663	1311
46735		Repair of high imperforate anus without fistula; combined transabdominal and sacroperineal approaches	110.0	2532	2929	1592
46740		Repair of high imperforate anus with rectourethral or rectovaginal fistula; perineal or sacroperineal approach	120.0	2762	3196	1410
46742		Repair of high imperforate anus with rectourethral or rectovaginal fistula; combined transabdominal and sacroperineal approaches	132.0	3039	3515	1927
46744		Repair of cloacal anomaly by anorectovaginoplasty and urethroplasty, sacroperineal approach	163.0	3752	4341	2163
46746		Repair of cloacal anomaly by anorectovaginoplasty and urethroplasty, combined abdominal and sacroperineal approach;	179.5	4132	4780	2367
46748		Repair of cloacal anomaly by anorectovaginoplasty and urethroplasty, combined abdominal and sacroperineal approach; with vaginal lengthening by intestinal graft or pedicle flaps	198.5	4569	5286	2637
46750		Sphincteroplasty, anal, for incontinence or prolapse; adult	55.00	1266	1465	583

Code		Description	Medicode RVU	50th	75th	Medicare Nat'l Avg
46751		Sphincteroplasty, anal, for incontinence or prolapse; child	50.00	1151	1332	497
46753		Graft (Thiersch operation) for rectal incontinence and/or prolapse	35.00	806	932	474
46754		Removal of Thiersch wire or suture, anal canal	8.00	184	213	129
46760		Sphincteroplasty, anal, for incontinence, adult; muscle transplant	70.00	1611	1864	733
46761		Sphincteroplasty, anal, for incontinence, adult; levator muscle imbrication (Park posterior anal repair)	100.0	2302	2663	714
46762		Sphincteroplasty, anal, for incontinence, adult; implantation artificial sphincter	125.0	2877	3329	630
46900	*	Destruction of lesion(s), anus (eg, condyloma, papilloma, molluscum contagiosum, herpetic vesicle), simple; chemical	4.00	92	107	84
46910	*	Destruction of lesion(s), anus (eg, condyloma, papilloma, molluscum contagiosum, herpetic vesicle), simple; electrodesiccation	7.50	173	200	98
46916		Destruction of lesion(s), anus (eg, condyloma, papilloma, molluscum contagiosum, herpetic vesicle), simple; cryosurgery	9.00	207	240	98
46917		Destruction of lesion(s), anus (eg, condyloma, papilloma, molluscum contagiosum, herpetic vesicle), simple; laser surgery	20.00	460	533	162
46922		Destruction of lesion(s), anus (eg, condyloma, papilloma, molluscum contagiosum, herpetic vesicle), simple; surgical excision	13.50	311	360	137
46924		Destruction of lesion(s), anus (eg, condyloma, papilloma, molluscum contagiosum, herpetic vesicle), extensive, any method	30.00	691	799	237
46934		Destruction of hemorrhoids, any method; internal	13.50	311	360	172
46935		Destruction of hemorrhoids, any method; external	13.25	305	353	145
46936		Destruction of hemorrhoids, any method; internal and external	28.00	645	746	227
46937		Cryosurgery of rectal tumor; benign	15.00	345	399	212
46938		Cryosurgery of rectal tumor; malignant	25.00	575	666	292
46940		Curettage or cauterization of anal fissure, including dilation of anal sphincter (separate procedure); initial	5.00	115	133	110
46942		Curettage or cauterization of anal fissure, including dilation of anal sphincter (separate procedure); subsequent	5.00	115	133	99
46945		Ligation of internal hemorrhoids; single procedure	8.00	184	213	141
46946		Ligation of internal hemorrhoids; multiple procedures	12.00	276	320	197
46999		Unlisted procedure, anus	0.00	0	0	–

47000–47999
Liver/Biliary Tract

Coding Insight
Liver transplants are oftentimes a subject that payers and providers may not fully agree upon. Make sure payers are informed of certain key facts about liver transplants. Some of the key facts a payer should know are:

- More than one surgeon may be required to be present during the transplant. (Some edit systems may deny the second surgeon's claim.)
- More than one transplant may be performed. (If the transplant fails during the hospital stay, due to blockage/infarct of an artery or vein, if another liver is available it will be transplanted)
- More than one assistant may be present at the transplant. (Again, some edit systems may deny a claim if more than one assistant-at-surgery is reported.)
- More than one anesthesiologist may be required to be present during a tranplant. (Some edit systems may deny the second anesthesiologist's claim.)
- Multiple consultants in various specialties may advise the surgeon, depending upon the patient's post-transplant course of treatment. These claims may be denied by payers when they receive claims from more than one consultant — especially if they consulted on the same day

Costs for surgical removal of the donor liver may be reported to the payer. The payer may not have negotiated this cost in a global per case hospital fee, depending upon the arrangement between the surgeons and the hospital.

Nota Bene: Liver transplants are still considered investigational or experimental by some payers and may not be covered by the employeer due to the extra cost for coverage. Showing them which procedures Medicare covers can change their position. Physicians who perform transplants should request the hospital administration actively to seek contracts for the hospitalization cost on a per case basis. Contracts negotiated with hospitals could also include a fee-for-service discount in effect for all other providers who work on the case — this helps the payers because they will not have to call different departments to negotiate a discount.

Medicare Liver Transplant Coverage
Adult liver transplantation is covered under Medicare when performed in a facility approved by HCFA as meeting institutional coverage criteria, and for patients with one of the following conditions:

- Primary biliary cirrhosis
- Primary sclerosing cholangitis
- Post-necrotic cirrhosis, hepatitis B surface antigen negative
- Alcoholic cirrhosis
- Alpha-1 antitrypsin deficiency disease
- Wilson's disease
- Primary hemochromatosis

Subsidiary Codes

Subsidiary codes have relative values that require no further adjustment:

20926 is "in addition" to 47000–47999
38102 is "in addition" to 47000–47999
38747 is "in addition" to 47000–47999
44015 is "in addition" to 47000–47999
44955 is "in addition" to 47000–47999
45355 is "in addition" to 47000–47999
47001 is "in addition" to 47000–47999
47550 is "in addition" to 47420–47610
49905 is "in addition" to 47000–47999
58611 is "in addition" to 47010–47130, 47300–47480, 47600–47900

Because these are subsidiary or "in addition to" codes, reimbursement reduction and modifier -51 do not apply.

Medicare Alert

Medicare rebundles certain codes in the surgery section when the listed codes are considered a component of a more comprehensive service.

38500, 44005, 44950, 47480, and 49000 will not be reimbursed when reported with 47600, 47605, 47610, 47612, 47620
49255 will not be reimbursed when reported with 47600 and 47605
47420 will not be reimbursed when reported with 47605, 47610, 47612, 47620
47600 will not be reimbursed when reported with 47605, 47610, 47612, 47620
47605 will not be reimbursed when reported with 47610, 47612, 47620
44020 will not be reimbursed when reported with 47612
47610 will not be reimbursed when reported with 44612, 47620

Code		Description	Medicode RVU	50th	75th	Medicare Nat'l Avg
47000	*	Biopsy of liver, needle; percutaneous	13.00	312	369	121
47001		Biopsy of liver, needle; when done for indicated purpose at time of other major procedure	7.00	168	199	137
47010		Hepatotomy for drainage of abscess or cyst, one or two stages	60.00	1440	1703	669
47015		Laparotomy, with aspiration and/or injection of hepatic parasitic (eg, amoebic or echinococcal) cyst(s) or abscess(es)	60.00	1440	1703	670
47100		Biopsy of liver, wedge	45.00	1080	1277	463
47120		Hepatectomy, resection of liver; partial lobectomy	107.0	2567	3036	1375
47122		Hepatectomy, resection of liver; trisegmentectomy	150.0	3599	4256	2102
47125		Hepatectomy, resection of liver; total left lobectomy	150.0	3599	4256	1938
47130		Hepatectomy, resection of liver; total right lobectomy	150.0	3599	4256	2143
47133		Donor hepatectomy, with preparation and maintenance of allograft; from cadaver donor	0.00	0	0	–

	Code	Description	Medicode RVU	50th	75th	Medicare Nat'l Avg
	47134	Donor hepatectomy, with preparation and maintenance of allograft; partial, from living donor	0.00	0	0	2503
	47135	Liver allotransplantation; orthotopic, partial or whole, from cadaver or living donor, any age	0.00	0	0	7210
	47136	Liver allotransplantation; heterotopic, partial or whole, from cadaver or living donor, any age	0.00	0	0	6360
	47300	Marsupialization of cyst or abscess of liver	73.00	1751	2071	731
▲	**47350**	Management of liver hemorrhage; simple suture of liver wound or injury	73.00	1751	2071	815
▲	**47360**	Management of liver hemorrhage; complex suture of liver wound or injury, with or without hepatic artery ligation	100.0	2399	2838	1118
●	**47361**	Management of liver hemorrhage; exploration of hepatic wound, extensive debridement, coagulation and/or suture, with or without packing of liver	120.0	2879	3405	–
●	**47362**	Management of liver hemorrhage; re-exploration of hepatic wound for removal of packing	60.00	1440	1703	–
	47399	Unlisted procedure, liver	0.00	0	0	–
	47400	Hepaticotomy or hepaticostomy with exploration, drainage, or removal of calculus	100.0	2283	2668	1133
	47420	Choledochotomy or choledochostomy with exploration, drainage, or removal of calculus, with or without cholecystotomy; without transduodenal sphincterotomy or sphincteroplasty	85.00	1940	2268	1078
	47425	Choledochotomy or choledochostomy with exploration, drainage, or removal of calculus, with or without cholecystotomy; with transduodenal sphincterotomy or sphincteroplasty	110.5	2522	2949	1154
	47460	Transduodenal sphincterotomy or sphincteroplasty, with or without transduodenal extraction of calculus (separate procedure)	85.00	1940	2268	1103
	47480	Cholecystotomy or cholecystostomy with exploration, drainage, or removal of calculus (separate procedure)	68.00	1552	1815	718
	47490	Percutaneous cholecystostomy	30.00	685	801	344
	47500	Injection procedure for percutaneous transhepatic cholangiography	16.50	377	440	127
	47505	Injection procedure for cholangiography through an existing catheter (eg, percutaneous transhepatic or T-tube)	7.50	171	200	79
	47510	Introduction of percutaneous transhepatic catheter for biliary drainage	18.00	411	480	361
	47511	Introduction of percutaneous transhepatic stent for internal and external biliary drainage	24.00	548	640	439
	47525	Change of percutaneous biliary drainage catheter	15.00	342	400	240
	47530	Revision and/or reinsertion of transhepatic tube	19.00	434	507	248
	47550	Biliary endoscopy, intraoperative (choledochoscopy)	15.00	342	400	206

Code	Description	Medicode RVU	50th	75th	Medicare Nat'l Avg
47552	Biliary endoscopy, percutaneous via T-tube or other tract; diagnostic, with or without collection of specimen(s) by brushing and/or washing (separate procedure)	20.00	457	534	300
47553	Biliary endoscopy, percutaneous via T-tube or other tract; with biopsy, single or multiple	24.00	548	640	367
47554	Biliary endoscopy, percutaneous via T-tube or other tract; with removal of stone(s)	24.00	548	640	532
47555	Biliary endoscopy, percutaneous via T-tube or other tract; with dilation of biliary duct stricture(s) without stent	24.00	548	640	359
47556	Biliary endoscopy, percutaneous via T-tube or other tract; with dilation of biliary duct stricture(s) with stent	24.00	548	640	395
47600	Cholecystectomy;	75.00	1712	2001	792
47605	Cholecystectomy; with cholangiography	84.00	1918	2241	849
47610	Cholecystectomy with exploration of common duct;	88.00	2009	2348	995
47612	Cholecystectomy with exploration of common duct; with choledochoenterostomy	135.0	3082	3602	1312
47620	Cholecystectomy with exploration of common duct; with transduodenal sphincterotomy or sphincteroplasty, with or without cholangiography	100.0	2283	2668	1181
47630	Biliary duct stone extraction, percutaneous via T-tube tract, basket or snare (eg, Burhenne technique)	30.00	685	801	427
47700	Exploration for congenital atresia of bile ducts, without repair, with or without liver biopsy, with or without cholangiography	75.00	1712	2001	911
47701	Portoenterostomy (eg, Kasai procedure)	138.0	3150	3682	1429
47711	Excision of bile duct tumor, with or without primary repair of bile duct; extrahepatic	121.0	2762	3229	1293
47712	Excision of bile duct tumor, with or without primary repair of bile duct; intrahepatic	131.0	2990	3496	1498
47715	Excision of choledochal cyst	89.00	2032	2375	951
47716	Anastomosis, choledochal cyst, without excision	75.00	1712	2001	804
47720	Cholecystoenterostomy; direct	75.00	1712	2001	937
47721	Cholecystoenterostomy; with gastroenterostomy	95.00	2169	2535	1158
47740	Cholecystoenterostomy; Roux-en-Y	85.00	1940	2268	1061
47741	Cholecystoenterostomy; Roux-en-Y with gastroenterostomy	105.0	2397	2802	1420
47760	Anastomosis, of extrahepatic biliary ducts and gastrointestinal tract	105.0	2397	2802	1355
47765	Anastomosis, of intrahepatic ducts and gastrointestinal tract	115.0	2625	3069	1453

Code	Description	Medicode RVU	50th	75th	Medicare Nat'l Avg
47780	Anastomosis, Roux-en-Y, of extrahepatic biliary ducts and gastrointestinal tract	135.0	3082	3602	1457
47785	Anastomosis, Roux-en-Y, of intrahepatic biliary ducts and gastrointestinal tract	150.0	3424	4003	1565
47800	Reconstruction, plastic, of extrahepatic biliary ducts with end-to-end anastomosis	110.0	2511	2935	1300
47801	Placement of choledochal stent	66.00	1507	1761	692
47802	U-tube hepaticoenterostomy	115.0	2625	3069	1096
47900	Suture of extrahepatic biliary duct for pre-existing injury (separate procedure)	65.00	1484	1734	1223
47999	Unlisted procedure, biliary tract	0.00	0	0	–

48000–48999
Pancreas

SUBSIDIARY CODES

Subsidiary codes have relative values that require no further adjustment:

20926 is "in addition" to 48000–48999
38102 is "in addition" to 48000–48999
38747 is "in addition" to 48000–48999
44015 is "in addition" to 48000–48999
44955 is "in addition" to 48000–48999
45355 is "in addition" to 48000–48999
47001 is "in addition" to 48000–48999
49905 is "in addition" to 48000–48999
58611 is "in addition" to 48120–48180, 48500–48547

Because these are subsidiary or "in addition to" codes, reimbursement reduction and modifier -51 do not apply.

Code		Description	Medicode RVU	50th	75th	Medicare Nat'l Avg
48000		Placement of drains, peripancreatic, for acute pancreatitis;	65.00	1526	1798	850
48001		Placement of drains, peripancreatic, for acute pancreatitis; with cholecystostomy, gastrostomy, and jejunostomy	164.0	3850	4537	993
48005		Resection or debridement of pancreas and peripancreatic tissue for acute necrotizing pancreatitis	105.0	2465	2905	1123
48020		Removal of pancreatic calculus	90.00	2113	2490	830
48100		Biopsy of pancreas, open, any method (eg, fine needle aspiration, needle core biopsy, wedge biopsy)	70.00	1643	1937	627
48102	*	Biopsy of pancreas, percutaneous needle	17.00	399	470	244

Code	Description	Medicode RVU	50th	75th	Medicare Nat'l Avg
48120	Excision of lesion of pancreas (eg, cyst, adenoma)	90.00	2113	2490	981
48140	Pancreatectomy, distal subtotal, with or without splenectomy; without pancreaticojejunostomy	105.0	2465	2905	1390
48145	Pancreatectomy, distal subtotal, with or without splenectomy; with pancreaticojejunostomy	120.0	2817	3320	1495
48146	Pancreatectomy, distal, near-total with preservation of duodenum (Child-type procedure)	140.0	3287	3873	1577
48148	Excision of ampulla of Vater	120.0	2817	3320	952
48150	Pancreatectomy, proximal subtotal with total duodenectomy, partial gastrectomy, choledochoenterostomy and gastrojejunostomy (Whipple-type procedure); with pancreatojejunostomy	200.0	4695	5533	2625
48152	Pancreatectomy, proximal subtotal with total duodenectomy, partial gastrectomy, choledochoenterostomy and gastrojejunostomy (Whipple-type procedure); without pancreatojejunostomy	185.0	4343	5118	2505
48153	Pancreatectomy, proximal subtotal with near-total duodenectomy, choledochoenterostomy and duodenojejunostomy (pylorus-sparing, Whipple-type procedure); with pancreatojejunostomy	200.0	4695	5533	2625
48154	Pancreatectomy, proximal subtotal with near-total duodenectomy, choledochoenterostomy and duodenojejunostomy (pylorus-sparing, Whipple-type procedure); without pancreatojejunostomy	185.0	4343	5118	2505
48155	Pancreatectomy, total	170.0	3991	4703	1764
48160	Pancreatectomy, total or subtotal, with autologous transplantation of pancreas or pancreatic islets	205.0	4813	5672	–
48180	Pancreaticojejunostomy, side-to-side anastomosis (Puestow-type operation)	140.0	3287	3873	1431
48400	Injection procedure for intraoperative pancreatography	16.00	376	443	110
48500	Marsupialization of cyst of pancreas	75.00	1761	2075	871
48510	External drainage, pseudocyst of pancreas	100.0	2348	2767	806
48520	Internal anastomosis of pancreatic cyst to gastrointestinal tract; direct	85.00	1996	2352	1076
48540	Internal anastomosis of pancreatic cyst to gastrointestinal tract; Roux-en-Y	100.0	2348	2767	1225
48545	Pancreatorrhaphy for trauma	88.00	2066	2435	937
48547	Duodenal exclusion with gastrojejunostomy for pancreatic trauma	180.0	4226	4980	1354
48550	Donor pancreatectomy, with preparation and maintenance of allograft from cadaver donor, with or without duodenal segment for transplantation	0.00	0	0	–
48554	Transplantation of pancreatic allograft	0.00	0	0	–

Code	Description	Medicode RVU	50th	75th	Medicare Nat'l Avg
48556	Removal of transplanted pancreatic allograft	0.00	0	0	888
48999	Unlisted procedure, pancreas	0.00	0	0	–

49000-49999
Abdomen, Peritoneum, and Omentum

CODING INSIGHT

One particularly difficult aspect for coders is in the area of separate procedures, especially involving code 49000 for exploratory laparotomy. Some of the following guidelines, which payers and CPT coding rules impose, may be helpful:

- Exploratory laparotomy includes simple biopsy(s) regardless of where the biopsy(s) originate
- It is unbundling to report 47000 *Biopsy of liver, needle; percutaneous* and 47100 *Biopsy of liver, wedge*, with code 49000
- Exploratory laparotomy is diagnostic in nature and is not considered a "major procedure" in CPT
- Examples of major procedures in CPT include a cholecystectomy or pancreatectomy
- The Medicare Fee Schedule rules for "major procedure" apply to 49000 *Exploratory laparotomy, exploratory celiotomy with or without biopsy(s) (separate procedure)* because 49000 has 90 follow-up days assigned
- It is incorrect to report 47001 *Biopsy of liver, needle; percutaneous* when done for indicated purposes at time of other major procedure (not as separate procedure) with 49000
- Exploratory laparotomy is considered an integral part of any other major intra-abdominal procedure and is not separately reportable

It is unbundling to report 49000 with 49201 *Excision or destruction by any method of intra-abdominal or retroperitoneal tumors or cysts or endometriomas; extensive.*

Nota Bene: Payers interpret the rules and guidelines for separate procedures for their individual companies. They may base payment guidelines on definitions established by outside consultants or on their own internal reference sources. They may interpret the guideline "alone and for a specific purpose" to mean the procedure would not be performed with any other procedure, or they may interpret it to mean it may be performed with another procedure as long as it is not an integral part of the other procedure. If you feel a separate procedure is not an integral part of another procedure done at the same operative session, appeal the decision if you recieve a denial. Use information from coding resources such as *CPT Assistant* to document and back up the appeal.

SUBSIDIARY CODES

Subsidiary codes have relative values that require no further adjustment:

20926 is "in addition" to 49000–49999
38102 is "in addition" to 49000–49999
38747 is "in addition" to 49000–49999
44015 is "in addition" to 49000–49999

44955 is "in addition" to 49000–49999
45355 is "in addition" to 49000–49999
47001 is "in addition" to 49000–49999
49568 is "in addition" to 49560–49566
49905 is "in addition" to 49000–49999
58611 is "in addition" to 49010–49085, 49200–49255

Because these are subsidiary or "in addition to" codes, reimbursement reduction and modifier -51 do not apply.

Medicare Alert

Medicare rebundles certain codes in the surgery section when the listed codes are considered a component of a more comprehensive service.

38500 will not be reimbursed when reported with 49201, 49505, 49510, 49520, 49530
44005 will not be reimbursed when reported with 49201, 49520, 49530, 49565
44950 will not be reimbursed when reported with 49201
49000 will not be reimbursed when reported with 49201, 49530, 49581
49200, 49255 will not be reimbursed when reported with 49201
49505 will not be reimbursed when reported with 49510, 49515, 49520, 49530
54520 will not be reimbursed when reported with 49510
55040 will not be reimbursed when reported with 49515
44600 will not be reimbursed when reported with 49530
49560 will not be reimbursed when reported with 49565

Code		Description	Medicode RVU	50th	75th	Medicare Nat'l Avg
49000		Exploratory laparotomy, exploratory celiotomy with or without biopsy(s) (separate procedure)	60.00	1417	1665	692
49002		Reopening of recent laparotomy	60.00	1417	1665	670
49010		Exploration, retroperitoneal area with or without biopsy(s) (separate procedure)	60.00	1417	1665	777
49020		Drainage of peritoneal abscess or localized peritonitis, exclusive of appendiceal abscess, transabdominal	55.00	1299	1526	596
49040		Drainage of subdiaphragmatic or subphrenic abscess	68.00	1605	1887	680
49060		Drainage of retroperitoneal abscess	65.00	1535	1804	679
49080	*	Peritoneocentesis, abdominal paracentesis, or peritoneal lavage (diagnostic or therapeutic); initial	8.00	189	222	78
49081	*	Peritoneocentesis, abdominal paracentesis, or peritoneal lavage (diagnostic or therapeutic); subsequent	6.00	142	167	70
49085		Removal of peritoneal foreign body from peritoneal cavity	47.00	1110	1304	468
49180	*	Biopsy, abdominal or retroperitoneal mass, percutaneous needle	15.00	354	416	132
49200		Excision or destruction by any method of intra-abdominal or retroperitoneal tumors or cysts or endometriomas;	80.00	1889	2220	816
49201		Excision or destruction by any method of intra-abdominal or retroperitoneal tumors or cysts or endometriomas; extensive	100.0	2361	2775	1167

Code		Description	Medicode RVU	50th	75th	Medicare Nat'l Avg
49215		Excision of presacral or sacrococcygeal tumor	113.0	2668	3136	1209
49220		Staging celiotomy (laparotomy) for Hodgkin's disease or lymphoma (includes splenectomy, needle or open biopsies of both liver lobes, possibly also removal of abdominal nodes, abdominal node and/or bone marrow biopsies, ovarian repositioning)	100.0	2361	2775	1143
49250		Umbilectomy, omphalectomy, excision of umbilicus (separate procedure)	35.00	826	971	516
49255		Omentectomy, epiploectomy, resection of omentum (separate procedure)	50.00	1180	1388	489
49400	*	Injection of air or contrast into peritoneal cavity (separate procedure)	7.00	163	189	123
49420	*	Insertion of intraperitoneal cannula or catheter for drainage or dialysis; temporary	19.00	443	514	159
49421		Insertion of intraperitoneal cannula or catheter for drainage or dialysis; permanent	40.00	933	1082	400
49422		Removal of permanent intraperitoneal cannula or catheter	30.00	700	812	425
49425		Insertion of peritoneal-venous shunt	63.00	1469	1705	845
49426		Revision of peritoneal-venous shunt	63.00	1469	1705	596
49427		Injection procedure (eg, contrast media) for evaluation of previously placed peritoneal-venous shunt	6.50	152	176	58
49428		Ligation of peritoneal-venous shunt	20.00	466	541	127
49429		Removal of peritoneal-venous shunt	51.00	1189	1380	406
49495		Repair initial inguinal hernia, under age 6 months, with or without hydrocelectomy; reducible	50.00	1155	1325	466
49496		Repair initial inguinal hernia, under age 6 months, with or without hydrocelectomy; incarcerated or strangulated	57.00	1317	1510	589
49500		Repair initial inguinal hernia, age 6 months to under 5 years, with or without hydrocelectomy; reducible	45.00	1039	1192	419
49501		Repair initial inguinal hernia, age 6 months to under 5 years, with or without hydrocelectomy; incarcerated or strangulated	52.00	1201	1378	551
49505		Repair initial inguinal hernia, age 5 years or over; reducible	48.00	1109	1272	465
49507		Repair initial inguinal hernia, age 5 years or over; incarcerated or strangulated	55.00	1270	1457	556
49520		Repair recurrent inguinal hernia, any age; reducible	55.00	1257	1461	557
49521		Repair recurrent inguinal hernia, any age; incarcerated or strangulated	63.00	1440	1674	624
49525		Repair inguinal hernia, sliding, any age	52.00	1189	1382	549
49540		Repair lumbar hernia	52.00	1189	1382	567

Code	Description	Medicode RVU	50th	75th	Medicare Nat'l Avg
49550	Repair initial femoral hernia, any age, reducible;	45.00	1029	1196	502
49553	Repair initial femoral hernia, any age, reducible; incarcerated or strangulated	52.00	1189	1382	514
49555	Repair recurrent femoral hernia; reducible	49.00	1120	1302	588
49557	Repair recurrent femoral hernia; incarcerated or strangulated	56.00	1280	1488	633
49560	Repair initial incisional hernia; reducible	60.00	1371	1594	638
49561	Repair initial incisional hernia; incarcerated or strangulated	69.00	1577	1833	698
49565	Repair recurrent incisional hernia; reducible	69.00	1577	1833	682
49566	Repair recurrent incisional hernia; incarcerated or strangulated	79.00	1806	2099	737
49568	Implantation of mesh or other prosthesis for incisional hernia repair (list separately in addition to code for the incisional hernia repair)	16.00	366	425	312
49570	Repair epigastric hernia (eg, preperitoneal fat); reducible (separate procedure)	35.00	800	930	397
49572	Repair epigastric hernia (eg, preperitoneal fat); incarcerated or strangulated	43.75	1000	1162	497
49580	Repair umbilical hernia, under age 5 years; reducible	39.00	891	1036	336
49582	Repair umbilical hernia, under age 5 years; incarcerated or strangulated	45.00	1029	1196	419
49585	Repair umbilical hernia, age 5 years or over; reducible	45.00	1029	1196	426
49587	Repair umbilical hernia, age 5 years or over; incarcerated or strangulated	52.00	1189	1382	452
49590	Repair spigelian hernia	50.00	1143	1329	546
49600	Repair of small omphalocele, with primary closure	55.00	1257	1461	605
49605	Repair of large omphalocele or gastroschisis; with or without prosthesis	90.00	2057	2391	1253
49606	Repair of large omphalocele or gastroschisis; with removal of prosthesis, final reduction and closure, in operating room	67.50	1543	1794	1059
49610	Repair of omphalocele (Gross type operation); first stage	55.00	1257	1461	645
49611	Repair of omphalocele (Gross type operation); second stage	55.00	1257	1461	694
49900	Suture, secondary, of abdominal wall for evisceration or dehiscence	50.00	1143	1329	370
49905	Omental flap (eg, for reconstruction of sternal and chest wall defects) (list separately in addition to code for primary procedure)	40.00	914	1063	419

Code	Description	Medicode RVU	50th	75th	Medicare Nat'l Avg
49999	Unlisted procedure, abdomen, peritoneum and omentum	0.00	0	0	–

Surgery Codes 50010–58999

Some of the codes in this section are for incisional, percutaneous, and/or other (e.g., lithotripsy) procedures for removal of calculus. When lithotripsy (crushing of calculus by shock waves) is performed one of the following codes should be used:

- 50080 *Percutaneous nephrostolithotomy or pyelostolithotomy, with or without dilation, endoscopy, lithotripsy, stenting, or basket extraction; up to 2 cm*
- 50081 *Percutaneous nephrostolithotomy or pyelostolithotomy, with or without dilation, endoscopy, lithotripsy, stenting, or basket extraction; over 2 cm*
- 50590 *Lithotripsy, extracorporeal shock wave (which includes the kidney and ureter, as listed in the index).*
- 52337 *Cystourethroscopy with ureteroscopy and/or pyeloscopy (includes dilation of the ureter and/or pyeloureteral junction, by any method); with lithotripsy (ureteral catheterization is included)*

If the procedure is difficult, complex, or requires significant additional time and effort, append modifier -22. Be sure to submit a cover letter and operative report with the claim.

Nota Bene: Contracts negotiated between hospitals or other facilities where lithotripsy is performed are often negotiated on a flat rate for the entire service, including the part of the service performed by the physician. The payer in this type of contract pays the amount due for the full service directly to the hospital/facility and it disperses the money between the facility and the physician. A problem occurs when the physician's office also bills the payer for their part of the service; in effect creating a type of double billing.

These types of contracts are often difficult for payers to administer because they are an exception to the normal reporting patterns, which are separate contracts and claims from the facility and the provider. Because of this, the payer's claims department may duplicate the payment. Knowing payment errors are made, auditors working for the payer target these types of contracts for audit. Do not make the mistake of double billing these services; review all contracts. If auditors find double billing they may assume you are unaware of your contract for this service and could be making mistakes on another contract with them. They may then decide to audit more of your claims.

50010–50135
Kidney Incision

Coding Insight

This code specifies that when the renal exploration is performed it does not necessitate other specific procedures. When using this code keep in mind that an exploratory surgery should not be reported with another major open procedure. If there is a specific reason for the exploration and significant time is required during another surgery, generally modifier -22 would be appended to the main code rather than a separate code being listed on the claim.

Code 50010 *Renal exploration, not necessitating other specific procedures*, should be reported when the kidney and renal pelvis is explored but not incised, and no other procedure(s) is performed. Use 50045 *Nephrotomy, with exploration* when there is an incision into the kidney and the interior of the kidney is explored and no other procedure(s) is performed. Code 50120 *Pyelotomy, with exploration* should be reported when an incision is made into the renal pelvis for exploration; again no other procedure(s) is performed.

Code	Description	Medicode RVU	Medicare 50th	Medicare 75th	Medicare Nat'l Avg
50010	Renal exploration, not necessitating other specific procedures	75.00	1731	2064	848
50020	Drainage of perirenal or renal abscess (separate procedure)	67.00	1547	1844	799
50040	Nephrostomy, nephrotomy with drainage	90.00	2078	2477	761
50045	Nephrotomy, with exploration	90.00	2078	2477	984
50060	Nephrolithotomy; removal of calculus	95.00	2193	2615	1248
50065	Nephrolithotomy; secondary surgical operation for calculus	120.0	2770	3303	1364
50070	Nephrolithotomy; complicated by congenital kidney abnormality	116.0	2678	3193	1303
50075	Nephrolithotomy; removal of large staghorn calculus filling renal pelvis and calyces (including anatrophic pyelolithotomy)	123.0	2840	3385	1667
50080	Percutaneous nephrostolithotomy or pyelostolithotomy, with or without dilation, endoscopy, lithotripsy, stenting or basket extraction; up to 2 cm	97.00	2239	2670	1120
50081	Percutaneous nephrostolithotomy or pyelostolithotomy, with or without dilation, endoscopy, lithotripsy, stenting or basket extraction; over 2 cm	111.5	2574	3069	1462
50100	Transection or repositioning of aberrant renal vessels (separate procedure)	60.00	1385	1651	1044
50120	Pyelotomy; with exploration	90.00	2078	2477	1063
50125	Pyelotomy; with drainage, pyelostomy	90.00	2078	2477	1075
50130	Pyelotomy; with removal of calculus (pyelolithotomy, pelviolithotomy, including coagulum pyelolithotomy)	90.00	2078	2477	1195
50135	Pyelotomy; complicated (eg, secondary operation, congenital kidney abnormality)	110.0	2539	3028	1445

50200–50590
Kidney Excision

Coding Insight

Biopsy is not reported separately if a therapeutic excision is performed during the same surgical session.

Use 50230 when the surrounding fat, Gerots' fascia, adrenal gland, and periaortic lymph nodes are removed along with the kidney, upper ureter, and neural and vascular structures (with regional lymphadenectomy and/or vena cava thrombectomy). When vena cava resection with reconstruction is also necessary, CPT directs you to 37799.

Most insurance plans cover transplants (50300–50380) with prior authorization. However, patients should be alerted that immunosuppressive drugs, such as cyclosporin, may have limited or no coverage.

Code 50393 *Introduction of ureteral catheter or stent into ureter through renal pelvis for drainage and or injection, percutaneous* is a unilateral procedure. If bilateral stents are placed, 50393 should be reported twice with modifier -50 appended to the second code.

Nota Bene: Trauma cases frequently require the services of physicians from different specialties. Procedures such as nephorrhaphy (suture of kidney wound or injury, code 50500) and complicated cystorrhaphy (suture of bladder wound, injury, or rupture, code 51865) may be necessary as well as repair of fractures, lacerations, and other services. When this is the case, each surgeon reports services separately, appending modifiers as appropriate to the second and any subsequent codes. The only time a procedure would be reported as "co-surgeons" is when it requires the skill of two surgeons to perform the surgery/surgeries. An example would be when the patient has a crush injury and one physician performs a pyeloplasty (plastic operation on renal pelvis) and/or other structures, and the other physician performs repairs of the renal artery(s) and vein(s). In a co-surgery situation, see modifier -62 for instructions.

SUBSIDIARY CODES

Subsidiary codes have relative values that require no further adjustment:

20926 is "in addition" to 50010–50590
38102 is "in addition" to 50010–50590
38747 is "in addition" to 50010–50590
44015 is "in addition" to 50010–50590
44955 is "in addition" to 50010–50590
45355 is "in addition" to 50010–50590
47001 is "in addition" to 50010–50590
49905 is "in addition" to 50010–50590

Because these are subsidiary or "in addition to" codes, reimbursement reduction and modifier -51 do not apply.

MEDICARE ALERT

Immunosuppressive Coverage

Medicare pays for FDA-approved immunosuppressive drugs and for drugs used in immunosuppressive therapy (generally, self-administered immunosuppressive drugs specifically labeled and approved for marketing as such by the FDA, or identified in FDA-approved labeling for use in conjunction with immunosuppressive drug therapy). The benefit is subject to the Part B deductible and coinsurance provision and is limited to the one-year period after the date of the transplant. Payment is also allowed for immunosuppressive drugs provided beyond the one-year period if they are covered under another provision of the law (e.g., as inpatient hospital services or when furnished incidental to a physician's service).

One-year period after date of transplant means 365 days from the day on which an inpatient is discharged from the hospital. From surgery to hospital discharge, payment for these drugs is included in Medicare's Part A payment to the hospital. If the same patient receives a subsequent transplant operation within the 365 days, the period begins anew.

Prescriptions generally should be nonrefillable and limited to a 30-day supply — unless there are special circumstances.

Medicare rebundles certain codes in the surgery section when the listed codes are considered a component of a more comprehensive service.

50230 will not be reimbursed when reported with 32020, 35761, 38100, 49010, 49255, 50080–50081, 50220, 50370, 50526, and 50780

Code		Description	Medicode RVU	50th	75th	Medicare Nat'l Avg
50200	*	Renal biopsy; percutaneous, by trocar or needle	18.00	416	495	194
50205		Renal biopsy; by surgical exposure of kidney	45.00	1039	1239	741
50220		Nephrectomy, including partial ureterectomy, any approach including rib resection;	90.00	2078	2477	1225
50225		Nephrectomy, including partial ureterectomy, any approach including rib resection; complicated because of previous surgery on same kidney	110.0	2539	3028	1478
50230		Nephrectomy, including partial ureterectomy, any approach including rib resection; radical, with regional lymphadenectomy and/or vena caval thrombectomy	143.0	3301	3936	1676
50234		Nephrectomy with total ureterectomy and bladder cuff; through same incision	110.0	2539	3028	1590
50236		Nephrectomy with total ureterectomy and bladder cuff; through separate incision	115.0	2655	3165	1699
50240		Nephrectomy, partial	110.0	2539	3028	1507
50280		Excision or unroofing of cyst(s) of kidney	80.00	1847	2202	1064
50290		Excision of perinephric cyst	80.00	1847	2202	930
50300		Donor nephrectomy, with preparation and maintenance of allograft; from cadaver donor, unilateral or bilateral	90.00	2078	2477	–
50320		Donor nephrectomy, with preparation and maintenance of allograft; from living donor	160.0	3694	4404	1584
50340		Recipient nephrectomy (separate procedure)	90.00	2078	2477	1016
50360		Renal allotransplantation, implantation of graft; excluding donor and recipient nephrectomy	193.0	4456	5312	2197
50365		Renal allotransplantation, implantation of graft; with recipient nephrectomy	243.0	5610	6688	2623
50370		Removal of transplanted renal allograft	80.00	1847	2202	966
50380		Renal autotransplantation, reimplantation of kidney	160.0	3694	4404	1109
50390	*	Aspiration and/or injection of renal cyst or pelvis by needle, percutaneous	14.00	323	385	172
50392		Introduction of intracatheter or catheter into renal pelvis for drainage and/or injection, percutaneous	21.00	485	578	279

Code		Description	Medicode RVU	50th	75th	Medicare Nat'l Avg
50393		Introduction of ureteral catheter or stent into ureter through renal pelvis for drainage and/or injection, percutaneous	22.00	508	606	341
50394		Injection procedure for pyelography (as nephrostogram, pyelostogram, antegrade pyeloureterograms) through nephrostomy or pyelostomy tube, or indwelling ureteral catheter	5.00	115	138	49
50395		Introduction of guide into renal pelvis and/or ureter with dilation to establish nephrostomy tract, percutaneous	30.00	693	826	313
50396		Manometric studies through nephrostomy or pyelostomy tube, or indwelling ureteral catheter	5.00	115	138	90
50398	*	Change of nephrostomy or pyelostomy tube	4.50	104	124	76
50400		Pyeloplasty (Foley Y-pyeloplasty), plastic operation on renal pelvis, with or without plastic operation on ureter, nephropexy, nephrostomy, pyelostomy, or ureteral splinting; simple	100.0	2309	2752	1317
50405		Pyeloplasty (Foley Y-pyeloplasty), plastic operation on renal pelvis, with or without plastic operation on ureter, nephropexy, nephrostomy, pyelostomy, or ureteral splinting; complicated (congenital kidney abnormality, secondary pyeloplasty, solitary kidney, calycoplasty)	120.0	2770	3303	1631
50500		Nephrorrhaphy, suture of kidney wound or injury	90.00	2078	2477	1263
50520		Closure of nephrocutaneous or pyelocutaneous fistula	90.00	2078	2477	1083
50525		Closure of nephrovisceral fistula (eg, renocolic), including visceral repair; abdominal approach	110.0	2539	3028	1369
50526		Closure of nephrovisceral fistula (eg, renocolic), including visceral repair; thoracic approach	110.0	2539	3028	1239
50540		Symphysiotomy for horseshoe kidney with or without pyeloplasty and/or other plastic procedure, unilateral or bilateral (one operation)	140.0	3232	3853	1332
50551		Renal endoscopy through established nephrostomy or pyelostomy, with or without irrigation, instillation, or ureteropyelography, exclusive of radiologic service;	10.00	231	275	309
50553		Renal endoscopy through established nephrostomy or pyelostomy, with or without irrigation, instillation, or ureteropyelography, exclusive of radiologic service; with ureteral catheterization, with or without dilation of ureter	21.00	485	578	298
50555		Renal endoscopy through established nephrostomy or pyelostomy, with or without irrigation, instillation, or ureteropyelography, exclusive of radiologic service; with biopsy	23.00	531	633	451
50557		Renal endoscopy through established nephrostomy or pyelostomy, with or without irrigation, instillation, or ureteropyelography, exclusive of radiologic service; with fulguration and/or incision, with or without biopsy	27.00	623	743	459
50559		Renal endoscopy through established nephrostomy or pyelostomy, with or without irrigation, instillation, or ureteropyelography, exclusive of radiologic service; with insertion of radioactive substance with or without biopsy and/or fulguration	30.00	693	826	323

Code	Description	Medicode RVU	50th	75th	Medicare Nat'l Avg
50561	Renal endoscopy through established nephrostomy or pyelostomy, with or without irrigation, instillation, or ureteropyelography, exclusive of radiologic service; with removal of foreign body or calculus	32.00	739	881	508
50570	Renal endoscopy through nephrotomy or pyelotomy, with or without irrigation, instillation, or ureteropyelography, exclusive of radiologic service;	12.00	277	330	433
50572	Renal endoscopy through nephrotomy or pyelotomy, with or without irrigation, instillation, or ureteropyelography, exclusive of radiologic service; with ureteral catheterization, with or without dilation of ureter	23.00	531	633	704
50574	Renal endoscopy through nephrotomy or pyelotomy, with or without irrigation, instillation, or ureteropyelography, exclusive of radiologic service; with biopsy	24.00	554	661	727
50575	Renal endoscopy through nephrotomy or pyelotomy, with or without irrigation, instillation, or ureteropyelography, exclusive of radiologic service; with endopyelotomy (includes cystoscopy, ureteroscopy, dilation of ureter and ureteral pelvic junction, incision of ureteral pelvic junction and insertion of endopyelotomy stent)	40.00	923	1101	968
50576	Renal endoscopy through nephrotomy or pyelotomy, with or without irrigation, instillation, or ureteropyelography, exclusive of radiologic service; with fulguration and/or incision, with or without biopsy	29.00	669	798	793
50578	Renal endoscopy through nephrotomy or pyelotomy, with or without irrigation, instillation, or ureteropyelography, exclusive of radiologic service; with insertion of radioactive substance, with or without biopsy and/or fulguration	32.00	739	881	635
50580	Renal endoscopy through nephrotomy or pyelotomy, with or without irrigation, instillation, or ureteropyelography, exclusive of radiologic service; with removal of foreign body or calculus	34.00	785	936	616
50590	Lithotripsy, extracorporeal shock wave	100.0	2333	2659	862

50600–50980
Ureter

Coding Insight

Code 50600 is by definition a separate procedure, making it the component of a more complex service and usually not identified separately. When performed alone and for a specific and documented purpose, it is reported. If incision into the ureter is used only as an approach for an endoscopy, report the appropriate code from 50970–50980. If the ureterotomy is for both an endoscopic procedure and another significantly identifiable service, report both 50600 and the appropriate code from 50970–50980.

If ureteral calculus is removed through an incision in the bladder, use 51065 instead of 50610–50630.

In 50725, the physician may elect to correct an aberrantly positioned ureter by dissecting the ureter on both sides of the vena cava and connecting the distal end to the upper ureter by fashioning a long, elliptical flap from the renal pelvis or by dissecting the vena cava and then reconnecting it once the ureter is repositioned in front. In either scenario the anastomosis is included in the procedure and is not reported separately.

Subsidiary Codes

Subsidiary codes have relative values that require no further adjustment:

20926 is "in addition" to 50600–50980
38102 is "in addition" to 50600–50980
38747 is "in addition" to 50600–50980
44015 is "in addition" to 50600–50980
44955 is "in addition" to 50600–50980
45355 is "in addition" to 50600–50980
47001 is "in addition" to 50600–50980
49905 is "in addition" to 50600–50980
58611 is "in addition" to 50600–50940

Because these are subsidiary or "in addition to" codes, reimbursement reduction and modifier -51 do not apply.

Code		Description	Medicode RVU	50th	75th	Medicare Nat'l Avg
50600		Ureterotomy with exploration or drainage (separate procedure)	80.00	1861	2217	1007
50605		Ureterotomy for insertion of indwelling stent, all types	50.00	1163	1386	844
50610		Ureterolithotomy; upper one-third of ureter	85.00	1977	2356	1110
50620		Ureterolithotomy; middle one-third of ureter	80.00	1861	2217	1068
50630		Ureterolithotomy; lower one-third of ureter	85.00	1977	2356	1127
50650		Ureterectomy, with bladder cuff (separate procedure)	90.00	2093	2494	1171
50660		Ureterectomy, total, ectopic ureter, combination abdominal, vaginal and/or perineal approach	105.0	2442	2910	1272
50684		Injection procedure for ureterography or ureteropyelography through ureterostomy or indwelling ureteral catheter	3.25	76	90	51
50686		Manometric studies through ureterostomy or indwelling ureteral catheter	4.00	93	111	75
50688	*	Change of ureterostomy tube	3.00	70	83	60
50690		Injection procedure for visualization of ileal conduit and/or ureteropyelography, exclusive of radiologic service	4.00	93	111	59
50700		Ureteroplasty, plastic operation on ureter (eg, stricture)	90.00	2093	2494	1110
50715		Ureterolysis, with or without repositioning of ureter for retroperitoneal fibrosis	90.00	2093	2494	1203
50722		Ureterolysis for ovarian vein syndrome	70.00	1628	1940	1065
50725		Ureterolysis for retrocaval ureter, with reanastomosis of upper urinary tract or vena cava	120.0	2791	3326	1206
50727		Revision of urinary-cutaneous anastomosis (any type urostomy);	60.00	1395	1663	524

Code	Description	Medicode RVU	50th	75th	Medicare Nat'l Avg
50728	Revision of urinary-cutaneous anastomosis (any type urostomy); with repair of fascial defect and hernia	80.00	1861	2217	771
50740	Ureteropyelostomy, anastomosis of ureter and renal pelvis	105.0	2442	2910	1251
50750	Ureterocalycostomy, anastomosis of ureter to renal calyx	110.0	2558	3049	1303
50760	Ureteroureterostomy	105.0	2442	2910	1282
50770	Transureteroureterostomy, anastomosis of ureter to contralateral ureter	110.0	2558	3049	1366
50780	Ureteroneocystostomy; anastomosis of single ureter to bladder	105.0	2442	2910	1295
50782	Ureteroneocystostomy; anastomosis of duplicated ureter to bladder	115.0	2675	3187	1335
50783	Ureteroneocystostomy; with extensive ureteral tailoring	120.0	2791	3326	1369
50785	Ureteroneocystostomy; with vesico-psoas hitch or bladder flap	125.0	2907	3464	1440
50800	Ureteroenterostomy, direct anastomosis of ureter to intestine	105.0	2442	2910	1159
50810	Ureterosigmoidostomy, with creation of sigmoid bladder and establishment of abdominal or perineal colostomy, including bowel anastomosis	160.0	3721	4434	1289
50815	Ureterocolon conduit, including bowel anastomosis	160.0	3721	4434	1592
50820	Ureteroileal conduit (ileal bladder), including bowel anastomosis (Bricker operation)	160.0	3721	4434	1691
50825	Continent diversion, including bowel anastomosis using any segment of small and/or large bowel (Kock pouch or Camey enterocystoplasty)	175.0	4070	4850	2352
50830	Urinary undiversion (eg, taking down of ureteroileal conduit, ureterosigmoidostomy or ureteroenterostomy with ureteroureterostomy or ureteroneocystostomy)	100.0	2326	2771	2041
50840	Replacement of all or part of ureter by bowel segment, including bowel anastomosis	160.0	3721	4434	1305
50845	Cutaneous appendico-vesicostomy	114.0	2651	3159	1352
50860	Ureterostomy, transplantation of ureter to skin	80.00	1861	2217	1030
50900	Ureterorrhaphy, suture of ureter (separate procedure)	90.00	2093	2494	938
50920	Closure of ureterocutaneous fistula	90.00	2093	2494	928
50930	Closure of ureterovisceral fistula (including visceral repair)	110.0	2558	3049	1221
50940	Deligation of ureter	90.00	2093	2494	952
50951	Ureteral endoscopy through established ureterostomy, with or without irrigation, instillation, or ureteropyelography, exclusive of radiologic service;	9.00	209	249	296

Code	Description	Medicode RVU	50th	75th	Medicare Nat'l Avg
50953	Ureteral endoscopy through established ureterostomy, with or without irrigation, instillation, or ureteropyelography, exclusive of radiologic service; with ureteral catheterization, with or without dilation of ureter	20.00	465	554	312
50955	Ureteral endoscopy through established ureterostomy, with or without irrigation, instillation, or ureteropyelography, exclusive of radiologic service; with biopsy	22.00	512	610	370
50957	Ureteral endoscopy through established ureterostomy, with or without irrigation, instillation, or ureteropyelography, exclusive of radiologic service; with fulguration and/or incision, with or without biopsy	26.00	605	721	370
50959	Ureteral endoscopy through established ureterostomy, with or without irrigation, instillation, or ureteropyelography, exclusive of radiologic service; with insertion of radioactive substance, with or without biopsy and/or fulguration (not including provision of material)	29.00	674	804	314
50961	Ureteral endoscopy through established ureterostomy, with or without irrigation, instillation, or ureteropyelography, exclusive of radiologic service; with removal of foreign body or calculus	31.00	721	859	349
50970	Ureteral endoscopy through ureterotomy, with or without irrigation, instillation, or ureteropyelography, exclusive of radiologic service;	11.00	256	305	493
50972	Ureteral endoscopy through ureterotomy, with or without irrigation, instillation, or ureteropyelography, exclusive of radiologic service; with ureteral catheterization, with or without dilation of ureter	22.00	512	610	334
50974	Ureteral endoscopy through ureterotomy, with or without irrigation, instillation, or ureteropyelography, exclusive of radiologic service; with biopsy	24.00	558	665	654
50976	Ureteral endoscopy through ureterotomy, with or without irrigation, instillation, or ureteropyelography, exclusive of radiologic service; with fulguration and/or incision, with or without biopsy	28.00	651	776	624
50978	Ureteral endoscopy through ureterotomy, with or without irrigation, instillation, or ureteropyelography, exclusive of radiologic service; with insertion of radioactive substance, with or without biopsy and/or fulguration (not including provision of material)	31.00	721	859	374
50980	Ureteral endoscopy through ureterotomy, with or without irrigation, instillation, or ureteropyelography, exclusive of radiologic service; with removal of foreign body or calculus	33.00	767	915	398

51000–51980
Bladder

CODING INSIGHT

Code 51715 is for endoscopic injection of implant material into the submucosal tissues of the urethra and/or bladder neck. In order to place the collagen or Teflon material, a cystoscopy is performed (52000) to insert the needle into the appropriate site and inject. Therefore, a cystoscope is inherent to this procedure and should not be reported separately. If a separate surgical cystourethroscopic procedure is performed simultaneously or at the same session, other codes may be reported along with code 51715.

Subsidiary Codes

Subsidiary codes have relative values that require no further adjustment:

20926 is "in addition" to 51000–51980
38102 is "in addition" to 51000–51980
38747 is "in addition" to 51000–51980
44015 is "in addition" to 51000–51980
44955 is "in addition" to 51000–51980
45355 is "in addition" to 51000–51980
47001 is "in addition" to 51000–51980
49905 is "in addition" to 51000–51980
58611 is "in addition" to 51020–51596, 51800–51960

Because these are subsidiary or "in addition to" codes, reimbursement reduction and modifier -51 do not apply.

Medicare Alert

Medicare rebundles certain codes in the surgery section when the listed codes are considered a component of a more comprehensive service.

44130, 51590, and 51840–51841 will not be reimbursed when reported with 51595
53670 will not be reimbursed when reported with 51600, 51605
51700, 53670, and 53675 will not be reimbursed when reported with 51720
51725, 53670 will not be reimbursed when reported with 51726
49000, 53660, 53661, 57240, 57289 will not be reimbursed when reported with 51840, 51845

Code		Description	Medicode RVU	50th	75th	Medicare Nat'l Avg
51000	*	Aspiration of bladder by needle	3.00	69	85	53
51005	*	Aspiration of bladder; by trocar or intracatheter	3.50	81	99	61
51010		Aspiration of bladder; with insertion of suprapubic catheter	10.00	231	282	141
51020		Cystotomy or cystostomy; with fulguration and/or insertion of radioactive material	60.00	1387	1694	563
51030		Cystotomy or cystostomy; with cryosurgical destruction of intravesical lesion	60.00	1387	1694	450
51040		Cystostomy, cystotomy with drainage	50.00	1155	1411	505
51045		Cystotomy, with insertion of ureteral catheter or stent (separate procedure)	55.00	1271	1553	494
51050		Cystolithotomy, cystotomy with removal of calculus, without vesical neck resection	60.00	1387	1694	599
51060		Transvesical ureterolithotomy	80.00	1849	2258	776
51065		Cystotomy, with stone basket extraction and/or ultrasonic or electrohydraulic fragmentation of ureteral calculus	70.00	1618	1976	630
51080		Drainage of perivesical or prevesical space abscess	45.00	1040	1270	447

Code		Description	Medicode RVU	50th	75th	Medicare Nat'l Avg
51500		Excision of urachal cyst or sinus, with or without umbilical hernia repair	65.00	1502	1835	697
51520		Cystotomy; for simple excision of vesical neck (separate procedure)	70.00	1618	1976	728
51525		Cystotomy; for excision of bladder diverticulum, single or multiple (separate procedure)	90.00	2080	2541	995
51530		Cystotomy; for excision of bladder tumor	70.00	1618	1976	861
51535		Cystotomy for excision, incision, or repair of ureterocele	70.00	1618	1976	800
51550		Cystectomy, partial; simple	70.00	1618	1976	1053
51555		Cystectomy, partial; complicated (eg, postradiation, previous surgery, difficult location)	90.00	2080	2541	1310
51565		Cystectomy, partial, with reimplantation of ureter(s) into bladder (ureteroneocystostomy)	110.0	2542	3105	1483
51570		Cystectomy, complete; (separate procedure)	120.0	2773	3387	1553
51575		Cystectomy, complete; with bilateral pelvic lymphadenectomy, including external iliac, hypogastric and obturator nodes	180.0	4160	5081	2098
51580		Cystectomy, complete, with ureterosigmoidostomy or ureterocutaneous transplantations;	177.0	4090	4996	1967
51585		Cystectomy, complete, with ureterosigmoidostomy or ureterocutaneous transplantations; with bilateral pelvic lymphadenectomy, including external iliac, hypogastric and obturator nodes	220.0	5084	6210	2339
51590		Cystectomy, complete, with ureteroileal conduit or sigmoid bladder, including bowel anastomosis;	228.0	5269	6436	2329
51595		Cystectomy, complete, with ureteroileal conduit or sigmoid bladder, including bowel anastomosis; with bilateral pelvic lymphadenectomy, including external iliac, hypogastric and obturator nodes	262.0	6055	7396	2907
51596		Cystectomy, complete, with continent diversion, any technique, using any segment of small and/or large bowel to construct neobladder	250.0	5777	7057	2974
51597		Pelvic exenteration, complete, for vesical, prostatic or urethral malignancy, with removal of bladder and ureteral transplantations, with or without hysterectomy and/or abdominoperineal resection of rectum and colon and colostomy, or any combination thereof	285.0	6586	8045	2819
51600	*	Injection procedure for cystography or voiding urethrocystography	3.00	69	85	44
51605		Injection procedure and placement of chain for contrast and/or chain urethrocystography	4.00	92	113	56
51610		Injection procedure for retrograde urethrocystography	4.50	104	127	69
51700	*	Bladder irrigation, simple, lavage and/or instillation	2.00	46	56	41
51705	*	Change of cystostomy tube; simple	3.00	69	85	52

Code		Description	Medicode RVU	50th	75th	Medicare Nat'l Avg
51710	*	Change of cystostomy tube; complicated	12.00	277	339	81
51715		Endoscopic injection of implant material into the submucosal tissues of the urethra and/or bladder neck	24.00	555	677	259
51720		Bladder instillation of anticarcinogenic agent (including detention time)	4.00	92	113	88
51725		Simple cystometrogram (CMG) (eg, spinal manometer)	6.50	146	180	101
-26				124	153	85
51726		Complex cystometrogram (eg, calibrated electronic equipment)	7.50	169	207	121
-26				143	176	100
51736		Simple uroflowmetry (UFR) (eg, stop-watch flow rate, mechanical uroflowmeter)	3.25	73	90	48
-26				62	76	44
51741		Complex uroflowmetry (eg, calibrated electronic equipment)	4.00	90	111	82
-26				76	94	75
51772		Urethral pressure profile studies (UPP) (urethral closure pressure profile), any technique	7.00	157	193	104
-26				134	164	85
51784		Electromyography studies (EMG) of anal or urethral sphincter, other than needle, any technique	7.00	157	193	104
-26				134	164	88
51785		Needle electromyography studies (EMG) of anal or urethral sphincter, any technique	7.00	157	193	104
-26				134	164	88
51792		Stimulus evoked response (eg, measurement of bulbocavernosus reflex latency time)	7.00	157	193	125
-26				134	164	68
51795		Voiding pressure studies (VP); bladder voiding pressure, any technique	6.50	146	180	119
-26				124	153	84
51797		Voiding pressure studies (VP); intra-abdominal voiding pressure (AP) (rectal, gastric, intraperitoneal)	7.50	169	207	104
-26				143	176	84
51800		Cystoplasty or cystourethroplasty, plastic operation on bladder and/or vesical neck (anterior Y-plasty, vesical fundus resection), any procedure, with or without wedge resection of posterior vesical neck	100.0	2481	2858	1179
51820		Cystourethroplasty with unilateral or bilateral ureteroneocystostomy	145.0	3597	4144	1025
51840		Anterior vesicourethropexy, or urethropexy (Marshall-Marchetti-Krantz type); simple	78.00	1935	2229	828
51841		Anterior vesicourethropexy, or urethropexy (Marshall-Marchetti-Krantz type); complicated (eg, secondary repair)	88.00	2183	2515	987
51845		Abdomino-vaginal vesical neck suspension, with or without endoscopic control (eg, Stamey, Raz, modified Pereyra)	75.00	1861	2144	880
51860		Cystorrhaphy, suture of bladder wound, injury or rupture; simple	70.00	1737	2001	794
51865		Cystorrhaphy, suture of bladder wound, injury or rupture; complicated	90.00	2233	2572	1047
51880		Closure of cystostomy (separate procedure)	45.00	1116	1286	499
51900		Closure of vesicovaginal fistula, abdominal approach	105.0	2605	3001	986
51920		Closure of vesicouterine fistula;	90.00	2233	2572	736

Code	Description	Medicode RVU	50th	75th	Medicare Nat'l Avg
51925	Closure of vesicouterine fistula; with hysterectomy	105.0	2605	3001	1028
51940	Closure of bladder exstrophy	60.00	1488	1715	1796
51960	Enterocystoplasty, including bowel anastomosis	160.0	3969	4573	1760
51980	Cutaneous vesicostomy	90.00	2233	2572	740

52000–52700
Endoscopy–Cystoscopy, Urethroscopy, Cystourethroscopy

CODING INSIGHT
Endoscopic codes in this section specify that they include minor related functions performed at the same time. Examples, such as meatotomy, are cited in CPT. It is further specified that "when the secondary procedure requires significant additional time and effort, it may be identified by the addition of either modifier -22 or the five-digit code 09922." Be sure to submit a cover letter and operative report if you use this modifier. Some payers may have strict guidelines that specify significant time is 45 minutes or greater. Other payers may not have a time qualifier, but may consider time equally with effort (i.e., difficult, complex).

CPT '96 notes on page 191 that stent insertion is included in 52320–52339, and when performed should not be reported separately.

SUBSIDIARY CODES
Subsidiary codes have relative values that require no further adjustment:

20926 is "in addition" to 52000–52700
38102 is "in addition" to 52000–52700
38747 is "in addition" to 52000–52700
44015 is "in addition" to 52000–52700
44955 is "in addition" to 52000–52700
45355 is "in addition" to 52000–52700
47001 is "in addition" to 52000–52700
49905 is "in addition" to 52000–52700

Because these are subsidiary or "in addition to" codes, reimbursement reduction and modifier -51 do not apply.

MEDICARE ALERT

Cystourethrosocpy with Urethral Catheterization
When filing Medicare claims, do not report 52005 (cystourethroscopy with urethral catheterization) with either modifier -50 (bilateral) or modifier -51 (multiple surgery). Because the basic procedure is an examination of the bladder and urethra (i.e., of organs that are not paired), no additional payment will be made if modifier -50 is appended to 52005. Likewise, modifier -51 is the multiple surgery modifier and is intended to be used when multiple, usually different, procedures are done on the same day. Only reimbursement for the unmodified code will be allowed by Medicare.

Medicare rebundles certain codes in the surgery section when the listed codes are considered a component of a more comprehensive service.

G0002, 53670 will not be reimbursed when reported with 52000
51700, 52000, 53670 will not be reimbursed when reported with 52005
51700, 52000, 52005 will not be reimbursed when reported with 52007
53670 will not be reimbursed when reported with 52204
51700, 52214, 52224, 52234 will not be reimbursed when reported with 52235
51700, 52214, 52224, 52234–52235 will not be reimbursed when reported with 52240
51700, 53600–53601, 53620–53621, 53660–53661 will not be reimbursed when reported with 52276
51700, 52000, 53600–53601, 53620, 53660–53661, 53675 will not be reimbursed when reported with 52281
51700, 52000, 52281 will not be reimbursed when reported with 52310
51700, 52000, 52005 will not be reimbursed when reported with 52332
51700, 52000, 52335 will not be reimbursed when reported with 52336–52337
52000, 52214, 52340, 52640 will not be reimbursed when reported with 52500
51700, 52000, 52214, 52275–52276, 52281, 52500, 53020, 53600–53601, 53620, 53675, 55250 will not be reimbursed when reported with 52601
53670 will not be reimbursed when reported with 52630

Code	Description	Medicode RVU	50th	75th	Medicare Nat'l Avg
52000	Cystourethroscopy (separate procedure)	11.00	267	306	137
52005	Cystourethroscopy, with ureteral catheterization, with or without irrigation, instillation, or ureteropyelography, exclusive of radiologic service;	18.00	437	501	193
52007	Cystourethroscopy, with ureteral catheterization, with or without irrigation, instillation, or ureteropyelography, exclusive of radiologic service; with brush biopsy of ureter and/or renal pelvis	20.00	485	556	247
52010	Cystourethroscopy, with ejaculatory duct catheterization, with or without irrigation, instillation, or duct radiography, exclusive of radiologic service	19.00	461	529	200
52204	Cystourethroscopy, with biopsy	19.00	457	528	203
52214	Cystourethroscopy, with fulguration (including cryosurgery or laser surgery) of trigone, bladder neck, prostatic fossa, urethra, or periurethral glands	19.00	457	528	267
52224	Cystourethroscopy, with fulguration (including cryosurgery or laser surgery) or treatment of MINOR (less than 0.5 cm) lesion(s) with or without biopsy	20.00	481	556	253
52234	Cystourethroscopy, with fulguration (including cryosurgery or laser surgery) and/or resection of; SMALL bladder tumor(s) (0.5 to 2.0 cm)	30.00	721	834	397
52235	Cystourethroscopy, with fulguration (including cryosurgery or laser surgery) and/or resection of; MEDIUM bladder tumor(s) (2.0 to 5.0 cm)	50.00	1201	1390	595
52240	Cystourethroscopy, with fulguration (including cryosurgery or laser surgery) and/or resection of; LARGE bladder tumor(s)	70.00	1682	1946	890
52250	Cystourethroscopy with insertion of radioactive substance, with or without biopsy or fulguration	23.00	553	639	307

Code	Description	Medicode RVU	50th	75th	Medicare Nat'l Avg
52260	Cystourethroscopy, with dilation of bladder for interstitial cystitis; general or conduction (spinal) anesthesia	18.00	433	500	244
52265	Cystourethroscopy, with dilation of bladder for interstitial cystitis; local anesthesia	19.00	457	528	170
52270	Cystourethroscopy, with internal urethrotomy; female	22.00	529	612	304
52275	Cystourethroscopy, with internal urethrotomy; male	27.00	649	751	337
52276	Cystourethroscopy with direct vision internal urethrotomy	37.00	889	1029	379
52277	Cystourethroscopy, with resection of external sphincter (sphincterotomy)	28.00	673	778	454
52281	Cystourethroscopy, with calibration and/or dilation of urethral stricture or stenosis, with or without meatotomy and injection procedure for cystography, male or female	18.00	433	500	213
52283	Cystourethroscopy, with steroid injection into stricture	17.50	420	487	210
52285	Cystourethroscopy for treatment of the female urethral syndrome with any or all of the following: urethral meatotomy, urethral dilation, internal urethrotomy, lysis of urethrovaginal septal fibrosis, lateral incisions of the bladder neck, and fulguration of polyp(s) of urethra, bladder neck, and/or trigone	22.50	541	626	268
52290	Cystourethroscopy; with ureteral meatotomy, unilateral or bilateral	20.00	481	556	280
52300	Cystourethroscopy; with resection or fulguration of ureterocele(s), unilateral or bilateral	27.00	649	751	362
52305	Cystourethroscopy; with incision or resection of orifice of bladder diverticulum, single or multiple	27.00	649	751	365
52310	Cystourethroscopy, with removal of foreign body, calculus, or ureteral stent from urethra or bladder (separate procedure); simple	20.00	481	556	252
52315	Cystourethroscopy, with removal of foreign body, calculus, or ureteral stent from urethra or bladder (separate procedure); complicated	33.00	793	918	393
52317	Litholapaxy: crushing or fragmentation of calculus by any means in bladder and removal of fragments; simple or small (less than 2.5 cm)	41.00	985	1140	558
52318	Litholapaxy: crushing or fragmentation of calculus by any means in bladder and removal of fragments; complicated or large (over 2.5 cm)	55.00	1322	1529	738
52320	Cystourethroscopy (including ureteral catheterization); with removal of ureteral calculus	37.50	849	985	414
52325	Cystourethroscopy (including ureteral catheterization); with fragmentation of ureteral calculus (eg, ultrasonic or electro-hydraulic technique)	65.00	1472	1707	567
52327	Cystourethroscopy (including ureteral catheterization); with subureteric injection of implant material	40.00	906	1051	360
52330	Cystourethroscopy (including ureteral catheterization); with manipulation, without removal of ureteral calculus	28.00	634	735	349

Code	Description	Medicode RVU	50th	75th	Medicare Nat'l Avg
52332	Cystourethroscopy, with insertion of indwelling ureteral stent (eg, Gibbons or double-J type)	27.00	611	709	273
52334	Cystourethroscopy with insertion of ureteral guide wire through kidney to establish a percutaneous nephrostomy, retrograde	25.00	566	657	356
52335	Cystourethroscopy, with ureteroscopy and/or pyeloscopy (includes dilation of the ureter and/or pyeloureteral junction by any method);	45.00	1019	1182	444
52336	Cystourethroscopy, with ureteroscopy and/or pyeloscopy (includes dilation of the ureter and/or pyeloureteral junction by any method); with removal or manipulation of calculus (ureteral catheterization is included)	80.00	1812	2101	744
52337	Cystourethroscopy, with ureteroscopy and/or pyeloscopy (includes dilation of the ureter and/or pyeloureteral junction by any method); with lithotripsy (ureteral catheterization is included)	100.0	2265	2627	829
52338	Cystourethroscopy, with ureteroscopy and/or pyeloscopy (includes dilation of the ureter and/or pyeloureteral junction by any method); with biopsy and/or fulguration of lesion	54.00	1223	1418	566
52339	Cystourethroscopy, with ureteroscopy and/or pyeloscopy (includes dilation of the ureter and/or pyeloureteral junction by any method); with resection of tumor	64.00	1449	1681	616
52340	Cystourethroscopy with incision, fulguration, or resection of bladder neck and/or posterior urethra (congenital valves, obstructive hypertrophic mucosal folds)	45.00	1063	1200	528
52450	Transurethral incision of prostate	39.00	921	1040	488
52500	Transurethral resection of bladder neck (separate procedure)	50.00	1181	1333	635
52510	Transurethral balloon dilation of the prostatic urethra, any method	43.00	1016	1147	576
52601	Transurethral electrosurgical resection of prostate, including control of postoperative bleeding, complete (vasectomy, meatotomy, cystourethroscopy, urethral calibration and/or dilation, and internal urethrotomy are included)	83.00	1960	2213	983
52606	Transurethral fulguration for postoperative bleeding occurring after the usual follow-up time	22.00	520	587	424
52612	Transurethral resection of prostate; first stage of two-stage resection (partial resection)	65.00	1535	1733	700
52614	Transurethral resection of prostate; second stage of two-stage resection (resection completed)	40.00	945	1067	563
52620	Transurethral resection; of residual obstructive tissue after 90 days postoperative	30.00	709	800	475
52630	Transurethral resection; of regrowth of obstructive tissue longer than one year postoperative	90.00	2126	2400	740
52640	Transurethral resection; of postoperative bladder neck contracture	48.00	1134	1280	531
52647	Non-contact laser coagulation of prostate, including control of postoperative bleeding, complete (vasectomy, meatotomy, cystourethroscopy, urethral calibration and/or dilation, and internal urethrotomy are included)	0.00	0	0	897

Code	Description	Medicode RVU	50th	75th	Medicare Nat'l Avg
52648	Contact laser vaporization with or without transurethral resection of prostate, including control of postoperative bleeding, complete (vasectomy, meatotomy, cystourethroscopy, urethral calibration and/or dilation, and internal urethrotomy are included)	0.00	0	0	923
52700	Transurethral drainage of prostatic abscess	37.00	874	987	398

53000–53899
Urethra

Coding Insight
Some of the procedures in this code range can also be performed through a cystourethroscope. They are often listed with a separate procedure designation. When a separate procedure is noted in the code description, double-check for another code that may report more accurately the complete procedure that was performed. An example is 53020 *Meatotomy, cutting of meatus (separate procedure); except infant*. When performed through a cystourethroscope, a meatotomy is considered a minor procedure in relation to the main procedure being performed and is not listed separately.

Watch for female or male designations made in 53230–53235. Payer software generally has edits that can match the patient's sex with a code designated for use by the opposite sex. This type of coding mistake could target your office for audit.

Subsidiary Codes
Subsidiary codes have relative values that require no further adjustment:

20926 is "in addition" to 53000–53899
38102 is "in addition" to 53000–53899
38747 is "in addition" to 53000–53899
44015 is "in addition" to 53000–53899
44955 is "in addition" to 53000–53899
45355 is "in addition" to 53000–53899
47001 is "in addition" to 53000–53899
49905 is "in addition" to 53000–53899

Because these are subsidiary or "in addition to" codes, reimbursement reduction and modifier -51 do not apply.

Medicare Alert
Medicare rebundles certain codes in the surgery section when the listed codes are considered a component of a more comprehensive service.

53670 will not be reimbursed when reported with 53600, 53660, 53675

Code	Description	Medicode RVU	50th	75th	Medicare Nat'l Avg
53000	Urethrotomy or urethrostomy, external (separate procedure); pendulous urethra	12.00	268	320	158
53010	Urethrotomy or urethrostomy, external (separate procedure); perineal urethra, external	25.00	558	667	281

Code	Description	Medicode RVU	50th	75th	Medicare Nat'l Avg
53020	Meatotomy, cutting of meatus (separate procedure); except infant	10.00	223	267	104
53025	Meatotomy, cutting of meatus (separate procedure); infant	5.00	112	133	78
53040	Drainage of deep periurethral abscess	15.00	335	400	311
53060	Drainage of Skene's gland abscess or cyst	6.00	134	160	123
53080	Drainage of perineal urinary extravasation; uncomplicated (separate procedure)	15.00	335	400	400
53085	Drainage of perineal urinary extravasation; complicated	25.00	558	667	677
53200	Biopsy of urethra	10.00	223	267	150
53210	Urethrectomy, total, including cystostomy; female	65.00	1452	1735	753
53215	Urethrectomy, total, including cystostomy; male	80.00	1787	2135	1019
53220	Excision or fulguration of carcinoma of urethra	50.00	1117	1335	469
53230	Excision of urethral diverticulum (separate procedure); female	60.00	1340	1601	701
53235	Excision of urethral diverticulum (separate procedure); male	60.00	1340	1601	523
53240	Marsupialization of urethral diverticulum, male or female	25.00	558	667	425
53250	Excision of bulbourethral gland (Cowper's gland)	55.00	1229	1468	397
53260	Excision or fulguration; urethral polyp(s), distal urethra	7.00	156	187	161
53265	Excision or fulguration; urethral caruncle	15.00	335	400	197
53270	Excision or fulguration; Skene's glands	15.00	335	400	154
53275	Excision or fulguration; urethral prolapse	20.00	447	534	272
53400	Urethroplasty; first stage, for fistula, diverticulum, or stricture (eg, Johannsen type)	50.00	1117	1335	785
53405	Urethroplasty; second stage (formation of urethra), including urinary diversion	70.00	1564	1868	984
53410	Urethroplasty, one-stage reconstruction of male anterior urethra	80.00	1787	2135	991
53415	Urethroplasty, transpubic or perineal, one stage, for reconstruction or repair of prostatic or membranous urethra	90.00	2011	2402	1241
53420	Urethroplasty, two-stage reconstruction or repair of prostatic or membranous urethra; first stage	90.00	2011	2402	990
53425	Urethroplasty, two-stage reconstruction or repair of prostatic or membranous urethra; second stage	90.00	2011	2402	993

Code		Description	Medicode RVU	50th	75th	Medicare Nat'l Avg
53430		Urethroplasty, reconstruction of female urethra	70.00	1564	1868	920
53440		Operation for correction of male urinary incontinence, with or without introduction of prosthesis	90.00	2011	2402	1042
53442		Removal of perineal prosthesis introduced for continence	30.00	670	801	553
53443		Urethroplasty with tubularization of posterior urethra and/or lower bladder for incontinence (eg, Tenago, Leadbetter procedure)	90.00	2011	2402	1175
53445		Operation for correction of urinary incontinence with placement of inflatable urethral or bladder neck sphincter, including placement of pump and/or reservoir	215.0	4803	5739	1368
53447		Removal, repair or replacement of inflatable sphincter including pump and/or reservoir and/or cuff	30.00	670	801	885
53449		Surgical correction of hydraulic abnormality of inflatable sphincter device	50.00	1117	1335	716
53450		Urethromeatoplasty, with mucosal advancement	20.00	447	534	338
53460		Urethromeatoplasty, with partial excision of distal urethral segment (Richardson type procedure)	22.00	491	587	366
53502		Urethrorrhaphy, suture of urethral wound or injury, female	50.00	1117	1335	498
53505		Urethrorrhaphy, suture of urethral wound or injury; penile	50.00	1117	1335	507
53510		Urethrorrhaphy, suture of urethral wound or injury; perineal	65.00	1452	1735	675
53515		Urethrorrhaphy, suture of urethral wound or injury; prostatomembranous	100.0	2234	2669	883
53520		Closure of urethrostomy or urethrocutaneous fistula, male (separate procedure)	35.00	782	934	570
53600	*	Dilation of urethral stricture by passage of sound or urethral dilator, male; initial	3.00	67	80	57
53601	*	Dilation of urethral stricture by passage of sound or urethral dilator, male; subsequent	2.25	50	60	47
53605		Dilation of urethral stricture or vesical neck by passage of sound or urethral dilator, male, general or conduction (spinal) anesthesia	7.00	156	187	70
53620	*	Dilation of urethral stricture by passage of filiform and follower, male; initial	4.25	95	113	80
53621	*	Dilation of urethral stricture by passage of filiform and follower, male; subsequent	3.40	76	91	65
53640	*	Passage of filiform and follower for acute vesical retention, male	4.50	101	120	84
53660	*	Dilation of female urethra including suppository and/or instillation; initial	2.50	56	67	39
53661	*	Dilation of female urethra including suppository and/or instillation; subsequent	2.00	45	53	37
53665		Dilation of female urethra, general or conduction (spinal) anesthesia	5.75	128	153	46

Code		Description	Medicode RVU	50th	75th	Medicare Nat'l Avg
53670	*	Catheterization, urethra; simple	1.90	42	51	28
53675	*	Catheterization, urethra; complicated (may include difficult removal of balloon catheter)	3.50	78	93	74
53899		Unlisted procedure, urinary system	0.00	0	0	–

54000–54450
Penis

CODING INSIGHT

Codes listed under destruction of lesion(s) of the penis (54050–54065) include:

- Lesions identified by physician and/or pathology as:

  Condyloma — wart-like eruption on the glans penis, anus, or vulva

  Papilloma — benign epithelial tumor

  Molluscum contagiosum — viral related infectious epithelial lesions

  Hepatic vesicle — infected groups of one or more vesicles caused by herpes type II virus

Nota Bene: These codes include destruction of lesion(s) listed above. For other than those listed, see the integumentary system for excision of benign or malignant lesions, destruction of benign, premalignant or malignant lesions, or other appropriate codes.

- Destruction methods:

  Simple, chemical — local application of a chemical

  Electrodesiccation — high frequency electrical current

  Cryosurgery — freezing cold mixtures used to destroy lesions

  Laser surgery — narrow beam of light amplified by stimulated emission of radiation used to destroy lesion(s)

  Surgical excision — removal of the lesion by cutting

- Extent of lesions:

  Extensive — lesion(s) removed by destruction methods listed above. However, when extensive removal is required it may be due to groups of lesions clustered closely together over a large area, the number of lesions in different areas, or the size and number of lesions. The physician must list the destruction as extensive in the operative report before this code should be used.

- Number of lesion(s) included:

  Single or multiple lesions

An excisional biopsy (code 54100) is not reported separately if a therapeutic excision is performed during the same surgical session.

Code 54115 reports removal of a foreign body from deep penile tissue. It is also used to report removal of a temporary penile prosthesis. If a removal, repair, or replacement of a permanent penile prosthesis is performed when the penile shaft was hollowed out, see 54407 or 54409.

For removal of foreign body from skin or subcutaneous tissue, see 10120–10121. For wound exploration, trauma, with removal of foreign body(s), see 20102 and applicable notes.

SUBSIDIARY CODES

Subsidiary codes have relative values that require no further adjustment:

20926 is "in addition" to 54000–54450
38102 is "in addition" to 54000–54450
38747 is "in addition" to 54000–54450
44015 is "in addition" to 54000–54450
44955 is "in addition" to 54000–54450
45355 is "in addition" to 54000–54450
47001 is "in addition" to 54000–54450
49905 is "in addition" to 54000–54450

Because these are subsidiary or "in addition to" codes, reimbursement reduction and modifier -51 do not apply.

MEDICARE ALERT

Coverage for Impotence

Program payment may be made for diagnosis and treatment of sexual impotence. (Impotence is a failure of a body part for which the diagnosis, and frequently the treatment, require medical expertise.) Depending upon the cause of the condition, treatment may be surgical (e.g., implantation of a penile prosthesis) or nonsurgical (e.g., medical or psychotherapeutic treatment). Since treatment varies with cause, documentation may be required in certain instances, and if treatment is furnished to patients (other than hospital inpatients) in connection with a mental condition, apply the psychiatric service limitation.

Medicare rebundles certain codes in the surgery section when the listed codes are considered a component of a more comprehensive service.

49000, 49010, 54400 will not be reimbursed when reported with 54405

Code		Description	Medicode RVU	50th	75th	Medicare Nat'l Avg
54000		Slitting of prepuce, dorsal or lateral (separate procedure); newborn	5.50	117	136	85
54001		Slitting of prepuce, dorsal or lateral (separate procedure); except newborn	8.00	171	198	117
54015		Incision and drainage of penis, deep	13.00	277	322	232
54050	*	Destruction of lesion(s), penis (eg, condyloma, papilloma, molluscum contagiosum, herpetic vesicle), simple; chemical	3.50	75	87	61
54055	*	Destruction of lesion(s), penis (eg, condyloma, papilloma, molluscum contagiosum, herpetic vesicle), simple; electrodesiccation	6.00	128	149	81
54056		Destruction of lesion(s), penis (eg, condyloma, papilloma, molluscum contagiosum, herpetic vesicle), simple; cryosurgery	6.25	133	155	70
54057		Destruction of lesion(s), penis (eg, condyloma, papilloma, molluscum contagiosum, herpetic vesicle), simple; laser surgery	20.00	426	495	124

Code		Description	Medicode RVU	50th	75th	Medicare Nat'l Avg
54060		Destruction of lesion(s), penis (eg, condyloma, papilloma, molluscum contagiosum, herpetic vesicle), simple; surgical excision	13.00	277	322	128
54065		Destruction of lesion(s), penis (eg, condyloma, papilloma, molluscum contagiosum, herpetic vesicle), extensive, any method	27.00	576	669	208
54100		Biopsy of penis; cutaneous (separate procedure)	6.00	128	149	99
54105		Biopsy of penis; deep structures	11.00	235	272	174
54110		Excision of penile plaque (Peyronie disease);	42.00	896	1040	637
54111		Excision of penile plaque (Peyronie disease); with graft to 5 cm in length	62.00	1322	1535	903
54112		Excision of penile plaque (Peyronie disease); with graft greater than 5 cm in length	82.00	1748	2030	1059
54115		Removal foreign body from deep penile tissue (eg, plastic implant)	27.50	586	681	401
54120		Amputation of penis; partial	50.00	1066	1238	644
54125		Amputation of penis; complete	60.00	1279	1486	1020
54130		Amputation of penis, radical; with bilateral inguinofemoral lymphadenectomy	120.0	2559	2971	1366
54135		Amputation of penis, radical; in continuity with bilateral pelvic lymphadenectomy, including external iliac, hypogastric and obturator nodes	150.0	3198	3714	1737
54150		Circumcision, using clamp or other device; newborn	5.75	134	155	93
54152		Circumcision, using clamp or other device; except newborn	14.00	326	377	167
54160		Circumcision, surgical excision other than clamp, device or dorsal slit; newborn	6.50	151	175	167
54161		Circumcision, surgical excision other than clamp, device or dorsal slit; except newborn	19.25	448	519	224
54200	*	Injection procedure for Peyronie disease;	3.50	78	94	53
54205		Injection procedure for Peyronie disease; with surgical exposure of plaque	35.00	778	944	500
54220		Irrigation of corpora cavernosa for priapism	13.00	289	350	170
54230		Injection procedure for corpora cavernosography	10.50	233	283	109
54231		Dynamic cavernosometry, including intracavernosal injection of vasoactive drugs (eg, papaverine, phentolamine)	16.50	367	445	141
54235		Injection of corpora cavernosa with pharmacologic agent(s) (eg, papaverine, phentolamine)	6.25	139	168	63
54240		Penile plethysmography	8.00	178	216	93
-26				151	183	73

Code	Description	Medicode RVU	50th	75th	Medicare Nat'l Avg
54250	Nocturnal penile tumescence and/or rigidity test	10.00	222	270	117
-26			189	229	107
54300	Plastic operation of penis for straightening of chordee (eg, hypospadias), with or without mobilization of urethra	53.00	1178	1429	688
54304	Plastic operation on penis for correction of chordee or for first stage hypospadias repair with or without transplantation of prepuce and/or skin flaps	65.00	1445	1752	848
54308	Urethroplasty for second stage hypospadias repair (including urinary diversion); less than 3 cm	80.00	1778	2157	712
54312	Urethroplasty for second stage hypospadias repair (including urinary diversion); greater than 3 cm	90.00	2000	2426	912
54316	Urethroplasty for second stage hypospadias repair (including urinary diversion) with free skin graft obtained from site other than genitalia	100.0	2223	2696	1110
54318	Urethroplasty for third stage hypospadias repair to release penis from scrotum (eg, third stage Cecil repair)	50.00	1111	1348	743
54322	One stage distal hypospadias repair (with or without chordee or circumcision); with simple meatal advancement (eg, Magpi, V-flap)	62.50	1389	1685	808
54324	One stage distal hypospadias repair (with or without chordee or circumcision); with urethroplasty by local skin flaps (eg, flip-flap, prepucial flap)	85.00	1889	2292	1073
54326	One stage distal hypospadias repair (with or without chordee or circumcision); with urethroplasty by local skin flaps and mobilization of urethra	96.00	2134	2588	1026
54328	One stage distal hypospadias repair (with or without chordee or circumcision); with extensive dissection to correct chordee and urethroplasty with local skin flaps, skin graft patch, and/or island flap	113.0	2511	3046	1042
54332	One stage proximal penile or penoscrotal hypospadias repair requiring extensive dissection to correct chordee and urethroplasty by use of skin graft tube and/or island flap	104.0	2311	2804	1162
54336	One stage perineal hypospadias repair requiring extensive dissection to correct chordee and urethroplasty by use of skin graft tube and/or island flap	119.5	2656	3222	1523
54340	Repair of hypospadias complications (ie, fistula, stricture, diverticula); by closure, incision, or excision, simple	60.00	1334	1618	592
54344	Repair of hypospadias complications (ie, fistula, stricture, diverticula); requiring mobilization of skin flaps and urethroplasty with flap or patch graft	80.00	1778	2157	1281
54348	Repair of hypospadias complications (ie, fistula, stricture, diverticula); requiring extensive dissection and urethroplasty with flap, patch or tubed graft (includes urinary diversion)	91.00	2022	2453	1135
54352	Repair of hypospadias cripple requiring extensive dissection and excision of previously constructed structures including re-release of chordee and reconstruction of urethra and penis by use of local skin as grafts and island flaps and skin brought in as flaps or grafts	135.0	3000	3639	1616
54360	Plastic operation on penis to correct angulation	66.00	1467	1779	746

Code	Description	Medicode RVU	50th	75th	Medicare Nat'l Avg
54380	Plastic operation on penis for epispadias distal to external sphincter;	60.00	1334	1618	887
54385	Plastic operation on penis for epispadias distal to external sphincter; with incontinence	100.0	2223	2696	1018
54390	Plastic operation on penis for epispadias distal to external sphincter; with exstrophy of bladder	120.0	2667	3235	1406
54400	Insertion of penile prosthesis; non-inflatable (semi-rigid)	88.00	1956	2372	909
54401	Insertion of penile prosthesis; inflatable (self-contained)	109.0	2423	2939	1060
54402	Removal or replacement of non-inflatable (semi-rigid) or inflatable (self-contained) penile prosthesis	50.00	1111	1348	598
54405	Insertion of inflatable (multi-component) penile prosthesis, including placement of pump, cylinders, and/or reservoir	145.0	3223	3909	1407
54407	Removal, repair, or replacement of inflatable (multi-component) penile prosthesis, including pump and/or reservoir and/or cylinders	88.00	1956	2372	988
54409	Surgical correction of hydraulic abnormality of inflatable (multi-component) prosthesis including pump and/or reservoir and/or cylinders	80.00	1778	2157	838
54420	Corpora cavernosa-saphenous vein shunt (priapism operation), unilateral or bilateral	70.00	1556	1887	758
54430	Corpora cavernosa-corpus spongiosum shunt (priapism operation), unilateral or bilateral	70.00	1556	1887	686
54435	Corpora cavernosa-glans penis fistulization (eg, biopsy needle, Winter procedure, rongeur, or punch) for priapism	40.00	889	1078	403
54440	Plastic operation of penis for injury	55.00	1222	1483	845
54450	Foreskin manipulation including lysis of preputial adhesions and stretching	6.50	144	175	74

54500–54680
Testes

Coding Insight
Orchiectomy is frequently a treatment for prostate cancer, depending upon the stage of the disease. Hormonal therapy, which is the alternative, also lowers testosterone levels and decreases the tumor size; but, it carries serious side effects, especially in high doses, such as cardiovascular disease. When performed bilaterally report the code twice and append modifier -50 to the second code. See discussion of modifiers for additional information on the use of modifier -50.

Subsidiary Codes
Subsidiary codes have relative values that require no further adjustment:

20926 is "in addition" to 54500–54680
38102 is "in addition" to 54500–54680

38747 is "in addition" to 54500–54680
44015 is "in addition" to 54500–54680
44955 is "in addition" to 54500–54680
45355 is "in addition" to 54500–54680
47001 is "in addition" to 54500–54680
49905 is "in addition" to 54500–54680

Because these are subsidiary or "in addition to" codes, reimbursement reduction and modifier -51 do not apply.

MEDICARE ALERT

Medicare rebundles certain codes in the surgery section when the listed codes are considered a component of a more comprehensive service.

49000, 49010 will not be reimbursed when reported with 54520

Code	Description	Medicode RVU	50th	75th	Medicare Nat'l Avg
54500	Biopsy of testis, needle (separate procedure)	6.00	139	161	70
54505	Biopsy of testis, incisional (separate procedure)	20.00	464	538	214
54510	Excision of local lesion of testis	30.00	696	807	342
54520	Orchiectomy, simple (including subcapsular), with or without testicular prosthesis, scrotal or inguinal approach	35.00	812	942	432
54530	Orchiectomy, radical, for tumor; inguinal approach	50.00	1160	1346	655
54535	Orchiectomy, radical, for tumor; with abdominal exploration	57.00	1323	1534	823
54550	Exploration for undescended testis (inguinal or scrotal area)	40.00	928	1077	520
54560	Exploration for undescended testis with abdominal exploration	57.00	1323	1534	723
54600	Reduction of torsion of testis, surgical, with or without fixation of contralateral testis	45.00	1044	1211	456
54620	Fixation of contralateral testis (separate procedure)	22.75	528	612	325
54640	Orchiopexy, inguinal approach, with or without hernia repair	57.00	1323	1534	611
54650	Orchiopexy, abdominal approach, for intra-abdominal testis (eg, Fowler-Stephens)	61.00	1416	1642	767
54660	Insertion of testicular prosthesis (separate procedure)	20.00	464	538	332
54670	Suture or repair of testicular injury	39.25	911	1056	420
54680	Transplantation of testis(es) to thigh (because of scrotal destruction)	50.00	1160	1346	799

54700–54901
Epididymis

Coding Insight
If epididymitis is caused by chlamydia, both the patient and the sexual partner must be treated with antibiotics.

Subsidiary Codes
Subsidiary codes have relative values that require no further adjustment:

20926 is “in addition” to 54700–54901
38102 is “in addition” to 54700–54901
38747 is “in addition” to 54700–54901
44015 is “in addition” to 54700–54901
44955 is “in addition” to 54700–54901
45355 is “in addition” to 54700–54901
47001 is “in addition” to 54700–54901
49905 is “in addition” to 54700–54901

Because these are subsidiary or “in addition to” codes, reimbursement reduction and modifier -51 do not apply.

Code	Description	Medicode RVU	50th	75th	Medicare Nat'l Avg
54700	Incision and drainage of epididymis, testis and/or scrotal space (eg, abscess or hematoma)	13.50	306	341	164
54800	Biopsy of epididymis, needle	6.00	136	152	174
54820	Exploration of epididymis, with or without biopsy	25.00	566	632	299
54830	Excision of local lesion of epididymis	25.00	566	632	353
54840	Excision of spermatocele, with or without epididymectomy	38.00	860	961	426
54860	Epididymectomy; unilateral	40.00	905	1011	472
54861	Epididymectomy; bilateral	60.25	1364	1523	654
54900	Epididymovasostomy, anastomosis of epididymis to vas deferens; unilateral	50.00	1132	1264	873
54901	Epididymovasostomy, anastomosis of epididymis to vas deferens; bilateral	73.25	1658	1852	1198

55000–55060
Tunica Vaginalis

Coding Insight
When a hydrocele has been aspirated the sac may be injected with a sclerosing medication to prevent accumulation of new fluid by stimulating scarring and hardening of the empty sac.

Starred (*) procedures report the surgical portion of the service only. Any pre- and postoperative services are reported separately.

Subsidiary Codes

Subsidiary codes have relative values that require no further adjustment:

20926 is "in addition" to 55000–55060
38102 is "in addition" to 55000–55060
38747 is "in addition" to 55000–55060
44015 is "in addition" to 55000–55060
44955 is "in addition" to 55000–55060
45355 is "in addition" to 55000–55060
47001 is "in addition" to 55000–55060
49905 is "in addition" to 55000–55060

Because these are subsidiary or "in addition to" codes, reimbursement reduction and modifier -51 do not apply.

Code		Description	Medicode RVU	50th	75th	Medicare Nat'l Avg
55000	*	Puncture aspiration of hydrocele, tunica vaginalis, with or without injection of medication	4.75	108	120	68
55040		Excision of hydrocele; unilateral	40.00	905	1011	438
55041		Excision of hydrocele; bilateral	62.00	1403	1568	642
55060		Repair of tunica vaginalis hydrocele (Bottle type)	30.00	679	759	392

55100–55180
Scrotum

Coding Insight

Use integumentary system codes to report excision of local lesions of the skin of the scrotum.

Starred (*) procedures report the surgical portion of the service only. Any pre- and postoperative services are reported separately.

Subsidiary Codes

Subsidiary codes have relative values that require no further adjustment:

20926 is "in addition" to 55100–55180
38102 is "in addition" to 55100–55180
38747 is "in addition" to 55100–55180
44015 is "in addition" to 55100–55180
44955 is "in addition" to 55100–55180
45355 is "in addition" to 55100–55180
47001 is "in addition" to 55100–55180
49905 is "in addition" to 55100–55180

Because these are subsidiary or "in addition to" codes, reimbursement reduction and modifier -51 do not apply.

Code		Description	Medicode RVU	50th	75th	Medicare Nat'l Avg
55100	*	Drainage of scrotal wall abscess	5.75	130	145	103
55110		Scrotal exploration	30.00	679	759	364
55120		Removal of foreign body in scrotum	17.00	385	430	265
55150		Resection of scrotum	50.00	1132	1264	517
55175		Scrotoplasty; simple	40.00	905	1011	399
55180		Scrotoplasty; complicated	60.00	1358	1517	689

55200–55450
Vas Deferens

Coding Insight
There are procedures that simply are not covered or are infrequently covered by payers. These procedures may require prior authorization or may be flagged for audit 100 percent of the time. Code 55400, which may be performed to correct a previous vasectomy or for infertility, is one of these codes. Carefully document the reason for the surgery and request prior authorization; submit a cover letter and operative report with the claim.

Subsidiary Codes
Subsidiary codes have relative values that require no further adjustment:

20926 is "in addition" to 55200–55450
38102 is "in addition" to 55200–55450
38747 is "in addition" to 55200–55450
44015 is "in addition" to 55200–55450
44955 is "in addition" to 55200–55450
45355 is "in addition" to 55200–55450
47001 is "in addition" to 55200–55450
49905 is "in addition" to 55200–55450

Because these are subsidiary or "in addition to" codes, reimbursement reduction and CPT modifier -51 do not apply.

Code	Description	Medicode RVU	50th	75th	Medicare Nat'l Avg
55200	Vasotomy, cannulization with or without incision of vas, unilateral or bilateral (separate procedure)	20.50	472	526	246
55250	Vasectomy, unilateral or bilateral (separate procedure), including postoperative semen examination(s)	20.00	460	514	240
55300	Vasotomy for vasograms, seminal vesiculograms, or epididymograms, unilateral or bilateral	22.00	506	565	252
55400	Vasovasostomy, vasovasorrhaphy	85.00	1956	2182	604

Code	Description	Medicode RVU	50th	75th	Medicare Nat'l Avg
55450	Ligation (percutaneous) of vas deferens, unilateral or bilateral (separate procedure)	14.00	322	359	266

55500–55540
Spermatic Cord

Coding Insight
Code 55530 may be a noncovered benefit when performed to correct infertility. If symptomatic varicocele is present and surgery is performed for pain or scrotal fullness, documentation should clearly reflect the reason for the surgery (otherwise, in an audit situation, payment may be denied). Prior authorization of this service should be requested. Submit a cover letter and operative report with the claim.

Subsidiary Codes
Subsidiary codes have relative values that require no further adjustment:

20926 is "in addition" to 55500–55540
38102 is "in addition" to 55500–55540
38747 is "in addition" to 55500–55540
44015 is "in addition" to 55500–55540
44955 is "in addition" to 55500–55540
45355 is "in addition" to 55500–55540
47001 is "in addition" to 55500–55540
49905 is "in addition" to 55500–55540

Because these are subsidiary or "in addition to" codes, reimbursement reduction and modifier -51 do not apply.

Code	Description	Medicode RVU	50th	75th	Medicare Nat'l Avg
55500	Excision of hydrocele of spermatic cord, unilateral (separate procedure)	30.00	690	770	402
55520	Excision of lesion of spermatic cord (separate procedure)	30.00	690	770	371
55530	Excision of varicocele or ligation of spermatic veins for varicocele; (separate procedure)	47.00	1081	1207	444
55535	Excision of varicocele or ligation of spermatic veins for varicocele; abdominal approach	50.00	1150	1284	439
55540	Excision of varicocele or ligation of spermatic veins for varicocele; with hernia repair	47.50	1093	1220	500

55600–55680
Seminal Vesicles

CODING INSIGHT
Codes 55600–55650 are unilateral procedures. If performed bilaterally, report 55600 or 55605 twice and append modifier -50 to the second code. Modifier -50 identifies a procedure performed identically on the opposite side of the body (mirror image).

SUBSIDIARY CODES
Subsidiary codes have relative values that require no further adjustment:

20926 is "in addition" to 55600–55680
38102 is "in addition" to 55600–55680
38747 is "in addition" to 55600–55680
44015 is "in addition" to 55600–55680
44955 is "in addition" to 55600–55680
45355 is "in addition" to 55600–55680
47001 is "in addition" to 55600–55680
49905 is "in addition" to 55600–55680

Because these are subsidiary or "in addition to" codes, reimbursement reduction and modifier -51 do not apply.

Code	Description	Medicode RVU	50th	75th	Medicare Nat'l Avg
55600	Vesiculotomy;	40.00	920	1027	428
55605	Vesiculotomy; complicated	65.00	1496	1669	537
55650	Vesiculectomy, any approach	100.0	2301	2568	753
55680	Excision of Mullerian duct cyst	100.0	2301	2568	376

55700–55899
Prostate

CODING INSIGHT
Code 55859 *Transperineal placement of needles or catheters into prostate for interstitial radioelement application, with or without cystoscopy* was added to CPT in 1996. Use this code when needles or catheters are inserted for radioelement application (radioactive seeds) placement. If an incision or other approach is performed, see 55860–55865.

SUBSIDIARY CODES
Subsidiary codes have relative values that require no further adjustment:

20926 is "in addition" to 55700–55865
38102 is "in addition" to 55700–55865
38747 is "in addition" to 55700–55865
44015 is "in addition" to 55700–55865
44955 is "in addition" to 55700–55865
45355 is "in addition" to 55700–55865

47001 is "in addition" to 55700–55865
49905 is "in addition" to 55700–55865

Because these are subsidiary or "in addition to" codes, reimbursement reduction and modifier -51 do not apply.

Medicare Alert

Medicare rebundles certain codes in the surgery section when the listed codes are considered a component of a more comprehensive service.

49010, 51010, 51550, 51700, 52000, 53020, 53620, 55250, 55840, 55842 will not be reimbursed when reported with 55845
51040, 51010, 51700, 53020, 53600, 55250 will not be reimbursed when reported with 55821
51010, 51040, 51700, 52281, 53020, 53600, 55250 will not be reimbursed when reported with 55831

Code	Description	Medicode RVU	50th	75th	Medicare Nat'l Avg
55700	Biopsy, prostate; needle or punch, single or multiple, any approach	12.50	283	327	131
55705	Biopsy, prostate; incisional, any approach	45.00	1019	1178	327
55720	Prostatotomy, external drainage of prostatic abscess, any approach; simple	45.00	1019	1178	447
55725	Prostatotomy, external drainage of prostatic abscess, any approach; complicated	58.00	1314	1519	545
55801	Prostatectomy, perineal, subtotal (including control of postoperative bleeding, vasectomy, meatotomy, urethral calibration and/or dilation, and internal urethrotomy)	90.00	2038	2356	1194
55810	Prostatectomy, perineal radical;	130.0	2944	3404	1612
55812	Prostatectomy, perineal radical; with lymph node biopsy(s) (limited pelvic lymphadenectomy)	155.0	3511	4058	1766
55815	Prostatectomy, perineal radical; with bilateral pelvic lymphadenectomy, including external iliac, hypogastric and obturator nodes	185.0	4190	4844	2205
55821	Prostatectomy (including control of postoperative bleeding, vasectomy, meatotomy, urethral calibration and/or dilation, and internal urethrotomy); suprapubic, subtotal, one or two stages	100.0	2265	2618	1127
55831	Prostatectomy (including control of postoperative bleeding, vasectomy, meatotomy, urethral calibration and/or dilation, and internal urethrotomy); retropubic, subtotal	100.0	2265	2618	1214
55840	Prostatectomy, retropubic radical, with or without nerve sparing;	130.0	2944	3404	1571
55842	Prostatectomy, retropubic radical, with or without nerve sparing; with lymph node biopsy(s) (limited pelvic lymphadenectomy)	130.0	2944	3404	1739
55845	Prostatectomy, retropubic radical, with or without nerve sparing; with bilateral pelvic lymphadenectomy, including external iliac, hypogastric and obturator nodes	170.0	3850	4451	2204

Code	Description	Medicode RVU	50th	75th	Medicare Nat'l Avg
● 55859	Transperineal placement of needles or catheters into prostate for interstitial radioelement application, with or without cystoscopy	50.00	1132	1309	–
55860	Exposure of prostate, any approach, for insertion of radioactive substance;	40.00	906	1047	837
55862	Exposure of prostate, any approach, for insertion of radioactive substance; with lymph node biopsy(s) (limited pelvic lymphadenectomy)	68.00	1540	1780	1168
55865	Exposure of prostate, any approach, for insertion of radioactive substance; with bilateral pelvic lymphadenectomy, including external iliac, hypogastric and obturator nodes	120.0	2718	3142	1907
55870	Electroejaculation	0.00	0	0	157
55899	Unlisted procedure, male genital system	0.00	0	0	–

55970–55980
Intersex Surgery

Cosmetic Warning
This section contains codes that 85 percent of the time or more are considered cosmetic. The codes are 55970 and 55980.

Subsidiary Codes
Subsidiary codes have relative values that require no further adjustment:

20926 is "in addition" to 55970–55980
38102 is "in addition" to 55970–55980
38747 is "in addition" to 55970–55980
44015 is "in addition" to 55970–55980
44955 is "in addition" to 55970–55980
45355 is "in addition" to 55970–55980
47001 is "in addition" to 55970–55980
49905 is "in addition" to 55970–55980

Because these are subsidiary or "in addition to" codes, reimbursement reduction and modifier -51 do not apply.

Code	Description	Medicode RVU	50th	75th	Medicare Nat'l Avg
55970	Intersex surgery; male to female	0.00	0	0	–
55980	Intersex surgery; female to male	0.00	0	0	–

56300–56399
Laparoscopy/Peritoneoscopy/Hysteroscopy

Coding Insight
Note the following for diagnostic laparoscopy only:

- Codes 56300 *Laparoscopy, diagnostic (separate procedure)* and 56360 *Peritoneoscopy; without biopsy* identify performance of essentially the same procedure. Both procedures involve direct inspection of the surface area of the liver, gallbladder, spleen, peritoneum, and pelvic organs
- Codes 56360 *Peritoneoscopy; without biopsy* and 56361 *Peritoneoscopy; with biopsy* should each be treated as a "separate procedure." Laparoscopy and peritoneoscopy are incidental when performed with other endoscopic therapeutic intra-abdominal procedures
- Code 56362 *Peritoneoscopy with guided transhepatic cholangiography; without biopsy* includes 56360 (Peritoneoscopy; without biopsy)
- Code 56362 *Peritoneoscopy with guided transhepatic cholangiography; without biopsy* includes 56361 (Peritoneoscopy; with biopsy)

Multiple Related Procedures through the Endoscope:
Modifier -22 should be used to report secondary procedures requiring significant additional time and effort rather than reporting multiple procedures with modifier -51. Modifier -50 should not be used to report bilateral procedures. However, new *CPT '96* codes 56343 and 56344 specify they are unilateral procedures unless otherwise specified, which may be an exception to the general rule for the use of modifier -50.

When 56304 *Laparoscopy, surgical; with lysis of adhesions* is performed with 56308 *Laparoscopy, surgical; with vaginal hysterectomy with or without removal of tube(s), with or without removal of ovary(s) (laparoscopic assisted vaginal hysterectomy)*, 56308 is reported with modifier -22 for unusual services added.

Note that certain payers may specifically instruct providers to report 56304 with modifier -51 for multiple procedures added instead of using the CPT guidelines, which instruct use of modifier -22.

Multiple Unrelated Procedures through Endoscope
Modifier -51 (multiple procedure) should be used to report performance of procedures that are not in the same code family or multiple unrelated procedures — usually different systems or anatomic structures.

The following examples illustrate the use of modifier -51 for multiple endoscopic procedures:

- 56341 *Laparoscopy, surgical; cholecystectomy with cholangiography*
  56302-51 *Laparoscopy, surgical; with occlusion of oviducts by device (e.g., band, clip, or Falope ring)*
- 56324 *Laparoscopy, surgical; cholecystoenterostomy*
  56302-51 *Laparoscopy, surgical; with occlusion of oviducts by device (e.g., band, clip, or Falope ring)*

Diagnostic with Therapeutic Endoscopy
Diagnostic endoscopy is always incidental to any intra-abdominal therapeutic endoscopy, regardless of code family.

Code 56341 *Laparoscopy, surgical; cholecystectomy with cholangiography* inherently includes 56300 *Laparoscopy, diagnostic (separate procedure)* or 56361 *Peritoneoscopy; with biopsy*.

Diagnostic Endoscopy with Open Procedure

Diagnostic endoscopy is separately reportable with nonendoscopic surgery when the need for therapeutic surgery has not been determined prior to the procedure.

The following examples illustrate the use of modifier -51 for open procedure endoscopies:

- 58925 *Ovarian cystectomy, unilateral or bilateral (separate procedure)*
  56300-51 *Laparoscopy, diagnostic (separate procedure)*
- 44950 *Appendectomy*
  56300-51 *Laparoscopy, diagnostic (separate procedure)*

Combined Endoscopic and Open Procedures

If a major procedure is performed as an open procedure and a minor procedure (e.g., lysis of adhesions, biopsy) is done through the endoscope, the procedures should be reported using the procedure codes for diagnostic endoscopy (specify diagnostic laparoscopy, peritoneoscopy, or hysteroscopy) and the code for the open procedure.

The following examples illustrate the use of modifier -51 for these endoscopic procedures.

Laparoscopically-aided colectomy should be reported with codes:

- 44140 *Colectomy, partial; with anastomosis*
  56300-51 *Laparoscopy, diagnostic (separate procedure) or*
  56360-51 *Peritoneoscopy; without biopsy*
- Fulguration of oviducts with vaginal hysterectomy with partial colpectomy should be reported with codes:

  58275 *Vaginal hysterectomy, with total or partial colpectomy*

  56300-51 *Laparoscopy, diagnostic (separate procedure)*

If two major procedures are performed, one endoscopically and one open (e.g., laparotomy), both services should be reported using modifier -51 on the secondary service.

- 56308 *Laparoscopy, surgical; with vaginal hysterectomy with or without removal of tube(s), with or without removal of ovary(s) (laparoscopic assisted vaginal hysterectomy)*

  47605-51 *Cholecystectomy; with cholangiography*

Hysteroscopy

Hysteroscopy is unrelated to laparoscopy and peritoneoscopy. The hysteroscope is passed through the vagina and cervix into the uterus to visualize the uterine cavity. Hysteroscopy is not incidental to or an integral part of laparoscopy and peritoneoscopy procedures.

If two procedures are performed, one through a laparoscope or peritoneoscope and one through a hysteroscope, both services should be reported using modifier -51 on the secondary service:

- 56300 *Laparoscopy, diagnostic (separate procedure)*

  56350-51 *Hysteroscopy, diagnostic (separate procedure)*

Failed Endoscopic Procedures Followed by Open Procedure

The open procedure is reported as the primary procedure and a diagnostic endoscopy is reported as a secondary procedure with modifier -51:

- 47605 *Cholecystectomy; with cholangiography*

  56300-51 *Laparoscopy, diagnostic (separate procedure)*

- 59120 *Surgical treatment of ectopic pregnancy; tubal or ovarian, requiring salpingectomy and/or oophorectomy, abdominal or vaginal approach*

    56300-51 *Laparoscopy, diagnostic (separate procedure)*

New Endoscopic Procedures

New endoscopic procedures are being performed even though they have not yet been proven efficacious. These procedures should be considered experimental until medical groups (such as the American College of Surgeons) have shown that the procedures have at least the same outcome and standard of care as demonstrated by an open procedure:

- New endoscopic procedures without a specific CPT code should be reported with the unlisted code 56399 *Unlisted procedure, laparoscopy, peritoneoscopy, hysteroscopy*, based on the anatomic structure addressed
- A CPT code specific to an open procedure should never be used to report an endoscopic procedure

Subsidiary Codes

Subsidiary codes have relative values that require no further adjustment:

20926 is "in addition" to 56300–56399
38102 is "in addition" to 56300–56399
38747 is "in addition" to 56300–56399
44015 is "in addition" to 56300–56399
44955 is "in addition" to 56300–56399
45355 is "in addition" to 56300–56399
47001 is "in addition" to 56300–56399
49905 is "in addition" to 56300–56399

Because these are subsidiary or "in addition to" codes, reimbursement reduction and modifier -51 do not apply.

Code	Description	Medicode RVU	50th	75th	Medicare Nat'l Avg
56300	Laparoscopy, diagnostic (separate procedure)	48.00	1096	1285	385
56301	Laparoscopy, surgical; with fulguration of oviducts (with or without transection)	50.00	1142	1339	410
56302	Laparoscopy, surgical; with occlusion of oviducts by device (eg, band, clip, or Falope ring)	50.00	1142	1339	426
56303	Laparoscopy, surgical; with fulguration or excision of lesions of the ovary, pelvic viscera, or peritoneal surface by any method	78.00	1781	2089	485
56304	Laparoscopy, surgical; with lysis of adhesions	69.50	1587	1861	467
56305	Laparoscopy, surgical; with biopsy of peritoneal surface(s), single or multiple	58.00	1324	1553	401
56306	Laparoscopy, surgical; with aspiration (single or multiple)	61.00	1393	1633	400
56307	Laparoscopy, surgical; with removal of adnexal structures (partial or total oophorectomy and/or salpingectomy)	87.00	1986	2330	559
56308	Laparoscopy, surgical; with vaginal hysterectomy with or without removal of tube(s), with or without removal of ovary(s) (laparoscopic assisted vaginal hysterectomy)	123.0	2808	3294	995

	Code	Description	Medicode RVU	50th	75th	Medicare Nat'l Avg
	56309	Laparoscopy, surgical; with removal of leiomyomata, subserosal (single or multiple)	80.00	1826	2142	453
	56311	Laparoscopy, surgical; with retroperitoneal lymph node sampling (biopsy), single or multiple	85.00	1941	2276	651
	56312	Laparoscopy, surgical; with bilateral total pelvic lymphadenectomy	90.00	2055	2410	835
	56313	Laparoscopy, surgical; with bilateral total pelvic lymphadenectomy and peri-aortic lymph node sampling (biopsy), single or multiple	108.0	2466	2892	1021
	56315	Laparoscopy, surgical; appendectomy	58.00	1324	1553	485
	56316	Laparoscopy, surgical; repair of initial inguinal hernia	61.00	1393	1633	465
	56317	Laparoscopy, surgical; repair of recurrent inguinal hernia	67.00	1530	1794	557
	56320	Laparoscopy, surgical; with ligation of spermatic veins for varicocele	50.00	1142	1339	439
	56322	Laparoscopy, surgical; transection of vagus nerves, truncal	70.00	1598	1874	620
	56323	Laparoscopy, surgical; transection of vagus nerves, selective or highly selective	110.0	2511	2946	744
	56324	Laparoscopy, surgical; cholecystoenterostomy	75.00	1712	2008	937
	56340	Laparoscopy, surgical; cholecystectomy (any method)	92.00	2100	2464	807
	56341	Laparoscopy, surgical; cholecystectomy with cholangiography	100.0	2283	2678	864
	56342	Laparoscopy, surgical; cholecystectomy with exploration of common duct	109.0	2488	2919	995
●	**56343**	Laparoscopy, surgical; with salpingostomy (salpingoneostomy)	139.0	3173	3722	–
●	**56344**	Laparoscopy, surgical; with fimbrioplasty	129.0	2945	3454	–
	56350	Hysteroscopy, diagnostic (separate procedure)	29.00	662	777	210
	56351	Hysteroscopy, surgical; with sampling (biopsy) of endometrium and/or polypectomy, with or without D & s	47.00	1073	1259	225
	56352	Hysteroscopy, surgical; with lysis of intrauterine adhesions (any method)	56.00	1278	1500	303
	56353	Hysteroscopy, surgical; with division or resection of intrauterine septum (any method)	61.00	1393	1633	318
	56354	Hysteroscopy, surgical; with removal of leiomyomata	72.00	1644	1928	397
	56355	Hysteroscopy, surgical; with removal of impacted foreign body	54.00	1233	1446	233
	56356	Hysteroscopy, surgical; with endometrial ablation (any method)	80.00	1826	2142	388
	56360	Peritoneoscopy; without biopsy	35.00	799	937	330

Code	Description	Medicode RVU	50th	75th	Medicare Nat'l Avg
56361	Peritoneoscopy; with biopsy	40.00	913	1071	387
56362	Peritoneoscopy with guided transhepatic cholangiography; without biopsy	45.00	1027	1205	307
56363	Peritoneoscopy with guided transhepatic cholangiography; with biopsy	50.00	1142	1339	377
56399	Unlisted procedure, laparoscopy, peritoneoscopy, hysteroscopy	0.00	0	0	–

56405–56810

Female Genital System

Vulva, Perineum, and Introitus

Coding Insight

The vulva includes the clitoris, labia majora, labia minora, opening of the urethra, mons pubis, bulb of the vestibule, vestibule of the vagina, greater and lesser vestibular glands, and vaginal orifice. The perineum is the area between the vulva and the anus. The introitus is the entrance to the vagina. When the term external genitalia is used it refers to the vulva. These terms may become confusing when trying to decide which code to use for excision of benign or malignant lesions, repair of laceration in the integumentary system, or from codes listed under vulva, perineum, and introitus.

The key to the use of these codes is to use them for biopsy(s), incisions of hematoma and/or cyst, and excision of lesions — unless CPT directs you to use other codes. For example:

- Directions for excision of local lesion (see 11420–11426, 11620–11626) is given between 56606 *Biopsy of vulva or perineum (separate procedure; each separate additional lesion* and 56620 *Vulvectomy simple; partial*
- Directions for repair of wounds to genitalia (see 12001–12007, 12041–12047, 13131, 13132) is given under 56810 *Perineoplasty, repair of perineum, nonobstetrical (separate procedure)*

Cosmetic Warning

This section contains codes that 85 percent of the time or more are considered cosmetic, e.g., 56805.

Subsidiary Codes

Subsidiary codes have relative values that require no further adjustment:

20926 is "in addition" to 56405–56810
38102 is "in addition" to 56405–56810
38747 is "in addition" to 56405–56810
44015 is "in addition" to 56405–56810
44955 is "in addition" to 56405–56810
45355 is "in addition" to 56405–56810
47001 is "in addition" to 56405–56810
49905 is "in addition" to 56405–56810
56606 is "in addition" to 56605

Because these are subsidiary or "in addition to" codes, reimbursement reduction and modifier -51 do not apply.

Code		Description	Medicode RVU	50th	75th	Medicare Nat'l Avg
56405	*	Incision and drainage of vulva or perineal abscess	7.50	171	201	89
56420	*	Incision and drainage of Bartholin's gland abscess	8.50	194	228	89
56440		Marsupialization of Bartholin's gland cyst	27.50	628	736	238
56441		Lysis of labial adhesions	5.50	126	147	150
56501		Destruction of lesion(s), vulva; simple, any method	8.50	194	228	104
56515		Destruction of lesion(s), vulva; extensive, any method	29.00	662	777	220
56605	*	Biopsy of vulva or perineum (separate procedure); one lesion	6.50	148	174	66
56606	*	Biopsy of vulva or perineum (separate procedure); each separate additional lesion	3.25	74	87	33
56620		Vulvectomy simple; partial	58.00	1324	1553	597
56625		Vulvectomy simple; complete	78.00	1781	2089	762
56630		Vulvectomy, radical, partial;	100.0	2283	2678	1104
56631		Vulvectomy, radical, partial; with unilateral inguinofemoral lymphadenectomy	125.0	2854	3347	1495
56632		Vulvectomy, radical, partial; with bilateral inguinofemoral lymphadenectomy	150.0	3425	4017	1734
56633		Vulvectomy, radical, complete;	125.0	2854	3347	1251
56634		Vulvectomy, radical, complete; with unilateral inguinofemoral lymphadenectomy	156.0	3561	4177	1647
56637		Vulvectomy, radical, complete; with bilateral inguinofemoral lymphadenectomy	171.5	3915	4592	1800
56640		Vulvectomy, radical, complete, with inguinofemoral, iliac, and pelvic lymphadenectomy	155.0	3539	4151	1738
56700		Partial hymenectomy or revision of hymenal ring	20.00	457	536	179
56720	*	Hymenotomy, simple incision	8.50	194	228	51
56740		Excision of Bartholin's gland or cyst	26.00	594	696	281
56800		Plastic repair of introitus	30.00	685	803	283
56805		Clitoroplasty for intersex state	29.00	662	777	1113
56810		Perineoplasty, repair of perineum, non-obstetrical (separate procedure)	30.00	685	803	289

57000–57460
Vagina

Coding Insight
When an anterior colporrhaphy (57240) is performed on the same date of service and at the same operative session as a Stamey abdomino-vaginal neck suspension (code 51845), the degree of redundant tissue excised should be specified in the operative report. When the claim is reviewed and/or audited by the payer it may be assumed that the Stamey procedure should have resulted in the complete take-up of the redundant tissue. This is usually the case when there is a first or second degree cystocele, but anterior colporrhaphy is usually needed when there is a third or fourth degree cystocele. The Stamey procedure should be listed first and the anterior colporrhaphy second. Append modifier -51 to the anterior colporrhaphy.

Code 57284 is a new code in *CPT '96*.

Cosmetic Warning
This section contains codes that 85 percent of the time or more are considered cosmetic, e.g., 57335.

Subsidiary Codes
Subsidiary codes have relative values that require no further adjustment:

20926 is "in addition" to 57000–57460
38102 is "in addition" to 57000–57460
38747 is "in addition" to 57000–57460
44015 is "in addition" to 57000–57460
44955 is "in addition" to 57000–57460
45355 is "in addition" to 57000–57460
47001 is "in addition" to 57000–57460
49905 is "in addition" to 57000–57460

Because these are subsidiary or "in addition to" codes, reimbursement reduction and modifier -51 do not apply.

Medicare Alert
Medicare rebundles certain codes in the surgery section when the listed codes are considered a component of a more comprehensive service.

57240, 57250, 53620, 53660 will not be reimbursed when reported with 57260
53670, 57240, 57250, 57260, 57268 will not be reimbursed when reported with 57265
57452 will not be reimbursed when reported with 57454

Code		Description	Medicode RVU	50th	75th	Medicare Nat'l Avg
57000		Colpotomy; with exploration	25.00	595	727	211
57010		Colpotomy; with drainage of pelvic abscess	27.50	655	800	333
57020	*	Colpocentesis (separate procedure)	7.50	179	218	89
57061		Destruction of vaginal lesion(s); simple, any method	15.00	357	436	90

Code		Description	Medicode RVU	50th	75th	Medicare Nat'l Avg
57065		Destruction of vaginal lesion(s); extensive, any method	30.00	714	873	260
57100	*	Biopsy of vaginal mucosa; simple (separate procedure)	6.00	143	175	68
57105		Biopsy of vaginal mucosa; extensive, requiring suture (including cysts)	14.75	351	429	143
57108		Colpectomy, obliteration of vagina; partial	52.00	1238	1513	483
57110		Colpectomy, obliteration of vagina; complete	65.00	1548	1891	895
57120		Colpocleisis (Le Fort type)	58.00	1381	1687	635
57130		Excision of vaginal septum	26.00	619	756	219
57135		Excision of vaginal cyst or tumor	20.00	476	582	205
57150	*	Irrigation of vagina and/or application of medicament for treatment of bacterial, parasitic, or fungoid disease	1.75	42	51	43
57160	*	Insertion of pessary	2.00	48	58	43
57170		Diaphragm or cervical cap fitting with instructions	2.10	50	61	50
57180		Introduction of any hemostatic agent or pack for spontaneous or traumatic nonobstetrical vaginal hemorrhage (separate procedure)	9.00	214	262	85
57200		Colporrhaphy, suture of injury of vagina (nonobstetrical)	30.00	690	820	276
57210		Colpoperineorrhaphy, suture of injury of vagina and/or perineum (nonobstetrical)	32.50	748	888	343
57220		Plastic operation on urethral sphincter, vaginal approach (eg, Kelly urethral plication)	37.50	863	1025	362
57230		Plastic repair of urethrocele	35.00	805	956	374
57240		Anterior colporrhaphy, repair of cystocele with or without repair of urethrocele	45.00	1035	1229	556
57250		Posterior colporrhaphy, repair of rectocele with or without perineorrhaphy	43.00	989	1175	520
57260		Combined anteroposterior colporrhaphy;	65.00	1495	1776	745
57265		Combined anteroposterior colporrhaphy; with enterocele repair	75.00	1725	2049	796
57268		Repair of enterocele, vaginal approach (separate procedure)	50.00	1150	1366	595
57270		Repair of enterocele, abdominal approach (separate procedure)	56.00	1288	1530	641
57280		Colpopexy, abdominal approach	70.00	1610	1912	759
57282		Sacrospinous ligament fixation for prolapse of vagina	70.00	1610	1912	775

	Code		Description	Medicode RVU	50th	75th	Medicare Nat'l Avg
●	**57284**		Paravaginal defect repair (including repair of cystocele, stress urinary incontinence, and/or incomplete vaginal prolapse)	74.00	1702	2022	–
	57288		Sling operation for stress incontinence (eg, fascia or synthetic)	77.00	1771	2104	971
	57289		Pereyra procedure, including anterior colporrhaphy	70.00	1610	1912	663
	57291		Construction of artificial vagina; without graft	60.00	1380	1639	543
	57292		Construction of artificial vagina; with graft	110.0	2530	3005	798
	57300		Closure of rectovaginal fistula; vaginal or transanal approach	60.00	1380	1639	669
	57305		Closure of rectovaginal fistula; abdominal approach	85.00	1955	2322	714
	57307		Closure of rectovaginal fistula; abdominal approach, with concomitant colostomy	90.00	2070	2459	702
	57310		Closure of urethrovaginal fistula;	72.50	1668	1981	437
	57311		Closure of urethrovaginal fistula; with bulbocavernosus transplant	110.0	2530	3005	517
	57320		Closure of vesicovaginal fistula; vaginal approach	72.50	1668	1981	713
	57330		Closure of vesicovaginal fistula; transvesical and vaginal approach	80.00	1840	2186	811
	57335		Vaginoplasty for intersex state	45.00	1035	1229	655
	57400	*	Dilation of vagina under anesthesia	12.50	288	342	50
	57410	*	Pelvic examination under anesthesia	9.00	207	246	44
	57415		Removal of impacted vaginal foreign body (separate procedure) under anesthesia	11.75	270	321	53
	57452	*	Colposcopy (vaginoscopy); (separate procedure)	7.50	180	212	70
	57454	*	Colposcopy (vaginoscopy); with biopsy(s) of the cervix and/or endocervical curettage	11.25	270	318	109
	57460		Colposcopy (vaginoscopy); with loop electrode excision procedure of the cervix	31.50	755	891	206

57500–57820
Cervix Uteri

Coding Insight
If cerclage of the uterine cervix is performed during pregnancy by a vaginal approach, use 59320; if performed by an abdominal approach, during pregnancy, use 59325.

Subsidiary Codes

Subsidiary codes have relative values that require no further adjustment:

20926 is "in addition" to 57500–57820
38102 is "in addition" to 57500–57820
38747 is "in addition" to 57500–57820
44015 is "in addition" to 57500–57820
44955 is "in addition" to 57500–57820
45355 is "in addition" to 57500–57820
47001 is "in addition" to 57500–57820
49905 is "in addition" to 57500–57820

Because these are subsidiary or "in addition to" codes, reimbursement reduction and modifier -51 do not apply.

Medicare Alert

Medicare rebundles certain codes in the surgery section when the listed codes are considered a component of a more comprehensive service.

53670, 57454, 58120 will not be reimbursed when reported with 57520

Code		Description	Medicode RVU	50th	75th	Medicare Nat'l Avg
57500	*	Biopsy, single or multiple, or local excision of lesion, with or without fulguration (separate procedure)	10.00	234	276	65
57505		Endocervical curettage (not done as part of a dilation and curettage)	6.00	140	166	82
57510		Cauterization of cervix; electro or thermal	9.00	210	248	91
57511	*	Cauterization of cervix; cryocautery, initial or repeat	8.50	199	235	109
57513		Cauterization of cervix; laser ablation	30.00	701	828	211
57520		Conization of cervix, with or without fulguration, with or without dilation and curettage, with or without repair; cold knife or laser	36.00	841	994	324
57522		Conization of cervix, with or without fulguration, with or without dilation and curettage, with or without repair; loop electrode excision	36.00	841	994	306
57530		Trachelectomy (cervicectomy), amputation of cervix (separate procedure)	28.50	666	787	353
57540		Excision of cervical stump, abdominal approach;	60.00	1402	1656	564
57545		Excision of cervical stump, abdominal approach; with pelvic floor repair	75.00	1752	2070	486
57550		Excision of cervical stump, vaginal approach;	45.00	1051	1242	528
57555		Excision of cervical stump, vaginal approach; with anterior and/or posterior repair	70.00	1636	1932	821
57556		Excision of cervical stump, vaginal approach; with repair of enterocele	54.00	1262	1490	740
57700		Cerclage of uterine cervix, nonobstetrical	35.00	818	966	236

Code		Description	Medicode RVU	50th	75th	Medicare Nat'l Avg
57720		Trachelorrhaphy, plastic repair of uterine cervix, vaginal approach	29.50	689	814	279
57800	*	Dilation of cervical canal, instrumental (separate procedure)	5.25	123	145	52
57820		Dilation and curettage of cervical stump	20.00	467	552	180

58100–58540
Corpus Uteri

Coding Insight
For postpartum curettage (for hemorrhage), see 59160.

Subsidiary Codes
Subsidiary codes have relative values that require no further adjustment:

20926 is "in addition" to 58100–58540
38102 is "in addition" to 58100–58540
38747 is "in addition" to 58100–58540
44015 is "in addition" to 58100–58540
44955 is "in addition" to 58100–58540
45355 is "in addition" to 58100–58540
47001 is "in addition" to 58100–58540
49905 is "in addition" to 58100–58540
58611 is "in addition" to 58400–58540
58611 is "in addition" to 58400–58540

Because these are subsidiary or "in addition to" codes, reimbursement reduction and modifier -51 do not apply.

Medicare Alert
Medicare rebundles certain codes in the surgery section when the listed codes are considered a component of a more comprehensive service.

53670, 57410, 57505 will not be reimbursed when reported with 58120
49000, 58270, 58700, 58720, 58740, 58940 will not be reimbursed when reported with 58150

	Code		Description	Medicode RVU	50th	75th	Medicare Nat'l Avg
▲	58100	*	Endometrial sampling (biopsy) with or without endocervical sampling (biopsy), without cervical dilation, any method (separate procedure)	7.00	166	195	61
	58120		Dilation and curettage, diagnostic and/or therapeutic (nonobstetrical)	27.50	650	764	230
	58140		Myomectomy, excision of fibroid tumor of uterus, single or multiple (separate procedure); abdominal approach	90.00	2128	2501	719
	58145		Myomectomy, excision of fibroid tumor of uterus, single or multiple (separate procedure); vaginal approach	65.00	1537	1806	676

Code		Description	Medicode RVU	50th	75th	Medicare Nat'l Avg
58150		Total abdominal hysterectomy (corpus and cervix), with or without removal of tube(s), with or without removal of ovary(s);	97.50	2263	2552	961
58152		Total abdominal hysterectomy (corpus and cervix), with or without removal of tube(s), with or without removal of ovary(s); with colpo-urethrocystopexy (Marshall-Marchetti-Krantz type)	125.0	2902	3272	1136
58180		Supracervical abdominal hysterectomy (subtotal hysterectomy), with or without removal of tube(s), with or without removal of ovary(s)	90.00	2089	2356	848
58200		Total abdominal hysterectomy, including partial vaginectomy, with para-aortic and pelvic lymph node sampling, with or without removal of tube(s), with or without removal of ovary(s)	118.5	2751	3102	1407
58210		Radical abdominal hysterectomy, with bilateral total pelvic lymphadenectomy and para-aortic lymph node sampling (biopsy), with or without removal of tube(s), with or without removal of ovary(s)	190.0	4411	4973	1799
58240		Pelvic exenteration for gynecologic malignancy, with total abdominal hysterectomy or cervicectomy, with or without removal of tube(s), with or without removal of ovary(s), with removal of bladder and ureteral transplantations, and/or abdominoperineal resection of rectum and colon and colostomy, or any combination thereof	210.0	4875	5497	2547
58260		Vaginal hysterectomy;	94.00	2182	2460	902
58262		Vaginal hysterectomy; with removal of tube(s), and/or ovary(s)	101.0	2345	2644	965
58263		Vaginal hysterectomy; with removal of tube(s), and/or ovary(s), with repair of enterocele	110.0	2554	2879	1057
58267		Vaginal hysterectomy; with colpo-urethrocystopexy (Marshall-Marchetti-Krantz type, Pereyra type, with or without endoscopic control)	116.0	2693	3036	1104
58270		Vaginal hysterectomy; with repair of enterocele	110.0	2554	2879	995
58275		Vaginal hysterectomy, with total or partial colpectomy;	112.0	2600	2932	1068
58280		Vaginal hysterectomy, with total or partial colpectomy; with repair of enterocele	115.0	2670	3010	1066
58285		Vaginal hysterectomy, radical (Schauta type operation)	125.0	2902	3272	1238
58300	*	Insertion of intrauterine device (IUD)	8.00	185	222	–
58301		Removal of intrauterine device (IUD)	3.00	69	83	49
58321		Artificial insemination; intra-cervical	6.50	150	180	69
58322		Artificial insemination; intra-uterine	7.50	173	208	76
58323		Sperm washing for artificial insemination	5.50	127	153	17

Code		Description	Medicode RVU	50th	75th	Medicare Nat'l Avg
58340	*	Injection procedure for hysterosalpingography	7.75	179	215	61
58345		Transcervical introduction of fallopian tube catheter for diagnosis and/or re-establishing patency (any method), with or without hysterosalpingography	26.00	601	722	331
58350	*	Chromotubation of oviduct, including materials	9.00	208	250	70
58400		Uterine suspension, with or without shortening of round ligaments, with or without shortening of sacrouterine ligaments; (separate procedure)	59.00	1363	1638	497
58410		Uterine suspension, with or without shortening of round ligaments, with or without shortening of sacrouterine ligaments; with presacral sympathectomy	80.00	1849	2221	513
58520		Hysterorrhaphy, repair of ruptured uterus (nonobstetrical)	50.00	1155	1388	454
58540		Hysteroplasty, repair of uterine anomaly (Strassman type)	75.00	1733	2082	628

58600–58770
Oviduct

Coding Insight
For laparoscopic treatment of ectopic pregnancy, see 59150–59151.

Nota Bene: An ectopic pregnancy or other problem may require surgery to correct, and at the same time the patient may desire a sterilization. Even though 58700 *Salpingectomy, complete or partial* specifies that it is unilateral or bilateral, the code is only accurate if used to report a salpingectomy performed on both sides — not if a salpingectomy was performed on one side and the other side required a salpingo-oophorectomy. If two separate and distinct procedures are performed, they are both coded. The procedure with the highest value is listed first, and modifier -50 is appended to the second code.

Subsidiary Codes
Subsidiary codes have relative values that require no further adjustment:

20926 is "in addition" to 58600–58770
38102 is "in addition" to 58600–58770
38747 is "in addition" to 58600–58770
44015 is "in addition" to 58600–58770
44955 is "in addition" to 58600–58770
45355 is "in addition" to 58600–58770
47001 is "in addition" to 58600–58770
49905 is "in addition" to 58600–58770

Because these are subsidiary or "in addition to" codes, reimbursement reduction and modifier -51 do not apply.

Medicare Alert
Medicare rebundles certain codes in the surgery section when the listed codes are considered a component of a more comprehensive service.

44950, 49000, 58700 will not be reimbursed when reported with 58720

Code	Description	Medicode RVU	50th	75th	Medicare Nat'l Avg
58600	Ligation or transection of fallopian tube(s), abdominal or vaginal approach, unilateral or bilateral	47.00	1081	1266	423
58605	Ligation or transection of fallopian tube(s), abdominal or vaginal approach, postpartum, unilateral or bilateral, during same hospitalization (separate procedure)	40.50	932	1091	335
58611	Ligation or transection of fallopian tube(s) when done at the time of cesarean section or intra-abdominal surgery (not a separate procedure)	30.00	690	808	50
58615	Occlusion of fallopian tube(s) by device (eg, band, clip, Falope ring) vaginal or suprapubic approach	45.00	1035	1212	277
58700	Salpingectomy, complete or partial, unilateral or bilateral (separate procedure)	60.00	1369	1615	550
58720	Salpingo-oophorectomy, complete or partial, unilateral or bilateral (separate procedure)	70.00	1597	1884	673
58740	Lysis of adhesions (salpingolysis, ovariolysis)	73.00	1665	1965	633
58750	Tubotubal anastomosis	120.0	2738	3230	651
58752	Tubouterine implantation	110.0	2510	2961	607
58760	Fimbrioplasty	115.0	2624	3095	525
58770	Salpingostomy (salpingoneostomy)	105.0	2395	2826	532

58800–58960
Ovary

Coding Insight
Wedge resection or bisection of the ovary, unilateral or bilateral, (58920) may be a noncovered benefit when performed for infertility. Request prior authorization for this procedure to determine patient responsibility.

Subsidiary Codes
Subsidiary codes have relative values that require no further adjustment:

20926 is "in addition" to 58800–58960
38102 is "in addition" to 58800–58960
38747 is "in addition" to 58800–58960
44015 is "in addition" to 58800–58960
44955 is "in addition" to 58800–58960
45355 is "in addition" to 58800–58960
47001 is "in addition" to 58800–58960
49905 is "in addition" to 58800–58960
58611 is "in addition" to 58805, 58822

Because these are subsidiary or "in addition to" codes, reimbursement reduction and modifier -51 do not apply.

Code	Description	Medicode RVU	50th	75th	Medicare Nat'l Avg
58800	Drainage of ovarian cyst(s), unilateral or bilateral, (separate procedure); vaginal approach	37.00	912	1092	274
58805	Drainage of ovarian cyst(s), unilateral or bilateral, (separate procedure); abdominal approach	54.00	1331	1593	521
58820	Drainage of ovarian abscess; vaginal approach	25.00	616	738	281
58822	Drainage of ovarian abscess; abdominal approach	60.00	1479	1770	410
58825	Transposition, ovary(s)	60.00	1479	1770	411
58900	Biopsy of ovary, unilateral or bilateral (separate procedure)	54.00	1331	1593	476
58920	Wedge resection or bisection of ovary, unilateral or bilateral	60.00	1479	1770	573
58925	Ovarian cystectomy, unilateral or bilateral	65.00	1602	1918	594
58940	Oophorectomy, partial or total, unilateral or bilateral;	65.00	1602	1918	621
58943	Oophorectomy, partial or total, unilateral or bilateral; for ovarian malignancy, with para-aortic and pelvic lymph node biopsies, peritoneal washings, peritoneal biopsies, diaphragmatic assessments, with or without salpingectomy(s), with or without omentectomy	107.0	2637	3157	1259
58950	Resection of ovarian malignancy with bilateral salpingo-oophorectomy and omentectomy;	100.0	2465	2950	1115
58951	Resection of ovarian malignancy with bilateral salpingo-oophorectomy and omentectomy; with total abdominal hysterectomy, pelvic and limited para-aortic lymphadenectomy	159.0	3919	4691	1699
58952	Resection of ovarian malignancy with bilateral salpingo-oophorectomy and omentectomy; with radical dissection for debulking	193.0	4757	5694	1708
58960	Laparotomy, for staging or restaging of ovarian malignancy ("second look"), with or without omentectomy, peritoneal washing, biopsy of abdominal and pelvic peritoneum, diaphragmatic assessment with pelvic and limited para-aortic lymphadenectomy	110.0	2711	3245	1078

58970–58976
In Vitro Fertilization

CODING INSIGHT

Procedures in this section are rarely, if at all, covered by payers.

Codes 58974 and 58976 have been revised in *CPT '96*. Code 58974 is no longer listed as a separate procedure; it is to be reported for intra-uterine embryo transfer instead of "by any method." Code 58976 now includes embryo intra-fallopian transfer, along with gamete or zygote transfer; the transfer can be performed by any method.

Subsidiary Codes

Subsidiary codes have relative values that require no further adjustment:

20926 is "in addition" to 58970–58976
38102 is "in addition" to 58970–58976
38747 is "in addition" to 58970–58976
44015 is "in addition" to 58970–58976
44955 is "in addition" to 58970–58976
45355 is "in addition" to 58970–58976
47001 is "in addition" to 58970–58976
49905 is "in addition" to 58970–58976

Because these are subsidiary or "in addition to" codes, reimbursement reduction and modifier -51 do not apply.

	Code	Description	Medicode RVU	50th	75th	Medicare Nat'l Avg
	58970	Follicle puncture for oocyte retrieval, any method	45.00	1109	1328	226
▲	**58974**	Embryo transfer, intrauterine	16.00	394	472	93
▲	**58976**	Gamete, zygote, or embryo intrafallopian transfer, any method	56.00	1380	1652	245

58999
Other Procedures

Subsidiary Codes

Subsidiary codes have relative values that require no further adjustment:

20926 is "in addition" to 58999–58999
38102 is "in addition" to 58999–58999
38747 is "in addition" to 58999–58999
44015 is "in addition" to 58999–58999
44955 is "in addition" to 58999–58999
45355 is "in addition" to 58999–58999
47001 is "in addition" to 58999–58999
49905 is "in addition" to 58999–58999

Because these are subsidiary or "in addition to" codes, reimbursement reduction and modifier -51 do not apply.

Code	Description	Medicode RVU	50th	75th	Medicare Nat'l Avg
58999	Unlisted procedure, female genital system (nonobstetrical)	0.00	0	0	–

59000–59160

Maternity Care and Delivery, Incision/Excision

Coding Insight

Molar pregnancies result from an abnormal condition in which cells that form the placenta invade the uterine lining and continue to invade and grow after the death of the fetus. This procedure (59100) is performed through an abdominal and uterine incision. It is similar to a cesarean section but the incisions are smaller. Be careful not to confuse this code with a vaginal dilation and curettage (D&C) for a molar pregnancy; if D&C is performed instead of hysterotomy, use 59870.

Subsidiary Codes

Subsidiary codes have relative values that require no further adjustment:

20926 is "in addition" to 59100–59140
58611 is "in addition" to 59100–59140

Because these are subsidiary or "in addition to" codes, reimbursement reduction and modifier -51 do not apply.

Code		Description	Medicode RVU	50th	75th	Medicare Nat'l Avg
59000	*	Amniocentesis, any method	10.00	230	278	96
59012		Cordocentesis (intrauterine), any method	23.00	529	638	248
59015		Chorionic villus sampling, any method	12.75	293	354	136
59020	*	Fetal contraction stress test	6.00	138	167	89
-26				117	142	66
59025		Fetal non-stress test	5.00	115	139	49
-26				98	118	39
59030	*	Fetal scalp blood sampling	6.00	138	167	147
59050		Fetal monitoring during labor by consulting physician (ie, non-attending physician) with written report (separate procedure); supervision and interpretation	7.50	173	208	76
59051		Fetal monitoring during labor by consulting physician (ie, non-attending physician) with written report (separate procedure); interpretation only	3.00	69	83	62
59100		Hysterotomy, abdominal (eg, for hydatidiform mole, abortion)	66.00	1519	1832	431
59120		Surgical treatment of ectopic pregnancy; tubal or ovarian, requiring salpingectomy and/or oophorectomy, abdominal or vaginal approach	75.00	1726	2082	646
59121		Surgical treatment of ectopic pregnancy; tubal or ovarian, without salpingectomy and/or oophorectomy	73.00	1680	2026	522
59130		Surgical treatment of ectopic pregnancy; abdominal pregnancy	70.00	1611	1943	566
59135		Surgical treatment of ectopic pregnancy; interstitial, uterine pregnancy requiring total hysterectomy	84.00	1933	2332	934

Code	Description	Medicode RVU	50th	75th	Medicare Nat'l Avg
59136	Surgical treatment of ectopic pregnancy; interstitial, uterine pregnancy with partial resection of uterus	82.00	1887	2276	634
59140	Surgical treatment of ectopic pregnancy; cervical, with evacuation	54.00	1243	1499	391
59150	Laparoscopic treatment of ectopic pregnancy; without salpingectomy and/or oophorectomy	73.00	1680	2026	463
59151	Laparoscopic treatment of ectopic pregnancy; with salpingectomy and/or oophorectomy	83.00	1910	2304	641
59160	Curettage, postpartum (separate procedure)	26.00	598	722	239

59200
Introduction

Coding Insight
If a cervical dilator (e.g., laminaria, prostaglandin) or hypertonic solution is introduced to initiate labor, for abortion, see 59850–59857. If used to initiate labor without abortion, use 59200.

Subsidiary Codes
Subsidiary codes have relative values that require no further adjustment:

20926 is "in addition" to 59100–59140

Because these are subsidiary or "in addition to" codes, reimbursement reduction and modifier -51 do not apply.

Code	Description	Medicode RVU	50th	75th	Medicare Nat'l Avg
59200	Insertion of cervical dilator (eg, laminaria, prostaglandin) (separate procedure)	8.75	201	243	57

59300–59350
Repair

Coding Insight
For cerclage of the uterine cervix (tracheloplasty), nonobstetrical, use 57700.

Subsidiary Codes
Subsidiary codes have relative values that require no further adjustment:

20926 is "in addition" to 59100–59140

Because these are subsidiary or "in addition to" codes, reimbursement reduction and modifier -51 do not apply.

Code	Description	Medicode RVU	50th	75th	Medicare Nat'l Avg
59300	Episiotomy or vaginal repair, by other than attending physician	18.75	432	521	138
59320	Cerclage of cervix, during pregnancy; vaginal	35.00	805	972	182
59325	Cerclage of cervix, during pregnancy; abdominal	50.00	1151	1388	282
59350	Hysterorrhaphy of ruptured uterus	55.00	1266	1527	361

59400–59525
Vaginal/Cesarean Delivery, Antepartum and Postpartum Care

CODING INSIGHT

According to CPT, "antepartum care includes the initial and subsequent history, physical examinations, recording of weight, blood pressures, fetal heart tones, routine chemical urinalysis, monthly visits up to 28 weeks gestation, biweekly visits to 36 weeks gestation, and weekly visits until delivery. Any other visits or services within this time period should be coded separately."

Delivery services include hospital admission, the history and physical examination, management of uncomplicated labor, vaginal delivery (with or without episotomy, with or without forceps), or cesarean delivery. Report medical problems such as cardiac problems, neurological problems, diabetes, hypertension, toxemia, or hyperemesis that complicate labor and delivery management and require additional resources with codes from the Medicine and E/M sections as well as codes for maternity care. Report surgical complications of pregnancy (e.g., appendectomy, ovarian cyst) with codes in the Surgery section.

Postpartum care includes hospital and office visits following vaginal or cesarean section delivery.

Using Modifier -22 with Delivery Codes

Many providers report a modifier -22 along with delivery codes, only to be frustrated when the extra payment for the modifier is denied. How payers determine payment for this modifier is a seemingly ongoing mystery. There are some good reasons for the denials. Listing some of them below will, hopefully, help coders understand the denials and even use the information appropriately to overturn a denial.

- CPT section notes clearly define, in maternity care and delivery, what is included in antepartum care. The instructions indicate that any other visits or services within the time period other than those indicated should be coded separately. To an auditor, these notes rule out payment for a modifier -22. To use this modifier would be inappropriate because there are separate codes listed throughout CPT — especially E/M codes — that more clearly define any circumstance requiring the extra care.

  Delivery codes also clearly define what is included in the code. Instructions once again specify that medical problems complicating labor and delivery management should be identified by using the E/M codes. However, it is not clear that there is a code for a prolonged labor listed elsewhere in CPT, and nowhere is it defined exactly what constitutes an uncomplicated labor; hence, auditors are as confused as coders. And, the question arises that since the code used for delivery is global, how many visits by the provider should be considered normal during the course of labor?

Auditors frequently see modifier -22 appended to delivery codes with an ICD•9 diagnostic code specifying that there were problems with the labor portion of the delivery, or they find a cover letter from the provider specifying a prolonged labor. The problem is in the definition of a prolonged labor: Is the patient a primagravida or multigravida? What is the normal average labor time for both of these types of patients? What made it more complicated?

It would be helpful if providers listed the normal for most of their patients in the same category and then how the particular case for which they are requesting additional payment does not meet the norm and why. Another suggestion is to attach a copy of a study indicating average labor time in different patient categories. All too often medical records do not indicate anything out of the norm occurred and no other charges, consults, additional tests, or other services were reported by the provider(s). The medical records usually do not indicate that the number of times the provider checked on the patient was out of the norm and how, or that the case was complicated or complex.

Postpartum care also defines what is included in the code. Services for postpartum care out of the norm could be reported by using other surgery or E/M codes and by applying the appropriate modifier. An example would be a return to the operating room for a postpartum hemorrhage, which would be paid separately and would carry its own global period follow-up days for any additional (normal) care connected with the hemorrhage.

- Modifier -22 appended to complete delivery code, which includes the delivery and antepartum and postpartum care, would be immediately denied by an auditor because other avenues could be used to express where additional care was rendered in any of the three separate categories that make up the code.
- High Risk Care is a fairly ambiguous term that does not define how the care rendered was different from care given to other patients. Many auditors, however, are nurses who do understand what may be involved in the care from the diagnostic codes listed during the pregnancy. Generally, auditors would think that providers who care for high-risk patients have adjusted their fees to reflect usual care given to this type of patient and that any other care rendered would be listed by the use of additional E/M or surgery codes.

Do all of these general rulings mean you can never report modifier -22 with these codes? No, they just mean that other codes, such as case management for a patient with premature labor, should be used or that documentation, studies, or other information necessary for the auditor to make a more informed decision is absolutely essential. Only append modifier -22 to a code for which the unusual service was actually performed.

Nota Bene: for delivery of a twin birth, modifier –22 should be appended to 59400; listing 59400 twice and appending modifier -51 to the second code is incorrect coding.

Subsidiary Codes

Subsidiary codes have relative values that require no further adjustment:

20926 is "in addition" to 59400–59525
58611 is "in addition" to 59510–59515
59412 is "in addition" to 59400, 59409, 59410, 59510, 59514, 59515
59525 is "in addition" to 59510 and 59515

Because these are subsidiary or "in addition to" codes, reimbursement reduction and modifier -51 do not apply.

Code	Description	Medicode RVU	50th	75th	Medicare Nat'l Avg
59400	Routine obstetric care including antepartum care, vaginal delivery (with or without episiotomy, and/or forceps) and postpartum care	90.00	2179	2374	1432
59409	Vaginal delivery only (with or without episiotomy and/or forceps);	47.00	1138	1240	914
59410	Vaginal delivery only (with or without episiotomy and/or forceps); including postpartum care	52.00	1259	1372	982
59412	External cephalic version, with or without tocolysis (list in addition to code(s) for delivery)	17.50	424	462	125
59414	Delivery of placenta (separate procedure)	14.00	339	369	118
59425	Antepartum care only; 4-6 visits	12.75	309	336	294
59426	Antepartum care only; 7 or more visits	38.00	920	1002	504
59430	Postpartum care only (separate procedure)	5.00	121	132	95
59510	Routine obstetric care including antepartum care, cesarean delivery, and postpartum care	108.0	2579	2864	1700
59514	Cesarean delivery only;	64.50	1540	1711	1122
59515	Cesarean delivery only; including postpartum care	69.50	1659	1843	1197
59525	Subtotal or total hysterectomy after cesarean delivery (list in addition to 59510 or 59515)	36.00	860	955	515

59610–59622
Delivery after Previous Cesarean Delivery

Coding Insight
Delivery after previous cesarean section codes 59610–59622 have been added to this section of *CPT '96*. They are commonly referred to as VBAC (vaginal birth after cesarean), codes that specify a failed attempted vaginal delivery after a cesarean section that eventually resulted in a repeat cesarean delivery. It has always been known that the risk is greater for a patient with a previous uterine scar who either delivers vaginally or fails an attempted vaginal delivery and requires cesarean section when they have already delivered by "C-section" in the past. These codes will help define this circumstance and will probably increase reimbursement over time.

In contract negotiations, check the reimbursement payers are allowing for these codes and that it is in line with your expectations of a fair reimbursement.

Subsidiary Codes
Subsidiary codes have relative values that require no further adjustment:

20926 is "in addition" to 59100–59140
59412 is "in addition" to 59400, 59409, 59410, 59510, 59514, 59515
58611 is "in addition" to 59510–59515
59525 is "in addition" to 59510, 59515

Because these are subsidiary or "in addition to" codes, reimbursement reduction and modifier -51 do not apply.

	Code	Description	Medicode RVU	50th	75th	Medicare Nat'l Avg
●	**59610**	Routine obstetric care including antepartum care, vaginal delivery (with or without episiotomy, and/or forceps) and postpartum care, after previous cesarean delivery	94.50	2256	2506	–
●	**59612**	Vaginal delivery only, after previous cesarean delivery (with or without episiotomy and/or forceps);	49.25	1176	1306	–
●	**59614**	Vaginal delivery only, after previous cesarean delivery (with or without episiotomy and/or forceps); including postpartum care	54.50	1301	1446	–
●	**59618**	Routine obstetric care including antepartum care, cesarean delivery, and postpartum care, following attempted vaginal delivery after previous cesarean delivery	113.5	2710	3010	–
●	**59620**	Cesarean delivery only, following attempted vaginal delivery after previous cesarean delivery;	67.75	1618	1797	–
●	**59622**	Cesarean delivery only, following attempted vaginal delivery after previous cesarean delivery; including postpartum care	73.00	1743	1936	–

59812–59857
Abortion

Coding Insight

Induced abortion (59840–59857) can be accomplished by different methods, including the following:

Dilation and curettage. The cervix is anesthetized after insertion of a vaginal speculum. Cervical dilators are used in ever-increasing sizes until dilatation is complete. The uterine lining and the products of conception are then curetted (scraped) out.

Dilation and evacuation. The cervix is anesthetized after insertion of a vaginal speculum. Cervical dilators are used in ever-increasing sizes until dilatation is complete. Forceps hold the cervix steady while a vacuum extractor aspirates the products of conception.

Intra-amniotic injections. After administration of a local anesthetic, a hollow needle is inserted through the abdomen into the amniotic sac. Amniotic fluid is removed through the needle. Injection(s) of a hypertonic solution is then administered by gravity drip into the amnotic sac, resulting in fetal death, from which labor usually ensues; alternatively, a dosage of prostaglandin may be infused into the amniotic sac to initiate uterine contractions.

Laminaria/Prostaglandin. Short pieces of seaweed (kelp) or synthetic material (laminaria) are inserted into the cervix. These expand as they draw fluid from the cervical canal, thus dilating the cervix. Once the cervical canal is dilated, vaginal suppositories of prostaglandin initiate uterine contractions.

Hysterotomy with induced abortion laminaria/prostaglandin. An incision is made through the abdominal wall into the uterus to remove tissue that remains when an induced abortion through use of a laminaria and vaginal suppositories fails to expel all the products of conception.

Nota Bene: In a spontaneous complete abortion the products of conception are completely (naturally) expelled by the body. In an incomplete abortion part of the products of conception are retained in the uterus. In a missed abortion the fetus has died and the fetus, along with the other products of conception, are retained in the uterus. Because the body has not expelled them naturally they must be manually removed. Medical treatment of spontaneous complete abortion, any trimester, should be reported by using E/M codes 99201–99233. For treatment of a missed abortion, completed surgically, select from 59820–59821. When an abortion is induced, select from 59840–59857.

SUBSIDIARY CODES

Subsidiary codes have relative values that require no further adjustment:

20926 is "in addition" to 59100–59140
58611 is "in addition" to 59812–59857

Because these are subsidiary or "in addition to" codes, reimbursement reduction and modifier -51 do not apply.

Code	Description	Medicode RVU	50th	75th	Medicare Nat'l Avg
59812	Treatment of incomplete abortion, any trimester, completed surgically	27.00	666	765	292
59820	Treatment of missed abortion, completed surgically; first trimester	28.00	691	793	322
59821	Treatment of missed abortion, completed surgically; second trimester	32.50	802	921	295
59830	Treatment of septic abortion, completed surgically	40.00	987	1133	428
59840	Induced abortion, by dilation and curettage	32.00	790	906	267
59841	Induced abortion, by dilation and evacuation	34.00	839	963	304
59850	Induced abortion, by one or more intra-amniotic injections (amniocentesis-injections), including hospital admission and visits, deliver of fetus and secundines;	49.00	1209	1388	401
59851	Induced abortion, by one or more intra-amniotic injections (amniocentesis-injections), including hospital admission and visits, deliver of fetus and secundines; with dilation and curettage and/or evacuation	52.00	1283	1473	421
59852	Induced abortion, by one or more intra-amniotic injections (amniocentesis-injections), including hospital admission and visits, deliver of fetus and secundines; with hysterotomy (failed intra-amniotic injection)	66.00	1629	1869	563
59855	Induced abortion, by one or more vaginal suppositories (eg, prostaglandin) with or without cervical dilation (eg, laminaria), including hospital admission and visits, delivery of fetus and secundines;	36.50	901	1034	346
59856	Induced abortion, by one or more vaginal suppositories (eg, prostaglandin) with or without cervical dilation (eg, laminaria), including hospital admission and visits, delivery of fetus and secundines; with dilation and curettage and/or evacuation	39.50	975	1119	522
59857	Induced abortion, by one or more vaginal suppositories (eg, prostaglandin) with or without cervical dilation (eg, laminaria), including hospital admission and visits, delivery of fetus and secundines; with hysterotomy (failed medical evaluation)	66.00	1629	1869	635

59870–59899
Other Procedures

Coding Insight
Molar pregnancies result from an abnormal condition where cells that form the placenta invade the uterine lining and continue to invade and grow after the death of the fetus. This procedure is the same as a dilation and evacuation, except that the uterus may also be curetted after the evacuation. If the procedure is perormed through an abdominal incision, use code 59100. Do not confuse this code with abortion coes performed to terminate a normal pregnancy.

Subsidiary Codes
Subsidiary codes have relative values that require no further adjustment:

20926 is "in addition" to 59100–59140

Because these are subsidiary or "in addition to" codes, reimbursement reduction and modifier -51 do not apply.

Code	Description	Medicode RVU	50th	75th	Medicare Nat'l Avg
59870	Uterine evacuation and curettage for hydatidiform mole	32.00	790	906	298
59899	Unlisted procedure, maternity care and delivery	0.00	0	0	–

Surgery Codes 60000–69979

60000–60281
Thyroid Gland

Coding Insight

Because many bilateral codes have been dropped from CPT, append modifier -50 when a surgery is performed bilaterally and a separate bilateral code is not listed.

Pituitary and pineal surgery are found in the Nervous System section of CPT.

Subsidiary Codes

Subsidiary codes have relative values that require no further adjustment:

20926 is "in addition" to 60000–60281

Because these are subsidiary or "in addition to" codes, reimbursement reduction and modifier -51 do not apply.

Code		Description	Medicode RVU	50th	75th	Medicare Nat'l Avg
60000	*	Incision and drainage of thyroglossal cyst, infected	6.00	142	165	81
60001		Aspiration and/or injection, thyroid cyst	3.70	88	102	77
60100	*	Biopsy thyroid, percutaneous core needle	8.00	189	220	77
60200		Excision of cyst or adenoma of thyroid, or transection of isthmus	55.00	1302	1514	633
60210		Partial thyroid lobectomy, unilateral; with or without isthmusectomy	75.00	1775	2064	855
60212		Partial thyroid lobectomy, unilateral; with contralateral subtotal lobectomy, including isthmusectomy	85.00	2012	2339	1018
60220		Total thyroid lobectomy, unilateral; with or without isthmusectomy	73.00	1728	2009	825
60225		Total thyroid lobectomy, unilateral; with contralateral subtotal lobectomy, including isthmusectomy	91.00	2154	2504	971
60240		Thyroidectomy, total or complete	90.00	2130	2477	1133
60252		Thyroidectomy, total or subtotal for malignancy; with limited neck dissection	130.0	3077	3578	1292
60254		Thyroidectomy, total or subtotal for malignancy; with radical neck dissection	160.0	3787	4403	1551

Code	Description	Medicode RVU	50th	75th	Medicare Nat'l Avg
60260	Thyroidectomy, removal of all remaining thyroid tissue following previous removal of a portion of thyroid	83.00	1965	2284	717
60270	Thyroidectomy, including substernal thyroid gland; sternal split or transthoracic approach	105.0	2485	2890	1300
60271	Thyroidectomy, including substernal thyroid gland; cervical approach	90.00	2130	2477	1136
60280	Excision of thyroglossal duct cyst or sinus;	60.00	1420	1651	576
60281	Excision of thyroglossal duct cyst or sinus; recurrent	63.00	1491	1734	546

60500–60699
Parathyroid, Thymus, Adrenal Glands, and Carotid Body

CODING INSIGHT

Because many bilateral codes have been dropped from CPT, append modifier -50 if a surgery is performed bilaterally and a separate bilateral code is not listed.

For excision of remote or disseminated pheochromocytoma, see 49200–49201.

SUBSIDIARY CODES

Subsidiary codes have relative values that require no further adjustment:

20926 is "in addition" to 60500–60699

Because these are subsidiary or "in addition to" codes, reimbursement reduction and modifier -51 do not apply.

Code	Description	Medicode RVU	50th	75th	Medicare Nat'l Avg
60500	Parathyroidectomy or exploration of parathyroid(s);	92.00	2178	2532	1190
60502	Parathyroidectomy or exploration of parathyroid(s); re-exploration	101.0	2391	2780	1284
60505	Parathyroidectomy or exploration of parathyroid(s); with mediastinal exploration, sternal split or transthoracic approach	120.0	2840	3303	1402
60512	Parathyroid autotransplantation	18.40	436	506	284
60520	Thymectomy, partial or total; transcervical approach (separate procedure)	103.0	2438	2835	1267
60521	Thymectomy, partial or total; sternal split or transthoracic approach, without radical mediastinal dissection (separate procedure)	105.0	2485	2890	1333
60522	Thymectomy, partial or total; sternal split or transthoracic approach, with radical mediastinal dissection (separate procedure)	130.5	3089	3591	1464
60540	Adrenalectomy, partial or complete, or exploration of adrenal gland with or without biopsy, transabdominal, lumbar or dorsal (separate procedure);	97.50	2308	2683	1200

Code	Description	Medicode RVU	50th	75th	Medicare Nat'l Avg
60545	Adrenalectomy, partial or complete, or exploration of adrenal gland with or without biopsy, transabdominal, lumbar or dorsal (separate procedure); with excision of adjacent retroperitoneal tumor	125.0	2959	3440	1388
60600	Excision of carotid body tumor; without excision of carotid artery	100.0	2367	2752	1149
60605	Excision of carotid body tumor; with excision of carotid artery	115.0	2722	3165	1221
60699	Unlisted procedure, endocrine system	0.00	0	0	–

61000*–61576
Skull, Meninges, and Brain

CODING INSIGHT

The following terminology will be helpful when coding procedures associated with the nervous system:

Microdissection is dissection of tissues under a microscope or magnifying glass, usually done by separating the tissue by means of needles.

Microsurgery is a surgical procedure(s) performed under the magnification of a surgical microscope.

Surgical operating microscope is a binocular microscope used to obtain good visualization of fine structures in the operating field. In the standing type of microscope, a motorized zoom lens system operated by hand or foot controls provides an adjustable working distance; in head-borne models, interchangeable oculars provide the magnification needed.

For injection, drainage, or aspiration of the spine and spinal cord, see 62268–62298.

MEDICARE ALERT

Medicare rebundles certain codes in the surgery section when the listed codes are considered a component of a more comprehensive service.

20550, 29075, 29125 will not be reimbursed when reported with 64721
61304, 61312–61313 will not be reimbursed when reported with 61510
61304, 61312 will not be reimbursed when reported with 61512
61304, 61312–61313 will not be reimbursed when reported with 61700
62278 will not be reimbursed when reported with 62289
62278–62279 will not be reimbursed when reported with 63005
62278–62279, 62289, 63005, 63012 will not be reimbursed when reported with 63017
62278–62279 will not be reimbursed when reported with 63030–63035
62278–62279, 63030, 63035 will not be reimbursed when reported with 63042
62278–62279, 63005, 63012will not be reimbursed when reported with 63047

SUBSIDIARY CODES

There are three subsidiary codes in *CPT '96* that specify certain techniques requiring the use of an operating microscope before they are reportable:

- 61712 *Microdissection, intracranial or spinal procedure (list separately in addition to code for primary repair)* is limited to use with codes 61304–61711, 62010–62100, 63081–63308, and 63704–63710

- 64727 *Internal neurolysis, requiring the use of operating microscope (list separately in addition to code for neuroplasty) (neuroplasty includes external neurolysis)* is limited to use with 64702–64726
- 64830 *Microdissection and/or microrepair of nerve (list separately in addition to code for nerve repair)* is limited to use with 64831–64876

Codes 61712, 64727, and 64830 may be identified more than once per operative session when multiple procedures are performed using the specified technique.

The specific code that describes microsurgical techniques should be used instead of modifier -20. Modifier -20 should not be used with primary procedure codes that correlate to subsidiary codes 61712, 64727, and 64830.

Code 64727 is usually reimbursed based on an assigned value. Reimbursement for 61712 and 64830 may be based on a variable percentage increase (typically 20 percent) or on an assigned dollar amount based on time increments (e.g., $100 per hour for time spent using the operating microscope).

All other nervous system procedures performed with a surgical operating microscope should be appended with modifier -20.

Use of magnifying loupes or binoculars during surgery does not warrant separate identification.

Nota Bene: Append the listed codes or modifier -20 only for the procedure(s) performed. In an audit situation close scrutiny will be paid to the operative report and comments about the microscope being moved out of the surgical field and then another procedure being performed.

Subsidiary codes have relative values that require no further adjustment:

20900 is "in addition" to 61000–61576
20902 is "in addition" to 61000–61576
20926 is "in addition" to 61000–61576
61106 is "in addition" to 61000–61576
61130 is "in addition" to 61000–61576
61712 is "in addition" to 61304–61576
61795 is "in addition" to 61000–61576

Because these are subsidiary or "in addition to" codes, reimbursement reduction and modifier -51 do not apply.

Code		Description	Medicode RVU	50th	75th	Medicare Nat'l Avg
61000	*	Subdural tap through fontanelle, or suture, infant, unilateral or bilateral; initial	10.00	246	289	110
61001	*	Subdural tap through fontanelle, or suture, infant, unilateral or bilateral; subsequent taps	7.00	172	202	99
61020	*	Ventricular puncture through previous burr hole, fontanelle, suture, or implanted ventricular catheter/reservoir; without injection	11.00	271	318	119
61026	*	Ventricular puncture through previous burr hole, fontanelle, suture, or implanted ventricular catheter/reservoir; with injection of drug or other substance for diagnosis or treatment	11.00	271	318	139
61050	*	Cisternal or lateral cervical (C1-C2) puncture; without injection (separate procedure)	10.00	246	289	100

Code		Description	Medicode RVU	50th	75th	Medicare Nat'l Avg
61055	*	Cisternal or lateral cervical (C1-C2) puncture; with injection of drug or other substance for diagnosis or treatment (eg, C1-C2)	16.00	394	462	147
61070	*	Puncture of shunt tubing or reservoir for aspiration or injection procedure	9.00	222	260	58
61105	*	Twist drill hole for subdural or ventricular puncture; not followed by other surgery	50.00	1231	1443	638
61106		Twist drill hole for subdural or ventricular puncture; followed by other surgery	35.00	861	1010	568
61107	*	Twist drill hole for subdural or ventricular puncture; for implanting ventricular catheter or pressure recording device	65.00	1600	1876	491
61108		Twist drill hole for subdural or ventricular puncture; for evacuation and/or drainage of subdural hematoma	100.0	2461	2887	993
61120		Burr hole(s) for ventricular puncture (including injection of gas, contrast media, dye, or radioactive material); not followed by other surgery	50.00	1231	1443	636
61130		Burr hole(s) for ventricular puncture (including injection of gas, contrast media, dye, or radioactive material); followed by other surgery	35.00	861	1010	479
61140		Burr hole(s) or trephine; with biopsy of brain or intracranial lesion	110.0	2707	3175	1258
61150		Burr hole(s) or trephine; with drainage of brain abscess or cyst	110.0	2707	3175	1324
61151		Burr hole(s) or trephine; with subsequent tapping (aspiration) of intracranial abscess or cyst	15.00	369	433	535
61154		Burr hole(s) with evacuation and/or drainage of hematoma, extradural or subdural	125.0	3076	3608	1424
61156		Burr hole(s); with aspiration of hematoma or cyst, intracerebral	110.0	2707	3175	1367
61210	*	Burr hole(s); for implanting ventricular catheter, reservoir, EEG electrode(s) or pressure recording device (separate procedure)	67.00	1649	1934	572
61215		Insertion of subcutaneous reservoir, pump or continuous infusion system for connection to ventricular catheter	65.00	1600	1876	814
61250		Burr hole(s) or trephine, supratentorial, exploratory, not followed by other surgery	65.00	1600	1876	801
61253		Burr hole(s) or trephine, infratentorial, unilateral or bilateral	100.0	2461	2887	946
61304		Craniectomy or craniotomy, exploratory; supratentorial	146.0	3593	4214	2051
61305		Craniectomy or craniotomy, exploratory; infratentorial (posterior fossa)	160.0	3938	4619	2317
61312		Craniectomy or craniotomy for evacuation of hematoma, supratentorial; extradural or subdural	170.0	4184	4907	1996
61313		Craniectomy or craniotomy for evacuation of hematoma, supratentorial; intracerebral	180.0	4430	5196	1992
61314		Craniectomy or craniotomy for evacuation of hematoma, infratentorial; extradural or subdural	150.0	3692	4330	2106

Code	Description	Medicode RVU	50th	75th	Medicare Nat'l Avg
61315	Craniectomy or craniotomy for evacuation of hematoma, infratentorial; intracerebellar	170.0	4184	4907	2171
61320	Craniectomy or craniotomy, drainage of intracranial abscess; supratentorial	175.0	4307	5052	1812
61321	Craniectomy or craniotomy, drainage of intracranial abscess; infratentorial	160.0	3938	4619	1943
61330	Decompression of orbit only, transcranial approach	137.0	3372	3955	1179
61332	Exploration of orbit (transcranial approach); with biopsy	142.0	3495	4099	1936
61333	Exploration of orbit (transcranial approach); with removal of lesion	152.0	3741	4388	1978
61334	Exploration of orbit (transcranial approach); with removal of foreign body	130.0	3199	3753	1309
61340	Other cranial decompression (eg, subtemporal), supratentorial	101.0	2486	2915	1126
61343	Craniectomy, suboccipital with cervical laminectomy for decompression of medulla and spinal cord, with or without dural graft (eg, Arnold-Chiari malformation)	254.0	6251	7332	2480
61345	Other cranial decompression, posterior fossa	95.00	2338	2742	1881
61440	Craniotomy for section of tentorium cerebelli (separate procedure)	119.0	2929	3435	1886
61450	Craniectomy, subtemporal, for section, compression, or decompression of sensory root of gasserian ganglion	160.0	3938	4619	1879
61458	Craniectomy, suboccipital; for exploration or decompression of cranial nerves	201.0	4947	5802	2294
61460	Craniectomy, suboccipital; for section of one or more cranial nerves	193.0	4750	5571	2179
61470	Craniectomy, suboccipital; for medullary tractotomy	129.0	3175	3724	1450
61480	Craniectomy, suboccipital; for mesencephalic tractotomy or pedunculotomy	116.0	2855	3348	1310
61490	Craniotomy for lobotomy, including cingulotomy	114.0	2806	3291	1147
61500	Craniectomy; with excision of tumor or other bone lesion of skull	165.0	4061	4763	1653
61501	Craniectomy; for osteomyelitis	130.0	3199	3753	1343
61510	Craniectomy, trephination, bone flap craniotomy; for excision of brain tumor, supratentorial, except meningioma	225.0	5537	6495	2246
61512	Craniectomy, trephination, bone flap craniotomy; for excision of meningioma, supratentorial	225.0	5537	6495	2357
61514	Craniectomy, trephination, bone flap craniotomy; for excision of brain abscess, supratentorial	190.0	4676	5485	2117
61516	Craniectomy, trephination, bone flap craniotomy; for excision or fenestration of cyst, supratentorial	190.0	4676	5485	2119

Code	Description	Medicode RVU	50th	75th	Medicare Nat'l Avg
61518	Craniectomy for excision of brain tumor, infratentorial or posterior fossa; except meningioma, cerebellopontine angle tumor, or midline tumor at base of skull	225.0	5537	6495	2691
61519	Craniectomy for excision of brain tumor, infratentorial or posterior fossa; meningioma	233.0	5734	6726	2806
61520	Craniectomy for excision of brain tumor, infratentorial or posterior fossa; cerebellopontine angle tumor	233.0	5734	6726	3084
61521	Craniectomy for excision of brain tumor, infratentorial or posterior fossa; midline tumor at base of skull	252.0	6202	7274	3049
61522	Craniectomy, infratentorial or posterior fossa; for excision of brain abscess	190.0	4676	5485	2001
61524	Craniectomy, infratentorial or posterior fossa; for excision or fenestration of cyst	190.0	4676	5485	2285
61526	Craniectomy, bone flap craniotomy, transtemporal (mastoid) for excision of cerebellopontine angle tumor;	200.0	4922	5773	2673
61530	Craniectomy, bone flap craniotomy, transtemporal (mastoid) for excision of cerebellopontine angle tumor; combined with middle/posterior fossa craniotomy/craniectomy	210.0	5168	6062	3136
61531	Subdural implantation of strip electrodes through one or more burr or trephine hole(s) for long term seizure monitoring	122.0	3003	3522	1465
61533	Craniotomy with elevation of bone flap; for subdural implantation of an electrode array, for long term seizure monitoring	195.0	4799	5629	1712
61534	Craniotomy with elevation of bone flap; for excision of epileptogenic focus without electrocorticography during surgery	203.0	4996	5860	1073
61535	Craniotomy with elevation of bone flap; for removal of epidural or subdural electrode array, without excision of cerebral tissue (separate procedure)	130.0	3199	3753	745
61536	Craniotomy with elevation of bone flap; for excision of cerebral epileptogenic focus, with electrocorticography during surgery (includes removal of electrode array)	200.0	4922	5773	2161
61538	Craniotomy with elevation of bone flap; for lobectomy with electrocorticography during surgery, temporal lobe	210.0	5168	6062	2438
61539	Craniotomy with elevation of bone flap; for lobectomy with electrocorticography during surgery, other than temporal lobe, partial or total	210.0	5168	6062	2234
61541	Craniotomy with elevation of bone flap; for transection of corpus callosum	250.0	6153	7217	1974
61542	Craniotomy with elevation of bone flap; for total hemispherectomy	250.0	6153	7217	1988
61543	Craniotomy with elevation of bone flap; for partial or subtotal hemispherectomy	250.0	6153	7217	1570
61544	Craniotomy with elevation of bone flap; for excision or coagulation of choroid plexus	175.0	4307	5052	2099
61545	Craniotomy with elevation of bone flap; for excision of craniopharyngioma	250.0	6153	7217	2524
61546	Craniotomy for hypophysectomy or excision of pituitary tumor, intracranial approach	215.0	5291	6206	2394

Code	Description	Medicode RVU	50th	75th	Medicare Nat'l Avg
61548	Hypophysectomy or excision of pituitary tumor, transnasal or transseptal approach, nonstereotactic	205.0	5045	5918	2011
61550	Craniectomy for craniosynostosis; single cranial suture	125.0	3076	3608	1060
61552	Craniectomy for craniosynostosis; multiple cranial sutures	150.0	3692	4330	1387
61556	Craniotomy for craniosynostosis; frontal or parietal bone flap	146.0	3593	4214	1550
61557	Craniotomy for craniosynostosis; bifrontal bone flap	175.0	4307	5052	1559
61558	Extensive craniectomy for multiple cranial suture craniosynostosis (eg, cloverleaf skull); not requiring bone grafts	180.0	4430	5196	1771
61559	Extensive craniectomy for multiple cranial suture craniosynostosis (eg, cloverleaf skull); recontouring with multiple osteotomies and bone autografts (eg, barrel-stave procedure) (includes obtaining grafts)	215.0	5291	6206	2297
61563	Excision, intra and extracranial, benign tumor of cranial bone (eg, fibrous dysplasia); without optic nerve decompression	197.0	4848	5687	1878
61564	Excision, intra and extracranial, benign tumor of cranial bone (eg, fibrous dysplasia); with optic nerve decompression	237.0	5833	6841	2369
61570	Craniectomy or craniotomy; with excision of foreign body from brain	224.0	5513	6466	1663
61571	Craniectomy or craniotomy; with treatment of penetrating wound of brain	224.0	5513	6466	1804
61575	Transoral approach to skull base, brain stem or upper spinal cord for biopsy, decompression or excision of lesion;	155.0	3815	4474	2799
61576	Transoral approach to skull base, brain stem or upper spinal cord for biopsy, decompression or excision of lesion; requiring splitting of tongue and/or mandible (including tracheostomy)	165.0	4061	4763	2564

61580–62258
Surgery of Skull Base

Coding Insight
As defined in CPT, when one physician performs the approach procedure, another performs the definitive procedure, and another performs the repair/reconstructive procedure, each physician reports only the code for the specific procedure performed. If one physician performs more than one procedure, then both codes are reported and modifier -51 is added to the secondary, additional procedure.

Subsidiary Codes
Subsidiary codes have relative values that require no further adjustment:

20900 is "in addition" to 61580–62258
20902 is "in addition" to 61580–62258
20926 is "in addition" to 61580–62258

61106 is "in addition" to 61000–61576
61130 is "in addition" to 61580–62258
61609 is "in addition" to 61605–61608
61610 is "in addition" to 61605–61608
61611 is "in addition" to 61605–61608
61612 is "in addition" to 61605–61608
61712 is "in addition" to 61580–61711, 62010–62100
61795 is "in addition" to 61580–62258

Because these are subsidiary or "in addition to" codes, reimbursement reduction and modifier -51 do not apply.

Code	Description	Medicode RVU	50th	75th	Medicare Nat'l Avg
61580	Craniofacial approach to anterior cranial fossa; extradural, including lateral rhinotomy, ethmoidectomy, sphenoidectomy, without maxillectomy or orbital exenteration	125.0	3076	3608	2097
61581	Craniofacial approach to anterior cranial fossa; extradural, including lateral rhinotomy, orbital exenteration, ethmoidectomy, sphenoidectomy and/or maxillectomy	175.0	4307	5052	2380
61582	Craniofacial approach to anterior cranial fossa; extradural, including unilateral or bifrontal craniotomy, elevation of frontal lobe(s), osteotomy of base of anterior cranial fossa	180.0	4430	5196	2161
61583	Craniofacial approach to anterior cranial fossa; intradural, including unilateral or bifrontal craniotomy, elevation or resection of frontal lobe, osteotomy of base of anterior cranial fossa	190.0	4676	5485	2466
61584	Orbitocranial approach to anterior cranial fossa, extradural, including supraorbital ridge osteotomy and elevation of frontal and/or temporal lobe(s); without orbital exenteration	125.0	3076	3608	2387
61585	Orbitocranial approach to anterior cranial fossa, extradural, including supraorbital ridge osteotomy and elevation of frontal and/or temporal lobe(s); with orbital exenteration	175.0	4307	5052	2671
61590	Infratemporal pre-auricular approach to middle cranial fossa (parapharyngeal space, infratemporal and midline skull base, nasopharynx), with or without disarticulation of the mandible, including parotidectomy, craniotomy, decompression and/or mobilization of the facial nerve and/or petrous carotid artery	0.00	0	0	2904
61591	Infratemporal post-auricular approach to middle cranial fossa (internal auditory meatus, petrous apex, tentorium, cavernous sinus, parasellar area, infratemporal fossa) including mastoidectomy, resection of sigmoid sinus, with or without decompression and/or mobilization of contents of auditory canal or petrous carotid artery	0.00	0	0	3046
61592	Orbitocranial zygomatic approach to middle cranial fossa (cavernous sinus and carotid artery, clivus, basilar artery or petrous apex) including osteotomy of zygoma, craniotomy, extra- or intradural elevation of temporal lobe	188.0	4627	5427	2763

Code	Description	Medicode RVU	50th	75th	Medicare Nat'l Avg
61595	Transtemporal approach to posterior cranial fossa, jugular foramen or midline skull base, including mastoidectomy, decompression of sigmoid sinus and/or facial nerve, with or without mobilization	167.0	4110	4821	2041
61596	Transcochlear approach to posterior cranial fossa, jugular foramen or midline skull base, including labyrinthectomy, decompression, with or without mobilization of facial nerve and/or petrous carotid artery	180.0	4430	5196	2480
61597	Transcondylar (far lateral) approach to posterior cranial fossa, jugular foramen or midline skull base, including occipital condylectomy, mastoidectomy, resection of C1-C3 vertebral body(s), decompression of vertebral artery, with or without mobilization	232.0	5710	6697	2621
61598	Transpetrosal approach to posterior cranial fossa, clivus or foramen magnum, including ligation of superior petrosal sinus and/or sigmoid sinus	150.0	3692	4330	2310
61600	Resection or excision of neoplastic, vascular or infectious lesion of base of anterior cranial fossa; extradural	166.0	4085	4792	1771
61601	Resection or excision of neoplastic, vascular or infectious lesion of base of anterior cranial fossa; intradural, including dural repair, with or without graft	178.0	4381	5138	1899
61605	Resection or excision of neoplastic, vascular or infectious lesion of infratemporal fossa, parapharyngeal space, petrous apex; extradural	188.0	4627	5427	2005
61606	Resection or excision of neoplastic, vascular or infectious lesion of infratemporal fossa, parapharyngeal space, petrous apex; intradural, including dural repair, with or without graft	251.0	6177	7245	2685
61607	Resection or excision of neoplastic, vascular or infectious lesion of parasellar area, cavernous sinus, clivus or midline skull base; extradural	235.0	5784	6784	2508
61608	Resection or excision of neoplastic, vascular or infectious lesion of parasellar area, cavernous sinus, clivus or midline skull base; intradural, including dural repair, with or without graft	273.0	6719	7880	2918
61609	Transection or ligation, carotid artery in cavernous sinus; without repair	67.00	1649	1934	717
61610	Transection or ligation, carotid artery in cavernous sinus; with repair by anastomosis or graft	202.0	4971	5831	2152
61611	Transection or ligation, carotid artery in petrous canal; without repair	50.00	1231	1443	538
61612	Transection or ligation, carotid artery in petrous canal; with repair by anastomosis or graft	189.0	4651	5456	2022
61613	Obliteration of carotid aneurysm, arteriovenous malformation, or carotid-cavernous fistula by dissection within cavernous sinus	268.0	6596	7736	2862
61615	Resection or excision of neoplastic, vascular or infectious lesion of base of posterior cranial fossa, jugular foramen, foramen magnum, or C1-C3 vertebral bodies; extradural	206.0	5070	5946	2203

Code	Description	Medicode RVU	50th	75th	Medicare Nat'l Avg
61616	Resection or excision of neoplastic, vascular or infectious lesion of base of posterior cranial fossa, jugular foramen, foramen magnum, or C1-C3 vertebral bodies; intradural, including dural repair, with or without graft	281.0	6916	8111	2997
61618	Secondary repair of dura for CSF leak, anterior, middle or posterior cranial fossa following surgery of the skull base; by free tissue graft (eg, pericranium, fascia, tensor fascia lata, adipose tissue, homologous or synthetic grafts)	150.0	3692	4330	1133
61619	Secondary repair of dura for CSF leak, anterior, middle or posterior cranial fossa following surgery of the skull base; by local or regionalized vascularized pedicle flap or myocutaneous flap (including galea, temporalis, frontalis or occipitalis muscle)	240.0	5907	6928	1417
61624	Transcatheter occlusion or embolization (eg, for tumor destruction, to achieve hemostasis, to occlude a vascular malformation), percutaneous, any method; central nervous system (intracranial, spinal cord)	170.0	4184	4907	1270
61626	Transcatheter occlusion or embolization (eg, for tumor destruction, to achieve hemostasis, to occlude a vascular malformation), percutaneous, any method; non-central nervous system, head or neck (extracranial, brachiocephalic branch)	117.0	2879	3377	1048
61680	Surgery of intracranial arteriovenous malformation; supratentorial, simple	225.0	5537	6495	2845
61682	Surgery of intracranial arteriovenous malformation; supratentorial, complex	270.0	6645	7794	3256
61684	Surgery of intracranial arteriovenous malformation; infratentorial, simple	270.0	6645	7794	2819
61686	Surgery of intracranial arteriovenous malformation; infratentorial, complex	324.0	7974	9353	3409
61690	Surgery of intracranial arteriovenous malformation; dural, simple	195.0	4799	5629	2542
61692	Surgery of intracranial arteriovenous malformation; dural, complex	234.0	5759	6755	2727
61700	Surgery of intracranial aneurysm, intracranial approach; carotid circulation	260.0	6399	7505	2880
61702	Surgery of intracranial aneurysm, intracranial approach; vertebral-basilar circulation	285.0	7014	8227	3186
61703	Surgery of intracranial aneurysm, cervical approach by application of occluding clamp to cervical carotid artery (Selverstone-Crutchfield type)	135.0	3322	3897	1202
61705	Surgery of aneurysm, vascular malformation or carotid-cavernous fistula; by intracranial and cervical occlusion of carotid artery	225.0	5537	6495	2749
61708	Surgery of aneurysm, vascular malformation or carotid-cavernous fistula; by intracranial electrothrombosis	200.0	4922	5773	2379
61710	Surgery of aneurysm, vascular malformation or carotid-cavernous fistula; by intra-arterial embolization, injection procedure, or balloon catheter	80.00	1969	2309	1831
61711	Anastomosis, arterial, extracranial-intracranial (eg, middle cerebral/cortical) arteries	210.0	5168	6062	2872

Code	Description	Medicode RVU	50th	75th	Medicare Nat'l Avg
61712	Microdissection, intracranial or spinal procedure (list separately in addition to code for primary procedure)	0.00	0	0	353
61720	Creation of lesion by stereotactic method, including burr hole(s) and localizing and recording techniques, single or multiple stages; globus pallidus or thalamus	188.0	4627	5427	1617
61735	Creation of lesion by stereotactic method, including burr hole(s) and localizing and recording techniques, single or multiple stages; subcortical structure(s) other than globus pallidus or thalamus	188.0	4627	5427	1238
61750	Stereotactic biopsy, aspiration, or excision, including burr hole(s), for intracranial lesion;	180.0	4430	5196	1327
61751	Stereotactic biopsy, aspiration, or excision, including burr hole(s), for intracranial lesion; with computerized axial tomography	188.0	4627	5427	1717
61760	Stereotactic implantation of depth electrodes into the cerebrum for long term seizure monitoring	180.0	4430	5196	1632
61770	Stereotactic localization, any method, including burr hole(s), with insertion of catheter(s) for brachytherapy	180.0	4430	5196	1481
61790	Creation of lesion by stereotactic method, percutaneous, by neurolytic agent (eg, alcohol, thermal, electrical, radiofrequency); gasserian ganglion	123.0	3027	3551	1113
61791	Creation of lesion by stereotactic method, percutaneous, by neurolytic agent (eg, alcohol, thermal, electrical, radiofrequency); trigeminal medullary tract	123.0	3027	3551	901
61793	Stereotactic focused proton beam or gamma radiosurgery	222.0	5464	6408	1573
61795	Stereotactic computer assisted volumetric intracranial procedure (list separately in addition to code for primary procedure)	48.00	1181	1386	467
61850	Twist drill or burr hole(s) for implantation of neurostimulator electrodes; cortical	107.0	2633	3089	1160
61855	Twist drill or burr hole(s) for implantation of neurostimulator electrodes; subcortical	107.0	2633	3089	965
61860	Craniectomy or craniotomy for implantation of neurostimulator electrodes, cerebral; cortical	150.0	3692	4330	817
61865	Craniectomy or craniotomy for implantation of neurostimulator electrodes, cerebral; subcortical	150.0	3692	4330	1575
61870	Craniectomy for implantation of neurostimulator electrodes, cerebellar; cortical	165.0	4061	4763	420
61875	Craniectomy for implantation of neurostimulator electrodes, cerebellar; subcortical	165.0	4061	4763	668
61880	Revision or removal of intracranial neurostimulator electrodes	168.0	4135	4849	437
61885	Incision and subcutaneous placement of cranial neurostimulator pulse generator or receiver, direct or inductive coupling	28.00	689	808	184
61888	Revision or removal of cranial neurostimulator pulse generator or receiver	28.00	689	808	229
62000	Elevation of depressed skull fracture; simple, extradural	106.0	2609	3060	723

Code	Description	Medicode RVU	50th	75th	Medicare Nat'l Avg
62005	Elevation of depressed skull fracture; compound or comminuted, extradural	140.0	3446	4041	1102
62010	Elevation of depressed skull fracture; with repair of dura and/or debridement of brain	164.0	4036	4734	1617
62100	Craniotomy for repair of dural/CSF leak, including surgery for rhinorrhea/otorrhea	175.0	4307	5052	1844
62115	Reduction of craniomegalic skull (eg, treated hydrocephalus); not requiring bone grafts or cranioplasty	0.00	0	0	1471
62116	Reduction of craniomegalic skull (eg, treated hydrocephalus); with simple cranioplasty	0.00	0	0	1611
62117	Reduction of craniomegalic skull (eg, treated hydrocephalus); requiring craniotomy and reconstruction with or without bone graft (includes obtaining grafts)	0.00	0	0	1821
62120	Repair of encephalocele, skull vault, including cranioplasty	150.0	3692	4330	1603
62121	Craniotomy for repair of encephalocele, skull base	150.0	3692	4330	1597
62140	Cranioplasty for skull defect; up to 5 cm diameter	129.0	3175	3724	1128
62141	Cranioplasty for skull defect; larger than 5 cm diameter	157.0	3864	4532	1397
62142	Removal of bone flap or prosthetic plate of skull	90.00	2215	2598	992
62143	Replacement of bone flap or prosthetic plate of skull	120.0	2953	3464	893
62145	Cranioplasty for skull defect with reparative brain surgery	160.0	3938	4619	1292
62146	Cranioplasty with autograft (includes obtaining bone grafts); up to 5 cm diameter	159.0	3913	4590	1097
62147	Cranioplasty with autograft (includes obtaining bone grafts); larger than 5 cm diameter	195.0	4799	5629	1316
62180	Ventriculocisternostomy (Torkildsen type operation)	122.0	3003	3522	1172
62190	Creation of shunt; subarachnoid/subdural-atrial, -jugular, -auricular	115.0	2830	3320	1046
62192	Creation of shunt; subarachnoid/subdural-peritoneal, -pleural, other terminus	115.0	2830	3320	1156
62194	Replacement or irrigation, subarachnoid/subdural catheter	50.00	1231	1443	179
62200	Ventriculocisternostomy, third ventricle;	175.0	4307	5052	1307
62201	Ventriculocisternostomy, third ventricle; stereotactic method	159.0	3913	4590	879
62220	Creation of shunt; ventriculo-atrial, -jugular, -auricular	125.0	3076	3608	1245
62223	Creation of shunt; ventriculo-peritoneal, -pleural, other terminus	135.0	3322	3897	1329

Code	Description	Medicode RVU	50th	75th	Medicare Nat'l Avg
62225	Replacement or irrigation, ventricular catheter	65.00	1600	1876	410
62230	Replacement or revision of CSF shunt, obstructed valve, or distal catheter in shunt system	95.00	2338	2742	879
62256	Removal of complete CSF shunt system; without replacement	59.00	1452	1703	547
62258	Removal of complete CSF shunt system; with replacement by similar or other shunt at same operation	137.0	3372	3955	1226

62268–62368
Spine and Spinal Cord

CODING INSIGHT
For injection, drainage, or aspiration of the skull, meninges, or brain, see 61000–61576. For stereotactic biopsy, aspiration, or excision of spinal cord lesion, see 63615.

Nota Bene: Codes 62274–62279 have been revised in *CPT '96*; the term "antispasmodic" is included in the official description. Although codes 62275–62279 are subordinate to the main description of 62274, they are not marked with the revision symbol; don't forget that they have also revised. The same is true for code 62289; the term "antispasmodic" has also been added to 62288, which affects the nomenclature of the subordinate code.

SUBSIDIARY CODES
Subsidiary codes have relative values that require no further adjustment:

20900 is "in addition" to 62268–62298
20902 is "in addition" to 62268–62298
20926 is "in addition" to 62268–62298
61795 is "in addition" to 62268–62298

Because these are subsidiary or "in addition to" codes, reimbursement reduction and modifier -51 do not apply.

Code	Description	Medicode RVU	50th	75th	Medicare Nat'l Avg
62268 *	Percutaneous aspiration, spinal cord cyst or syrinx	65.00	1504	1734	245
62269 *	Biopsy of spinal cord, percutaneous needle	55.00	1273	1467	210
62270 *	Spinal puncture, lumbar, diagnostic	6.65	154	177	65
62272 *	Spinal puncture, therapeutic, for drainage of spinal fluid (by needle or catheter)	9.00	208	240	92
62273 *	Injection, lumbar epidural, of blood or clot patch	16.00	370	427	123
▲ 62274 *	Injection of diagnostic or therapeutic anesthetic or antispasmodic substance (including narcotics); subarachnoid or subdural, single	15.00	347	400	92

	Code		Description	Medicode RVU	50th	75th	Medicare Nat'l Avg
▲	62275	*	Injection of anesthetic substance (including narcotics), diagnostic or therapeutic; epidural, cervical or thoracic, single	19.00	440	507	93
▲	62276	*	Injection of anesthetic substance (including narcotics), diagnostic or therapeutic; subarachnoid or subdural, differential	16.00	370	427	123
▲	62277	*	Injection of anesthetic substance (including narcotics), diagnostic or therapeutic; subarachnoid or subdural, continuous	16.00	370	427	112
▲	62278	*	Injection of anesthetic substance (including narcotics), diagnostic or therapeutic; epidural, lumbar or caudal, single	16.50	382	440	99
▲	62279	*	Injection of anesthetic substance (including narcotics), diagnostic or therapeutic; epidural, lumbar or caudal, continuous	22.00	509	587	97
	62280	*	Injection of neurolytic substance (eg, alcohol, phenol, iced saline solutions); subarachnoid	15.00	347	400	121
	62281	*	Injection of neurolytic substance (eg, alcohol, phenol, iced saline solutions); epidural, cervical or thoracic	19.00	440	507	135
	62282	*	Injection of neurolytic substance (eg, alcohol, phenol, iced saline solutions); epidural, lumbar or caudal	20.00	463	533	154
	62284	*	Injection procedure for myelography and/or computerized axial tomography, spinal (other than C1-C2 and posterior fossa)	19.00	440	507	160
	62287		Aspiration procedure, percutaneous, of nucleus pulposus of intervertebral disk, any method, single or multiple levels, lumbar	125.0	2893	3334	646
▲	62288	*	Injection of substance other than anesthetic, antispasmodic, contrast, or neurolytic solutions; subarachnoid (separate procedure)	15.00	347	400	110
▲	62289	*	Injection of substance other than anesthetic, contrast, or neurolytic solutions; lumbar or caudal epidural (separate procedure)	16.50	382	440	112
	62290	*	Injection procedure for diskography, each level; lumbar	17.00	393	453	196
	62291	*	Injection procedure for diskography, each level; cervical	18.00	417	480	176
	62292		Injection procedure for chemonucleolysis, including diskography, intervertebral disk, single or multiple levels, lumbar	100.0	2315	2667	755
	62294		Injection procedure, arterial, for occlusion of arteriovenous malformation, spinal	19.00	440	507	568
	62298	*	Injection of substance other than anesthetic, contrast, or neurolytic solutions, epidural, cervical or thoracic (separate procedure)	19.00	440	507	123
●	62350		Implantation, revision or repositioning of intrathecal or epidural catheter, for implantable reservoir or implantable infusion pump; without laminectomy	110.0	2546	2934	–
●	62351		Implantation, revision or repositioning of intrathecal or epidural catheter, for implantable reservoir or implantable infusion pump; with laminectomy	130.0	3009	3467	–
●	62355		Removal of previously implanted intrathecal or epidural catheter	50.00	1157	1334	–

	Code	Description	Medicode RVU	50th	75th	Medicare Nat'l Avg
●	**62360**	Implantation or replacement of device for intrathecal or epidural drug infusion; subcutaneous reservoir	52.00	1204	1387	–
●	**62361**	Implantation or replacement of device for intrathecal or epidural drug infusion; non-programmable pump	52.00	1204	1387	–
●	**62362**	Implantation or replacement of device for intrathecal or epidural drug infusion; programmable pump, including preparation of pump, with or without programming	55.00	1273	1467	–
●	**62365**	Removal of subcutaneous reservoir or pump, previously implanted for intrathecal or epidural infusion	33.00	764	880	–
●	**62367**	Electronic analysis of programmable, implanted pump for intrathecal or epidural drug infusion (includes evaluation of reservoir status); without reprogramming	0.00	0	0	–
●	**62368**	Electronic analysis of programmable, implanted pump for intrathecal or epidural drug infusion (includes evaluation of reservoir status, alarm status, drug prescription status, alarm status, drug prescription status); with reprogramming	0.00	0	0	–

63001–63048

Posterior Extradural Laminotomy or Laminectomy for Exploration/Decompression of Neural Elements or Excision of Herniated Intervertebral Disks

Coding Insight

Laminectomy is the excision of the whole lamina (posterior arch) of the vertebrae. Laminotomy is incision into the lamina (posterior arch) of the vertebrae. Laminotomy, when used with the term hemilaminectomy, describes an incision into the lamina of a vertebrae that results in part, half, or one side (unilateral) of the lamina of the vertebrae being removed.

When a laminotomy (hemilaminectomy) is performed it may be referred to in operative reports or staff notes as simply a laminectomy. In order to code a laminectomy or laminotomy accurately, be sure you read carefully to determine if all or part of the lamina of a vertebrae was removed. To make the proper code selection, note if a herniated intervertebral disk was removed and if a partial facetectomy or foramenotomy was performed.

Laminectomy Codes

Codes 63001–63011 do not include facetectomy, foramenotomy, or diskectomy, but do include a laminectomy performed on one or two vertebral segments. Use 63001 for cervical, 63003 for thoracic, 63005 for lumbar (except for spondylolisthesis), and 63017 for sacral. When more than two vertebral segments are involved, choose from 63015–63017.

Report 63012 if laminectomy is performed for lumbar spondylolisthesis, and 63015–63017 when laminectomy is performed on more than two vertebral segments (as described by 63001–63017).

When laminectomy, facetectomy, and foramenotomy are performed without excision of a herniated intervertebral disk for spinal or lateral recess stenosis, report 63045 for cervical, 63046 for thoracic, and 63047 for lumbar. When performed on more than one interspace, report 63048 for each additional interspace. (63048 is a subsidiary code; see below.)

Laminotomy Codes

For partial excision of the lamina (laminotomy, hemilaminectomy), which includes partial facetectomy, foramenotomy, and/or excision of herniated intervertebral disk, report 63020 for cervical and 63030 for lumbar. When performed on more than one interspace, report 63035 for each additional interspace. (63035 is a subsidiary code; see below).

Codes 63020 and 63030 describe unilateral procedures. If performed bilaterally, report twice and append modifier -50 to the second code. Modifier -50 identifies a procedure performed identically on the opposite side (mirror image).

For re-exploration laminotomy (hemilaminectomy) that includes partial facetectomy, foramenotomy, and/or excision of the herniated intervertebral disk, see 63040–63042.

When 63001–63048 are followed by arthrodesis, the arthrodesis is reported separately (see 22590–22650).

Subsidiary Codes

Subsidiary codes have relative values that require no further adjustment:

20900 is "in addition" to 63001–63048
20902 is "in addition" to 63001–63048
20926 is "in addition" to 63001–63048
61795 is "in addition" to 63001–63048
63035 is "in addition" to 63020, 63030
63048 is "in addition" to 63045, 63046, 63047

Because these are subsidiary or "in addition to" codes, reimbursement reduction and modifier -51 do not apply.

Code	Description	Medicode RVU	50th	75th	Medicare Nat'l Avg
63001	Laminectomy with exploration and/or decompression of spinal cord and/or cauda equina, without facetectomy, foraminotomy or diskectomy, (eg, spinal stenosis), one or two vertebral segments; cervical	140.0	3257	3790	1493
63003	Laminectomy with exploration and/or decompression of spinal cord and/or cauda equina, without facetectomy, foraminotomy or diskectomy, (eg, spinal stenosis), one or two vertebral segments; thoracic	160.0	3722	4331	1439
63005	Laminectomy with exploration and/or decompression of spinal cord and/or cauda equina, without facetectomy, foraminotomy or diskectomy, (eg, spinal stenosis), one or two vertebral segments; lumbar, except for spondylolisthesis	135.0	3140	3654	1390
63011	Laminectomy with exploration and/or decompression of spinal cord and/or cauda equina, without facetectomy, foraminotomy or diskectomy, (eg, spinal stenosis), one or two vertebral segments; sacral	152.0	3536	4114	903
63012	Laminectomy with removal of abnormal facets and/or pars inter-articularis with decompression of cauda equina and nerve roots for spondylolisthesis, lumbar (Gill type procedure)	160.0	3722	4331	1434
63015	Laminectomy with exploration and/or decompression of spinal cord and/or cauda equina, without facetectomy, foraminotomy or diskectomy, (eg, spinal stenosis), more than 2 vertebral segments; cervical	172.0	4001	4656	1739

Code	Description	Medicode RVU	50th	75th	Medicare Nat'l Avg
63016	Laminectomy with exploration and/or decompression of spinal cord and/or cauda equina, without facetectomy, foraminotomy or diskectomy, (eg, spinal stenosis), more than 2 vertebral segments; thoracic	180.0	4187	4872	1745
63017	Laminectomy with exploration and/or decompression of spinal cord and/or cauda equina, without facetectomy, foraminotomy or diskectomy, (eg, spinal stenosis), more than 2 vertebral segments; lumbar	172.0	4001	4656	1674
63020	Laminotomy (hemilaminectomy), with decompression of nerve root(s), including partial facetectomy, foraminotomy and/or excision of herniated intervertebral disk; one interspace, cervical	158.0	3675	4277	1363
63030	Laminotomy (hemilaminectomy), with decompression of nerve root(s), including partial facetectomy, foraminotomy and/or excision of herniated intervertebral disk; one interspace, lumbar	153.0	3559	4142	1234
63035	Laminotomy (hemilaminectomy), with decompression of nerve root(s), including partial facetectomy, foraminotomy and/or excision of herniated intervertebral disk; each additional interspace, cervical or lumbar	50.00	1163	1353	360
63040	Laminotomy (hemilaminectomy), with decompression of nerve root(s), including partial facetectomy, foraminotomy and/or excision of herniated intervertebral disk, re-exploration; cervical	172.0	4001	4656	1757
63042	Laminotomy (hemilaminectomy), with decompression of nerve root(s), including partial facetectomy, foraminotomy and/or excision of herniated intervertebral disk, re-exploration; lumbar	179.0	4164	4845	1790
63045	Laminectomy, facetectomy and foraminotomy (unilateral or bilateral with decompression of spinal cord, cauda equina and/or nerve root(s), (eg, spinal or lateral recess stenosis)), single vertebral segment; cervical	190.0	4420	5143	1675
63046	Laminectomy, facetectomy and foraminotomy (unilateral or bilateral with decompression of spinal cord, cauda equina and/or nerve root(s), (eg, spinal or lateral recess stenosis)), single vertebral segment; thoracic	185.0	4303	5008	1568
63047	Laminectomy, facetectomy and foraminotomy (unilateral or bilateral with decompression of spinal cord, cauda equina and/or nerve root(s), (eg, spinal or lateral recess stenosis)), single vertebral segment; lumbar	185.0	4303	5008	1645
63048	Laminectomy, facetectomy and foraminotomy (unilateral or bilateral with decompression of spinal cord, cauda equina and/or nerve root(s), (eg, spinal or lateral recess stenosis)), single vertebral segment; each additional segment, cervical, thoracic or lumbar	60.00	1396	1624	424

63055–63091

Other Exploration/Decompression Transpedicular or Costovertebral-Anterior or Anterolateral

Coding Insight

Codes 63081–63091 and 63300–63308 are used to report vertebral corpectomy (vertebral body resection). Codes 63081–63091 are used whether the resection is partial or complete and is performed with different approaches, depending upon the spinal level for decompression of the spinal cord and/or nerve root(s). Codes 63300–63308 are used for partial or complete resection of the vertebral body (corpectomy) for intraspinal lesions (extra- or intradural) with different approaches, depending upon the spinal level. Codes 22140–22152 for reconstruction of the spine following vertebral corpectomyhave been deleted in *CPT '96*, although parenthetical notes still reference them.

Procedures 63081–63091 include diskectomy above and/or below vertebral segment. If followed by arthrodesis, see 22554–22585. Codes 63075–63091 also include diskectomy above and below the vertebral segment.

SUBSIDIARY CODES

Subsidiary codes have relative values that require no further adjustment:

20900 is "in addition" to 63055–63091
20902 is "in addition" to 63055–63091
20926 is "in addition" to 63055–63091
61712 is "in addition" to 63081–63091
61795 is "in addition" to 63055–63091
63057 is "in addition" to 63055, 63056
63066 is "in addition" to 63064
63076 is "in addition" to 63075
63078 is "in addition" to 63077
63082 is "in addition" to 63081
63086 is "in addition" to 63085
63088 is "in addition" to 63087
63091 is "in addition" to 63090

Because these are subsidiary or "in addition to" codes, reimbursement reduction and modifier -51 do not apply.

Code	Description	Medicode RVU	50th	75th	Medicare Nat'l Avg
63055	Transpedicular approach with decompression of spinal cord, equina and/or nerve root(s) (eg, herniated intervertebral disk), single segment; thoracic	205.0	4769	5549	1904
63056	Transpedicular approach with decompression of spinal cord, equina and/or nerve root(s) (eg, herniated intervertebral disk), single segment; lumbar	188.0	4373	5089	1758
63057	Transpedicular approach with decompression of spinal cord, equina and/or nerve root(s) (eg, herniated intervertebral disk), single segment; each additional segment, thoracic or lumbar	68.00	1582	1841	314
63064	Costovertebral approach with decompression of spinal cord or nerve root(s), (eg, herniated intervertebral disk), thoracic; single segment	172.0	4001	4656	2015
63066	Costovertebral approach with decompression of spinal cord or nerve root(s), (eg, herniated intervertebral disk), thoracic; each additional segment	57.00	1326	1543	249
63075	Diskectomy, anterior, with decompression of spinal cord and/or nerve root(s), including osteophytectomy; cervical, single interspace	158.0	3675	4277	1641
63076	Diskectomy, anterior, with decompression of spinal cord and/or nerve root(s), including osteophytectomy; cervical, each additional interspace	53.00	1233	1435	428

Code	Description	Medicode RVU	50th	75th	Medicare Nat'l Avg
63077	Diskectomy, anterior, with decompression of spinal cord and/or nerve root(s), including osteophytectomy; thoracic, single interspace	150.0	3489	4060	1630
63078	Diskectomy, anterior, with decompression of spinal cord and/or nerve root(s), including osteophytectomy; thoracic, each additional interspace	50.00	1163	1353	254
63081	Vertebral corpectomy (vertebral body resection), partial or complete, anterior approach with decompression of spinal cord and/or nerve root(s); cervical, single segment	190.0	4420	5143	2103
63082	Vertebral corpectomy (vertebral body resection), partial or complete, anterior approach with decompression of spinal cord and/or nerve root(s); cervical, each additional segment	63.00	1465	1705	457
63085	Vertebral corpectomy (vertebral body resection), partial or complete, transthoracic approach with decompression of spinal cord and/or nerve root(s); thoracic, single segment	190.0	4420	5143	2256
63086	Vertebral corpectomy (vertebral body resection), partial or complete, transthoracic approach with decompression of spinal cord and/or nerve root(s); thoracic, each additional segment	63.00	1465	1705	355
63087	Vertebral corpectomy (vertebral body resection), partial or complete, combined thoracolumbar approach with decompression of spinal cord, cauda equina or nerve root(s), lower thoracic or lumbar; single segment	182.0	4234	4927	2377
63088	Vertebral corpectomy (vertebral body resection), partial or complete, combined thoracolumbar approach with decompression of spinal cord, cauda equina or nerve root(s), lower thoracic or lumbar; each additional segment	61.00	1419	1651	435
63090	Vertebral corpectomy (vertebral body resection), partial or complete, transperitoneal or retroperitoneal approach with decompression of spinal cord, cauda equina or nerve root(s), lower thoracic, lumbar, or sacral; single segment	180.0	4187	4872	2369
63091	Vertebral corpectomy (vertebral body resection), partial or complete, transperitoneal or retroperitoneal approach with decompression of spinal cord, cauda equina or nerve root(s), lower thoracic, lumbar, or sacral; each additional segment	60.00	1396	1624	251

63170–63200
Incision

SUBSIDIARY CODES

Subsidiary codes have relative values that require no further adjustment:

20900 is "in addition" to 63170–63200
20902 is "in addition" to 63170–63200
20926 is "in addition" to 63170–63200
61712 is "in addition" to 63170–63200
61795 is "in addition" to 63170–63200

Because these are subsidiary or "in addition to" codes, reimbursement reduction and CPT modifier -51 do not apply.

Code	Description	Medicode RVU	50th	75th	Medicare Nat'l Avg
63170	Laminectomy with myelotomy (eg, Bischof or DREZ type), cervical, thoracic or thoracolumbar	152.0	3536	4114	1580
63172	Laminectomy with drainage of intramedullary cyst/syrinx; to subarachnoid space	168.0	3908	4548	1623
63173	Laminectomy with drainage of intramedullary cyst/syrinx; to peritoneal space	185.0	4303	5008	1481
63180	Laminectomy and section of dentate ligaments, with or without dural graft, cervical; one or two segments	152.0	3536	4114	1189
63182	Laminectomy and section of dentate ligaments, with or without dural graft, cervical; more than two segments	182.0	4234	4927	1481
63185	Laminectomy with rhizotomy; one or two segments	152.0	3536	4114	1271
63190	Laminectomy with rhizotomy; more than two segments	182.0	4234	4927	1607
63191	Laminectomy with section of spinal accessory nerve	136.0	3164	3681	1231
63194	Laminectomy with cordotomy, with section of one spinothalamic tract, one stage; cervical	127.5	2966	3451	1283
63195	Laminectomy with cordotomy, with section of one spinothalamic tract, one stage; thoracic	127.5	2966	3451	1301
63196	Laminectomy with cordotomy, with section of both spinothalamic tracts, one stage; cervical	147.0	3419	3979	1481
63197	Laminectomy with cordotomy, with section of both spinothalamic tracts, one stage; thoracic	141.0	3280	3817	1420
63198	Laminectomy with cordotomy with section of both spinothalamic tracts, two stages within 14 days; cervical	160.0	3722	4331	1629
63199	Laminectomy with cordotomy with section of both spinothalamic tracts, two stages within 14 days; thoracic	160.0	3722	4331	1863
63200	Laminectomy, with release of tethered spinal cord, lumbar	160.0	3722	4331	1244

63250–63290
Excision by Laminectomy of Lesion Other Than Herniated Disk

Coding Insight
For arterial injection procedure and/or for occlusion of spinal arteriovenous malformation see 62294. For transcatheter occlusion or embolization (e.g., to occlude a vascular malformation), percutaneous, spinal cord, see 61624.

Subsidiary Codes
Subsidiary codes have relative values that require no further adjustment:

20900 is "in addition" to 63250–63290
20902 is "in addition" to 63250–63290
20926 is "in addition" to 63250–63290
61712 is "in addition" to 63250–63290
61795 is "in addition" to 63250–63290

Because these are subsidiary or "in addition to" codes, reimbursement reduction and modifier -51 do not apply.

Code	Description	Medicode RVU	50th	75th	Medicare Nat'l Avg
63250	Laminectomy for excision or occlusion of arteriovenous malformation of spinal cord; cervical	164.0	3815	4439	2788
63251	Laminectomy for excision or occlusion of arteriovenous malformation of spinal cord; thoracic	152.0	3536	4114	2567
63252	Laminectomy for excision or occlusion of arteriovenous malformation of spinal cord; thoracolumbar	192.0	4466	5197	2819
63265	Laminectomy for excision or evacuation of intraspinal lesion other than neoplasm, extradural; cervical	160.0	3722	4331	1808
63266	Laminectomy for excision or evacuation of intraspinal lesion other than neoplasm, extradural; thoracic	160.0	3722	4331	1968
63267	Laminectomy for excision or evacuation of intraspinal lesion other than neoplasm, extradural; lumbar	144.0	3350	3898	1706
63268	Laminectomy for excision or evacuation of intraspinal lesion other than neoplasm, extradural; sacral	122.0	2838	3302	1271
63270	Laminectomy for excision of intraspinal lesion other than neoplasm, intradural; cervical	168.0	3908	4548	1810
63271	Laminectomy for excision of intraspinal lesion other than neoplasm, intradural; thoracic	168.0	3908	4548	2195
63272	Laminectomy for excision of intraspinal lesion other than neoplasm, intradural; lumbar	180.0	4187	4872	1992
63273	Laminectomy for excision of intraspinal lesion other than neoplasm, intradural; sacral	152.0	3536	4114	1686
63275	Laminectomy for biopsy/excision of intraspinal neoplasm; extradural, cervical	184.0	4280	4981	2147
63276	Laminectomy for biopsy/excision of intraspinal neoplasm; extradural, thoracic	184.0	4280	4981	2100
63277	Laminectomy for biopsy/excision of intraspinal neoplasm; extradural, lumbar	168.0	3908	4548	1899
63278	Laminectomy for biopsy/excision of intraspinal neoplasm; extradural, sacral	142.0	3303	3844	1835
63280	Laminectomy for biopsy/excision of intraspinal neoplasm; intradural, extramedullary, cervical	200.0	4652	5414	2329
63281	Laminectomy for biopsy/excision of intraspinal neoplasm; intradural, extramedullary, thoracic	200.0	4652	5414	2317
63282	Laminectomy for biopsy/excision of intraspinal neoplasm; intradural, extramedullary, lumbar	220.0	5117	5955	2093
63283	Laminectomy for biopsy/excision of intraspinal neoplasm; intradural, sacral	170.0	3954	4602	1777
63285	Laminectomy for biopsy/excision of intraspinal neoplasm; intradural, intramedullary, cervical	220.0	5117	5955	2454
63286	Laminectomy for biopsy/excision of intraspinal neoplasm; intradural, intramedullary, thoracic	220.0	5117	5955	2629
63287	Laminectomy for biopsy/excision of intraspinal neoplasm; intradural, intramedullary, thoracolumbar	240.0	5583	6497	2524
63290	Laminectomy for biopsy/excision of intraspinal neoplasm; combined extradural-intradural lesion, any level	0.00	0	0	2600

63300–63308
Excision Anterior or Anterolateral Approach, Intraspinal Lesion

Coding Insight
Codes 63300–63308 and 63081–63091 report vertebral corpectomy (vertebral body resection). Codes 63300–63308 report a partial or complete resection of the vertebral body (corpectomy) for intraspinal lesions, extra- or intradural, with different approaches, depending upon the spinal level. Codes 63081–63091 report partial or complete resection performed with different approaches, depending upon the spinal level for decompression of the spinal cord and/or nerve root(s). Codes 22140–22152 for reconstruction of the spine following vertebral corpectomyhave been deleted in *CPT '96*, although parenthetical notes still reference them.

If followed by arthrodesis, see 22554–22585.

Subsidiary Codes
Subsidiary codes have relative values that require no further adjustment:

20900 is "in addition" to 63300–63308
20902 is "in addition" to 63300–63308
20926 is "in addition" to 63300–63308
61712 is "in addition" to 63300–63308
61795 is "in addition" to 63300–63308
63308 is "in addition" to 63300–63307

Because these are subsidiary or "in addition to" codes, reimbursement reduction and modifier -51 do not apply.

Code	Description	Medicode RVU	50th	75th	Medicare Nat'l Avg
63300	Vertebral corpectomy (vertebral body resection), partial or complete, for excision of intraspinal lesion, single segment; extradural, cervical	124.0	2884	3357	1663
63301	Vertebral corpectomy (vertebral body resection), partial or complete, for excision of intraspinal lesion, single segment; extradural, thoracic by transthoracic approach	128.0	2977	3465	1845
63302	Vertebral corpectomy (vertebral body resection), partial or complete, for excision of intraspinal lesion, single segment; extradural, thoracic by thoracolumbar approach	128.0	2977	3465	1948
63303	Vertebral corpectomy (vertebral body resection), partial or complete, for excision of intraspinal lesion, single segment; extradural, lumbar or sacral by transperitoneal or retroperitoneal approach	128.0	2977	3465	1979
63304	Vertebral corpectomy (vertebral body resection), partial or complete, for excision of intraspinal lesion, single segment; intradural, cervical	124.0	2884	3357	2020
63305	Vertebral corpectomy (vertebral body resection), partial or complete, for excision of intraspinal lesion, single segment; intradural, thoracic by transthoracic approach	128.0	2977	3465	2169
63306	Vertebral corpectomy (vertebral body resection), partial or complete, for excision of intraspinal lesion, single segment; intradural, thoracic by thoracolumbar approach	128.0	2977	3465	2156
63307	Vertebral corpectomy (vertebral body resection), partial or complete, for excision of intraspinal lesion, single segment; intradural, lumbar or sacral by transperitoneal or retroperitoneal approach	128.0	2977	3465	2213

Code	Description	Medicode RVU	50th	75th	Medicare Nat'l Avg
63308	Vertebral corpectomy (vertebral body resection), partial or complete, for excision of intraspinal lesion, single segment; each additional segment (list separately in addition to codes for single segment 63300-63307)	43.00	1000	1164	392

63600–63615
Stereotaxis

Coding Insight
Stereotactic surgery allows a structure to be located by three-dimensional coordinates. It differs from 62269 *Biopsy of spinal cord, percutaneous needle*, which uses fluoroscopy, computerized tomography, or ultrasound, for guidance during the biopsy.

Subsidiary Codes
Subsidiary codes have relative values that require no further adjustment:

20900 is "in addition" to 63600–63615
20902 is "in addition" to 63600–63615
20926 is "in addition" to 63600–63615
61795 is "in addition" to 63600–63615

Because these are subsidiary or "in addition to" codes, reimbursement reduction and modifier -51 do not apply.

Code	Description	Medicode RVU	50th	75th	Medicare Nat'l Avg
63600	Creation of lesion of spinal cord by stereotactic method, percutaneous, any modality (including stimulation and/or recording)	100.0	2326	2707	905
63610	Stereotactic stimulation of spinal cord, percutaneous, separate procedure not followed by other surgery	80.00	1861	2166	598
63615	Stereotactic biopsy, aspiration, or excision of lesion, spinal cord	130.0	3024	3519	1130

63650–63691
Neurostimulators (Spinal)

Coding Insight
If neurostimulator electrodes were percutaneously inserted in a previous surgery, a laminectomy may be performed during a revision to gain access to the epidural space for location of an electrode in a different vertebral segment. Because no code exists for this surgical situation, it may be necessary to use 63655 *Laminectomy for implantation of neurostimulator electrodes; epidural*, and append modifier -22 for unusual procedure. Submit a cover letter and operative report with the claim.

Subsidiary Codes

Subsidiary codes have relative values that require no further adjustment:

20900 is "in addition" to 63650–63691
20902 is "in addition" to 63650–63691
20926 is "in addition" to 63650–63691
61795 is "in addition" to 63650–63691

Because these are subsidiary or "in addition to" codes, reimbursement reduction and modifier -51 do not apply.

Code	Description	Medicode RVU	50th	75th	Medicare Nat'l Avg
63650	Percutaneous implantation of neurostimulator electrodes; epidural	147.0	3419	3979	650
63655	Laminectomy for implantation of neurostimulator electrodes; epidural	168.0	3908	4548	1113
63660	Revision or removal of spinal neurostimulator electrodes	75.00	1745	2030	586
63685	Incision and subcutaneous placement of spinal neurostimulator pulse generator or receiver, direct or inductive coupling	60.50	1407	1638	630
63688	Revision or removal of implanted spinal neurostimulator pulse generator or receiver	50.00	1163	1353	501
63690	Electronic analysis of implanted neurostimulator pulse generator system (may include rate, pulse amplitude and duration, configuration of wave form, battery status, electrode selectability, output modulation, cycling, impedance and patient compliance measurements); without reprogramming of pulse generator	4.00	93	108	48
63691	Electronic analysis of implanted neurostimulator pulse generator system (may include rate, pulse amplitude and duration, configuration of wave form, battery status, electrode selectability, output modulation, cycling, impedance and patient compliance measurements); with reprogramming of pulse generator	6.00	140	162	40

63700–63710
Repair

Coding Insight

A meningocele is a spinal birth defect consisting of a cystic sac, cerebrospinal fluid, and meninges. A myelomeningocele is a spinal birth defect consisting of a cystic sac, cerebrospinal fluid, meninges, and part of the spinal cord (depending upon the spinal level of the defect). Pseudomeningocele is an opening in the dura, which may be a postoperative complication caused by trauma or some other process. Be sure to read operative reports and code descriptions carefully to choose the correct code. Because skin closure of these procedures may be complex, see the Integumentary System for additional reportable codes.

Subsidiary Codes

Subsidiary codes have relative values that require no further adjustment:

20900 is "in addition" to 63700–63710
20902 is "in addition" to 63700–63710

20926 is "in addition" to 63700–63710
61712 is "in addition" to 63704–63710
61795 is "in addition" to 63700–63710

Because these are subsidiary or "in addition to" codes, reimbursement reduction and modifier -51 do not apply.

Code	Description	Medicode RVU	50th	75th	Medicare Nat'l Avg
63700	Repair of meningocele; less than 5 cm diameter	120.0	2791	3248	1133
63702	Repair of meningocele; larger than 5 cm diameter	130.0	3024	3519	1275
63704	Repair of myelomeningocele; less than 5 cm diameter	140.0	3257	3790	1416
63706	Repair of myelomeningocele; larger than 5 cm diameter	145.0	3373	3925	1629
63707	Repair of dural/CSF leak, not requiring laminectomy	150.0	3489	4060	1076
63709	Repair of dural/CSF leak or pseudomeningocele, with laminectomy	160.0	3722	4331	1340
63710	Dural graft, spinal	140.0	3257	3790	973

63740–63746
Shunt, Spinal CSF

SUBSIDIARY CODES
Subsidiary codes have relative values that require no further adjustment:

20900 is "in addition" to 63740–63746
20902 is "in addition" to 63740–63746
20926 is "in addition" to 63740–63746
61795 is "in addition" to 63740–63746

Because these are subsidiary or "in addition to" codes, reimbursement reduction and modifier -51 do not apply.

Code	Description	Medicode RVU	50th	75th	Medicare Nat'l Avg
63740	Creation of shunt, lumbar, subarachnoid-peritoneal, -pleural, or other; including laminectomy	120.0	2791	3248	1119
63741	Creation of shunt, lumbar, subarachnoid-peritoneal, -pleural, or other; percutaneous, not requiring laminectomy	65.00	1512	1759	754
63744	Replacement, irrigation or revision of lumbosubarachnoid shunt	60.00	1396	1624	663
63746	Removal of entire lumbosubarachnoid shunt system without replacement	45.00	1047	1218	484

64400–64530

Introduction/Injection of Anesthetic Agent (Nerve Block), Diagnostic or Therapeutic

Coding Insight

For phenol destruction (somatic nerve) see 64600–64640, and for subarachnoid or subdural injection, see 62274–62277. For epidural or caudal injection, see 62278, 62279.

Subsidiary Codes

Subsidiary codes have relative values that require no further adjustment:

20900 is "in addition" to 64400–64530
20902 is "in addition" to 64400–64530
20926 is "in addition" to 64400–64530
61795 is "in addition" to 64400–64999
64443 is "in addition" to 64442

Because these are subsidiary or "in addition to" codes, reimbursement reduction and modifier -51 do not apply.

Code		Description	Medicode RVU	50th	75th	Medicare Nat'l Avg
64400	*	Injection, anesthetic agent; trigeminal nerve, any division or branch	4.48	107	130	58
64402	*	Injection, anesthetic agent; facial nerve	6.00	144	174	76
64405	*	Injection, anesthetic agent; greater occipital nerve	7.00	168	203	69
64408	*	Injection, anesthetic agent; vagus nerve	6.00	144	174	87
64410	*	Injection, anesthetic agent; phrenic nerve	6.00	144	174	78
64412	*	Injection, anesthetic agent; spinal accessory nerve	8.50	204	247	65
64413	*	Injection, anesthetic agent; cervical plexus	8.00	192	233	79
64415	*	Injection, anesthetic agent; brachial plexus	7.50	180	218	65
64417	*	Injection, anesthetic agent; axillary nerve	7.50	180	218	77
64418	*	Injection, anesthetic agent; suprascapular nerve	7.00	168	203	78
64420	*	Injection, anesthetic agent; intercostal nerve, single	8.00	192	233	65
64421	*	Injection, anesthetic agent; intercostal nerves, multiple, regional block	12.50	299	363	96
64425	*	Injection, anesthetic agent; ilioinguinal, iliohypogastric nerves	8.50	204	247	82
64430	*	Injection, anesthetic agent; pudendal nerve	6.50	156	189	90

Code		Description	Medicode RVU	50th	75th	Medicare Nat'l Avg
64435	*	Injection, anesthetic agent; paracervical (uterine) nerve	6.00	144	174	79
64440	*	Injection, anesthetic agent; paravertebral nerve (thoracic, lumbar, sacral, coccygeal), single vertebral level	7.50	180	218	77
64441	*	Injection, anesthetic agent; paravertebral nerves, multiple levels (eg, regional block)	11.00	263	320	103
64442	*	Injection, anesthetic agent; paravertebral facet joint nerve, lumbar, single level	10.50	251	305	101
64443	*	Injection, anesthetic agent; paravertebral facet joint nerve, lumbar, each additional level	6.50	156	189	76
64445	*	Injection, anesthetic agent; sciatic nerve	6.50	156	189	69
64450	*	Injection, anesthetic agent; other peripheral nerve or branch	3.90	93	113	71
64505	*	Injection, anesthetic agent; sphenopalatine ganglion	5.00	120	145	71
64508	*	Injection, anesthetic agent; carotid sinus (separate procedure)	5.00	120	145	77
64510	*	Injection, anesthetic agent; stellate ganglion (cervical sympathetic)	14.00	335	407	78
64520	*	Injection, anesthetic agent; lumbar or thoracic (paravertebral sympathetic)	13.00	311	378	81
64530	*	Injection, anesthetic agent; celiac plexus, with or without radiologic monitoring	16.50	395	480	111

64550–64595
Neurostimulators (Peripheral Nerve)

SUBSIDIARY CODES
Subsidiary codes have relative values that require no further adjustment:

20900 is "in addition" to 64550–64595
20902 is "in addition" to 64550–64595
20926 is "in addition" to 64550–64595
61795 is "in addition" to 64550–64595

Because these are subsidiary or "in addition to" codes, reimbursement reduction and modifier -51 do not apply.

Code	Description	Medicode RVU	50th	75th	Medicare Nat'l Avg
64550	Application of surface (transcutaneous) neurostimulator	3.50	84	102	24
64553	Percutaneous implantation of neurostimulator electrodes; cranial nerve	8.00	192	233	117
64555	Percutaneous implantation of neurostimulator electrodes; peripheral nerve	8.00	192	233	99

Code	Description	Medicode RVU	50th	75th	Medicare Nat'l Avg
64560	Percutaneous implantation of neurostimulator electrodes; autonomic nerve	8.00	192	233	157
64565	Percutaneous implantation of neurostimulator electrodes; neuromuscular	8.00	192	233	88
64573	Incision for implantation of neurostimulator electrodes; cranial nerve	10.00	239	291	315
64575	Incision for implantation of neurostimulator electrodes; peripheral nerve	12.00	287	349	301
64577	Incision for implantation of neurostimulator electrodes; autonomic nerve	12.00	287	349	302
64580	Incision for implantation of neurostimulator electrodes; neuromuscular	12.00	287	349	279
64585	Revision or removal of peripheral neurostimulator electrodes	12.00	287	349	123
64590	Incision and subcutaneous placement of peripheral neurostimulator pulse generator or receiver, direct or inductive coupling	12.00	287	349	176
64595	Revision or removal of peripheral neurostimulator pulse generator or receiver	10.00	239	291	122

64600–64680
Destruction by Neurolytic Agent (e.g., Chemical, Thermal, Electrical, Radiofrequency)

CODING INSIGHT
Other names for this procedure (on the somatic nerve) include rhizotomy, radiculectomy, and radicotomy. Nerve roots are sectioned by use of chemical, thermal, electrical, or radiofrequency. The procedure may be performed to relieve pain or for other reasons.

SUBSIDIARY CODES
Subsidiary codes have relative values that require no further adjustment:

20900 is "in addition" to 64600–64680
20902 is "in addition" to 64600–64680
20926 is "in addition" to 64600–64680
61795 is "in addition" to 64600–64680
64623 is "in addition" to 64622

Because these are subsidiary or "in addition to" codes, reimbursement reduction and modifier -51 do not apply.

Code	Description	Medicode RVU	50th	75th	Medicare Nat'l Avg
64600	Destruction by neurolytic agent, trigeminal nerve; supraorbital, infraorbital, mental, or inferior alveolar branch	10.50	251	292	180
64605	Destruction by neurolytic agent, trigeminal nerve; second and third division branches at foramen ovale	15.00	358	418	258

Code	Description	Medicode RVU	50th	75th	Medicare Nat'l Avg
64610	Destruction by neurolytic agent, trigeminal nerve; second and third division branches at foramen ovale under radiologic monitoring	17.00	406	473	535
64612	Destruction by neurolytic agent (chemodenervation of muscle endplate); muscles enervated by facial nerve (eg, for blepharospasm, hemifacial spasm)	17.00	406	473	137
64613	Destruction by neurolytic agent (chemodenervation of muscle endplate); cervical spinal muscles (eg, for spasmodic torticollis)	17.00	406	473	137
64620	Destruction by neurolytic agent; intercostal nerve	8.25	197	230	137
64622	Destruction by neurolytic agent; paravertebral facet joint nerve, lumbar, single level	13.50	322	376	176
64623	Destruction by neurolytic agent; paravertebral facet joint nerve, lumbar, each additional level	7.50	179	209	70
64630	Destruction by neurolytic agent; pudendal nerve	13.50	322	376	173
64640	Destruction by neurolytic agent; other peripheral nerve or branch	9.00	215	251	123
64680	Destruction by neurolytic agent, celiac plexus, with or without radiologic monitoring	12.00	287	334	162

64702–64727
Neuroplasty (Exploration, Neurolysis, or Nerve Decompression)

Coding Insight
Neuroplasty decompresses an intact nerve from scar tissue. The codes include external neurolysis and/or transposition. A frequently performed procedure for carpal tunnel syndrome, 64721, freeing of the median nerve at carpal tunnel, is listed in this section. For cubital tunnel syndrome, freeing of the ulnar nerve at the elbow, use 64718.

Subsidiary Codes
Subsidiary codes have relative values that require no further adjustment:

20900 is "in addition" to 64702–64727
20902 is "in addition" to 64702–64727
20926 is "in addition" to 64702–64727
61795 is "in addition" to 64702–64727
64727 is "in addition" to 64702–64726

Because these are subsidiary or "in addition to" codes, reimbursement reduction and modifier -51 do not apply.

Code	Description	Medicode RVU	50th	75th	Medicare Nat'l Avg
64702	Neuroplasty; digital, one or both, same digit	30.00	716	835	356
64704	Neuroplasty; nerve of hand or foot	36.00	860	1002	437

Code	Description	Medicode RVU	50th	75th	Medicare Nat'l Avg
64708	Neuroplasty, major peripheral nerve, arm or leg; other than specified	60.00	1433	1670	594
64712	Neuroplasty, major peripheral nerve, arm or leg; sciatic nerve	70.00	1672	1948	723
64713	Neuroplasty, major peripheral nerve, arm or leg; brachial plexus	74.00	1767	2060	840
64714	Neuroplasty, major peripheral nerve, arm or leg; lumbar plexus	55.00	1314	1531	683
64716	Neuroplasty and/or transposition; cranial nerve (specify)	65.00	1552	1809	444
64718	Neuroplasty and/or transposition; ulnar nerve at elbow	65.00	1552	1809	549
64719	Neuroplasty and/or transposition; ulnar nerve at wrist	43.50	1039	1211	427
64721	Neuroplasty and/or transposition; median nerve at carpal tunnel	46.00	1099	1280	385
64722	Decompression; unspecified nerve(s) (specify)	46.00	1099	1280	475
64726	Decompression; plantar digital nerve	20.00	478	557	192
64727	Internal neurolysis, requiring use of operating microscope (list separately in addition to code for neuroplasty) (Neuroplasty includes external neurolysis)	0.00	0	0	287

64732–64772
Transection or Avulsion

Coding Insight
Because many bilateral codes have been dropped from CPT, it is often necessary to append modifier -50 when a surgery is performed bilaterally and a separate bilateral code is not listed.

Subsidiary Codes
Subsidiary codes have relative values that require no further adjustment:

20900 is "in addition" to 64732–64772
20902 is "in addition" to 64732–64772
20926 is "in addition" to 64732–64772
61795 is "in addition" to 64732–64772

Because these are subsidiary or "in addition to" codes, reimbursement reduction and modifier -51 do not apply.

Code	Description	Medicode RVU	50th	75th	Medicare Nat'l Avg
64732	Transection or avulsion of; supraorbital nerve	30.00	716	835	365
64734	Transection or avulsion of; infraorbital nerve	30.00	716	835	392

Code	Description	Medicode RVU	50th	75th	Medicare Nat'l Avg
64736	Transection or avulsion of; mental nerve	36.00	860	1002	364
64738	Transection or avulsion of; inferior alveolar nerve by osteotomy	44.00	1051	1225	441
64740	Transection or avulsion of; lingual nerve	55.00	1314	1531	432
64742	Transection or avulsion of; facial nerve, differential or complete	55.00	1314	1531	453
64744	Transection or avulsion of; greater occipital nerve	35.00	836	974	471
64746	Transection or avulsion of; phrenic nerve	25.00	597	696	395
64752	Transection or avulsion of; vagus nerve (vagotomy), transthoracic	75.00	1791	2088	456
64755	Transection or avulsion of; vagi limited to proximal stomach (selective proximal vagotomy, proximal gastric vagotomy, parietal cell vagotomy, supra- or highly selective vagotomy)	110.0	2627	3062	1014
64760	Transection or avulsion of; vagus nerve (vagotomy), abdominal	70.00	1672	1948	584
64761	Transection or avulsion of; pudendal nerve	25.00	597	696	438
64763	Transection or avulsion of obturator nerve, extrapelvic, with or without adductor tenotomy	30.00	716	835	484
64766	Transection or avulsion of obturator nerve, intrapelvic, with or without adductor tenotomy	45.00	1075	1253	629
64771	Transection or avulsion of other cranial nerve, extradural	50.00	1194	1392	552
64772	Transection or avulsion of other spinal nerve, extradural	30.00	716	835	589

64774–64876
Excision

Subsidiary Codes

Subsidiary codes have relative values that require no further adjustment:

20900 is "in addition" to 64774–64876
20902 is "in addition" to 64774–64876
20926 is "in addition" to 64774–64876
61795 is "in addition" to 64774–64876
64778 is "in addition" to 64776
64783 is "in addition" to 64782
64787 is "in addition" to 64774–64786
64830 is "in addition" to 64831–64876
64832 is "in addition" to 64831
64837 is "in addition" to 64834, 64835, 64836
64859 is "in addition" to 64856, 64857, 64858
64872 is "in addition" to 64831–64865

64874 is "in addition" to 64831, 64834–64836, 64840, 64858, 64861–64865
64876 is "in addition" to 64831, 64834–64836

Because these are subsidiary or "in addition to" codes, reimbursement reduction and modifier -51 do not apply.

Code	Description	Medicode RVU	50th	75th	Medicare Nat'l Avg
64774	Excision of neuroma; cutaneous nerve, surgically identifiable	23.00	549	640	313
64776	Excision of neuroma; digital nerve, one or both, same digit	24.00	573	668	312
64778	Excision of neuroma; digital nerve, each additional digit (list separately by this number)	9.75	233	271	243
64782	Excision of neuroma; hand or foot, except digital nerve	32.00	764	891	428
64783	Excision of neuroma; hand or foot, each additional nerve, except same digit (list separately by this number)	16.00	382	445	289
64784	Excision of neuroma; major peripheral nerve, except sciatic	47.00	1123	1308	630
64786	Excision of neuroma; sciatic nerve	67.00	1600	1865	1154
64787	Implantation of nerve end into bone or muscle (list separately in addition to neuroma excision)	35.00	836	974	326
64788	Excision of neurofibroma or neurolemmoma; cutaneous nerve	36.00	860	1002	338
64790	Excision of neurofibroma or neurolemmoma; major peripheral nerve	55.00	1314	1531	758
64792	Excision of neurofibroma or neurolemmoma; extensive (including malignant type)	65.00	1552	1809	982
64795	Biopsy of nerve	20.00	478	557	231
64802	Sympathectomy, cervical	72.50	1732	2018	584
64804	Sympathectomy, cervicothoracic	106.0	2532	2950	1131
64809	Sympathectomy, thoracolumbar	103.0	2460	2867	993
64818	Sympathectomy, lumbar	75.00	1791	2088	809
64820	Sympathectomy, digital arteries, with magnification, each digit	37.00	884	1030	661
64830	Microdissection and/or microrepair of nerve (list separately in addition to code for nerve repair)	0.00	0	0	218
64831	Suture of digital nerve, hand or foot; one nerve	37.50	896	1044	491
64832	Suture of digital nerve, hand or foot; each additional digital nerve	25.00	597	696	282
64834	Suture of one nerve, hand or foot; common sensory nerve	41.00	979	1141	537
64835	Suture of one nerve, hand or foot; median motor thenar	43.00	1027	1197	678

Code	Description	Medicode RVU	50th	75th	Medicare Nat'l Avg
64836	Suture of one nerve, hand or foot; ulnar motor	50.00	1194	1392	717
64837	Suture of each additional nerve, hand or foot	25.00	597	696	448
64840	Suture of posterior tibial nerve	60.00	1433	1670	907
64856	Suture of major peripheral nerve, arm or leg, except sciatic; including transposition	75.00	1791	2088	879
64857	Suture of major peripheral nerve, arm or leg, except sciatic; without transposition	60.00	1433	1670	950
64858	Suture of sciatic nerve	70.00	1672	1948	1107
64859	Suture of each additional major peripheral nerve	31.00	740	863	323
64861	Suture of; brachial plexus	70.00	1672	1948	1274
64862	Suture of; lumbar plexus	88.00	2102	2449	1606
64864	Suture of facial nerve; extracranial	68.00	1624	1893	821
64865	Suture of facial nerve; infratemporal, with or without grafting	85.00	2030	2366	1113
64866	Anastomosis; facial-spinal accessory	120.0	2866	3340	1088
64868	Anastomosis; facial-hypoglossal	120.0	2866	3340	1038
64870	Anastomosis; facial-phrenic	120.0	2866	3340	1198
64872	Suture of nerve; requiring secondary or delayed suture (list separately in addition to code for primary neurorrhaphy)	0.00	0	0	144
64874	Suture of nerve; requiring extensive mobilization, or transposition of nerve (list separately in addition to code for nerve suture)	0.00	0	0	217
64876	Suture of nerve; requiring shortening of bone of extremity (list separately in addition to code for nerve suture)	0.00	0	0	215

64885–64999
Neurorrhaphy with Nerve Graft

Cosmetic Warning
Code 64886 is considered cosmetic 85 percent of the time or more.

Subsidiary Codes
Subsidiary codes have relative values that require no further adjustment:

20900 is "in addition" to 64885–64999
20902 is "in addition" to 64885–64999
20926 is "in addition" to 64885–64999

61795 is "in addition" to 64885–64999
64830 is "in addition" to 64885–64907
64901 is "in addition" to 64885–64893
64902 is "in addition" to 64885, 64886, 64895–64898

Because these are subsidiary or "in addition to" codes, reimbursement reduction and modifier -51 do not apply.

Code	Description	Medicode RVU	50th	75th	Medicare Nat'l Avg
64885	Nerve graft (includes obtaining graft), head or neck; up to 4 cm in length	81.25	1940	2262	1202
64886	Nerve graft (includes obtaining graft), head or neck; more than 4 cm in length	100.0	2388	2783	1433
64890	Nerve graft (includes obtaining graft), single strand, hand or foot; up to 4 cm length	65.00	1552	1809	1115
64891	Nerve graft (includes obtaining graft), single strand, hand or foot; more than 4 cm length	80.00	1911	2227	1064
64892	Nerve graft (includes obtaining graft), single strand, arm or leg; up to 4 cm length	65.00	1552	1809	1034
64893	Nerve graft (includes obtaining graft), single strand, arm or leg; more than 4 cm length	80.00	1911	2227	1195
64895	Nerve graft (includes obtaining graft), multiple strands (cable), hand or foot; up to 4 cm length	98.00	2341	2728	1322
64896	Nerve graft (includes obtaining graft), multiple strands (cable), hand or foot; more than 4 cm length	120.0	2866	3340	1510
64897	Nerve graft (includes obtaining graft), multiple strands (cable), arm or leg; up to 4 cm length	98.00	2341	2728	1261
64898	Nerve graft (includes obtaining graft), multiple strands (cable), arm or leg; more than 4 cm length	120.0	2866	3340	1364
64901	Nerve graft, each additional nerve; single strand	32.50	776	905	827
64902	Nerve graft, each additional nerve; multiple strands (cable)	49.00	1170	1364	961
64905	Nerve pedicle transfer; first stage	40.00	955	1113	908
64907	Nerve pedicle transfer; second stage	57.00	1361	1587	1300
64999	Unlisted procedure, nervous system	0.00	0	0	–

EYE AND OCULAR ADNEXA

CODING INSIGHT

When coding, keep in mind that there are many outdated or infrequently used procedure codes in CPT, such as 66150 *Fistulization of sclera for glaucoma; trephination with iridectomy*, or 66820 *Discission of secondary membranous cataract (opacified posterior lens capsule and/or anterior hyaloid; stab incision technique (Ziegler or Wheeler knife)*. Procedures once popular often become obsolete when other treatment methods are developed, and very few physicians will continue using the old method. Always check with your provider if you are not sure which method was used to accomplish a procedure.

Several of the codes listed in the Ophthalmology section of CPT specify that they may be performed in one or more stages or sessions. Note the following:

- If the procedure specifies one or more stages, subsequent stages necessary to complete the procedure should not be reported.
- If the procedure specifies one or more sessions, subsequent sessions necessary to complete the procedure should not be reported.
- If the procedure does not specify one or more stages or sessions, but is performed in two stages, only one code should be used to report the procedure unless significant other services are performed. Examples are 66180 *Aqueous shunt to extraocular reservoir, (e.g., Molteno, Schocket, Denver-Krupin)* and 66185 *Revision of aqueous shunt to extraocular reservoir*. Although 66180 is sometimes done as a two-stage procedure, the code should only be reported once. The amount assigned to the code by payers assumes that the procedure will be completed. The second stage could not be considered a revision (66185) because the initial surgery was never completed. If extenuating conditions cause the procedure to be completed at a later date, modifier -22 may be warranted if the service provided is greater than that usually required to accomplish the procedure. Another way to report this type of situation is to report the code and use modifier -52 to reduce the procedure until it is completed, at which time the same code and modifier are used again — but the charge cannot exceed the usual charge. In either scenario the operative reports and a cover letter should be submitted with the claims to clarify that two stages were needed to complete the procedure.

65091–65175
Removal of Eye/Secondary Implant(s) Procedures

Coding Insight
For prescription, fitting, supply of ocular prosthesis (artificial eye) with medical supervision of adaptation or prescription of ocular prosthesis (artificial eye), and direction of fitting and supply by independent technician with medical supervision of adaptation, see 92330–92335.

Nota Bene: An implant is always placed after an evisceration to maintain the viability of the scleral shell. If the patient must be monitored for a period of time before an implant is permanently affixed, a temporary implant is used and 65091 ("without implant") is reported. Code 65130 is only used if the initial implant is a permanent one. Rearrangement of conjunctival tissues following evisceration and the placement of a permanent artificial eye can be separately reported with 68320–68340.

Subsidiary Codes
Subsidiary codes have relative values that require no further adjustment:

20900 is "in addition" to 65091–65175
20902 is "in addition" to 65091–65175
20920 is "in addition" to 65091–65175
20922 is "in addition" to 65091–65175
20926 is "in addition" to 65091–65175

Because these are subsidiary or "in addition to" codes, reimbursement reduction and modifier -51 do not apply.

Code	Description	Medicode RVU	50th	75th	Medicare Nat'l Avg
65091	Evisceration of ocular contents; without implant	55.00	1241	1466	579
65093	Evisceration of ocular contents; with implant	60.00	1354	1599	635
65101	Enucleation of eye; without implant	55.00	1241	1466	618
65103	Enucleation of eye; with implant, muscles not attached to implant	60.00	1354	1599	679
65105	Enucleation of eye; with implant, muscles attached to implant	75.00	1692	1999	747
65110	Exenteration of orbit (does not include skin graft), removal of orbital contents; only	100.0	2256	2665	1196
65112	Exenteration of orbit (does not include skin graft), removal of orbital contents; with therapeutic removal of bone	112.5	2538	2998	1124
65114	Exenteration of orbit (does not include skin graft), removal of orbital contents; with muscle or myocutaneous flap	120.0	2707	3198	1225
65125	Modification of ocular implant with placement or replacement of pegs (eg, drilling receptacle for prosthesis appendage) (separate procedure)	0.00	0	0	217
65130	Insertion of ocular implant secondary; after evisceration, in scleral shell	55.00	1241	1466	631
65135	Insertion of ocular implant secondary; after enucleation, muscles not attached to implant	62.50	1410	1666	501
65140	Insertion of ocular implant secondary; after enucleation, muscles attached to implant	75.00	1692	1999	555
65150	Reinsertion of ocular implant; with or without conjunctival graft	55.00	1241	1466	604
65155	Reinsertion of ocular implant; with use of foreign material for reinforcement and/or attachment of muscles to implant	75.00	1692	1999	797
65175	Removal of ocular implant	40.00	902	1066	552

65205–65290
Removal of Foreign Body/ Repair of Laceration

Coding Insight
For diagnostic x-ray for foreign body, see 70030; for echography, see 76529.

Nota Bene: Codes 65205–65265 are for removal of foreign body without repair, if repair is made to the conjunctiva or cornea, codes 65270–65290 for repair of laceration should also be reported. Any ophthalmic exam to rule out retinal problems is reported separately. If a therapeutic contact lens is applied, it also can be reported separately with 92070. Remember to report surgical trays (HCPCS code A4550) when they are used.

Subsidiary Codes
Subsidiary codes have relative values that require no further adjustment:

20900 is "in addition" to 65205–65290
20902 is "in addition" to 65205–65290

20920 is "in addition" to 65205–65290
20922 is "in addition" to 65205–65290
20926 is "in addition" to 65205–65290

Because these are subsidiary or "in addition to" codes, reimbursement reduction and modifier -51 do not apply.

Code		Description	Medicode RVU	50th	75th	Medicare Nat'l Avg
65205	*	Removal of foreign body, external eye; conjunctival superficial	2.90	65	77	44
65210	*	Removal of foreign body, external eye; conjunctival embedded (includes concretions), subconjunctival, or scleral nonperforating	3.25	73	87	52
65220	*	Removal of foreign body, external eye; corneal, without slit lamp	3.60	81	96	44
65222	*	Removal of foreign body, external eye; corneal, with slit lamp	4.10	93	109	60
65235		Removal of foreign body, intraocular; from anterior chamber or lens	65.00	1466	1732	525
65260		Removal of foreign body, intraocular; from posterior segment, magnetic extraction, anterior or posterior route	65.00	1466	1732	758
65265		Removal of foreign body, intraocular; from posterior segment, nonmagnetic extraction	75.00	1692	1999	890
65270	*	Repair of laceration; conjunctiva, with or without nonperforating laceration sclera, direct closure	6.00	135	160	121
65272		Repair of laceration; conjunctiva, by mobilization and rearrangement, without hospitalization	9.00	203	240	208
65273		Repair of laceration; conjunctiva, by mobilization and rearrangement, with hospitalization	15.00	338	400	285
65275		Repair of laceration; cornea, nonperforating, with or without removal foreign body	13.00	293	346	234
65280		Repair of laceration; cornea and/or sclera, perforating, not involving uveal tissue	60.00	1354	1599	679
65285		Repair of laceration; cornea and/or sclera, perforating, with reposition or resection of uveal tissue	80.00	1805	2132	1010
65286		Repair of laceration; application of tissue glue, wounds of cornea and/or sclera	30.00	677	800	399
65290		Repair of wound, extraocular muscle, tendon and/or Tenon's capsule	40.00	902	1066	457

65400–65775
Anterior Segment, Cornea

CODING INSIGHT

Keratoplasty excludes refractive keratoplasty procedures 65760, 65765, and 65767.

Nota Bene: Code 65400 *Excision of lesion, cornea (keratectomy, lamellar, partial, except pterygium* and 65410 *Biopsy of cornea* are frequently and incorrectly reported together. Biopsy is not reported separately when a therapeutic excision is performed during the same operative session.

Code 65710 is also used to report the rotation of a patient's own lamellar corneal tissue in an uncommon procedure where the patient's corneal tissue is excised, rotated, and reattached to move a corneal defect out of the visual field.

The difference in codes 65730–65755 is the status of the patient's lens. Code 65730 refers to those who still have a natural lens and are "aphakic, with lens." Code 65750 is for those who have had cataract surgery and are "aphakic, without lens." Code 65755 is for those who have an artificial intraocular lens and are "pseudoaphakic, without natural lens."

Code 65760, performed to correct high degrees of myopia, has largely been replaced by the anterior lamellar keratoplasty (ALK), which should be reported with 66999 *Unlisted procedure* (anterior chamber of eye). Submit a cover letter and operative report with the claim.

Codes 65765–65771 for the correction of refractive errors are usually not done out of medical necessity; hence, patients are usually responsible for all charges connected with this surgery. However, 65767 may be paid in cases where patients are aphakic (without lens) and lens implantation is contraindicated. Reimbursement may also be considered if a prior authorization is requested for these procedures and a cover letter accompanies the claim explaining the unusual circumstance.

Code 65772 *Corneal relaxing incision for correction of surgically induced astigmatism* is rarely done. Most physicians prefer the corneal wedge resection, 65775. The procedure is usually performed with a subconjunctival or retrobulbar injection rather than a general anesthesia.

Some payers require the repair to be performed within a certain time frame (e.g., within one year of the original surgery). Check with your Medicare carrier for policy guidelines when using 65772 or 65775.

SUBSIDIARY CODES

Subsidiary codes have relative values that require no further adjustment:

20900 is "in addition" to 65400–65775
20902 is "in addition" to 65400–65775
20920 is "in addition" to 65400–65775
20922 is "in addition" to 65400–65775
20926 is "in addition" to 65400–65775

Because these are subsidiary or "in addition to" codes, reimbursement reduction and modifier -51 do not apply.

MEDICARE ALERT

Medicare rebundles certain codes in the surgery section when the listed codes are considered a component of a more comprehensive service.

65710, 66030, 67500, 92504 will not be reimbursed when reported with 65730, 65750

Code		Description	Medicode RVU	50th	75th	Medicare Nat'l Avg
65400		Excision of lesion, cornea (keratectomy, lamellar, partial), except pterygium	42.00	952	1098	499
65410	*	Biopsy of cornea	7.50	170	196	132
65420		Excision or transposition of pterygium; without graft	33.00	748	863	344
65426		Excision or transposition of pterygium; with graft	45.00	1020	1177	493

Code		Description	Medicode RVU	50th	75th	Medicare Nat'l Avg
65430	*	Scraping of cornea, diagnostic, for smear and/or culture	3.50	79	92	59
65435	*	Removal of corneal epithelium; with or without chemocauterization (abrasion, curettage)	5.00	113	131	68
65436		Removal of corneal epithelium; with application of chelating agent (eg, EDTA)	10.00	227	261	217
65450		Destruction of lesion of cornea by cryotherapy, photocoagulation or thermocauterization	8.00	181	209	255
65600		Multiple punctures of anterior cornea (eg, for corneal erosion, tattoo)	27.00	612	706	235
65710		Keratoplasty (corneal transplant); lamellar	110.0	2494	2876	1152
65730		Keratoplasty (corneal transplant); penetrating (except in aphakia)	135.0	3060	3530	1451
65750		Keratoplasty (corneal transplant); penetrating (in aphakia)	140.0	3174	3661	1529
65755		Keratoplasty (corneal transplant); penetrating (in pseudophakia)	145.0	3287	3792	1587
65760		Keratomileusis	125.0	2834	3269	–
65765		Keratophakia	145.0	3287	3792	–
65767		Epikeratoplasty	135.0	3060	3530	–
65770		Keratoprosthesis	135.0	3060	3530	1222
65771		Radial keratotomy	73.50	1666	1922	–
65772		Corneal relaxing incision for correction of surgically induced astigmatism	36.00	816	941	402
65775		Corneal wedge resection for correction of surgically induced astigmatism	45.00	1020	1177	542

65800–65860
Anterior Chamber–Incision

Coding Insight

Note that 65815 reports the aspiration of blood and should not be confused with 65930, which reports aspiration of a blood clot. Gonioscopy performed for 65820 can be reported separately with 92020.

Subsidiary Codes

Subsidiary codes have relative values that require no further adjustment:

20900 is "in addition" to 65800–65860
20902 is "in addition" to 65800–65860
20920 is "in addition" to 65800–65860
20922 is "in addition" to 65800–65860
20926 is "in addition" to 65800–65860

Because these are subsidiary or "in addition to" codes, reimbursement reduction and modifier -51 do not apply.

Medicare Alert
Medicare rebundles certain codes in the surgery section when the listed codes are considered a component of a more comprehensive service.

67500, 92504 will not be reimbursed when reported with 65855

Code		Description	Medicode RVU	50th	75th	Medicare Nat'l Avg
65800	*	Paracentesis of anterior chamber of eye (separate procedure); with diagnostic aspiration of aqueous	8.00	190	218	153
65805	*	Paracentesis of anterior chamber of eye (separate procedure); with therapeutic release of aqueous	8.00	190	218	156
65810		Paracentesis of anterior chamber of eye (separate procedure); with removal of vitreous and/or discission of anterior hyaloid membrane, with or without air injection	40.00	948	1092	425
65815		Paracentesis of anterior chamber of eye (separate procedure); with removal of blood, with or without irrigation and/or air injection	45.00	1066	1228	377
65820		Goniotomy	65.00	1540	1774	693
65850		Trabeculotomy ab externo	60.00	1422	1638	946
65855		Trabeculoplasty by laser surgery, one or more sessions (defined treatment series)	54.00	1280	1474	582
65860		Severing adhesions of anterior segment, laser technique (separate procedure)	40.00	948	1092	426

65865–66030
Other Procedures

Coding Insight
Laser surgery has largely replaced procedure codes 65865–65880. For laser surgery, see 66821.

Code 65920 is also used if the physician amputates the haptics of an anterior chamber lens. If the old lens is replaced with a new one, report 66986.

Subsidiary Codes
Subsidiary codes have relative values that require no further adjustment:

20900 is "in addition" to 65865–66030
20902 is "in addition" to 65865–66030
20920 is "in addition" to 65865–66030
20922 is "in addition" to 65865–66030
20926 is "in addition" to 65865–66030

Because these are subsidiary or "in addition to" codes, reimbursement reduction and modifier -51 do not apply.

Code		Description	Medicode RVU	50th	75th	Medicare Nat'l Avg.
65865		Severing adhesions of anterior segment of eye, incisional technique (with or without injection of air or liquid) (separate procedure); goniosynechiae	60.00	1422	1638	520
65870		Severing adhesions of anterior segment of eye, incisional technique (with or without injection of air or liquid) (separate procedure); anterior synechiae, except goniosynechiae	43.00	1019	1174	483
65875		Severing adhesions of anterior segment of eye, incisional technique (with or without injection of air or liquid) (separate procedure); posterior synechiae	43.00	1019	1174	517
65880		Severing adhesions of anterior segment of eye, incisional technique (with or without injection of air or liquid) (separate procedure); corneovitreal adhesions	43.00	1019	1174	551
65900		Removal of epithelial downgrowth, anterior chamber eye	62.00	1469	1692	757
65920		Removal of implanted material, anterior segment eye	80.00	1896	2183	739
65930		Removal of blood clot, anterior segment eye	51.00	1209	1392	610
66020		Injection, anterior chamber (separate procedure); air or liquid	10.00	237	273	156
66030	*	Injection, anterior chamber (separate procedure); medication	7.00	166	191	77

66130–66250
Anterior Sclera

Coding Insight
Procedure codes 66150 and 66165 are rarely performed. For operations on posterior sclera, see 67250 and 67235. If 66165 is performed, include a cover letter with the claims submission.

Procedures 66170–66172 are nearly identical to 65850 with two exceptions: the scleral dissection is shallower here, and the full thickness wedge of trabecular meshwork is removed rather than simply opened.

Subsidiary Codes
Subsidiary codes have relative values that require no further adjustment:

20900 is "in addition" to 66130–66250
20902 is "in addition" to 66130–66250
20920 is "in addition" to 66130–66250
20922 is "in addition" to 66130–66250
20926 is "in addition" to 66130–66250

Because these are subsidiary or "in addition to" codes, reimbursement reduction and modifier -51 do not apply.

Medicare Alert
Medicare rebundles certain codes in the surgery section when the listed codes are considered a component of a more comprehensive service.

65850, 66030, 66625, 67500, 92504 will not be reimbursed when reported with 66170

Code	Description	Medicode RVU	50th	75th	Medicare Nat'l Avg
66130	Excision of lesion, sclera	50.00	1089	1273	518
66150	Fistulization of sclera for glaucoma; trephination with iridectomy	80.00	1742	2037	722
66155	Fistulization of sclera for glaucoma; thermocauterization with iridectomy	75.00	1633	1910	707
66160	Fistulization of sclera for glaucoma; sclerectomy with punch or scissors, with iridectomy	75.00	1633	1910	832
66165	Fistulization of sclera for glaucoma; iridencleisis or iridotasis	75.00	1633	1910	674
66170	Fistulization of sclera for glaucoma; trabeculectomy ab externo in absence of previous surgery	85.00	1851	2165	987
66172	Fistulization of sclera for glaucoma; trabeculectomy ab externo with scarring from previous ocular surgery or trauma (includes injection of antifibrotic agents)	102.0	2221	2598	1058
66180	Aqueous shunt to extraocular reservoir (eg, Molteno, Schocket, Denver-Krupin)	95.00	2068	2419	1178
66185	Revision of aqueous shunt to extraocular reservoir	57.00	1241	1452	706
66220	Repair of scleral staphyloma; without graft	110.0	2395	2801	549
66225	Repair of scleral staphyloma; with graft	130.0	2830	3311	1011
66250	Revision or repair of operative wound of anterior segment, any type, early or late, major or minor procedure	55.00	1197	1401	555

66500–66770

Iris, Ciliary Body

Coding Insight

For excision of lesion, use 66600 or 66605. For the removal of an epithelial down-growth, see 65900.

Subsidiary Codes

Subsidiary codes have relative values that require no further adjustment:

20900 is "in addition" to 66500–66770
20902 is "in addition" to 66500–66770
20920 is "in addition" to 66500–66770
20922 is "in addition" to 66500–66770
20926 is "in addition" to 66500–66770

Because these are subsidiary or "in addition to" codes, reimbursement reduction and modifier -51 do not apply.

Medicare Alert

Medicare rebundles certain codes in the surgery section when the listed codes are considered a component of a more comprehensive service.

66762, 67500, 92504 will not be reimbursed when reported with 66761

Code	Description	Medicode RVU	50th	75th	Medicare Nat'l Avg
66500	Iridotomy by stab incision (separate procedure); except transfixion	25.00	544	637	334
66505	Iridotomy by stab incision (separate procedure); with transfixion as for iris bombe	20.00	435	509	290
66600	Iridectomy, with corneoscleral or corneal section; for removal of lesion	75.00	1633	1910	724
66605	Iridectomy, with cyclectomy	102.0	2221	2598	973
66625	Iridotomy by stab incision (separate procedure); peripheral for glaucoma (separate procedure)	56.00	1219	1426	556
66630	Iridotomy by stab incision (separate procedure); sector for glaucoma (separate procedure)	56.00	1219	1426	550
66635	Iridotomy by stab incision (separate procedure); "optical" (separate procedure)	56.00	1219	1426	579
66680	Repair of iris, ciliary body (as for iridodialysis)	46.00	1001	1171	506
66682	Suture of iris, ciliary body (separate procedure) with retrieval of suture through small incision (eg, McCannel suture)	55.00	1197	1401	585
66700	Ciliary body destruction; diathermy	48.00	1045	1222	471
66710	Ciliary body destruction; cyclophotocoagulation	50.00	1089	1273	486
66720	Ciliary body destruction; cryotherapy	48.00	1045	1222	474
66740	Ciliary body destruction; cyclodialysis	65.00	1415	1655	476
66761	Iridotomy/iridectomy by laser surgery (eg, for glaucoma) (one or more sessions)	50.00	1089	1273	500
66762	Iridoplasty by photocoagulation (one or more sessions) (eg, for improvement of vision, for widening of anterior chamber angle)	51.00	1110	1299	520
66770	Destruction of cyst or lesion iris or ciliary body (nonexcisional procedure)	50.00	1089	1273	488

66820–66999
Lens Incision, Removal Cataract, Anterior Segment

Coding Insight
Most secondary membranous cataracts (66820) today are treated with laser surgery, not knife discission. If tissue is removed, use 66830.

The use of viscoelastic agents, enzymatic zonulysis, and other pharmacologic agents — as well as subconjunctival or sub-Tenon injections — are included in 66830–66940.

Code 66983 is performed less commonly than extracapsular extraction, and is generally reserved for patients whose natural lenses are not secure.

Procedure code 66985 is usually reserved for patients who have undergone traditional cataract surgery without lens implantation many years before or who experienced a complication during initial cataract surgery that precluded lens implantation at that time. Use 66983 or 66984 for implant concurrent with cataract surgery.

SUBSIDIARY CODES

Subsidiary codes have relative values that require no further adjustment:

20900 is "in addition" to 66830–66986
20902 is "in addition" to 66830–66986
20920 is "in addition" to 66830–66986
20922 is "in addition" to 66830–66986
20926 is "in addition" to 66830–66986

Because these are subsidiary or "in addition to" codes, reimbursement reduction and modifier -51 do not apply.

MEDICARE ALERT

Medicare rebundles certain codes in the surgery section when the listed codes are considered a component of a more comprehensive service.

63030, 66625, 66820–66821, 67005, 67500 will not be reimbursed when reported with 66830, 66983–66984
63030, 66625, 67500 will not be reimbursed when reported with 66985

Code	Description	Medicode RVU	50th	75th	Medicare Nat'l Avg
66820	Discission of secondary membranous cataract (opacified posterior lens capsule and/or anterior hyaloid); stab incision technique (Ziegler or Wheeler knife)	38.00	814	933	363
66821	Discission of secondary membranous cataract (opacified posterior lens capsule and/or anterior hyaloid); laser surgery (eg, YAG laser) (one or more stages)	42.50	911	1044	401
66825	Repositioning of intraocular lens prosthesis, requiring an incision (separate procedure)	74.00	1586	1818	649
66830	Removal of secondary membranous cataract (opacified posterior lens capsule and/or anterior hyaloid) with corneo-scleral section, with or without iridectomy (iridocapsulotomy, iridocapsulectomy)	51.00	1159	1279	633
66840	Removal of lens material; aspiration technique, one or more stages	93.00	2113	2333	729
66850	Removal of lens material; phacofragmentation technique (mechanical or ultrasonic) (eg, phacoemulsification), with aspiration	100.0	2272	2509	864
66852	Removal of lens material; pars plana approach, with or without vitrectomy	120.0	2727	3011	927
66920	Removal of lens material; intracapsular	88.00	2000	2208	813
66930	Removal of lens material; intracapsular, for dislocated lens	100.0	2272	2509	843
66940	Removal of lens material; extracapsular (other than 66840, 66850, 66852)	95.00	2159	2383	838
66983	Intracapsular cataract extraction with insertion of intraocular lens prosthesis (one stage procedure)	99.00	2250	2484	1033

Code	Description	Medicode RVU	50th	75th	Medicare Nat'l Avg
66984	Extracapsular cataract removal with insertion of intraocular lens prosthesis (one stage procedure), manual or mechanical technique (eg, irrigation and aspiration or phacoemulsification)	104.0	2363	2609	1117
66985	Insertion of intraocular lens prosthesis (secondary implant), not associated with concurrent cataract removal	84.00	1909	2107	818
66986	Exchange of intraocular lens	0.00	0	0	992
66999	Unlisted procedure, anterior segment of eye	0.00	0	0	–

67005–67040
Posterior Segment, Vitreous

Coding Insight
Use 67005–67010 cautiously as these procedures are rarely performed today. For vitreous removal by paracentesis of anterior chamber, see 65810. For removal of corneo-vitreal adhesions, see 65880.

Subsidiary Codes
Subsidiary codes have relative values that require no further adjustment:

20900 is "in addition" to 67005–67040
20902 is "in addition" to 67005–67040
20920 is "in addition" to 67005–67040
20922 is "in addition" to 67005–67040
20926 is "in addition" to 67005–67040

Because these are subsidiary or "in addition to" codes, reimbursement reduction and modifier -51 do not apply.

Medicare Alert
Medicare rebundles certain codes in the surgery section when the listed codes are considered a component of a more comprehensive service.

66030, 67500 will not be reimbursed when reported with 67005
66030, 67005, 67500 will not be reimbursed when reported with 67010
67005, 67010, 67015, 67025, 67028, 67031, 67500will not be reimbursed when reported with 67036, 67038
67028 will not be reimbursed when reported with 67039–67040

Code	Description	Medicode RVU	50th	75th	Medicare Nat'l Avg
67005	Removal of vitreous, anterior approach (open sky technique or limbal incision); partial removal	90.00	2113	2405	952
67010	Removal of vitreous, anterior approach (open sky technique or limbal incision); subtotal removal with mechanical vitrectomy	105.0	2465	2806	1022
67015	Aspiration or release of vitreous, subretinal or choroidal fluid, pars plana approach (posterior sclerotomy)	42.00	986	1122	551

Code	Description	Medicode RVU	50th	75th	Medicare Nat'l Avg
67025	Injection of vitreous substitute, pars plana or limbal approach, (fluid-gas exchange), with or without aspiration (separate procedure)	50.00	1174	1336	551
67028	Intravitreal injection of a pharmacologic agent (separate procedure)	19.50	458	521	244
67030	Discission of vitreous strands (without removal), pars plana approach	60.00	1409	1604	495
67031	Severing of vitreous strands, vitreous face adhesions, sheets, membranes or opacities, laser surgery (one or more stages)	50.00	1174	1336	591
67036	Vitrectomy, mechanical, pars plana approach;	145.0	3404	3875	1587
67038	Vitrectomy, mechanical, pars plana approach; with epiretinal membrane stripping	185.0	4343	4944	2062
67039	Vitrectomy, mechanical, pars plana approach; with focal endolaser photocoagulation	160.0	3756	4276	1502
67040	Vitrectomy, mechanical, pars plana approach; with endolaser panretinal photocoagulation	170.0	3991	4543	1883

67101–67228
Retina or Choroid

Coding Insight
If diathermy, cryotherapy, and/or photocoagulation are combined during a surgical session, report under the principal method used from 67101–67105.

Procedure 67208 has largely been replaced by laser surgery. For photocoagulation, see 67210.

Treatment of one eye at a time, 67227–67228, is recommended in bilateral disease.

Nota Bene: Codes 67105–67112 have been revised in *CPT '96*. The words "laser or xenon arc, one or more sessions" has been deleted from 67105, and the other codes have had wording changes. Read the code nomenclature carefully when using these codes.

Subsidiary Codes
Subsidiary codes have relative values that require no further adjustment:

20900 is "in addition" to 67101–67228
20902 is "in addition" to 67101–67228
20920 is "in addition" to 67101–67228
20922 is "in addition" to 67101–67228
20926 is "in addition" to 67101–67228

Because these are subsidiary or "in addition to" codes, reimbursement reduction and modifier -51 do not apply.

Medicare Alert
Medicare rebundles certain codes in the surgery section when the listed codes are considered a component of a more comprehensive service.

67015, 67028, 67101, 67141, 67145, 67208, 67210, 67227–67228, 67500 will not be reimbursed when reported with 67105

67015, 67101, 67105, 67141, 67145, 67208, 67210, 67500 will not be reimbursed when reported with 67107
67015, 67025, 67028, 67031, 67036, 67039–67040, 67101, 67105, 67107, 67141, 67145, 67208, 67210, 67500 will not be reimbursed when reported with 67108
67028, 67101, 67105, 67107–67108, 67110 will not be reimbursed when reported with 67109
67028 will not be reimbursed when reported with 67112
67141, 67500 will not be reimbursed when reported with 67145
67208, 67500 will not be reimbursed when reported with 67210
67141, 67145, 67208, 67210, 67500 will not be reimbursed when reported with 67227–67228

	Code	Description	Medicode RVU	50th	75th	Medicare Nat'l Avg
	67101	Repair of retinal detachment, one or more sessions; cryotherapy or diathermy, with or without drainage of subretinal fluid	85.00	1996	2272	774
▲	**67105**	Repair of retinal detachment, one or more sessions; photocoagulation, with or without drainage of subretinal fluid	85.00	1996	2272	820
▲	**67107**	Repair of retinal detachment; scleral buckling (such as lamellar scleral dissection, imbrication or encircling procedure), with or without implant, with or without cryotherapy, photocoagulation, and drainage of subretinal fluid	128.0	3005	3421	1396
▲	**67108**	Repair of retinal detachment; with vitrectomy, any method, with or without air or gas tamponade, focal endolaser photocoagulation, cryotherapy, drainage of subretinal fluid, scleral buckling, and/or removal of lens by same technique	200.0	4695	5345	2008
▲	**67110**	Repair of retinal detachment, one or more sessions; by injection of air or other gas (eg, pneumatic retinopexy)	100.0	2348	2673	872
▲	**67112**	Repair of retinal detachment; by scleral buckling or vitrectomy, on patient having previous ipsilateral retinal detachment repair(s) using scleral buckling or vitrectomy techniques	113.0	2653	3020	1366
	67115	Release of encircling material (posterior segment)	38.00	892	1016	480
	67120	Removal of implanted material, posterior segment; extraocular	48.00	1127	1283	552
	67121	Removal of implanted material, posterior segment; intraocular	55.00	1291	1470	791
	67141	Prophylaxis of retinal detachment (eg, retinal break, lattice degeneration) without drainage, one or more sessions; cryotherapy, diathermy	53.00	1244	1416	562
	67145	Prophylaxis of retinal detachment (eg, retinal break, lattice degeneration) without drainage, one or more sessions; photocoagulation (laser or xenon arc)	55.00	1291	1470	581
	67208	Destruction of localized lesion of retina (eg, maculopathy, choroidopathy, small tumors), one or more sessions; cryotherapy, diathermy	55.00	1260	1422	631
	67210	Destruction of localized lesion of retina (eg, maculopathy, choroidopathy, small tumors), one or more sessions; photocoagulation (laser or xenon arc)	57.00	1306	1474	748

Code	Description	Medicode RVU	50th	75th	Medicare Nat'l Avg
67218	Destruction of localized lesion of retina (eg, maculopathy, choroidopathy, small tumors), one or more sessions; radiation by implantation of source (includes removal of source)	110.0	2521	2844	1081
67227	Destruction of extensive or progressive retinopathy (eg, diabetic retinopathy), one or more sessions; cryotherapy, diathermy	59.00	1352	1526	643
67228	Destruction of extensive or progressive retinopathy (eg, diabetic retinopathy), one or more sessions; photocoagulation (laser or xenon arc)	61.00	1398	1577	857

67250–67299
Sclera

For repair of a protrusion of the contents of the eyeball at a point where the sclera has become too thin (scleral staphyloma), see 66220 and 66225.

SUBSIDIARY CODES
Subsidiary codes have relative values that require no further adjustment:

20900 is "in addition" to 67250–67299
20902 is "in addition" to 67250–67299
20920 is "in addition" to 67250–67299
20922 is "in addition" to 67250–67299
20926 is "in addition" to 67250–67299

Because these are subsidiary or "in addition to" codes, reimbursement reduction and modifier -51 do not apply.

Code	Description	Medicode RVU	50th	75th	Medicare Nat'l Avg
67250	Scleral reinforcement (separate procedure); without graft	80.00	1833	2068	647
67255	Scleral reinforcement (separate procedure); with graft	100.0	2291	2586	920
67299	Unlisted procedure, posterior segment	0.00	0	0	–

67311–67399
Ocular Adnexa

CODING INSIGHT
Code 67345 is for chemodenervation of extraocular muscle; for chemodenervation for blepharospasm and other neurological disorders, see 64612 and 64613.

67350 is for biopsy of extraocular muscle; for repair of wound, extraocular muscle, tendon, or Tenon's capsule, see 65290.

SUBSIDIARY CODES

Subsidiary codes have relative values that require no further adjustment:

20900 is "in addition" to 67311–67399
20902 is "in addition" to 67311–67399
20920 is "in addition" to 67311–67399
20922 is "in addition" to 67311–67399
20926 is "in addition" to 67311–67399
67320 is "in addition" to 67311–67318
67331 is "in addition" to 67311–67318
67332 is "in addition" to 67311–67318
67335 is "in addition" to 67311–67318
67340 is "in addition" to 67311–67318

Because these are subsidiary or "in addition to" codes, reimbursement reduction and modifier -51 do not apply.

Code	Description	Medicode RVU	50th	75th	Medicare Nat'l Avg
67311	Strabismus surgery, recession or resection procedure (patient not previously operated on); one horizontal muscle	60.00	1446	1678	635
67312	Strabismus surgery, recession or resection procedure (patient not previously operated on); two horizontal muscles	75.00	1807	2098	751
67314	Strabismus surgery, recession or resection procedure (patient not previously operated on); one vertical muscle (excluding superior oblique)	66.00	1590	1846	713
67316	Strabismus surgery, recession or resection procedure (patient not previously operated on); two or more vertical muscles (excluding superior oblique)	82.50	1988	2308	805
67318	Strabismus surgery, any procedure (patient not previously operated on), superior oblique muscle	75.00	1807	2098	604
67320	Transposition procedure (eg, for paretic extraocular muscle), any extraocular muscle (specify)	83.50	2012	2336	783
67331	Strabismus surgery on patient with previous eye surgery or injury that did not involve the extraocular muscles	35.00	843	979	719
67332	Strabismus surgery on patient with scarring of extraocular muscles (eg, prior ocular injury, strabismus or retinal detachment surgery) or restrictive myopathy (eg, dysthyroid ophthalmopathy)	42.50	1024	1189	803
67334	Strabismus surgery by posterior fixation suture technique, with or without muscle recession	66.00	1590	1846	553
67335	Placement of adjustable suture(s) during strabismus surgery, including postoperative adjustment(s) of suture(s) (Report in addition to code for specific strabismus surgery)	20.00	482	559	342
67340	Strabismus surgery involving exploration and/or repair of detached extraocular muscle(s)	37.50	903	1049	693
67343	Release of extensive scar tissue without detaching extraocular muscle (separate procedure)	30.00	723	839	512
67345	Chemodenervation of extraocular muscle	19.00	458	531	211
67350	Biopsy of extraocular muscle	18.00	434	504	210

Code	Description	Medicode RVU	50th	75th	Medicare Nat'l Avg
67399	Unlisted procedure, ocular muscle	0.00	0	0	–

67400–67599
Orbit

Coding Insight

Codes 67400–67415 are for orbitotomy and fine needle aspiration. For exenteration, enucleation, and repair, see 65101 and sequence; for optic nerve decompression, see 67570.

Codes 67420–67450 are for orbitotomy, lateral approach. For orbitotomy, transcranial approach, see 61330–61334. For removal of eyeball or for repair after removal, see 65091–65175, and for orbital implant, see 67550, 67560.

Subsidiary Codes

Subsidiary codes have relative values that require no further adjustment:

20900 is "in addition" to 67400–67599
20902 is "in addition" to 67400–67599
20920 is "in addition" to 67400–67599
20922 is "in addition" to 67400–67599
20926 is "in addition" to 67400–67599

Because these are subsidiary or "in addition to" codes, reimbursement reduction and CPT modifier -51 do not apply.

Code	Description	Medicode RVU	50th	75th	Medicare Nat'l Avg
67400	Orbitotomy without bone flap (frontal or transconjunctival approach); for exploration, with or without biopsy	85.00	2048	2378	824
67405	Orbitotomy without bone flap (frontal or transconjunctival approach); with drainage only	70.00	1687	1958	696
67412	Orbitotomy without bone flap (frontal or transconjunctival approach); with removal of lesion	80.00	1927	2238	868
67413	Orbitotomy without bone flap (frontal or transconjunctival approach); with removal of foreign body	80.00	1927	2238	726
67414	Orbitotomy without bone flap (frontal or transconjunctival approach); with removal of bone for decompression	0.00	0	0	736
67415	Fine needle aspiration of orbital contents	12.00	289	336	157
67420	Orbitotomy with bone flap or window, lateral approach (eg, Kroenlein); with removal of lesion	140.0	3373	3916	1235
67430	Orbitotomy with bone flap or window, lateral approach (eg, Kroenlein); with removal of foreign body	132.0	3180	3692	936
67440	Orbitotomy with bone flap or window, lateral approach (eg, Kroenlein); with drainage	125.0	3012	3497	1155
67445	Orbitotomy with bone flap or window, lateral approach (eg, Kroenlein); with removal of bone for decompression	0.00	0	0	976

Code		Description	Medicode RVU	50th	75th	Medicare Nat'l Avg
67450		Orbitotomy with bone flap or window, lateral approach (eg, Kroenlein); for exploration, with or without biopsy	98.00	2361	2741	1146
67500	*	Retrobulbar injection; medication (separate procedure, does not include supply of medication)	4.60	111	129	65
67505		Retrobulbar injection; alcohol	10.00	241	280	81
67515	*	Injection of therapeutic agent into Tenon's capsule	4.50	108	126	48
67550		Orbital implant (implant outside muscle cone); insertion	60.00	1446	1678	790
67560		Orbital implant (implant outside muscle cone); removal or revision	60.00	1446	1678	737
67570		Optic nerve decompression (eg, incision or fenestration of optic nerve sheath)	100.0	2409	2797	798
67599		Unlisted procedure, orbit	0.00	0	0	–

67700–67999
Eyelids

Coding Insight
Code 67715 is for a canthotomy, separate procedure. For canthoplasty, see 67950, and for division of symblepharon, see 68340.

Codes 67800–67850 are for lesion excision involving more than skin. For removal of lesion, involving mainly skin of eyelid, see 11440–11446, 11640–11646, and 17000–17010. For repair of wounds, blepharoplasty, grafts, or reconstructive surgery, see 67930–67975.

Nota Bene: Code 67825 has been revised *in CPT '96*. The words "by other than forceps" have been added and the word "or" deleted from the description.

Subsidiary Codes
Subsidiary codes have relative values that require no further adjustment:

20900 is "in addition" to 67700–67999
20902 is "in addition" to 67700–67999
20920 is "in addition" to 67700–67999
20922 is "in addition" to 67700–67999
20926 is "in addition" to 67700–67999

Because these are subsidiary or "in addition to" codes, reimbursement reduction and modifier -51 do not apply.

Medicare Alert
Medicare rebundles certain codes in the surgery section when the listed codes are considered a component of a more comprehensive service.

15822–15823 will not be reimbursed when reported with 67904
67500, 67914, 67916, 67950 will not be reimbursed when reported with 67917
67500, 67921, 67923, 67950 will not be reimbursed when reported with 67924

Code		Description	Medicode RVU	50th	75th	Medicare Nat'l Avg
67700	*	Blepharotomy, drainage of abscess, eyelid	4.00	91	111	67
67710	*	Severing of tarsorrhaphy	5.00	114	138	85
67715	*	Canthotomy (separate procedure)	6.00	137	166	109
67800		Excision of chalazion; single	6.00	137	166	91
67801		Excision of chalazion; multiple, same lid	8.00	183	221	129
67805		Excision of chalazion; multiple, different lids	9.00	206	249	143
67808		Excision of chalazion; under general anesthesia and/or requiring hospitalization, single or multiple	15.50	354	429	225
67810	*	Biopsy of eyelid	6.00	137	166	90
67820	*	Correction of trichiasis; epilation, by forceps only	2.50	57	69	48
▲ 67825	*	Correction of trichiasis; epilation by other than forceps (eg, by electrosurgery, cryotherapy, laser surgery)	6.00	137	166	90
67830		Correction of trichiasis; incision of lid margin	7.00	160	194	177
67835		Correction of trichiasis; incision of lid margin, with free mucous membrane graft	50.00	1144	1382	507
67840	*	Excision of lesion of eyelid (except chalazion) without closure or with simple direct closure	8.50	194	235	128
67850	*	Destruction of lesion of lid margin (up to 1 cm)	7.50	172	207	97
67875		Temporary closure of eyelids by suture (eg, Frost suture)	10.00	229	276	127
67880		Construction of intermarginal adhesions, median tarsorrhaphy, or canthorrhaphy;	24.50	560	677	326
67882		Construction of intermarginal adhesions, median tarsorrhaphy, or canthorrhaphy; with transposition of tarsal plate	35.00	800	968	460
67900		Repair of brow ptosis (supraciliary, mid-forehead or coronal approach)	0.00	0	0	332
67901		Repair of blepharoptosis; frontalis muscle technique with suture or other material	65.00	1487	1797	686
67902		Repair of blepharoptosis; frontalis muscle technique with fascial sling (includes obtaining fascia)	65.00	1487	1797	659
67903		Repair of blepharoptosis; (tarso)levator resection or advancement, internal approach	94.50	2161	2612	705
67904		Repair of blepharoptosis; (tarso)levator resection or advancement, external approach	90.00	2058	2488	728
67906		Repair of blepharoptosis; superior rectus technique with fascial sling (includes obtaining fascia)	85.50	1955	2364	496
67908		Repair of blepharoptosis; conjunctivo-tarso-Muller's muscle-levator resection (eg, Fasanella-Servat type)	70.00	1601	1935	586

Code	Description	Medicode RVU	50th	75th	Medicare Nat'l Avg
67909	Reduction of overcorrection of ptosis	60.00	1372	1659	499
67911	Correction of lid retraction	80.00	1830	2212	588
67914	Repair of ectropion; suture	28.00	640	774	394
67915	Repair of ectropion; thermocauterization	8.50	194	235	172
67916	Repair of ectropion; blepharoplasty, excision tarsal wedge	41.00	938	1133	499
67917	Repair of ectropion; blepharoplasty, extensive (eg, Kuhnt-Szymanowski or tarsal strip operations)	50.00	1144	1382	577
67921	Repair of entropion; suture	21.50	492	594	305
67922	Repair of entropion; thermocauterization	8.50	194	235	161
67923	Repair of entropion; blepharoplasty, excision tarsal wedge	41.00	938	1133	534
67924	Repair of entropion; blepharoplasty, extensive (eg, Wheeler operation)	52.00	1189	1438	555
67930	Suture of recent wound, eyelid, involving lid margin, tarsus, and/or palpebral conjunctiva direct closure; partial thickness	18.50	423	511	192
67935	Suture of recent wound, eyelid, involving lid margin, tarsus, and/or palpebral conjunctiva direct closure; full thickness	25.00	572	691	399
67938	Removal of embedded foreign body, eyelid	5.00	114	138	79
67950	Canthoplasty (reconstruction of canthus)	60.00	1372	1659	568
67961	Excision and repair of eyelid, involving lid margin, tarsus, conjunctiva, canthus, or full thickness, may include preparation for skin graft or pedicle flap with adjacent tissue transfer or rearrangement; up to one-fourth of lid margin	55.00	1258	1520	557
67966	Excision and repair of eyelid, involving lid margin, tarsus, conjunctiva, canthus, or full thickness, may include preparation for skin graft or pedicle flap with adjacent tissue transfer or rearrangement; over one-fourth of lid margin	70.00	1601	1935	675
67971	Reconstruction of eyelid, full thickness by transfer of tarsoconjunctival flap from opposing eyelid; up to two-thirds of eyelid, one stage or first stage	70.00	1601	1935	837
67973	Reconstruction of eyelid, full thickness by transfer of tarsoconjunctival flap from opposing eyelid; total eyelid, lower, one stage or first stage	80.00	1830	2212	1067
67974	Reconstruction of eyelid, full thickness by transfer of tarsoconjunctival flap from opposing eyelid; total eyelid, upper, one stage or first stage	90.00	2058	2488	1086
67975	Reconstruction of eyelid, full thickness by transfer of tarsoconjunctival flap from opposing eyelid; second stage	25.00	572	691	509

Code	Description	Medicode RVU	50th	75th	Medicare Nat'l Avg
67999	Unlisted procedure, eyelids	0.00	0	0	–

68020–68399
Conjunctiva

Coding Insight
Code 68200 is a subconjunctival injection procedure; for injection into Tenon's capsule or retrobulbar injection, see 67500–67515.

Subsidiary Codes
Subsidiary codes have relative values that require no further adjustment:

20900 is "in addition" to 68020–68399
20902 is "in addition" to 68020–68399
20920 is "in addition" to 68020–68399
20922 is "in addition" to 68020–68399
20926 is "in addition" to 68020–68399

Because these are subsidiary or "in addition to" codes, reimbursement reduction and modifier -51 do not apply.

Code		Description	Medicode RVU	50th	75th	Medicare Nat'l Avg
68020		Incision of conjunctiva, drainage of cyst	4.50	103	124	76
68040		Expression of conjunctival follicles, eg, for trachoma	4.50	103	124	51
68100		Biopsy of conjunctiva	7.00	160	194	95
68110		Excision of lesion, conjunctiva; up to 1 cm	9.50	217	263	117
68115		Excision of lesion, conjunctiva; over 1 cm	15.00	343	415	179
68130		Excision of lesion, conjunctiva; with adjacent sclera	30.00	686	829	356
68135	*	Destruction of lesion, conjunctiva	8.00	183	221	101
68200	*	Subconjunctival injection	4.00	91	111	42
68320		Conjunctivoplasty; with conjunctival graft or extensive rearrangement	60.00	1372	1659	517
68325		Conjunctivoplasty; with buccal mucous membrane graft (includes obtaining graft)	70.00	1601	1935	660
68326		Conjunctivoplasty, reconstruction cul-de-sac; with conjunctival graft or extensive rearrangement	65.00	1487	1797	631
68328		Conjunctivoplasty, reconstruction cul-de-sac; with buccal mucous membrane graft (includes obtaining graft)	75.00	1715	2073	733

Code	Description	Medicode RVU	50th	75th	Medicare Nat'l Avg
68330	Repair of symblepharon; conjunctivoplasty, without graft	30.00	686	829	428
68335	Repair of symblepharon; with free graft conjunctiva or buccal mucous membrane (includes obtaining graft)	45.00	1029	1244	658
68340	Repair of symblepharon; division of symblepharon, with or without insertion of conformer or contact lens	45.00	1029	1244	292
68360	Conjunctival flap; bridge or partial (separate procedure)	35.00	800	968	388
68362	Conjunctival flap; total (such as Gunderson thin flap or purse string flap)	50.00	1144	1382	612
68399	Unlisted procedure, conjunctiva	0.00	0	0	–

68400–68899
Lacrimal System

SUBSIDIARY CODES
Subsidiary codes have relative values that require no further adjustment:

20900 is "in addition" to 68400–68899
20902 is "in addition" to 68400–68899
20920 is "in addition" to 68400–68899
20922 is "in addition" to 68400–68899
20926 is "in addition" to 68400–68899

Because these are subsidiary or "in addition to" codes, reimbursement reduction and modifier -51 do not apply.

MEDICARE ALERT
Medicare rebundles certain codes in the surgery section when the listed codes are considered a component of a more comprehensive service.

68820 will not be reimbursed when reported with 68830

Code		Description	Medicode RVU	50th	75th	Medicare Nat'l Avg
68400		Incision, drainage of lacrimal gland	11.00	245	297	106
68420		Incision, drainage of lacrimal sac (dacryocystotomy or dacryocystostomy)	9.00	201	243	128
68440	*	Snip incision of lacrimal punctum	5.00	111	135	68
68500		Excision of lacrimal gland (dacryoadenectomy), except for tumor; total	60.00	1337	1621	736
68505		Excision of lacrimal gland (dacryoadenectomy), except for tumor; partial	50.00	1115	1351	766
68510		Biopsy of lacrimal gland	10.00	223	270	332

Code		Description	Medicode RVU	50th	75th	Medicare Nat'l Avg
68520		Excision of lacrimal sac (dacryocystectomy)	45.00	1003	1216	673
68525		Biopsy of lacrimal sac	10.00	223	270	324
68530		Removal of foreign body or dacryolith, lacrimal passages	35.00	780	946	262
68540		Excision of lacrimal gland tumor; frontal approach	75.00	1672	2026	742
68550		Excision of lacrimal gland tumor; involving osteotomy	75.00	1672	2026	964
68700		Plastic repair of canaliculi	55.00	1226	1486	392
68705		Correction of everted punctum, cautery	8.00	178	216	119
68720		Dacryocystorhinostomy (fistulization of lacrimal sac to nasal cavity)	80.00	1783	2161	830
68745		Conjunctivorhinostomy (fistulization of conjunctiva to nasal cavity); without tube	85.00	1895	2296	620
68750		Conjunctivorhinostomy (fistulization of conjunctiva to nasal cavity); with insertion of tube or stent	90.00	2006	2431	875
68760		Closure of the lacrimal punctum; by thermocauterization, ligation, or laser surgery	8.00	178	216	101
68761		Closure of the lacrimal punctum; by plug, each	6.00	134	162	89
68770		Closure of lacrimal fistula (separate procedure)	25.00	557	675	431
68800	*	Dilation of lacrimal punctum, with or without irrigation, unilateral or bilateral	3.00	67	81	57
68820	*	Probing of nasolacrimal duct, with or without irrigation, unilateral or bilateral;	7.50	167	203	76
68825		Probing of nasolacrimal duct, with or without irrigation, unilateral or bilateral; requiring general anesthesia	17.50	390	473	128
68830		Probing of nasolacrimal duct, with or without irrigation, unilateral or bilateral; with insertion of tube or stent	22.00	490	594	166
68840	*	Probing of lacrimal canaliculi, with or without irrigation	4.00	89	108	64
68850	*	Injection of contrast medium for dacryocystography	5.00	111	135	53
68899		Unlisted procedure, lacrimal system	0.00	0	0	–

AUDITORY SYSTEM

Coding Insight

When diagnostic services (e.g., audiometry or vestibular tests) are performed, see 92502 and sequence.

Because many bilateral codes have been dropped from CPT, append modifier -50 when a surgery is performed bilaterally and a separate bilateral code is not listed.

Don't forget to report a surgical tray (CPT code 99070 or HCPCS A4550) if the procedure is performed in the physician's office (for non-Medicare patients). When a procedure is performed in the physician's office and a specimen is sent to an outside laboratory, report 99000 for handling or conveyance.

If a procedure in this section of CPT is completed through an operating microscope, append modifier -20. Head gear (e.g., loupes or binoculars) is considered an integral part of most of these procedures.

69000–69399
External Ear

Coding Insight
An excisional biopsy (69100–69105) is not reported separately if a therapeutic excision is performed during the same surgical session.

For reconstruction of the ear after complete amputation (69120), see 15120 and sequence. For skin flap, see 15576 or 15630, and for a skin graft, see 15260 or 15261. If during the postoperative period an impression and custom preparation of an auricular prosthesis is performed, see 21086.

Code 69140 includes the excision of one or more exostosis(es).

For 69150 the radical dissection may include bone, the tympanic membrane, parotid gland, facial nerve, and portions of the mandible and mastoid. If neck dissection is necessary, as in 69155, lymph nodes from that side of the neck, the jugular vein, spinal accessory nerve, or sternocleidomastoid muscle may be removed. Usually the carotid artery, vagus, sympathetic, phrenic, brachial plexus, hypoglossal, and lingual nerves are spared. A separately reportable graft or flap may also be performed at the time of either of these surgeries.

Routine mastoid cavity debridement is required every three to six months in patients who have undergone a radical or modified radical mastoidectomy. The physician may use suction, a cerumen spoon, and delicate forceps to remove skin debris and drainage from the mastoid cavity (a bony extension of the ear canal). In 69220 the mastoid cavity is cleaned simply. If more extensive cleaning, is required (e.g., infection or extensive debris) report 69222. Extensive cleaning may require the use of general anesthesia and the use of a laser to remove granulation tissue. In either case, the procedures include any method (e.g., suction, laser) necessary to complete the cleaning.

Reconstruction of the external auditory canal, 69310–69320, may require middle ear reconstruction be performed at the same time. When external reconstruction is performed in combination with reconstruction of the middle ear, see 69631 or 69641.

For otoscopy under general anesthesia, see 69399.

Cosmetic Warning
Codes 69090 and 69300 are considered cosmetic 85 percent of the time or more.

Subsidiary Codes
Subsidiary codes have relative values that require no further adjustment:

20900 is "in addition" to 69000–69399
20902 is "in addition" to 69000–69399
20910 is "in addition" to 69000–69399
20912 is "in addition" to 69000–69155
20920 is "in addition" to 69000–69399
20922 is "in addition" to 69000–69399
20926 is "in addition" to 69000–69399

Because these are subsidiary or "in addition to" codes, reimbursement reduction and modifier -51 do not apply.

MEDICARE ALERT

Medicare rebundles certain codes in the surgery section when the listed codes are considered a component of a more comprehensive service.

92504 will not be reimbursed when reported with 69210

Code		Description	Medicode RVU	50th	75th	Medicare Nat'l Avg
69000	*	Drainage external ear, abscess or hematoma; simple	5.50	122	143	65
69005		Drainage external ear, abscess or hematoma; complicated	18.00	400	469	135
69020	*	Drainage external auditory canal, abscess	6.00	133	156	71
69090		Ear piercing	2.50	56	65	–
69100		Biopsy external ear	7.50	167	195	59
69105		Biopsy external auditory canal	7.50	167	195	69
69110		Excision external ear; partial, simple repair	30.00	667	781	255
69120		Excision external ear; complete amputation	70.00	1557	1822	210
69140		Excision exostosis(es), external auditory canal	120.0	2668	3123	657
69145		Excision soft tissue lesion, external auditory canal	20.00	445	521	220
69150		Radical excision external auditory canal lesion; without neck dissection	75.00	1668	1952	977
69155		Radical excision external auditory canal lesion; with neck dissection	110.0	2446	2863	1350
69200		Removal foreign body from external auditory canal; without general anesthesia	5.50	122	143	40
69205		Removal foreign body from external auditory canal; with general anesthesia	22.00	489	573	94
69210		Removal impacted cerumen (separate procedure), one or both ears	2.20	49	57	28
69220		Debridement, mastoidectomy cavity, simple (eg, routine cleaning)	3.00	67	78	52
69222		Debridement, mastoidectomy cavity, complex (eg, with anesthesia or more than routine cleaning)	13.50	300	351	90
69300		Otoplasty, protruding ear, with or without size reduction	65.00	1445	1692	465
69310		Reconstruction of external auditory canal (meatoplasty) (eg, for stenosis due to trauma, infection) (separate procedure)	95.00	2113	2473	881
69320		Reconstruction external auditory canal for congenital atresia, single stage	95.00	2113	2473	1281

Code	Description	Medicode RVU	50th	75th	Medicare Nat'l Avg
69399	Unlisted procedure, external ear	0.00	0	0	–

69400–69799
Middle Ear

Coding Insight

Middle ear exploration (69440) is not reported when a therapeutic procedure is performed during the same operative session.

Complex surgeries may include many different procedures that are inherent and should not be reported separately. For example, in 69530 the tegmen (bony plate separating the mastoid and middle cranial fossa) is exposed. Various cell tracts around the semicircular canals are explored in an attempt to drain the petrous apex. If this is unsuccessful, the posterior and superior bony canal walls are taken down to the level of the facial nerve. The ossicles, except for the stapes if possible, are removed as well as the eustachian tube orifice mucosa, middle ear mucosa, granulations, and cholesteatoma. Cell tracts between the carotid artery and cochlea or the jugular bulb and cochlea are followed to open the petrous apex and drain any infection. A meatoplasty is performed.

For planned secondary tympanoplasty after mastoidectomy, see 69631 and 69632.

For extracranial suture of facial nerve, see 64864.

Subsidiary Codes

Subsidiary codes have relative values that require no further adjustment:

20900 is “in addition” to 69400–69799
20902 is “in addition” to 69400–69799
20910 is “in addition” to 69400–69799
20912 is “in addition” to 69400–69799
20920 is "in addition" to 69400–69799
20922 is "in addition" to 69400–69799
20926 is "in addition" to 69400–69799

Because these are subsidiary or “in addition to” codes, reimbursement reduction and modifier -51 do not apply.

Code		Description	Medicode RVU	50th	75th	Medicare Nat'l Avg
69400		Eustachian tube inflation, transnasal; with catheterization	4.00	90	108	50
69401		Eustachian tube inflation, transnasal; without catheterization	2.00	45	54	35
69405		Eustachian tube catheterization, transtympanic	4.00	90	108	121
69410		Focal application of phase control substance, middle ear (baffle technique)	4.00	90	108	39
69420	*	Myringotomy including aspiration and/or eustachian tube inflation	11.00	248	296	78

Code		Description	Medicode RVU	50th	75th	Medicare Nat'l Avg
69421	*	Myringotomy including aspiration and/or eustachian tube inflation requiring general anesthesia	15.00	339	404	116
69424		Ventilating tube removal when originally inserted by another physician	10.00	226	269	61
69433	*	Tympanostomy (requiring insertion of ventilating tube), local or topical anesthesia	15.00	339	404	117
69436		Tympanostomy (requiring insertion of ventilating tube), general anesthesia	20.00	452	539	178
69440		Middle ear exploration through postauricular or ear canal incision	65.00	1468	1751	680
69450		Tympanolysis, transcanal	65.00	1468	1751	583
69501		Transmastoid antrotomy ("simple" mastoidectomy)	70.00	1581	1886	818
69502		Mastoidectomy; complete	93.00	2101	2506	1056
69505		Mastoidectomy; modified radical	105.0	2372	2829	1216
69511		Mastoidectomy; radical	120.0	2710	3233	1253
69530		Petrous apicectomy including radical mastoidectomy	150.0	3388	4041	1433
69535		Resection temporal bone, external approach	150.0	3388	4041	2432
69540		Excision aural polyp	12.00	271	323	103
69550		Excision aural glomus tumor; transcanal	100.0	2259	2694	1078
69552		Excision aural glomus tumor; transmastoid	120.0	2710	3233	1464
69554		Excision aural glomus tumor; extended (extratemporal)	150.0	3388	4041	2001
69601		Revision mastoidectomy; resulting in complete mastoidectomy	75.00	1694	2021	1111
69602		Revision mastoidectomy; resulting in modified radical mastoidectomy	120.0	2710	3233	1231
69603		Revision mastoidectomy; resulting in radical mastoidectomy	120.0	2710	3233	1297
69604		Revision mastoidectomy; resulting in tympanoplasty	120.0	2710	3233	1416
69605		Revision mastoidectomy; with apicectomy	130.0	2936	3502	1359
69610		Tympanic membrane repair, with or without site preparation or perforation for closure, with or without patch	9.00	203	242	212
69620		Myringoplasty (surgery confined to drumhead and donor area)	80.00	1807	2155	659

Code	Description	Medicode RVU	50th	75th	Medicare Nat'l Avg
69631	Tympanoplasty without mastoidectomy (including canalplasty, atticotomy and/or middle ear surgery), initial or revision; without ossicular chain reconstruction	108.0	2439	2910	1009
69632	Tympanoplasty without mastoidectomy (including canalplasty, atticotomy and/or middle ear surgery), initial or revision; with ossicular chain reconstruction (eg, postfenestration)	122.0	2755	3287	1198
69633	Tympanoplasty without mastoidectomy (including canalplasty, atticotomy and/or middle ear surgery), initial or revision; with ossicular chain reconstruction and synthetic prosthesis (eg, partial ossicular replacement prosthesis, (PORP), total ossicular replacement prosthesis (TORP))	130.0	2936	3502	1147
69635	Tympanoplasty with antrotomy or mastoidotomy (including canalplasty, atticotomy, middle ear surgery, and/or tympanic membrane repair); without ossicular chain reconstruction	125.0	2823	3368	1267
69636	Tympanoplasty with antrotomy or mastoidotomy (including canalplasty, atticotomy, middle ear surgery, and/or tympanic membrane repair); with ossicular chain reconstruction	133.0	3004	3583	1426
69637	Tympanoplasty with antrotomy or mastoidotomy (including canalplasty, atticotomy, middle ear surgery, and/or tympanic membrane repair); with ossicular chain reconstruction and synthetic prosthesis (eg, partial ossicular replacement prosthesis, (PORP), total ossicular replacement prosthesis (TORP))	140.0	3162	3772	1421
69641	Tympanoplasty with mastoidectomy (including canalplasty, middle ear surgery, tympanic membrane repair); without ossicular chain reconstruction	135.0	3049	3637	1240
69642	Tympanoplasty with mastoidectomy (including canalplasty, middle ear surgery, tympanic membrane repair); with ossicular chain reconstruction	142.0	3207	3826	1546
69643	Tympanoplasty with mastoidectomy (including canalplasty, middle ear surgery, tympanic membrane repair); with intact or reconstructed wall, without ossicular chain reconstruction	140.0	3162	3772	1470
69644	Tympanoplasty with mastoidectomy (including canalplasty, middle ear surgery, tympanic membrane repair); with intact or reconstructed canal wall, with ossicular chain reconstruction	148.0	3343	3987	1608
69645	Tympanoplasty with mastoidectomy (including canalplasty, middle ear surgery, tympanic membrane repair); radical or complete, without ossicular chain reconstruction	135.0	3049	3637	1532
69646	Tympanoplasty with mastoidectomy (including canalplasty, middle ear surgery, tympanic membrane repair); radical or complete, with ossicular chain reconstruction	145.0	3275	3906	1635
69650	Stapes mobilization	70.00	1581	1886	888
69660	Stapedectomy or stapedotomy with reestablishment of ossicular continuity, with or without use of foreign material;	112.0	2530	3017	1172
69661	Stapedectomy or stapedotomy with reestablishment of ossicular continuity, with or without use of foreign material; with footplate drill out	112.0	2530	3017	1395
69662	Revision of stapedectomy or stapedotomy	134.0	3027	3610	1359

Code	Description	Medicode RVU	50th	75th	Medicare Nat'l Avg
69666	Repair oval window fistula	100.0	2259	2694	976
69667	Repair round window fistula	100.0	2259	2694	951
69670	Mastoid obliteration (separate procedure)	120.0	2710	3233	874
69676	Tympanic neurectomy	70.00	1581	1886	733
69700	Closure postauricular fistula, mastoid (separate procedure)	30.00	678	808	646
69710	Implantation or replacement of electromagnetic bone conduction hearing device in temporal bone	0.00	0	0	–
69711	Removal or repair of electromagnetic bone conduction hearing device in temporal bone	0.00	0	0	742
69720	Decompression facial nerve, intratemporal; lateral to geniculate ganglion	120.0	2710	3233	1336
69725	Decompression facial nerve, intratemporal; including medial to geniculate ganglion	200.0	4517	5388	1370
69740	Suture facial nerve, intratemporal, with or without graft or decompression; lateral to geniculate ganglion	140.0	3162	3772	1141
69745	Suture facial nerve, intratemporal, with or without graft or decompression; including medial to geniculate ganglion	200.0	4517	5388	1305
69799	Unlisted procedure, middle ear	0.00	0	0	–

69801–69949
Inner Ear

Coding Insight
Codes 69801–69802 include any method which may be employed to accomplish the procedure.

Subsidiary Codes
Subsidiary codes have relative values that require no further adjustment:

20900 is "in addition" to 69801–69949
20902 is "in addition" to 69801–69949
20910 is "in addition" to 69801–69949
20912 is "in addition" to 69801–69949
20920 is "in addition" to 69801–69949
20922 is "in addition" to 69801–69949
20926 is "in addition" to 69801–69949

Because these are subsidiary or "in addition to" codes, reimbursement reduction and modifier -51 do not apply.

Code	Description	Medicode RVU	50th	75th	Medicare Nat'l Avg
69801	Labyrinthotomy, with or without cryosurgery or other nonexcisional destructive procedures or tack procedure; transcanal	90.00	2033	2425	897
69802	Labyrinthotomy, with or without cryosurgery or other nonexcisional destructive procedures or tack procedure; with mastoidectomy	120.0	2710	3233	974
69805	Endolymphatic sac operation; without shunt	120.0	2710	3233	1047
69806	Endolymphatic sac operation; with shunt	144.0	3252	3880	1295
69820	Fenestration semicircular canal	120.0	2710	3233	789
69840	Revision fenestration operation	65.00	1468	1751	745
69905	Labyrinthectomy; transcanal	100.0	2259	2694	1076
69910	Labyrinthectomy; with mastoidectomy	120.0	2710	3233	1332
69915	Vestibular nerve section, translabyrinthine approach	180.0	4065	4849	1547
69930	Cochlear device implantation, with or without mastoidectomy	140.0	3162	3772	1595
69949	Unlisted procedure, inner ear	0.00	0	0	–

69950–69979
Temporal Bone, Middle Fossa Approach

Coding Insight
For resection of the temporal bone by external approach, see 69535.

Code 69955 includes decompression, repair, and graft. For decompression of facial nerve, intratemporal, see 69720 and 69725. For suture of facial nerve, intratemporal, see 69740 and 69745.

Subsidiary Codes
Subsidiary codes have relative values that require no further adjustment:

20900 is "in addition" to 69950–69979
20902 is "in addition" to 69950–69979
20910 is "in addition" to 69950–69979
20912 is "in addition" to 69950–69979
20920 is "in addition" to 69950–69979
20922 is "in addition" to 69950–69979
20926 is "in addition" to 69950–69970

Because these are subsidiary or "in addition to" codes, reimbursement reduction and modifier -51 do not apply.

Code	Description	Medicode RVU	50th	75th	Medicare Nat'l Avg
69950	Vestibular nerve section, transcranial approach	200.0	4517	5388	1616
69955	Total facial nerve decompression and/or repair (may include graft)	200.0	4517	5388	1741
69960	Decompression internal auditory canal	200.0	4517	5388	1540
69970	Removal of tumor, temporal bone	250.0	5647	6735	1727
69979	Unlisted procedure, temporal bone, middle fossa approach	0.00	0	0	–

Radiology Codes 70010–79999

Physicians most often choose codes from within this section of CPT to report procedures used in a variety of healthcare settings: practitioner offices, free standing facilities, and hospitals. Therefore, it is important to understand how to use and correctly report the code that identifies the service provided.

Radiological procedures are divided into four sections in CPT: (1) diagnostic radiology (diagnostic imaging), which includes CT (computerized tomography), MRI (magnetic resonance imaging), and interventional radiology procedures; (2) diagnostic ultrasound; (3) radiation oncology; and (4) diagnostic and therapeutic nuclear medicine. Organization is according to anatomic site and body system.

Procedures are generally described by type of service (modality) and specific body site, followed by additional information regarding contrast material, the complexity of the procedure etc. Radiation oncology is organized according to treatment planning, medical radiation physics, treatment delivery, and treatment management.

TECHNICAL AND PROFESSIONAL COMPONENTS

The majority of radiology procedures are comprised of two components: technical and professional. The technical component includes the provision of the equipment, supplies, technical personnel, and costs attendant to the performance of the procedure other than the professional services.

The professional component encompasses all of the physician's work in providing the service, including interpretation and report of the procedure. Costs of education, malpractice insurance, and other expenses incident to maintaining a practice are also included in the professional component.

The term global service pertains to the complete cost of a procedure (100 percent), which includes the technical and professional components.

A common division for routine diagnostic procedures is 60 percent for the technical component and 40 percent for the professional component. It is important to note that this ratio varies widely depending on the particular service.

One problem in coding radiology services centers in reporting the technical component. The sophisticated and expensive equipment required for many radiology services has traditionally been owned by hospitals and large facilities. Naturally, hospitals reported the use of the equipment, the specially trained personnel, and related costs associated with the technical component. However, a trend has developed toward freestanding medical facilities capable of offering imaging services as well as catheterizations and other diagnostic and therapeutic services. Physicians in these practices can have problems securing reimbursement that includes the cost of the technical component.

CPT reports only the professional component of physician services. Indeed, coders will find no modifier in CPT to reflect technical services. Although CPT codes for a radiology procedure may be assigned a technical (TC), professional (PC) or -26 or a global (G) modifier by those who use radiology and other CPT codes to designate the different components of a radiology procedure.

A physician reading films after another party has performed the technical component (such as a hospital) should select the appropriate CPT code and add modifier -26 to indicate that the professional component only was provided. This also signals payers to expect the other entity to report the technical portion.

A global service may be reported when one physician provides both components of the radiology procedure, such as owning the equipment, employing the technologist, and providing a written interpretation of the examination. However, be aware that in some geographical areas a state-specific modifier is required to report a global service.

DOCUMENTATION

Radiologists should maintain good patient documentation to aid in coding. In most instances, the physician's dictated notes are the coder's basis for selection of ICD-9 diagnostic codes. When the information is poor, coders are more prone to error in selecting diagnostic codes. A patient history outlining the reason for the encounter can be provided with documentation, and codes can then be drawn from this information when a definitive diagnosis is not indicated in the report.

Dictated reports should also include the anatomy reviewed, number of views, whether or not the study required a contrast medium, type and amount of contrast medium, and other pertinent information relative to the procedure. Interventional vascular procedures should be documented by the access route(s), identification of selective and nonselective vessel catheterization and injection, and a description of any deviation from normal anatomy. This information will support the code selection and assist in reimbursement when documentation is requested by a payer.

Avoiding Denials with Good Documentation

Payers may not reimburse providers for their interpretation of x-ray procedures. This is especially true when the services are performed in an office, clinic, or operating room setting. The office or clinic provider may own the x-ray equipment, employ a technologist, and interpret the x-ray, and be reimbursed for the technical component of the service but denied the professional component. The facility will be reimbursed the technical portion of a radiology procedure performed in the operating room, but the physician performing the procedure and interpreting the radiology procedure at the same time may be denied the professional component.

The key to the denials may be in the way the services were documented. Payers may feel that a notation in the medical records (e.g., normal chest x-ray, fractured ulna) or in an operative report (e.g., fluoroscopy was utilized) does not constitute a written interpretation of the examination. Additionally, payers dislike the practice of some providers who routinely have a radiologist review the x-ray and expect both them and the radiologist to be paid for reading the same x-ray.

Providers generally expect to be reimbursed because they have the burden of liability associated with performing the interpretation, but payers continue to disagree. Check EOBs or with payers for their guidelines on this issue and discuss them when negotiating a contract.

Documenting Diagnostic Codes

Radiology providers need to be specific when reporting ICD-9 diagnostic codes. Many payers, frustrated by paying claims for normal exams, are excluding claims based on diagnosis.

Without a specific diagnosis that fits their guidelines or without prior authorization, some claims may be denied.

In addition, many plan benefits do not cover or limit coverage (e.g., once per year) of routine or preventive services. Often, this type of exam includes a chest or other x-ray. Check with your payer for their plan benefits for preventative coverage.

CODE SELECTION

To select the correct code, first look up the procedure in the CPT index. Go to the code located in one of the four radiology sections that best describes the procedure performed. Read the code description carefully, noting any includes or excludes comments (e.g., with contrast, without contrast, number and type of views).

Then, read the codes listed before and after the code to verify that the procedure code selected fits the service performed. Read all parenthetical phrases both before and after the code. Page back, as necessary, to the subsection and/or heading notes and read them for information pertaining to that section. Determine if you are reporting the technical or professional component or a global procedure.

When the selection is made, list the appropriate code(s) on a HCFA-1500 form along with any pertinent modifiers.

INTERVENTIONAL RADIOLOGY

Interventional radiology services involve both an invasive component (such as a biopsy or injection) and a radiological component. In the past, interventional radiology services could be reported either with "complete procedure" codes or with surgical or procedural codes in conjunction with "radiological supervision and interpretation" codes. Confusion was common among providers and payers. Reimbursement for identical services was, on average, much lower when reported as a complete procedure than when reported by separate components.

CPT introduced "component coding" to standardize the reporting of interventional radiological services. Component coding allows a physician, regardless of specialty, to identify and report those specific aspects of the service he or she provided — whether the procedural component, the radiological component, or both.

New surgery codes were added to CPT when it became apparent the existing series of codes did not adequately address the needs of interventionalists. Coders will find some interventional radiology codes have a one-to-one match with corresponding codes in surgery, while others may match to many surgery codes. Parenthetical guidelines in CPT help direct coders to the appropriate surgery codes.

The following list illustrates some surgical codes that may be used with interventional radiology codes:

Surgery Code(s)	*Corresponding Radiology S&I Code(s)*
19290, 19291	76096
27370	73580
35450–35476	75962–75968, 75978
36011–36015	See CPT Radiology section
36216–36218	See CPT Radiology section
37200	75970
37204, 61624-61626	75894
43260–43272	74328–74330
47511, 47556	75982
59000	76946
62291	72285, 72295

MODIFIERS

As in other specialties, modifiers are used in radiology to denote circumstances that affect the way services and procedures are performed. The modifier most frequently used by radiologists is modifier -26, which separately reports the physician (professional) component of a service from the technical portion. The HCPCS modifiers most frequently used are 'RT and 'LT'. These modifiers are used to identify procedures performed on the right side and left side of the body, respectively. The 'RT' and 'LT' modifiers are commonly used to report bilateral extremity exams (e.g., right foot and left foot). For a complete listing of modifiers, see the modifier section in this book. For other modifiers specific to radiology, see the Radiology Section of CPT.

MEDICARE ALERT

Medicare Bilateral Radiology Procedures
Under Medicare the bilateral concept and payment for radiology procedures are not subject to the special payment rules for bilateral surgeries (paid at 150 percent). A different bilateral concept is applied to radiology.

Bilateral Codes
Bilateral payment may be inappropriate for codes because: (1) of physiology or anatomy, or (2) the code description specifically states that it is a unilateral procedure and there is an existing code for the bilateral procedure.

If a procedure is reported with modifier -50, or is reported twice on the same day, e.g., with HCPCS Level II modifers -RT (right side) and/or -LT (left side), or a 2 in the units field, payment for both sides is based the lower of the total charge for both sides, or the fee schedule amount for one procedure

Billing for a Purchased Technical Component
Medicare law does not allow a provider to mark up the cost of a purchased diagnostic test. Accordingly, when physicians bill for diagnostic tests they did not perform or supervise, Medicare pays the lower of (1) the actual acquisition cost including any discount, or (2) the physician fee schedule amount for the test. The billing physician must identify the supplier, the supplier's provider number, and the amount the supplier charged. No payment may be made to the physician without this information unless the statement "No purchased tests are included" is noted on the claims. Most Medicare carriers have local Level III modifiers (available from your carrier assigned to designate this situation).

UPIN AND PIN

Coders serving radiology practices should be aware that this year HCFA is replacing the national unique physician identification number (UPIN) with a national provider identifier (NPI) number. The UPIN number has been different from the carrier-assigned physician identification number (PIN), or the more commonly used provider number. The UPIN system was created by HCFA to track referral patterns among physicians doing business with Medicare. The new NPI will accomplish the same purpose but has some advantages over the UPIN system.

NEW IDENTIFICATION SYSTEM
The new identification (NPI) system applies to all providers in the healthcare industry, including physicians, suppliers, home health agencies, hospitals, and affiliated providers.

The new national provider identifier system assigns each provider just one number, meaning providers do not have to use different numbers for different payers. The NPI number will stay the same throughout the provider's career, even if he or she changes specialties.

HCFA believes that having just one number for each provider will help curtail fraud and abuse by allowing cross-referencing of a physician's claims. Federal officials hope the NPI will eliminate the need for separate ID numbers for all commercial payers as well, making the NPI a universal identifying number.

Providers who already have a UPIN will automatically receive an NPI by April 1996. New physicians should call their state Medicare carriers and request an application. By January 1, 1997 NPIs will be required in the processing of all claims. Physician information will reside in a new National Provider System (NPS) database.

Here is a schedule of NPI implementation:

- Spring 1996 — education and training for users of the NPS database system
- Summer 1996 — HCFA will be able to support other government subscribers
- July 1996 — conversion of Medicare providers to new NPIs
- January 1, 1997 — NPIs will be required in all processing of claims

The UPIN of an ordering/referring physician should still be placed on line 17a of the HCFA-1500 claim form for specified radiology services. Consult your carrier's newsletter for instructions on placement of the new NPI. For a complete listing of the radiology services requiring the use of the UPIN and/or NPI number, request a copy from your local carrier.

GLOSSARY

The radiology section contains some unusual terms unique to those codes:

Anteroposterior (AP)	Front to back
Anteroposterior and Lateral	Two projections included in this examination
Cineradiography	Movies done by x-ray
Contrast Material	Usually a radiopaque material placed into the body to enable a system or body structure to be visualized. Common terms include: non-ionic and low osmolar contrast media (LOCM), ionic and high osmolar contrast media (HOCM), barium, and gadolinium.
Decubitus (DEC)	Patient lying on the side
Frontal	Face forward
Lateral (LAT)	Side view
Modality	A form of imaging, including x-ray, fluoroscopy, ultrasound, nuclear medicine, duplex Doppler, CT, and MRI
Oblique (OBL)	Oblique view of the object being x-rayed
Posteroanterior (PA)	Back to front
Subtraction	The removal of an overlying structure in order to better visualize the structure in question. This is done in a series by imposing one x-ray on top of another.
Tomography	A specialized type of x-ray imaging that provides slices through a body section to obliterate overlying structures. This is commonly performed for studies on the kidneys or the temporomandibular joint.

70010–76499
Diagnostic Radiology

Coding Insight

When a baseline (one-or two-view) general diagnostic exam is reported with a contrast procedure, interventional radiology procedure, CT, or MRI/MRA exam, it may not be reimbursed by the payer. Many assume a scout film or preliminary study is consistent with standard practice protocol and is incidental to the primary service. However, a radiological procedure code above the clinically standard scout film usually can be reported with an invasive diagnostic radiological procedure code. In this case it may be assumed by the payer that a complete standard exam preceded the invasive procedure.

Other times a payer may consider that a procedure code represents additional scout films and is incident to the invasive procedure, such as a complete knee x-ray (73564) reported with the code for an arthrogram of the knee (73580).

Other examples are:

- A single view abdomen code (74000), when reported with most radiological procedure codes, is generally thought to represent a scout film or a follow-up film; in which case the code for the (KUB) is inherent to the principal procedure
- Fluoroscopy (real-time x-ray) codes 76000 and 76001 should not be reported with most radiological examinations because the fluoroscopy may be considered incidental to the majority of radiological procedures

Two radiological procedure codes, each stating the same type of modality and referring to the same anatomical area, reported together may be transferred to a procedure code (if available) that includes both studies. For example, when the head computerized axial tomography (CT) scan with contrast material (code 70460) is reported with the head CT scan without contrast material (code 70450), both codes may be transferred by the payer to the head CT scan without contrast material, followed by the contrast material(s) code (70470).

A venipuncture code should not be reported with any diagnostic procedure code that involves the use of an intravenous contrast medium (e.g., venipuncture code 36000 reported with the code 74400 for intravenous urography).

A therapeutic/diagnostic injection procedure code (90782 or 90784) should not be reported with a computerized axial tomography (CT) scan, magnetic resonance imaging scan (MRI), magnetic resonance angiography (MRA), or nuclear medicine (NM) procedure code, or with any diagnostic procedure that involves the use of intravenous contrast material. The payer may assume that the injection IV contrast is inherent to these services, and injection of local anesthesia or anti-anxiety agents is incident to the primary procedure.

Analysis of information stored in computers (99090) should not be reported with any CT, MRI, MRA, or NM procedure.

CT/MRI

Payer utilization guidelines regarding CT scans and MRIs are frequently changing. For a long time it was a common practice in utilization guidelines to require a CT scan be performed prior to an MRI for certain procedures. However, payers have found that too often a CT scan did not eliminate the need for an MRI and that their guidelines were actually costing them more. Due to data acquisition, payers are now more likely to request an MRI without requiring a CT scan be performed first.

Contracts for MRI services frequently allow additional reimbursement for scans requiring imaging beyond what is normal for the examination. Modifier -22 is often added to the CPT code to identify the additional work. Radiologists are well advised to identify clearly the services provided, and in a manner that assures clear understanding for coders.

Do a "mini" audit of submitted claims for a one month period. Determine if any extra services were missed and look at EOBs to see if they were paid according to the contract. Extra imaging is usually one of the only ways to increase reimbursement beyond the normal payment for interpreting MRIs.

If charges were missed, resubmit the claims and check the contract to see how long resubmissions will be accepted. If additional reimbursement is not being made according to contract, resubmit the claims along with a letter of explanation and contact the provider relations department.

Missed services can add up to considerable amounts of lost revenue. Although it may take some time to do the audit, the extra time is time well spent.

Consultation On X-ray Examination
Code 76140 *Consultation on x-ray examination made elsewhere, written report* should be used by a physician who interprets and reports on radiological procedures performed at a source outside of the physician's practice and at the request of another physician. Maintain the written report as part of the patient's medical record and document the specific procedure reviewed and its complexity, e.g., number of views.

Do not use 76140 for review of outside films reviewed in conjunction with evaluation and management services. The medical decision making component of evaluation and management codes includes "amount and/or complexity of data to be reviewed."

Medicare Consultation on X-Ray Examination
Medicare does not recognize code 76140 *Consultation on x-ray examination made elsewhere, written report*.

Interventional Radiology

CODING INSIGHT
X-ray, CT, and ultrasound guidance codes (e.g., for biopsy, drainage, aspiration, and amniocentesis) do not include full examination of the organ or area involved. If a complete evaluation is performed (either preceding or following the guidance procedure), this should be separately coded. However, radiologic supervision and interpretation do include the work inherent in the actual guidance, documentation, and interpretation of images obtained during the intervention.

Exception: 76936 — diagnostic ultrasound evaluation is included in the CPT description for this intervention and is therefore not separately allowed.

MRA and MRI
MRA (magnetic resonance angiography) can be performed as an independent procedure or in conjunction with conventional MRI (magnetic resonance imaging). Although the two procedures are generally complementary, MRI should not be reported in addition to MRA when performed as other than a primary study (e.g., to report a preliminary or survey exam, or to report additional sequences).

Computerized Tomography
A limited or localized follow-up CT scan code (76380) may be reported with a specific complete CT scan code when they are performed on two separate areas.

Subsidiary Codes

Subsidiary codes have relative values that require no further adjustment:

74301 is "in addition" to 74300
75774 is "in addition" to 75650–75743
75964 is "in addition" to 75962
75968 is "in addition" to 75966
75993 is "in addition" to 75992
75996 is "in addition" to 75995
76125 is "in addition" to 70332, 70370, 70373, 74240–74283, 74305–74320, 74328–74330, 74425–74455
76350 is "in addition" to 70332, 72240–72295, 73040, 73085, 73115, 73525, 73580, 73615, 75600–75790, 75810–75891

Because these are subsidiary or "in addition to" codes, reimbursement reduction and CPT modifier -51 do not apply.

Medicare Alert

Medicare rebundles certain codes in the surgery section when the listed codes are considered a component of a more comprehensive service.

36000 will not be reimbursed when reported with 70552, 74400–74405, 74415–74420
70100 will not be reimbursed when reported with 70110
70120 will not be reimbursed when reported with 70130
70140 will not be reimbursed when reported with 70150
70210 will not be reimbursed when reported with 70220
70250 will not be reimbursed when reported with 70260
70300–70310 will not be reimbursed when reported with 70320
70328 will not be reimbursed when reported with 70330
70450, 70460 will not be reimbursed when reported with 70470
70480–70481 will not be reimbursed when reported with 70482
70486–70487 will not be reimbursed when reported with 70488
70490–70491 will not be reimbursed when reported with 70492
70551–70552 will not be reimbursed when reported with 70553
71010, 74000–74020 will not be reimbursed when reported with 74022
71250, 71260 will not be reimbursed when reported with 71270
72020, 72040 will not be reimbursed when reported with 72050–72052
72070 will not be reimbursed when reported with 72072–72074
72072 will not be reimbursed when reported with 72074
72020, 72100 will not be reimbursed when reported with72110
72125–72126 will not be reimbursed when reported with 72127
72128–72129 will not be reimbursed when reported with 72130
72131–72132 will not be reimbursed when reported with 72133
72192–72193 will not be reimbursed when reported with 72194
72200 will not be reimbursed when reported with 72202
73020 will not be reimbursed when reported with 73030
73100 will not be reimbursed when reported with 73110
73120 will not be reimbursed when reported with 73130
73200–73201 will not be reimbursed when reported with 73202
73500 will not be reimbursed when reported with 73510
72170, 73500, 73510 will not be reimbursed when reported with 73520
73560–73562 will not be reimbursed when reported with 73562–73564
73600 will not be reimbursed when reported with 73610
73620 will not be reimbursed when reported with 73630

73700–73701 will not be reimbursed when reported with 73702
74000–74010 will not be reimbursed when reported with 74010–74020
74000, 74010, 74240 will not be reimbursed when reported with 74241–74247, 74270–74280, 74400–74405, 74415
74000–74010 will not be reimbursed when reported with 74270
74000–74010, 74270 will not be reimbursed when reported with 74280
74150, 74160 will not be reimbursed when reported with 74170
74241 will not be reimbursed when reported with 74245–74247
74245 will not be reimbursed when reported with 74246
74246 will not be reimbursed when reported with 74247
74400 will not be reimbursed when reported with 74405–74415
74410 will not be reimbursed when reported with 74415
76090 will not be reimbursed when reported with 76091
76370 will not be reimbursed when reported with 77315

Code	Description	Medicode RVU	50th	75th	Medicare Nat'l Avg
70010	Myelography, posterior fossa, radiological supervision and interpretation	220.0	279	342	214
-26			98	120	65
70015	Cisternography, positive contrast, radiological supervision and interpretation	180.0	228	280	116
-26			80	98	64
70030	Radiologic examination, eye, for detection of foreign body	70.00	89	109	24
-26			36	44	9
70100	Radiologic examination, mandible; partial, less than four views	45.00	57	70	28
-26			23	28	10
70110	Radiologic examination, mandible; complete, minimum of four views	76.00	96	118	35
-26			39	47	14
70120	Radiologic examination, mastoids; less than three views per side	45.00	57	70	32
-26			23	28	10
70130	Radiologic examination, mastoids; complete, minimum of three views per side	85.00	108	132	46
-26			43	53	19
70134	Radiologic examination, internal auditory meati, complete	98.00	124	152	44
-26			50	61	19
70140	Radiologic examination, facial bones; less than three views	65.00	82	101	32
-26			33	40	10
70150	Radiologic examination, facial bones; complete, minimum of three views	80.00	101	124	42
-26			41	50	14
70160	Radiologic examination, nasal bones, complete, minimum of three views	50.00	63	78	28
-26			25	31	9
70170	Dacryocystography, nasolacrimal duct, radiological supervision and interpretation	78.00	99	121	49
-26			35	42	16
70190	Radiologic examination; optic foramina	64.00	81	99	33
-26			32	40	12
70200	Radiologic examination; orbits, complete, minimum of four views	81.00	103	126	43
-26			41	50	16
70210	Radiologic examination, sinuses, paranasal, less than three views	55.00	70	85	31
-26			28	34	9
70220	Radiologic examination, sinuses, paranasal, complete, minimum of three views	90.00	114	140	41
-26			46	56	14
70240	Radiologic examination, sella turcica	55.00	70	85	25
-26			28	34	11

Code	Description	Medicode RVU	50th	75th	Medicare Nat'l Avg
70250	Radiologic examination, skull; less than four views, with or without stereo	65.00	82	101	35
-26			33	40	13
70260	Radiologic examination, skull; complete, minimum of four views, with or without stereo	90.00	114	140	50
-26			46	56	19
70300	Radiologic examination, teeth; single view	19.00	24	30	15
-26			10	12	6
70310	Radiologic examination, teeth; partial examination, less than full mouth	36.00	46	56	23
-26			18	22	9
70320	Radiologic examination, teeth; complete, full mouth	68.00	86	106	39
-26			34	42	12
70328	Radiologic examination, temporomandibular joint, open and closed mouth; unilateral	82.00	104	127	27
-26			42	51	10
70330	Radiologic examination, temporomandibular joint, open and closed mouth; bilateral	120.0	152	186	42
-26			61	75	13
70332	Temporomandibular joint arthrography, radiological supervision and interpretation	187.0	237	291	102
-26			83	102	30
70336	Magnetic resonance (eg, proton) imaging, temporomandibular joint	815.0	1033	1267	440
-26			207	253	53
70350	Cephalogram, orthodontic	60.00	76	93	22
-26			30	37	9
70355	Orthopantogram	59.00	75	92	31
-26			30	37	11
70360	Radiologic examination; neck, soft tissue	62.00	79	96	24
-26			31	39	9
70370	Radiologic examination; pharynx or larynx, including fluoroscopy and/or magnification technique	137.0	174	213	62
-26			69	85	17
70371	Complex dynamic pharyngeal and speech evaluation by cine or video recording	238.0	302	370	117
-26			121	148	45
70373	Laryngography, contrast, radiological supervision and interpretation	150.0	190	233	85
-26			67	82	24
70380	Radiologic examination, salivary gland for calculus	75.00	95	117	32
-26			38	47	9
70390	Sialography, radiological supervision and interpretation	152.0	193	236	82
-26			67	83	21
70450	Computerized axial tomography, head or brain; without contrast material	378.0	497	577	210
-26			149	173	47
70460	Computerized axial tomography, head or brain; with contrast material(s)	456.0	600	696	257
-26			162	188	62
70470	Computerized axial tomography, head or brain; without contrast material, followed by contrast material(s) and further sections	555.0	730	847	313
-26			182	212	70
70480	Computerized axial tomography, orbit, sella, or posterior fossa or outer, middle, or inner ear; without contrast material	411.0	540	628	233
-26			162	188	71
70481	Computerized axial tomography, orbit, sella, or posterior fossa or outer, middle, or inner ear; with contrast material(s)	479.0	630	731	270
-26			170	197	76
70482	Computerized axial tomography, orbit, sella, or posterior fossa or outer, middle, or inner ear; without contrast material, followed by contrast material(s) and further sections	572.0	752	873	323
-26			188	218	80

Code	Description	Medicode RVU	50th	75th	Medicare Nat'l Avg
70486	Computerized axial tomography, maxillofacial area; without contrast material	425.0	559	649	225
-26			168	195	63
70487	Computerized axial tomography, maxillofacial area; with contrast material(s)	489.0	643	747	265
-26			174	202	71
70488	Computerized axial tomography, maxillofacial area; without contrast material, followed by contrast material(s) and further sections	581.0	764	887	321
-26			191	222	78
70490	Computerized axial tomography, soft tissue neck; without contrast material	459.0	604	701	233
-26			181	210	71
70491	Computerized axial tomography, soft tissue neck; with contrast material(s)	513.0	675	783	270
-26			182	212	76
70492	Computerized axial tomography, soft tissue neck; without contrast material followed by contrast material(s) and further sections	639.0	840	976	322
-26			210	244	80
70540	Magnetic resonance (eg, proton) imaging, orbit, face, and neck	878.0	1155	1341	467
-26			231	-268	82
70541	Magnetic resonance angiography, head and/or neck, with or without contrast material(s)	1000	1315	1527	473
-26			-263	305	88
70551	Magnetic resonance (eg, proton) imaging, brain (including brain stem); without contrast material	820.0	1078	1252	468
-26			216	250	82
70552	Magnetic resonance (eg, proton) imaging, brain (including brain stem); with contrast material(s)	1000	1315	1527	560
-26			-263	305	98
70553	Magnetic resonance (eg, proton) imaging, brain (including brain stem); without contrast material, followed by contrast material(s) and further sequences	1132	1489	1729	979
-26			298	346	127
71010	Radiologic examination, chest; single view, frontal	50.00	68	77	26
-26			27	31	10
71015	Radiologic examination, chest; stereo, frontal	58.00	79	90	29
-26			31	36	11
71020	Radiologic examination, chest, two views, frontal and lateral;	58.00	79	90	33
-26			31	36	12
71021	Radiologic examination, chest, two views, frontal and lateral; with apical lordotic procedure	85.00	115	131	40
-26			46	53	15
71022	Radiologic examination, chest, two views, frontal and lateral; with oblique projections	87.00	118	134	42
-26			47	54	17
71023	Radiologic examination, chest, two views, frontal and lateral; with fluoroscopy	100.0	136	154	48
-26			54	62	21
71030	Radiologic examination, chest, complete, minimum of four views;	95.00	129	147	44
-26			52	59	17
71034	Radiologic examination, chest, complete, minimum of four views; with fluoroscopy	150.0	203	232	75
-26			81	93	25
71035	Radiologic examination, chest, special views (eg, lateral decubitus, Bucky studies)	63.00	85	97	28
-26			34	39	10
71036	Needle biopsy of intrathoracic lesion, including follow-up films, fluoroscopic localization only, radiological supervision and interpretation	168.0	228	259	84
-26			80	91	30
71038	Fluoroscopic localization for transbronchial biopsy or brushing	151.0	205	233	88
-26			82	93	30
71040	Bronchography, unilateral, radiological supervision and interpretation	120.0	163	185	82
-26			57	65	32

Code	Description	Medicode RVU	50th	75th	Medicare Nat'l Avg
71060	Bronchography, bilateral, radiological supervision and	162.0	220	250	116
-26	interpretation		77	88	41
71090	Insertion pacemaker, fluoroscopy and radiography, radiological	156.0	212	241	87
-26	supervision and interpretation		74	84	30
71100	Radiologic examination, ribs, unilateral; two views	66.00	90	102	32
-26			36	41	12
71101	Radiologic examination, ribs, unilateral; including	76.00	103	117	38
-26	posteroanterior chest, minimum of three views		41	47	15
71110	Radiologic examination, ribs, bilateral; three views	80.00	108	124	42
-26			43	49	15
71111	Radiologic examination, ribs, bilateral; including posteroanterior	95.00	129	147	49
-26	chest, minimum of four views		52	59	18
71120	Radiologic examination; sternum, minimum of two views	58.00	79	90	33
-26			31	36	11
71130	Radiologic examination; sternoclavicular joint or joints, minimum	70.00	95	108	36
-26	of three views		38	43	12
71250	Computerized axial tomography, thorax; without contrast	430.0	613	698	267
-26	material		184	210	64
71260	Computerized axial tomography, thorax; with contrast	500.0	713	812	312
-26	material(s)		192	219	68
71270	Computerized axial tomography, thorax; without contrast	600.0	855	974	380
-26	material, followed by contrast material(s) and further sections		214	244	76
71550	Magnetic resonance (eg, proton) imaging, chest (eg, for	1042	1485	1692	474
-26	evaluation of hilar and mediastinal lymphadenopathy)		297	338	88
71555	Magnetic resonance angiography, chest (excluding	1060	1511	1721	475
-26	myocardium), with or without contrast material(s)		302	344	90
72010	Radiologic examination, spine, entire, survey study,	136.5	183	219	60
-26	anteroposterior and lateral		73	88	25
72020	Radiologic examination, spine, single view, specify level	50.00	67	80	23
-26			27	32	8
72040	Radiologic examination, spine, cervical; anteroposterior and	71.50	96	115	33
-26	lateral		38	46	12
72050	Radiologic examination, spine, cervical; minimum of four views	91.00	122	146	48
-26			49	59	17
72052	Radiologic examination, spine, cervical; complete, including	108.0	145	174	59
-26	oblique and flexion and/or extension studies		58	69	20
72069	Radiologic examination, spine, thoracolumbar, standing	70.00	94	112	30
-26	(scoliosis)		38	45	12
72070	Radiologic examination, spine; thoracic, anteroposterior and	69.00	92	111	34
-26	lateral		37	44	12
72072	Radiologic examination, spine; thoracic, anteroposterior and	74.00	99	119	37
-26	lateral, including swimmer's view of the cervicothoracic junction		40	48	12
72074	Radiologic examination, spine; thoracic, complete, including	85.00	114	137	44
-26	obliques, minimum of four views		46	55	12
72080	Radiologic examination, spine; thoracolumbar, anteroposterior	72.00	96	116	35
-26	and lateral		39	46	12
72090	Radiologic examination, spine; scoliosis study, including supine	85.00	114	137	39
-26	and erect studies		46	55	15

Code	Description	Medicode RVU	50th	75th	Medicare Nat'l Avg
72100	Radiologic examination, spine, lumbosacral; anteroposterior and lateral	65.00	87	104	35
-26			35	42	12
72110	Radiologic examination, spine, lumbosacral; complete, with oblique views	95.00	127	153	49
-26			51	61	17
72114	Radiologic examination, spine, lumbosacral; complete, including bending views	120.0	161	193	60
-26			64	77	20
72120	Radiologic examination, spine, lumbosacral, bending views only, minimum of four views	93.00	125	149	43
-26			50	60	12
72125	Computerized axial tomography, cervical spine; without contrast material	483.0	639	749	267
-26			192	225	64
72126	Computerized axial tomography, cervical spine; with contrast material	550.0	728	853	309
-26			197	230	67
72127	Computerized axial tomography, cervical spine; without contrast material, followed by contrast material(s) and further sections	661.0	875	1025	373
-26			219	256	69
72128	Computerized axial tomography, thoracic spine; without contrast material	483.0	639	749	267
-26			192	225	64
72129	Computerized axial tomography, thoracic spine; with contrast material	550.0	728	853	309
-26			197	230	67
72130	Computerized axial tomography, thoracic spine; without contrast material, followed by contrast material(s) and further sections	661.0	875	1025	373
-26			219	256	69
72131	Computerized axial tomography, lumbar spine; without contrast material	483.0	639	749	267
-26			192	225	64
72132	Computerized axial tomography, lumbar spine; with contrast material	550.0	728	853	309
-26			197	230	67
72133	Computerized axial tomography, lumbar spine; without contrast material, followed by contrast material(s) and further sections	661.0	875	1025	373
-26			219	256	70
72141	Magnetic resonance (eg, proton) imaging, spinal canal and contents, cervical; without contrast material	825.0	1092	1279	474
-26			218	256	89
72142	Magnetic resonance (eg, proton) imaging, spinal canal and contents, cervical; with contrast material(s)	1021	1352	1583	567
-26			270	317	105
72146	Magnetic resonance (eg, proton) imaging, spinal canal and contents, thoracic; without contrast material	900.0	1192	1395	512
-26			238	279	89
72147	Magnetic resonance (eg, proton) imaging, spinal canal and contents, thoracic; with contrast material(s)	990.0	1311	1535	568
-26			-262	307	105
72148	Magnetic resonance (eg, proton) imaging, spinal canal and contents, lumbar; without contrast material	855.0	1132	1325	506
-26			226	-265	82
72149	Magnetic resonance (eg, proton) imaging, spinal canal and contents, lumbar; with contrast material(s)	977.0	1294	1514	561
-26			259	303	97
72156	Magnetic resonance (eg, proton) imaging, spinal canal and contents, without contrast material, followed by contrast material(s) and further sequences; cervical	1190	1576	1845	989
-26			315	369	138
72157	Magnetic resonance (eg, proton) imaging, spinal canal and contents, without contrast material, followed by contrast material(s) and further sequences; thoracic	1225	1622	1899	989
-26			324	380	138
72158	Magnetic resonance (eg, proton) imaging, spinal canal and contents, without contrast material, followed by contrast material(s) and further sequences; lumbar	1161	1537	1800	979
-26			307	360	127

Code	Description	Medicode RVU	50th	75th	Medicare Nat'l Avg
72159	Magnetic resonance angiography, spinal canal and contents, with or without contrast material(s)	1064	1409	1649	515
-26			282	330	88
72170	Radiologic examination, pelvis; anteroposterior only	57.00	75	88	27
-26			30	35	9
72190	Radiologic examination, pelvis; complete, minimum of three views	72.00	95	112	35
-26			38	45	12
72192	Computerized axial tomography, pelvis; without contrast material	404.0	535	626	263
-26			160	188	60
72193	Computerized axial tomography, pelvis; with contrast material(s)	460.0	609	713	299
-26			164	193	64
72194	Computerized axial tomography, pelvis; without contrast material, followed by contrast material(s) and further sections	556.0	736	862	359
-26			184	215	67
72196	Magnetic resonance (eg, proton) imaging, pelvis	844.0	1117	1308	474
-26			223	-262	88
72198	Magnetic resonance angiography, pelvis, with or without contrast material(s)	1035	1370	1604	475
-26			274	321	90
72200	Radiologic examination, sacroiliac joints; less than three views	60.00	79	93	27
-26			32	37	9
72202	Radiologic examination, sacroiliac joints; three or more views	71.00	94	110	32
-26			38	44	11
72220	Radiologic examination, sacrum and coccyx, minimum of two views	61.00	81	95	29
-26			32	38	9
72240	Myelography, cervical, radiological supervision and interpretation	320.0	424	496	212
-26			148	174	50
72255	Myelography, thoracic, radiological supervision and interpretation	298.0	395	462	198
-26			138	162	50
72265	Myelography, lumbosacral, radiological supervision and interpretation	314.0	416	487	187
-26			146	170	46
72270	Myelography, entire spinal canal, radiological supervision and interpretation	422.0	559	654	282
-26			196	229	73
72285	Diskography, cervical, radiological supervision and interpretation	503.0	666	780	334
-26			233	273	45
72295	Diskography, lumbar, radiological supervision and interpretation	475.0	629	736	315
-26			220	258	45
73000	Radiologic examination; clavicle, complete	62.00	82	98	27
-26			33	39	9
73010	Radiologic examination; scapula, complete	65.00	86	103	27
-26			34	41	9
73020	Radiologic examination, shoulder; one view	55.00	73	87	25
-26			29	35	8
73030	Radiologic examination, shoulder; complete, minimum of two views	70.00	92	111	30
-26			37	44	10
73040	Radiologic examination, shoulder, arthrography, radiological supervision and interpretation	187.0	247	295	102
-26			86	103	30
73050	Radiologic examination; acromioclavicular joints, bilateral, with or without weighted distraction	62.00	82	98	34
-26			33	39	11
73060	Radiologic examination; humerus, minimum of two views	58.00	77	92	29
-26			31	37	9

Code	Description	Medicode RVU	50th	75th	Medicare Nat'l Avg
73070	Radiologic examination, elbow; anteroposterior and lateral views	52.00	69	82	26
-26			27	33	8
73080	Radiologic examination, elbow; complete, minimum of three views	58.00	77	92	29
-26			31	37	9
73085	Radiologic examination, elbow, arthrography, radiological supervision and interpretation	184.0	243	291	102
-26			85	102	30
73090	Radiologic examination; forearm, anteroposterior and lateral views	50.00	66	79	27
-26			-26	32	9
73092	Radiologic examination; upper extremity, infant, minimum of two views	53.00	70	84	25
-26			28	33	8
73100	Radiologic examination, wrist; anteroposterior and lateral views	46.00	61	73	26
-26			24	29	9
73110	Radiologic examination, wrist; complete, minimum of three views	52.00	69	82	28
-26			27	33	9
73115	Radiologic examination, wrist, arthrography, radiological supervision and interpretation	132.0	174	208	84
-26			61	73	30
73120	Radiologic examination, hand; two views	47.00	62	74	26
-26			25	30	9
73130	Radiologic examination, hand; minimum of three views	52.00	69	82	28
-26			27	33	9
73140	Radiologic examination, finger(s), minimum of two views	39.50	52	62	22
-26			21	25	7
73200	Computerized axial tomography, upper extremity; without contrast material	404.0	534	638	230
-26			160	191	60
73201	Computerized axial tomography, upper extremity; with contrast material(s)	460.0	608	726	266
-26			164	196	64
73202	Computerized axial tomography, upper extremity; without contrast material, followed by contrast material(s) and further sections	556.0	734	878	322
-26			184	219	66
73220	Magnetic resonance (eg, proton) imaging, upper extremity, other than joint	845.0	1116	1334	467
-26			223	-267	82
73221	Magnetic resonance (eg, proton) imaging, any joint of upper extremity	824.0	1089	1301	438
-26			218	-260	53
73225	Magnetic resonance angiography, upper extremity, with or without contrast material(s)	891.0	1177	1407	470
-26			235	281	85
73500	Radiologic examination, hip unilateral; one view	50.00	64	77	26
-26			-26	31	9
73510	Radiologic examination, hip unilateral; complete, minimum of two views	62.00	79	95	31
-26			32	38	12
73520	Radiologic examination, hips, bilateral, minimum of two views of each hip, including anteroposterior view of pelvis	80.00	102	123	38
-26			41	49	14
73525	Radiologic examination, hip, arthrography, radiological supervision and interpretation	187.0	239	288	102
-26			84	101	30
73530	Radiologic examination, hip, during operative procedure	83.00	106	128	34
-26			43	51	16
73540	Radiologic examination, pelvis and hips, infant or child, minimum of two views	68.00	87	105	31
-26			35	42	11
73550	Radiologic examination, femur, anteroposterior and lateral views	60.00	77	92	29
-26			31	37	9

Code	Description	Medicode RVU	50th	75th	Medicare Nat'l Avg
73560	Radiologic examination, knee; anteroposterior and lateral views	55.00	70	85	27
-26			28	34	9
73562	Radiologic examination, knee; anteroposterior and lateral, with	65.00	83	100	30
-26	oblique(s), minimum of three views		33	40	10
73564	Radiologic examination, knee; complete, including oblique(s),	73.00	93	112	34
-26	and tunnel, and/or patellar and/or standing views		37	45	12
73565	Radiologic examination, knee; both knees, standing,	55.00	70	85	28
-26	anteroposterior		28	34	10
73580	Radiologic examination, knee, arthrography, radiological	222.0	284	341	120
-26	supervision and interpretation		99	120	30
73590	Radiologic examination; tibia and fibula, anteroposterior and	60.00	77	92	27
-26	lateral views		31	37	9
73592	Radiologic examination; lower extremity, infant, minimum of two	60.00	77	92	26
-26	views		31	37	8
73600	Radiologic examination, ankle; anteroposterior and lateral views	54.00	69	83	26
-26			28	33	9
73610	Radiologic examination, ankle; complete, minimum of three	58.00	74	89	28
-26	views		30	36	9
73615	Radiologic examination, ankle, arthrography, radiological	184.0	236	283	102
-26	supervision and interpretation		82	99	30
73620	Radiologic examination, foot; anteroposterior and lateral views	56.00	72	86	26
-26			29	34	9
73630	Radiologic examination, foot; complete, minimum of three	58.00	74	89	28
-26	views		30	36	9
73650	Radiologic examination; calcaneus, minimum of two views	50.00	64	77	25
-26			-26	31	9
73660	Radiologic examination; toe(s), minimum of two views	44.00	56	68	22
-26			23	27	7
73700	Computerized axial tomography, lower extremity; without	404.0	531	617	230
-26	contrast material		159	185	60
73701	Computerized axial tomography, lower extremity; with contrast	460.0	605	702	266
-26	material(s)		163	190	64
73702	Computerized axial tomography, lower extremity; without	556.0	731	848	321
-26	contrast material, followed by contrast material(s) and further sections		183	212	66
73720	Magnetic resonance (eg, proton) imaging, lower extremity,	845.0	1111	1289	467
-26	other than joint		222	258	82
73721	Magnetic resonance (eg, proton) imaging, any joint of lower	824.0	1084	1257	438
-26	extremity		217	251	53
73725	Magnetic resonance angiography, lower extremity, with or	915.0	1203	1396	473
-26	without contrast material(s)		241	279	88
74000	Radiologic examination, abdomen; single anteroposterior view	52.00	70	80	28
-26			28	32	10
74010	Radiologic examination, abdomen; anteroposterior and	65.00	88	100	33
-26	additional oblique and cone views		35	40	13
74020	Radiologic examination, abdomen; complete, including	72.00	97	111	37
-26	decubitus and/or erect views		39	44	15

Code	Description	Medicode RVU	50th	75th	Medicare Nat'l Avg
74022	Radiologic examination, abdomen; complete acute abdomen series, including supine, erect, and/or decubitus views, upright PA chest	100.0	135	154	43
-26			54	62	18
74150	Computerized axial tomography, abdomen; without contrast material	450.0	613	700	260
-26			184	210	65
74160	Computerized axial tomography, abdomen; with contrast material(s)	522.0	711	812	305
-26			192	219	70
74170	Computerized axial tomography, abdomen; without contrast material, followed by contrast material(s) and further sections	630.0	859	980	369
-26			215	245	77
74181	Magnetic resonance (eg, proton) imaging, abdomen	844.0	1150	1313	474
-26			230	-263	89
74185	Magnetic resonance angiography, abdomen, with or without contrast material(s)	1015	1383	1579	475
-26			277	316	90
74190	Peritoneogram (eg, after injection of air or contrast), radiological supervision and interpretation	80.00	109	124	66
-26			38	44	22
74210	Radiologic examination; pharynx and/or cervical esophagus	99.00	137	160	60
-26			55	64	19
74220	Radiologic examination; esophagus	103.0	143	166	66
-26			57	66	-26
74230	Swallowing function, pharynx and/or esophagus, with cineradiography and/or video	125.0	174	202	74
-26			69	81	30
74235	Removal of foreign body(s), esophageal, with use of balloon catheter, radiological supervision and interpretation	250.0	347	403	155
-26			121	141	64
74240	Radiologic examination, gastrointestinal tract, upper; with or without delayed films, without KUB	138.0	192	223	89
-26			77	89	38
74241	Radiologic examination, gastrointestinal tract, upper; with or without delayed films, with KUB	139.0	193	224	90
-26			77	90	38
74245	Radiologic examination, gastrointestinal tract, upper; with small bowel, includes multiple serial films	225.0	312	363	132
-26			125	145	50
74246	Radiological examination, gastrointestinal tract, upper, air contrast, with specific high density barium, effervescent agent, with or without glucagon; with or without delayed films, without KUB	148.0	205	239	95
-26			82	95	38
74247	Radiological examination, gastrointestinal tract, upper, air contrast, with specific high density barium, effervescent agent, with or without glucagon; with or without delayed films, with KUB	155.0	215	250	96
-26			86	100	38
74249	Radiological examination, gastrointestinal tract, upper, air contrast, with specific high density barium, effervescent agent, with or without glucagon; with small bowel follow-through	230.0	319	371	138
-26			128	148	50
74250	Radiologic examination, small bowel, includes multiple serial films;	115.0	160	186	71
-26			64	74	-26
74251	Radiologic examination, small bowel, includes multiple serial films; via enteroclysis tube	133.0	185	215	76
-26			74	86	30
74260	Duodenography, hypotonic	134.0	186	216	79
-26			74	86	28
74270	Radiologic examination, colon; barium enema, with or without KUB	162.0	225	261	97
-26			90	105	38
74280	Radiologic examination, colon; air contrast with specific high density barium, with or without glucagon	212.0	294	342	131
-26			118	137	55

Code	Description	Medicode RVU	50th	75th	Medicare Nat'l Avg
74283	Barium enema, therapeutic, for reduction of intussusception	244.0	339	394	196
-26			135	157	108
74290	Cholecystography, oral contrast;	83.00	115	134	43
-26			46	54	18
74291	Cholecystography, oral contrast; additional or repeat	52.00	72	84	25
-26	examination or multiple day examination		29	34	11
74300	Cholangiography and/or pancreatography; intraoperative,	100.0	139	161	64
-26	radiological supervision and interpretation		49	56	20
74301	Cholangiography and/or pancreatography; additional set	57.00	79	92	40
-26	intraoperative, radiological supervision and interpretation		28	32	11
74305	Cholangiography and/or pancreatography; postoperative,	103.0	143	166	50
-26	radiological supervision and interpretation		50	58	23
74320	Cholangiography, percutaneous, transhepatic, radiological	254.0	353	410	138
-26	supervision and interpretation		123	143	30
74327	Postoperative biliary duct stone removal, percutaneous via T-	325.0	451	524	101
-26	tube tract, basket or snare (eg, Burhenne technique), radiological supervision and interpretation		158	183	39
74328	Endoscopic catheterization of the biliary ductal system,	277.0	384	447	146
-26	radiological supervision and interpretation		135	156	39
74329	Endoscopic catheterization of the pancreatic ductal system,	276.0	383	445	147
-26	radiological supervision and interpretation		134	156	39
74330	Combined endoscopic catheterization of the biliary and	293.0	407	473	146
-26	pancreatic ductal systems, radiological supervision and interpretation		142	165	39
74340	Introduction of long gastrointestinal tube (eg, Miller-Abbott),	150.0	208	242	120
-26	including multiple fluoroscopies and films, radiological supervision and interpretation		73	85	30
74350	Percutaneous placement of gastrostomy tube, radiological	218.0	303	352	150
-26	supervision and interpretation		106	123	42
74355	Percutaneous placement of enteroclysis tube, radiological	219.0	304	353	132
-26	supervision and interpretation		106	124	42
74360	Intraluminal dilation of strictures and/or obstructions (eg,	289.0	401	466	138
-26	esophagus), radiological supervision and interpretation		140	163	30
74363	Percutaneous transhepatic dilatation of biliary duct stricture with	208.0	289	336	255
-26	or without placement of stent, radiological supervision and interpretation		101	117	65
74400	Urography (pyelography), intravenous, with or without KUB,	150.0	193	226	85
-26	with or without tomography;		77	90	27
74405	Urography (pyelography), intravenous, with or without KUB,	173.0	222	261	95
-26	with or without tomography; with special hypertensive contrast concentration and/or clearance studies		89	104	27
74410	Urography, infusion, drip technique and/or bolus technique;	160.0	206	241	94
-26			82	96	27
74415	Urography, infusion, drip technique and/or bolus technique;	180.0	231	271	100
-26	with nephrotomography		93	108	27
74420	Urography, retrograde, with or without KUB	100.0	129	151	110
-26			51	60	19
74425	Urography, antegrade, (pyelostogram, nephrostogram,	115.0	148	173	64
-26	loopogram), radiological supervision and interpretation		52	61	19

Code	Description	Medicode RVU	50th	75th	Medicare Nat'l Avg
74430	Cystography, minimum of three views, radiological supervision	94.00	121	142	54
-26	and interpretation		42	50	18
74440	Vasography, vesiculography, or epididymography, radiological	105.0	135	158	60
-26	supervision and interpretation		47	55	21
74445	Corpora cavernosography, radiological supervision and	139.0	179	209	100
-26	interpretation		63	73	62
74450	Urethrocystography, retrograde, radiological supervision and	125.0	161	188	68
-26	interpretation		56	66	18
74455	Urethrocystography, voiding, radiological supervision and	137.0	176	206	72
-26	interpretation		62	72	18
74470	Radiologic examination, renal cyst study, translumbar, contrast	130.0	167	196	73
-26	visualization, radiological supervision and interpretation		58	69	30
74475	Introduction of intracatheter or catheter into renal pelvis for	364.0	468	548	169
-26	drainage and/or injection, percutaneous, radiological supervision and interpretation		164	192	30
74480	Introduction of ureteral catheter or stent into ureter through	442.0	568	666	170
-26	renal pelvis for drainage and/or injection, percutaneous, radiological supervision and interpretation		199	233	31
74485	Dilation of nephrostomy, ureters, or urethra, radiological	243.0	312	366	138
-26	supervision and interpretation		109	128	30
74710	Pelvimetry, with or without placental localization	96.00	123	145	55
-26			49	58	19
74740	Hysterosalpingography, radiological supervision and	120.0	154	181	65
-26	interpretation		54	63	21
74742	Transcervical catheterization of fallopian tube, radiological	135.0	173	203	139
-26	supervision and interpretation		61	71	31
74775	Perineogram (eg, vaginogram, for sex determination or extent	155.0	199	233	84
-26	of anomalies)		80	93	34
75552	Cardiac magnetic resonance imaging for morphology; without	875.0	1160	1425	472
-26	contrast material		232	285	87
75553	Cardiac magnetic resonance imaging for morphology; with	900.0	1193	1465	484
-26	contrast material		239	293	98
75554	Cardiac magnetic resonance imaging for function, with or	890.0	1180	1449	479
-26	without morphology; complete study (eg, multiple chambers)		236	290	93
75555	Cardiac magnetic resonance imaging for function, with or	884.0	1172	1439	476
-26	without morphology; limited study (eg, single chamber)		234	288	91
75556	Cardiac magnetic resonance imaging for velocity flow mapping	0.00	0	0	–
-26			0	0	
75600	Aortography, thoracic, without serialography, radiological	741.0	983	1206	441
-26	supervision and interpretation		98	121	27
75605	Aortography, thoracic, by serialography, radiological	861.0	1142	1402	486
-26	supervision and interpretation		171	210	62
75625	Aortography, abdominal, by serialography, radiological	868.0	1151	1413	486
-26	supervision and interpretation		173	212	62
75630	Aortography, abdominal plus bilateral iliofemoral lower	916.0	1215	1491	517
-26	extremity, catheter, by serialography, radiological supervision and interpretation		182	224	72
75650	Angiography, cervicocerebral, catheter, including vessel origin,	943.0	1250	1535	506
-26	radiological supervision and interpretation		188	230	81

Code	Description	Medicode RVU	50th	75th	Medicare Nat'l Avg
75658	Angiography, brachial, retrograde, radiological supervision and	862.0	1143	1403	496
-26	interpretation		171	211	71
75660	Angiography, external carotid, unilateral, selective, radiological	775.0	1028	1262	496
-26	supervision and interpretation		154	189	71
75662	Angiography, external carotid, bilateral, selective, radiological	986.0	1307	1605	517
-26	supervision and interpretation		196	241	90
75665	Angiography, carotid, cerebral, unilateral, radiological	882.0	1170	1436	496
-26	supervision and interpretation		175	215	72
75671	Angiography, carotid, cerebral, bilateral, radiological	935.0	1240	1522	517
-26	supervision and interpretation		186	228	91
75676	Angiography, carotid, cervical, unilateral, radiological	875.0	1160	1425	496
-26	supervision and interpretation		174	214	72
75680	Angiography, carotid, cervical, bilateral, radiological supervision	903.0	1197	1470	517
-26	and interpretation		180	221	91
75685	Angiography, vertebral, cervical, and/or intracranial,	883.0	1171	1438	496
-26	radiological supervision and interpretation		176	216	71
75705	Angiography, spinal, selective, radiological supervision and	730.0	968	1188	549
-26	interpretation		194	238	119
75710	Angiography, extremity, unilateral, radiological supervision and	752.0	997	1224	485
-26	interpretation		150	184	63
75716	Angiography, extremity, bilateral, radiological supervision and	930.0	1233	1514	496
-26	interpretation		185	227	72
75722	Angiography, renal, unilateral, selective (including flush	859.0	1139	1398	486
-26	aortogram), radiological supervision and interpretation		171	210	62
75724	Angiography, renal, bilateral, selective (including flush	1038	1376	1690	507
-26	aortogram), radiological supervision and interpretation		206	253	81
75726	Angiography, visceral, selective or supraselective, (with or	922.0	1223	1501	486
-26	without flush aortogram), radiological supervision and interpretation		183	225	62
75731	Angiography, adrenal, unilateral, selective, radiological	448.0	594	729	486
-26	supervision and interpretation		89	109	62
75733	Angiography, adrenal, bilateral, selective, radiological	700.0	928	1140	496
-26	supervision and interpretation		139	171	71
75736	Angiography, pelvic, selective or supraselective, radiological	874.0	1159	1423	486
-26	supervision and interpretation		174	213	62
75741	Angiography, pulmonary, unilateral, selective, radiological	859.0	1139	1398	495
-26	supervision and interpretation		171	210	71
75743	Angiography, pulmonary, bilateral, selective, radiological	903.0	1197	1470	517
-26	supervision and interpretation		180	221	90
75746	Angiography, pulmonary, by nonselective catheter or venous	740.0	981	1205	486
-26	injection, radiological supervision and interpretation		147	181	62
75756	Angiography, internal mammary, radiological supervision and	840.0	1114	1368	485
-26	interpretation		167	205	62
75774	Angiography, selective, each additional vessel studied after	159.0	211	259	430
-26	basic examination, radiological supervision and interpretation		21	-26	19
75790	Angiography, arteriovenous shunt (eg, dialysis patient),	260.0	345	423	162
-26	radiological supervision and interpretation		121	148	101
75801	Lymphangiography, extremity only, unilateral, radiological	395.0	547	681	228
-26	supervision and interpretation		109	136	44

Code	Description	Medicode RVU	50th	75th	Medicare Nat'l Avg
75803	Lymphangiography, extremity only, bilateral, radiological supervision and interpretation	476.0	659	820	249
-26			132	164	63
75805	Lymphangiography, pelvic/abdominal, unilateral, radiological supervision and interpretation	513.0	710	884	251
-26			142	177	44
75807	Lymphangiography, pelvic/abdominal, bilateral, radiological supervision and interpretation	550.0	761	948	272
-26			152	190	63
75809	Shuntogram for investigation of previously placed indwelling nonvascular shunt (eg, LeVeen shunt, ventriculoperitoneal shunt), radiological supervision and interpretation	170.0	235	293	51
-26			82	103	24
75810	Splenoportography, radiological supervision and interpretation	762.5	1055	1314	486
-26			158	197	62
75820	Venography, extremity, unilateral, radiological supervision and interpretation	180.0	249	310	73
-26			87	109	39
75822	Venography, extremity, bilateral, radiological supervision and interpretation	271.0	375	467	111
-26			131	163	58
75825	Venography, caval, inferior, with serialography, radiological supervision and interpretation	762.5	1055	1314	485
-26			158	197	62
75827	Venography, caval, superior, with serialography, radiological supervision and interpretation	762.5	1055	1314	486
-26			158	197	62
75831	Venography, renal, unilateral, selective, radiological supervision and interpretation	743.0	1028	1280	482
-26			154	192	62
75833	Venography, renal, bilateral, selective, radiological supervision and interpretation	888.0	1229	1530	506
-26			184	230	81
75840	Venography, adrenal, unilateral, selective, radiological supervision and interpretation	477.0	660	822	486
-26			99	123	62
75842	Venography, adrenal, bilateral, selective, radiological supervision and interpretation	783.0	1084	1349	506
-26			163	202	81
75860	Venography, sinus or jugular, catheter, radiological supervision and interpretation	697.0	965	1201	486
-26			145	180	62
75870	Venography, superior sagittal sinus, radiological supervision and interpretation	624.0	864	1075	486
-26			130	161	62
75872	Venography, epidural, radiological supervision and interpretation	797.0	1103	1373	486
-26			165	206	62
75880	Venography, orbital, radiological supervision and interpretation	229.0	317	395	72
-26			48	59	38
75885	Percutaneous transhepatic portography with hemodynamic evaluation, radiological supervision and interpretation	925.0	1280	1594	504
-26			192	239	78
75887	Percutaneous transhepatic portography without hemodynamic evaluation, radiological supervision and interpretation	455.0	630	784	504
-26			94	118	78
75889	Hepatic venography, wedged or free, with hemodynamic evaluation, radiological supervision and interpretation	819.0	1134	1411	486
-26			170	212	62
75891	Hepatic venography, wedged or free, without hemodynamic evaluation, radiological supervision and interpretation	793.0	1098	1366	486
-26			165	205	62
75893	Venous sampling through catheter, with or without angiography (eg, for parathyroid hormone, renin), radiological supervision and interpretation	327.0	453	563	429
-26			45	56	30
75894	Transcatheter therapy, embolization, any method, radiological supervision and interpretation	404.0	559	696	880
-26			56	70	71

Code	Description	Medicode RVU	50th	75th	Medicare Nat'l Avg
75896	Transcatheter therapy, infusion, any method (eg, thrombolysis other than coronary), radiological supervision and interpretation	1218	1686	2099	777
-26			169	210	71
75898	Angiogram through existing catheter for follow-up study for transcatheter therapy, embolization or infusion	496.0	686	855	126
-26			137	171	91
75900	Exchange of a previously placed arterial catheter during thrombolytic therapy with contrast monitoring, radiological supervision and interpretation	401.0	555	691	746
-26			56	69	-26
75940	Percutaneous placement of IVC filter, radiological supervision and interpretation	887.0	1228	1528	452
-26			123	153	30
75960	Transcatheter introduction of intravascular stent(s), (non-coronary vessel), percutaneous and/or open, radiological supervision and interpretation, each vessel	1182	1636	2037	554
-26			164	204	43
75961	Transcatheter retrieval, percutaneous, of intravascular foreign body (eg, fractured venous or arterial catheter), radiological supervision and interpretation	2020	2796	3480	601
-26			280	348	231
75962	Transluminal balloon angioplasty, peripheral artery, radiological supervision and interpretation	1218	1686	2099	558
-26			169	210	30
75964	Transluminal balloon angioplasty, each additional peripheral artery, radiological supervision and interpretation	669.0	926	1153	301
-26			93	115	19
75966	Transluminal balloon angioplasty, renal or other visceral artery, radiological supervision and interpretation	1436	1987	2474	601
-26			199	247	71
75968	Transluminal balloon angioplasty, each additional visceral artery, radiological supervision and interpretation	669.0	926	1153	301
-26			93	115	19
75970	Transcatheter biopsy, radiological supervision and interpretation	768.0	1063	1323	434
-26			106	132	45
75978	Transluminal balloon angioplasty, venous (eg, subclavian stenosis), radiological supervision and interpretation	1405	1945	2421	577
-26			194	242	38
75980	Percutaneous transhepatic biliary drainage with contrast monitoring, radiological supervision and interpretation	460.0	637	793	264
-26			191	238	78
75982	Percutaneous placement of drainage catheter for combined internal and external biliary drainage or of a drainage stent for internal biliary drainage in patients with an inoperable mechanical biliary obstruction, radiological supervision and interpretation	495.0	685	853	287
-26			206	256	78
75984	Change of percutaneous tube or drainage catheter with contrast monitoring (eg, gastrointestinal system, genitourinary system, abscess), radiological supervision and interpretation	172.0	238	296	106
-26			83	104	40
75989	Radiological guidance for percutaneous drainage of abscess, or specimen collection (ie, fluoroscopy, ultrasound, or computed tomography), with or without placement of indwelling catheter, radiological supervision and interpretation	347.0	480	598	172
-26			168	209	65
75992	Transluminal atherectomy, peripheral artery, radiological supervision and interpretation	1604	2220	2764	558
-26			222	276	30
75993	Transluminal atherectomy, each additional peripheral artery, radiological supervision and interpretation	530.0	734	913	301
-26			73	91	19
75994	Transluminal atherectomy, renal, radiological supervision and interpretation	1000	1384	1723	601
-26			138	172	71
75995	Transluminal atherectomy, visceral, radiological supervision and interpretation	1677	2321	2889	601
-26			232	289	71
75996	Transluminal atherectomy, each additional visceral artery, radiological supervision and interpretation	925.0	1280	1594	301
-26			128	159	19

Code	Description	Medicode RVU	50th	75th	Medicare Nat'l Avg
76000	Fluoroscopy (separate procedure), up to one hour physician	110.0	137	169	54
-26	time, other than 71023 or 71034 (eg, cardiac fluoroscopy)		48	59	11
76001	Fluoroscopy, physician time more than one hour, assisting a	0.00	0	0	127
-26	non-radiologic physician (eg, nephrostolithotomy, ERCP, bronchoscopy, transbronchial biopsy)		0	0	41
76003	Fluoroscopic localization for needle biopsy or fine needle	149.0	186	228	75
-26	aspiration		65	80	30
76010	Radiologic examination from nose to rectum for foreign body,	57.00	71	87	28
-26	single film, child		25	31	10
76020	Bone age studies	72.00	90	110	28
-26			31	39	10
76040	Bone length studies (orthoroentgenogram, scanogram)	85.00	106	130	42
-26			37	46	15
76061	Radiologic examination, osseous survey; limited (eg, for	120.0	150	184	59
-26	metastases)		60	74	25
76062	Radiologic examination, osseous survey; complete (axial and	160.0	200	245	80
-26	appendicular skeleton)		80	98	30
76065	Radiologic examination, osseous survey, infant	75.00	94	115	41
-26			37	46	15
76066	Joint survey, single view, one or more joints (specify)	74.00	92	113	55
-26			37	45	17
76070	Computerized tomography, bone density study	454.0	567	696	116
-26			142	174	14
76075	Dual energy x-ray absorptiometry (DEXA), bone density study	164.0	205	251	119
-26			82	101	15
76080	Radiologic examination, fistula or sinus tract study, radiological	92.00	115	141	66
-26	supervision and interpretation		40	49	30
76086	Mammary ductogram or galactogram, single duct, radiological	167.0	209	256	110
-26	supervision and interpretation		42	51	20
76088	Mammary ductogram or galactogram, multiple ducts,	197.0	246	302	150
-26	radiological supervision and interpretation		49	60	24
76090	Mammography; unilateral	87.50	109	134	50
-26			44	54	14
76091	Mammography; bilateral	110.0	137	169	67
-26			55	67	23
76092	Screening mammography, bilateral (two view film study of each	75.00	94	115	–
-26	breast)		37	46	
76093	Magnetic resonance imaging, breast, without and/or with	1269	1585	1945	653
-26	contrast material(s); unilateral		317	389	89
76094	Magnetic resonance imaging, breast, without and/or with	1667	2082	2556	827
-26	contrast material(s); bilateral		416	511	89
76095	Stereotactic localization for breast biopsy, each lesion,	223.5	279	343	329
-26	radiological supervision and interpretation		112	137	82
76096	Preoperative placement of needle localization wire, breast,	125.0	156	192	74
-26	radiological supervision and interpretation		62	77	30
76098	Radiological examination, surgical specimen	45.00	56	69	23
-26			22	28	9
76100	Radiologic examination, single plane body section (eg,	130.0	162	199	75
-26	tomography), other than with urography		65	80	33

Code	Description	Medicode RVU	50th	75th	Medicare Nat'l Avg
76101	Radiologic examination, complex motion (ie, hypercycloidal) body section (eg, mastoid polytomography), other than with urography; unilateral	160.0	200	245	81
-26			80	98	32
76102	Radiologic examination, complex motion (ie, hypercycloidal) body section (eg, mastoid polytomography), other than with urography; bilateral	210.0	262	322	92
-26			105	129	32
76120	Cineradiography, except where specifically included	110.0	137	169	57
-26			55	67	21
76125	Cineradiography to complement routine examination	90.00	112	138	42
-26			45	55	15
76140	Consultation on x-ray examination made elsewhere, written report	0.00	0	0	–
-26			0	0	
76150	Xeroradiography	50.00	62	77	15
-26			0	0	
76350	Subtraction in conjunction with contrast studies	58.00	72	89	90
-26			14	18	
76355	Computerized tomography guidance for stereotactic localization	426.0	532	653	349
-26			133	163	66
76360	Computerized tomography guidance for needle biopsy, radiological supervision and interpretation	584.0	729	895	346
-26			146	179	63
76365	Computerized tomography guidance for cyst aspiration, radiological supervision and interpretation	574.0	717	880	346
-26			143	176	63
76370	Computerized tomography guidance for placement of radiation therapy fields	375.0	468	575	148
-26			117	144	47
76375	Computerized tomography, coronal, sagittal, multiplanar, oblique and/or 3-dimensional reconstruction	305.0	381	468	131
-26			38	47	9
76380	Computerized tomography, limited or localized follow-up study	0.00	0	0	171
-26			0	0	51
76400	Magnetic resonance (eg, proton) imaging, bone marrow blood supply	875.0	1093	1341	473
-26			219	-268	87
76499	Unlisted diagnostic radiologic procedure	0.00	0	0	–

76506–76999
Ultrasound

Coding Insight
The code for a complete abdominal ultrasound study (76700) refers to examination of the upper abdomen from the diaphragm to the level of the umbilicus.

A limited retroperitoneal study (76775) may be denied when billed with a complete abdominal study code (76770). It may be assumed the limited retroperitoneal code represents imaging of the kidneys. Although the kidneys are technically retroperitoneal organs, their inclusion is essential to a complete study of the abdomen and a separate imaging code should not be used.

Subsidiary Codes
Subsidiary codes have relative values that require no further adjustment:

93325 is "in addition" to 76825–76828

Because these are subsidiary or "in addition to" codes, reimbursement reduction and CPT modifier -51 do not apply.

MEDICARE ALERT

Medicare rebundles certain codes in the ultrasound section when the listed codes are considered a component of a more comprehensive service.

76516 will not be reimbursed when reported with 76519
76705 will not be reimbursed when reported with 76700
76775 will not be reimbursed when reported with 76770
76816, 76856 will not be reimbursed when reported with 76805
76857 will not be reimbursed when reported with 76856

Medicare Non-interventional Diagnostic Imaging

The Correct Coding Initiative 1996 contains valuable information for the reporting of many different radiology procedures including Non-interventional diagnostic imaging. It includes information on how HCFA has established the definition of these services and what will or will not be covered. Because this initiative is too large to include in this publication you can obtain a copy of the Correct Coding Policy Manual from NTIS (703) 487-4650.

Code	Description	Medicode RVU	50th	75th	Medicare Nat'l Avg
76506	Echoencephalography, B-scan and/or real time with image documentation (gray scale) (for determination of ventricular size, delineation of cerebral contents and detection of fluid masses or other intracranial abnormalities), including A-mode encephalography as secondary component where indicated	174.0	218	267	83
-26			98	120	35
76511	Ophthalmic ultrasound, echography, diagnostic; A-scan only, with amplitude quantification	190.0	238	291	85
-26			107	131	41
76512	Ophthalmic ultrasound, echography, diagnostic; contact B-scan (with or without simultaneous A-scan)	210.0	263	322	89
-26			118	145	37
76513	Ophthalmic ultrasound, echography, diagnostic; immersion (water bath) B-scan	210.0	263	322	89
-26			118	145	36
76516	Ophthalmic biometry by ultrasound echography, A-scan;	200.0	250	306	73
-26			113	138	30
76519	Ophthalmic biometry by ultrasound echography, A-scan; with intraocular lens power calculation	200.0	250	306	73
-26			113	138	30
76529	Ophthalmic ultrasonic foreign body localization	180.0	225	276	78
-26			101	124	31
76536	Echography, soft tissues of head and neck (eg, thyroid, parathyroid, parotid), B-scan and/or real time with image documentation	159.0	199	244	80
-26			90	110	31
76604	Echography, chest, B-scan (includes mediastinum) and/or real time with image documentation	200.0	260	308	75
-26			117	139	31
76645	Echography, breast(s) (unilateral or bilateral), B-scan and/or real time with image documentation	149.0	194	229	66
-26			87	103	30
76700	Echography, abdominal, B-scan and/or real time with image documentation; complete	200.0	269	312	112
-26			121	140	45
76705	Echography, abdominal, B-scan and/or real time with image documentation; limited (eg, single organ, quadrant, follow-up)	150.0	202	234	81
-26			91	105	33
76770	Echography, retroperitoneal (eg, renal, aorta, nodes), B-scan and/or real time with image documentation; complete	191.0	257	298	109
-26			116	134	41

Code	Description	Medicode RVU	50th	75th	Medicare Nat'l Avg
76775	Echography, retroperitoneal (eg, renal, aorta, nodes), B-scan and/or real time with image documentation; limited	123.0	165	192	81
-26			74	86	32
76778	Echography of transplanted kidney, B-scan and/or real time with image documentation, with or without duplex Doppler studies	207.5	279	323	109
-26			126	145	41
76800	Echography, spinal canal and contents	218.0	293	340	110
-26			132	153	61
76805	Echography, pregnant uterus, B-scan and/or real time with image documentation; complete (complete fetal and maternal evaluation)	177.0	233	278	127
-26			105	125	55
76810	Echography, pregnant uterus, B-scan and/or real time with image documentation; complete (complete fetal and maternal evaluation), multiple gestation, after the first trimester	258.0	340	406	246
-26			153	183	102
76815	Echography, pregnant uterus, B-scan and/or real time with image documentation; limited (gestational age, heart beat, placental location, fetal position, or emergency in the delivery room)	130.0	171	204	84
-26			77	92	36
76816	Echography, pregnant uterus, B-scan and/or real time with image documentation; follow-up or repeat	114.0	150	179	69
-26			68	81	31
76818	Fetal biophysical profile	185.0	244	291	97
-26			110	131	42
76825	Echocardiography, fetal, cardiovascular system, real time with image documentation (2D) with or without M-mode recording;	235.0	310	370	116
-26			139	166	47
76826	Echocardiography, fetal, cardiovascular system, real time with image documentation (2D) with or without M-mode recording; follow-up or repeat study	141.0	186	222	85
-26			84	100	56
76827	Doppler echocardiography, fetal, cardiovascular system, pulsed wave and/or continuous wave with spectral display; complete	150.0	198	236	107
-26			89	106	49
76828	Doppler echocardiography, fetal, cardiovascular system, pulsed wave and/or continuous wave with spectral display; follow-up or repeat study	90.00	119	142	69
-26			53	64	31
76830	Echography, transvaginal	200.0	264	315	90
-26			119	142	38
76856	Echography, pelvic (nonobstetric), B-scan and/or real time with image documentation; complete	175.0	231	275	91
-26			104	124	39
76857	Echography, pelvic (nonobstetric), B-scan and/or real time with image documentation; limited or follow-up (eg, for follicles)	160.0	211	252	57
-26			95	113	21
76870	Echography, scrotum and contents	150.0	198	236	88
-26			89	106	35
76872	Echography, transrectal	214.0	282	337	91
-26			127	151	38
76880	Echography, extremity, non-vascular, B-scan and/or real time with image documentation	150.0	198	236	81
-26			89	106	33
76930	Ultrasonic guidance for pericardiocentesis, radiological supervision and interpretation	150.0	198	236	89
-26			89	106	37
76932	Ultrasonic guidance for endomyocardial biopsy, radiological supervision and interpretation	173.0	228	272	89
-26			103	122	37
76934	Ultrasonic guidance for thoracentesis or abdominal paracentesis, radiological supervision and interpretation	149.0	197	234	89
-26			88	105	37

Code	Description	Medicode RVU	50th	75th	Medicare Nat'l Avg
76936 **-26**	Ultrasound guided compression repair of arterial pseudo-aneurysm or arteriovenous fistulae (includes diagnostic ultrasound evaluation, compression of lesion and imaging)	531.0	700 315	835 376	291 75
76938 **-26**	Ultrasonic guidance for cyst (any location), or renal pelvis aspiration, radiological supervision and interpretation	195.0	257 116	307 138	89 37
76941 **-26**	Ultrasonic guidance for intrauterine fetal transfusion or cordocentesis, radiological supervision and interpretation	145.0	191 86	228 103	123 70
76942 **-26**	Ultrasonic guidance for needle biopsy, radiological supervision and interpretation	195.0	257 116	307 138	89 37
76945 **-26**	Ultrasonic guidance for chorionic villus sampling, radiological supervision and interpretation	145.0	191 86	228 103	100 47
76946 **-26**	Ultrasonic guidance for amniocentesis, radiological supervision and interpretation	162.0	214 96	255 115	73 21
76948 **-26**	Ultrasonic guidance for aspiration of ova, radiological supervision and interpretation	185.0	244 110	291 131	73 20
76950 **-26**	Echography for placement of radiation therapy fields, B-scan	180.0	237 107	283 127	77 32
76960 **-26**	Ultrasonic guidance for placement of radiation therapy fields, except for B-scan echography	180.0	237 107	283 127	77 32
● **76965** **-26**	Ultrasonic guidance for interstitial radioelement application	180.0	237 107	283 127	–
76970 **-26**	Ultrasound study follow-up (specify)	0.00	0 0	0 0	58 22
76975 **-26**	Gastrointestinal endoscopic ultrasound, radiological supervision and interpretation	262.0	346 156	412 185	94 41
76986 **-26**	Echography, intraoperative	353.0	466 210	555 250	158 65
76999	Unlisted ultrasound procedure	0.00	0	0	–

RADIATION ONCOLOGY
77261–77799

Clinical Treatment Management

Codes relative to the following services may not be reimbursed when reported with treatment management codes:

- Evaluation and Management
- Tattooing
- Treatment of first degree burns
- Application of dressings to, and/or debridement of, wounds resulting from the therapy
- Venipuncture
- Catheterization (urethra)
- IV infusion therapy
- Psychotherapy

- Analysis of information stored in computers
- Hyperbaric oxygen pressurization
- Hypothermia
- Anesthesia
- Care of infected skin
- Pain management
- Nutritional counseling

77261–77263

Code	Description	Medicode RVU	50th	75th	Medicare Nat'l Avg
77261	Therapeutic radiology treatment planning; simple	262.0	345	418	77
-26			345	418	
77262	Therapeutic radiology treatment planning; intermediate	343.0	451	547	116
-26			451	547	
77263	Therapeutic radiology treatment planning; complex	468.0	615	746	173
-26			615	746	

77280–77299

Therapeutic Radiology Simulation-aided Field Setting

CODING INSIGHT

Radiation oncology simulation codes (77280–77295) usually include the initial films taken to document the treatment portals. Scout or port films of the area being treated usually should not be reported with simulation codes and may be denied by payers. Additionally, injection of contrast (e.g., 90784, 51600) and fluoroscopy (76000) should not be reported with simulation.

Therapeutic radiology simulation is allowed only once per set-up procedure. Multiple simulation codes reported on the same date of service may be denied.

Clinical treatment planning includes interpretation of special testing and tumor localization. Consult CPT and the *User's Guide for the Radiation Oncology Related CPT Codes* for further information

Code	Description	Medicode RVU	50th	75th	Medicare Nat'l Avg
77280	Therapeutic radiology simulation-aided field setting; simple	445.0	585	709	157
-26			176	213	39
77285	Therapeutic radiology simulation-aided field setting; intermediate	653.0	859	1041	246
-26			258	312	57
77290	Therapeutic radiology simulation-aided field setting; complex	836.0	1099	1333	306
-26			330	400	86
▲ **77295**	Therapeutic radiology simulation-aided field setting; by three-dimensional reconstruction of tumor volume in preparation for treatment with non-coplanar therapy beams	1052	1383	1677	1124
-26			415	503	191
77299	Unlisted procedure, therapeutic radiology clinical treatment planning	0.00	0	0	

77300–77799

Medical Radiation Physics, Treatment Devices, and Special Services

CODING INSIGHT

As stated in *CPT '96*, "only one teletherapy isodose plan may be reported for a given course of therapy to a specific treatment area." Although many plans might be run, usually only one plan is accepted as the optimal for the course of therapy.

MEDICARE ALERT

Medicare rebundles certain codes in the radiology section when the listed codes are considered a component of a more comprehensive service.

77261 will not be reimbursed when reported with 77262–77263
77262 will not be reimbursed when reported with 77263
77280 will not be reimbursed when reported with 77285–77290
76370 will not be reimbursed when reported with 77315
77420 will not be reimbursed when reported with 77425
77420–77425 will not be reimbursed when reported with 77430

Code	Description	Medicode RVU	50th	75th	Medicare Nat'l Avg
77300	Basic radiation dosimetry calculation, central axis depth dose, TDF, NSD, gap calculation, off axis factor, tissue inhomogeneity factors, as required during course of treatment, only when prescribed by the treating physician	179.0	235	285	79
-26			118	143	34
77305	Teletherapy, isodose plan (whether hand or computer calculated); simple (one or two parallel opposed unmodified ports directed to a single area of interest)	225.0	296	359	101
-26			133	161	39
77310	Teletherapy, isodose plan (whether hand or computer calculated); intermediate (three or more treatment ports directed to a single area of interest)	243.0	320	387	136
-26			160	194	57
77315	Teletherapy, isodose plan (whether hand or computer calculated); complex (mantle or inverted Y, tangential ports, the use of wedges, compensators, complex blocking, rotational beam, or special beam considerations)	280.0	368	446	175
-26			203	245	86
77321	Special teletherapy port plan, particles, hemi-body, total body	334.0	439	532	189
-26			154	186	52
77326	Brachytherapy isodose calculation; simple (calculation made from single plane, one to four sources/ribbon application, remote afterloading brachytherapy, 1 to 8 sources)	200.0	263	319	131
-26			118	143	51
77327	Brachytherapy isodose calculation; intermediate (multiplane dosage calculations, application involving five to ten sources/ribbons, remote afterloading brachytherapy, 9 to 12 sources)	300.0	395	478	193
-26			178	215	76
77328	Brachytherapy isodose calculation; complex (multiplane isodose plan, volume implant calculations, over ten sources/ribbons used, special spatial reconstruction, remote afterloading brachytherapy, over 12 sources)	425.0	559	677	281
-26			279	339	114
77331	Special dosimetry (eg, TLD, microdosimetry) (specify), only when prescribed by the treating physician	119.0	156	190	64
-26			125	152	48
77332	Treatment devices, design and construction; simple (simple block, simple bolus)	160.0	210	255	75
-26			105	128	30

Code	Description	Medicode RVU	50th	75th	Medicare Nat'l Avg
77333	Treatment devices, design and construction; intermediate (multiple blocks, stents, bite blocks, special bolus)	196.0	258	312	110
-26			129	156	46
77334	Treatment devices, design and construction; complex (irregular blocks, special shields, compensators, wedges, molds or casts)	378.0	497	603	177
-26			224	271	68
77336	Continuing medical radiation physics consultation in support of therapeutic radiologist including continuing quality assurance reported per week of therapy	132.0	174	210	102
-26			0	0	
77370	Special medical radiation physics consultation	206.0	271	328	120
-26			0	0	
77399	Unlisted procedure, medical radiation physics, dosimetry and treatment devices	0.00	0	0	–
77401	Radiation treatment delivery, superficial and/or ortho voltage	86.00	113	137	61
-26			0	0	
77402	Radiation treatment delivery, single treatment area, single port or parallel opposed ports, simple blocks or no blocks; up to 5 MeV	87.50	115	139	61
-26			0	0	
77403	Radiation treatment delivery, single treatment area, single port or parallel opposed ports, simple blocks or no blocks; 6-10 MeV	101.0	133	161	61
-26			0	0	
77404	Radiation treatment delivery, single treatment area, single port or parallel opposed ports, simple blocks or no blocks; 11-19 MeV	113.0	149	180	63
-26			0	0	
77406	Radiation treatment delivery, single treatment area, single port or parallel opposed ports, simple blocks or no blocks; 20 MeV or greater	121.0	159	193	62
-26			0	0	
77407	Radiation treatment delivery, two separate treatment areas, three or more ports on a single treatment area, use of multiple blocks; up to 5 MeV	112.5	148	179	72
-26			0	0	
77408	Radiation treatment delivery, two separate treatment areas, three or more ports on a single treatment area, use of multiple blocks; 6-10 MeV	112.5	148	179	73
-26			0	0	
77409	Radiation treatment delivery, two separate treatment areas, three or more ports on a single treatment area, use of multiple blocks; 11-19 MeV	112.5	148	179	74
-26			0	0	
77411	Radiation treatment delivery, two separate treatment areas, three or more ports on a single treatment area, use of multiple blocks; 20 MeV or greater	112.5	148	179	73
-26			0	0	
77412	Radiation treatment delivery, three or more separate treatment areas, custom blocking, tangential ports, wedges, rotational beam, compensators, special particle beam (eg, electron or neutrons); up to 5 MeV	124.5	164	198	81
-26			0	0	
77413	Radiation treatment delivery, three or more separate treatment areas, custom blocking, tangential ports, wedges, rotational beam, compensators, special particle beam (eg, electron or neutrons); 6-10 MeV	137.0	180	218	82
-26			0	0	
77414	Radiation treatment delivery, three or more separate treatment areas, custom blocking, tangential ports, wedges, rotational beam, compensators, special particle beam (eg, electron or neutrons); 11-19 MeV	140.0	184	223	83
-26			0	0	
77416	Radiation treatment delivery, three or more separate treatment areas, custom blocking, tangential ports, wedges, rotational beam, compensators, special particle beam (eg, electron or neutrons); 20 MeV or greater	146.0	192	233	82
-26			0	0	

Code	Description	Medicode RVU	50th	75th	Medicare Nat'l Avg
77417	Therapeutic radiology port film(s)	87.00	114	139	20
-26			0	0	
77419	Weekly radiation therapy management; conformal	515.0	677	821	200
-26			677	821	
77420	Weekly radiation therapy management; simple	215.0	283	343	90
-26			283	343	
77425	Weekly radiation therapy management; intermediate	305.0	401	486	136
-26			401	486	
77430	Weekly radiation therapy management; complex	415.0	546	662	200
-26			546	662	
77431	Radiation therapy management with complete course of	116.0	153	185	92
-26	therapy consisting of one or two fractions only		153	185	
77432	Stereotactic radiation treatment management of cerebral	1013	1332	1615	454
-26	lesion(s) (complete course of treatment consisting of one session)		1332	1615	
77470	Special treatment procedure (eg, total body irradiation,	0.00	0	0	492
-26	hemibody irradiation, per oral, vaginal cone irradiation)		0	0	114
77499	Unlisted procedure, therapeutic radiology clinical treatment management	0.00	0	0	–
77600	Hyperthermia, externally generated; superficial (ie, heating to a	416.0	547	663	189
-26	depth of 4 cm or less)		274	332	85
77605	Hyperthermia, externally generated; deep (ie, heating to	560.0	736	893	251
-26	depths greater than 4 cm)		368	446	112
77610	Hyperthermia generated by interstitial probe(s); 5 or fewer	316.0	416	504	189
-26	interstitial applicators		208	252	85
77615	Hyperthermia generated by interstitial probe(s); more than 5	460.0	605	733	253
-26	interstitial applicators		302	367	113
77620	Hyperthermia generated by intracavitary probe(s)	270.0	355	430	188
-26			178	215	84
77750	Infusion or instillation of radioelement solution	500.0	658	797	294
-26			559	677	251
77761	Intracavitary radioelement application; simple	418.0	550	666	277
-26			412	500	198
77762	Intracavitary radioelement application; intermediate	618.0	813	985	411
-26			610	739	298
77763	Intracavitary radioelement application; complex	849.5	1117	1354	583
-26			894	1083	443
77776	Interstitial radioelement application; simple	550.0	723	877	328
-26			579	701	257
77777	Interstitial radioelement application; intermediate	900.0	1184	1435	523
-26			888	1076	387
77778	Interstitial radioelement application; complex	1250	1644	1993	742
-26			1315	1594	578
77781	Remote afterloading high intensity brachytherapy; 1-4 source	1004	1320	1600	783
-26	positions or catheters		198	240	84
77782	Remote afterloading high intensity brachytherapy; 5-8 source	1056	1389	1683	826
-26	positions or catheters		278	337	127

Code	Description	Medicode RVU	50th	75th	Medicare Nat'l Avg
77783	Remote afterloading high intensity brachytherapy; 9-12 source positions or catheters	1132	1489	1804	887
-26			372	451	188
77784	Remote afterloading high intensity brachytherapy; over 12 source positions or catheters	1249	1642	1991	982
-26			493	597	284
77789	Surface application of radioelement	103.0	135	164	72
-26			108	131	57
77790	Supervision, handling, loading of radioelement	130.0	171	207	74
-26			137	166	57
77799	Unlisted procedure, clinical brachytherapy	0.00	0	0	–

78000–79999
Nuclear Medicine

Coding Insight

Administration of radiopharmaceuticals by other than the intravenous route (e.g., intrathecal via endoscope) should be reported in addition to the imaging code. However, intravenous injection of radiopharmaceuticals is inherent to the codes describing nuclear medicine procedures and should not be separately coded.

A planar exam code may not be reimbursed when reported with a corresponding tomographic SPECT code listed in CPT under the same anatomical or procedural subheading. However, an exception may be when a whole body planar exam or three phase code is billed with a SPECT exam. It may be assumed it is necessary to perform a whole body planar exam prior to a SPECT study to determine if tomography is needed or to define the region to be selectively imaged. An exception would apply to the following coding combinations only:

- 78306 *Bone and/or joint imaging; whole body* with 78320 *Bone and/or joint imaging; tomographic (SPECT)*
- *78315 Bone and/or joint imagining; three phase study* with 78320 *Bone and/or joint imaging; tomographic (SPECT)*
- 78802 *Radiopharmaceutical localization of tumor; whole body* with 78803 *Radiopharmaceutical localization of tumor; tomographic (SPECT)*
- 78806 *Radiopharmaceutical localization of abscess; whole body* with 78807 *Radiopharmaceutical localization of abscess; tomographic (SPECT)*

The American College of Nuclear Physicians, the Society of Nuclear Medicine, and Medicare recommend that modifier -51 for multiple procedures be used when whole body planar exams and SPECT studies listed above are reported on the same date of service.

Vascular flow imaging (78445) should not be reported with a planar imaging code that states "with flow." If vascular flow imaging is reported with a planar imaging code that does not state "with flow," the payer may transfer both codes to an imaging code (if available) that includes the flow.

When PET and SPECT scans are performed together, the information from the two modalities will generally be complementary. However, in some areas (e.g., determination of cerebral perfusion) the two studies may be considered competitive and the payer may allow one scan and deny the second.

Subsidiary Codes

Subsidiary codes have relative values that require no further adjustment:

78478 is "in addition" to 78460–78465
78480 is "in addition" to 78460–78465

Because these are subsidiary or "in addition to" codes, reimbursement reduction and CPT modifier -51 do not apply.

Medicare Alert

Medicare rebundles certain codes in the surgery section when the listed codes are considered a component of a more comprehensive service.

36000 will not be reimbursed when reported with 78460, 78481–78483
78300–78305 will not be reimbursed when reported with 78305–78306
78305 will not be reimbursed when reported with 78306
78460–78465 will not be reimbursed when reported with 78465

For information on billing and payment of radiopharmaceuticals check with your local carrier for policy guidelines.

Code	Description	Medicode RVU	50th	75th	Medicare Nat'l Avg
78000	Thyroid uptake; single determination	75.00	106	134	44
-26			32	40	12
78001	Thyroid uptake; multiple determinations	100.0	141	178	60
-26			42	53	16
78003	Thyroid uptake; stimulation, suppression or discharge (not	90.00	127	160	52
-26	including initial uptake studies)		38	48	19
78006	Thyroid imaging, with uptake; single determination	166.0	235	296	110
-26			70	89	30
78007	Thyroid imaging, with uptake; multiple determinations	188.0	266	335	118
-26			80	101	31
78010	Thyroid imaging; only	113.0	160	201	84
-26			48	60	23
78011	Thyroid imaging; with vascular flow	180.0	255	321	109
-26			76	96	27
78015	Thyroid carcinoma metastases imaging; limited area (eg, neck	225.0	318	401	125
-26	and chest only)		95	120	38
78016	Thyroid carcinoma metastases imaging; with additional studies	239.0	338	426	166
-26	(eg, urinary recovery)		101	128	46
78017	Thyroid carcinoma metastases imaging; multiple areas	350.0	495	624	175
-26			148	187	48
78018	Thyroid carcinoma metastases imaging; whole body	375.0	530	668	238
-26			159	200	54
78070	Parathyroid imaging	100.0	141	178	92
-26			42	53	31
78075	Adrenal imaging, cortex and/or medulla	150.0	212	267	228
-26			64	80	43
78102	Bone marrow imaging; limited area	175.0	247	312	104
-26			62	78	33
78103	Bone marrow imaging; multiple areas	275.0	389	490	155
-26			97	123	44

Code	Description	Medicode RVU	50th	75th	Medicare Nat'l Avg
78104	Bone marrow imaging; whole body	300.0	424	535	189
-26			106	134	48
78110	Plasma volume, radiopharmaceutical volume-dilution technique	100.0	141	178	44
-26	(separate procedure); single sampling		35	45	11
78111	Plasma volume, radiopharmaceutical volume-dilution technique	150.0	212	267	100
-26	(separate procedure); multiple samplings		53	67	14
78120	Red cell volume determination (separate procedure); single	110.0	156	196	73
-26	sampling		39	49	15
78121	Red cell volume determination (separate procedure); multiple	185.0	262	330	117
-26	samplings		65	82	20
78122	Whole blood volume determination, including separate	280.0	396	499	180
-26	measurement of plasma volume and red cell volume (radiopharmaceutical volume-dilution technique)		99	125	25
78099	Unlisted endocrine procedure, diagnostic nuclear medicine	0.00	0	0	–
78130	Red cell survival study;	225.0	318	401	134
-26			80	100	35
78135	Red cell survival study; differential organ/tissue kinetics, (eg,	244.0	345	435	202
-26	splenic and/or hepatic sequestration)		86	109	37
78140	Labeled red cell sequestration, differential organ/tissue, (eg,	221.0	312	394	167
-26	splenic and/or hepatic)		78	98	34
78160	Plasma radioiron disappearance (turnover) rate	150.0	212	267	143
-26			53	67	20
78162	Radioiron oral absorption	235.0	332	419	134
-26			83	105	25
78170	Radioiron red cell utilization	227.0	321	405	203
-26			80	101	25
78172	Chelatable iron for estimation of total body iron	82.00	116	146	126
-26			29	37	29
78185	Spleen imaging only, with or without vascular flow	170.0	240	303	105
-26			60	76	25
78190	Kinetics, study of platelet survival, with or without differential	285.0	403	508	253
-26	organ/tissue localization		101	127	56
78191	Platelet survival study	321.0	454	572	284
-26			113	143	36
78195	Lymphatics and lymph glands imaging	277.0	392	494	178
-26			98	123	40
78201	Liver imaging; static only	200.0	277	337	109
-26			69	84	29
78202	Liver imaging; with vascular flow	220.0	305	371	131
-26			76	93	32
78205	Liver imaging (SPECT)	410.0	568	691	243
-26			142	173	42
78215	Liver and spleen imaging; static only	275.0	381	463	133
-26			95	116	33
78216	Liver and spleen imaging; with vascular flow	321.0	445	541	155
-26			111	135	37
78220	Liver function study with hepatobiliary agents, with serial	262.0	363	441	154
-26	images		91	110	31

Code	Description	Medicode RVU	50th	75th	Medicare Nat'l Avg
78223 **-26**	Hepatobiliary ductal system imaging, including gallbladder, with or without pharmacologic intervention, with or without quantitative measurement of gallbladder function	258.0	358 89	435 109	175 50
78199	Unlisted hematopoietic, reticuloendothelial and lymphatic procedure, diagnostic nuclear medicine	0.00	0	0	–
78230 **-26**	Salivary gland imaging;	169.0	234 59	285 71	100 -26
78231 **-26**	Salivary gland imaging; with serial images	176.0	244 61	297 74	138 31
78232 **-26**	Salivary gland function study	180.0	249 62	303 76	148 27
78258 **-26**	Esophageal motility	252.0	349 87	425 106	138 40
78261 **-26**	Gastric mucosa imaging	238.0	330 82	401 100	180 40
78262 **-26**	Gastroesophageal reflux study	260.0	360 90	438 110	185 41
78264 **-26**	Gastric emptying study	267.0	370 93	450 112	185 46
78270 **-26**	Vitamin B-12 absorption study (eg, Schilling test); without intrinsic factor	107.0	148 37	180 45	64 13
78271 **-26**	Vitamin B-12 absorption study (eg, Schilling test); with intrinsic factor	113.0	157 39	190 48	68 13
78272 **-26**	Vitamin B-12 absorption studies combined, with and without intrinsic factor	132.0	183 46	222 56	97 17
78278 **-26**	Acute gastrointestinal blood loss imaging	303.0	420 105	511 128	223 56
78282 **-26**	Gastrointestinal protein loss	168.0	233 58	283 71	107 22
78290 **-26**	Bowel imaging (eg, ectopic gastric mucosa, Meckel's localization, volvulus)	230.0	319 80	388 97	142 40
78291 **-26**	Peritoneal-venous shunt patency test (eg, for LeVeen, Denver shunt)	200.0	277 69	337 84	157 52
78300 **-26**	Bone and/or joint imaging; limited area	230.0	305 91	372 112	125 38
78305 **-26**	Bone and/or joint imaging; multiple areas	285.0	378 113	461 138	176 50
78306 **-26**	Bone and/or joint imaging; whole body	305.0	404 121	494 148	201 52
78315 **-26**	Bone and/or joint imaging; three phase study	325.0	431 129	526 158	218 58
78320 **-26**	Bone and/or joint imaging; tomographic (SPECT)	402.0	533 160	651 195	260 59
78299	Unlisted gastrointestinal procedure, diagnostic nuclear medicine	0.00	0	0	–
78350 **-26**	Bone density (bone mineral content) study; single photon absorptiometry	107.0	142 43	173 52	45 16
78351 **-26**	Bone density (bone mineral content) study; dual photon absorptiometry	147.0	195 58	238 71	–

Code	Description	Medicode RVU	50th	75th	Medicare Nat'l Avg
78414 **-26**	Determination of central c-v hemodynamics (non-imaging) (eg, ejection fraction with probe technique) with or without pharmacologic intervention or exercise, single or multiple determinations	260.0	341 102	420 126	109 29
78399	Unlisted musculoskeletal procedure, diagnostic nuclear medicine	0.00	0	0	–
78428 **-26**	Cardiac shunt detection	205.0	269 81	331 99	123 44
78445 **-26**	Vascular flow imaging (ie, angiography, venography)	247.0	324 97	399 120	95 32
78455 **-26**	Venous thrombosis study (eg, radioactive fibrinogen)	260.0	341 102	420 126	178 44
78457 **-26**	Venous thrombosis imaging (eg, venogram); unilateral	206.0	270 81	333 100	137 45
78458 **-26**	Venous thrombosis imaging (eg, venogram); bilateral	321.0	421 126	519 156	190 53
● **78459** **-26**	Myocardial imaging, positron emission tomography (PET), metabolic evaluation	0.00	0 0	0 0	–
78460 **-26**	Myocardial perfusion imaging; single study, at rest or stress (exercise and/or pharmacologic), qualitative or quantitative	325.0	426 128	525 158	139 51
78461 **-26**	Myocardial perfusion imaging; multiple studies, at rest and/or stress (exercise and/or pharmacologic), and redistribution and/or rest injection, qualitative or quantitative	511.0	670 201	826 248	258 81
78464 **-26**	Myocardial perfusion imaging; tomographic (SPECT), single study at rest or stress (exercise and/or pharmacologic), with or without quantitation	450.0	590 177	727 218	302 64
78465 **-26**	Myocardial perfusion imaging; tomographic (SPECT), multiple studies, at rest and/or stress (exercise and/or pharmacologic) and redistribution and/or rest injection, qualitative or quantitative	690.0	905 272	1115 335	488 90
78466 **-26**	Myocardial imaging, infarct avid, planar; qualitative or quantitative	311.0	408 122	503 151	134 44
78468 **-26**	Myocardial imaging, infarct avid, planar; with ejection fraction by first pass technique	285.0	374 112	461 138	172 46
78469 **-26**	Myocardial imaging, infarct avid, planar; tomographic SPECT with or without quantitation	333.0	437 131	538 161	229 52
78472 **-26**	Cardiac blood pool imaging, gated equilibrium; single study at rest or stress (exercise and/or pharmacologic), wall motion study plus ejection fraction, with or without additional quantitative processing	326.0	428 128	527 158	248 58
78473 **-26**	Cardiac blood pool imaging, gated equilibrium; multiple studies, wall motion study plus ejection fraction, at rest and stress (exercise and/or pharmacologic), with or without additional quantification	587.0	770 231	949 285	359 76
78478 **-26**	Myocardial perfusion study with wall motion, qualitative or quantitative study (list separately in addition to code for primary procedure)(Use only for codes 78460, 78461, 78464, 78465)	114.0	150 45	184 55	86 32
78480 **-26**	Myocardial perfusion study with ejection fraction (list separately in addition to code for primary procedure) (Use only for codes 78460, 78461, 78464, 78465)	109.0	143 43	176 53	86 32

Code	Description	Medicode RVU	50th	75th	Medicare Nat'l Avg
78481	Cardiac blood pool imaging, first pass technique; single study, at rest or during stress (exercise and/or pharmacologic), wall motion study plus ejection fraction, with or without quantitative processing	345.0	453	558	238
-26			136	167	58
78483	Cardiac blood pool imaging, first pass technique; multiple studies, at rest and during stress (exercise and/or pharmacologic), wall motion study plus ejection fraction, with or without additional quantitative processing	710.0	932	1147	347
-26			279	344	76
78499	Unlisted cardiovascular procedure, diagnostic nuclear medicine	0.00	0	0	–
78580	Pulmonary perfusion imaging, particulate	252.0	344	424	160
-26			86	106	45
78584	Pulmonary perfusion imaging, particulate, with ventilation; single breath	262.0	358	441	168
-26			89	110	57
78585	Pulmonary perfusion imaging, particulate, with ventilation; rebreathing and washout, with or without single breath	390.0	532	656	254
-26			133	164	65
78586	Pulmonary ventilation imaging, aerosol; single projection	166.0	227	279	117
-26			57	70	27
78587	Pulmonary ventilation imaging, aerosol; multiple projections (eg, anterior, posterior, lateral views)	212.0	289	357	129
-26			72	89	33
78591	Pulmonary ventilation imaging, gaseous, single breath, single projection	200.0	273	337	123
-26			68	84	25
78593	Pulmonary ventilation imaging, gaseous, with rebreathing and washout with or without single breath; single projection	233.0	318	392	148
-26			80	98	32
78594	Pulmonary ventilation imaging, gaseous, with rebreathing and washout with or without single breath; multiple projections (eg, anterior, posterior, lateral views)	280.0	382	471	205
-26			96	118	36
78596	Pulmonary quantitative differential function (ventilation/perfusion) study	158.0	216	266	311
-26			54	66	68
78600	Brain imaging, limited procedure; static	198.0	270	333	128
-26			68	83	28
78601	Brain imaging, limited procedure; with vascular flow	250.0	341	421	151
-26			85	105	34
78605	Brain imaging, complete study; static	245.0	334	412	150
-26			84	103	36
78606	Brain imaging, complete study; with vascular flow	281.0	384	473	176
-26			96	118	43
78607	Brain imaging, complete study; tomographic (SPECT)	429.0	586	722	292
-26			146	181	70
78608	Brain imaging, positron emission tomography (PET); metabolic evaluation	0.00	0	0	–
-26			0	0	
78609	Brain imaging, positron emission tomography (PET); perfusion evaluation	0.00	0	0	–
-26			0	0	
78610	Brain imaging, vascular flow only	114.0	156	192	72
-26			39	48	19
78615	Cerebral blood flow	256.0	349	431	157
-26			87	108	25
78599	Unlisted respiratory procedure, diagnostic nuclear medicine	0.00	0	0	–

Code	Description	Medicode RVU	50th	75th	Medicare Nat'l Avg
78630	Cerebrospinal fluid flow, imaging (not including introduction of material); cisternography	318.0	434	535	214
-26			109	134	46
78635	Cerebrospinal fluid flow, imaging (not including introduction of material); ventriculography	250.0	341	421	127
-26			85	105	37
78645	Cerebrospinal fluid flow, imaging (not including introduction of material); shunt evaluation	250.0	341	421	155
-26			85	105	37
78647	Cerebrospinal fluid flow, imaging (not including introduction of material); tomographic (SPECT)	368.0	502	619	253
-26			126	155	51
78650	CSF leakage detection and localization	350.0	478	589	195
-26			119	147	38
78660	Radiopharmaceutical dacryocystography	167.0	228	281	102
-26			57	70	30
78700	Kidney imaging; static only	213.0	301	364	130
-26			90	109	29
78701	Kidney imaging; with vascular flow	250.0	353	427	151
-26			106	128	33
78704	Kidney imaging; with function study (ie, imaging renogram)	286.0	404	488	176
-26			121	146	45
78707	Kidney imaging; with vascular flow and function study	285.0	402	487	212
-26			121	146	57
78710	Kidney imaging; tomographic (SPECT)	392.0	553	669	240
-26			166	201	38
78715	Kidney vascular flow only	120.0	169	205	75
-26			51	61	20
78725	Kidney function study without pharmacologic intervention	225.0	317	384	86
-26			95	115	24
78699	Unlisted nervous system procedure, diagnostic nuclear medicine	0.00	0	0	–
78726	Kidney function study including pharmacologic intervention	255.0	360	435	148
-26			108	131	48
78727	Kidney transplant evaluation	309.0	436	527	187
-26			131	158	54
78730	Urinary bladder residual study	100.0	141	171	72
-26			42	51	21
78740	Ureteral reflux study (radiopharmaceutical voiding cystogram)	179.0	253	306	105
-26			76	92	33
78760	Testicular imaging;	205.0	289	350	128
-26			87	105	37
78761	Testicular imaging; with vascular flow	239.0	337	408	150
-26			101	122	41
78800	Radiopharmaceutical localization of tumor; limited area	220.0	291	352	155
-26			73	88	40
78801	Radiopharmaceutical localization of tumor; multiple areas	278.0	368	445	191
-26			92	111	47
78802	Radiopharmaceutical localization of tumor; whole body	351.0	464	562	240
-26			116	140	53
78803	Radiopharmaceutical localization of tumor; tomographic (SPECT)	374.0	495	598	280
-26			124	150	60

Code	Description	Medicode RVU	50th	75th	Medicare Nat'l Avg
78805	Radiopharmaceutical localization of abscess; limited area	196.0	259	314	157
-26			65	78	42
78799	Unlisted genitourinary procedure, diagnostic nuclear medicine	0.00	0	0	–
78806	Radiopharmaceutical localization of abscess; whole body	336.0	445	538	267
-26			111	134	50
78807	Radiopharmaceutical localization of abscess; tomographic	374.0	495	598	280
-26	(SPECT)		124	150	60
● 78810	Tumor imaging, positron emission tomography (PET), metabolic	0.00	0	0	–
-26	evaluation		0	0	
78890	Generation of automated data: interactive process involving	100.0	132	160	–
-26	nuclear physician and/or allied health professional personnel; simple manipulations and interpretation, not to exceed 30 minutes		13	16	
78891	Generation of automated data: interactive process involving	150.0	198	240	–
-26	nuclear physician and/or allied health professional personnel; complex manipulations and interpretation, exceeding 30 minutes		20	24	
78990	Provision of diagnostic radiopharmaceutical(s)	0.00	0	0	–
-26			0	0	
78999	Unlisted miscellaneous procedure, diagnostic nuclear medicine	0.00	0	0	–
79000	Radiopharmaceutical therapy, hyperthyroidism; initial, including	351.0	464	562	197
-26	evaluation of patient		279	337	108
79001	Radiopharmaceutical therapy, hyperthyroidism; subsequent,	200.0	265	320	108
-26	each therapy		159	192	58
79020	Radiopharmaceutical therapy, thyroid suppression (euthyroid	345.0	456	552	197
-26	cardiac disease), including evaluation of patient		274	331	102
79030	Radiopharmaceutical ablation of gland for thyroid carcinoma	348.0	460	557	212
-26			276	334	118
79035	Radiopharmaceutical therapy for metastases of thyroid	441.0	583	706	236
-26	carcinoma		350	423	141
79100	Radiopharmaceutical therapy, polycythemia vera, chronic	261.0	345	418	163
-26	leukemia, each treatment		207	251	74
79200	Intracavitary radioactive colloid therapy	325.0	430	520	203
-26			258	312	112
79300	Interstitial radioactive colloid therapy	206.0	273	330	343
-26			164	198	92
79400	Radiopharmaceutical therapy, nonthyroid, nonhematologic	298.0	394	477	195
-26			237	286	105
79420	Intravascular radiopharmaceutical therapy, particulate	0.00	0	0	245
-26			0	0	83
79440	Intra-articular radiopharmaceutical therapy	396.0	524	634	201
-26			314	380	108
79900	Provision of therapeutic radiopharmaceutical(s)	0.00	0	0	201
-26			0	0	
79999	Unlisted radiopharmaceutical therapeutic procedure	0.00	0	0	–

Pathology & Laboratory 80002–89399

The Pathology and Laboratory section of CPT has undergone many changes in the past, the most significant changes affecting the way payers negotiate contracts for these services. Elements such as who can submit claims for pathology and laboratory services and how payment will be made for them are changing rapidly.

Some payers, realizing they were paying for test(s) that providers sent out to a reference lab (where they had a favorable contract) and then "marking-up" the cost of the test(s) are changing their contracting policy. New policy often allows payment only for laboratory tests based on their best contract. Now, providers must bring their contracted amounts in line with those of large laboratories (which offer volume discounts). This change in contracting strategy significantly affects both small and large providers.

Providers are increasingly required to show that tests performed are not "routine," but are performed for a specific reason. Some payers restrict payment by ICD-9 diagnostic codes. Claims reported with codes that do not match the codes acceptable to specific laboratory codes will be denied. Some local Medicare carriers are also adopting this method.

One thing is certain — both private and government payers have targeted lab services in recent cost containment strategies. Providers must understand the issues and correctly report for test(s) they perform.

The Pathology and Laboratory section is divided into 14 subsections. Most procedures are coded by analyte rather than method — in other words, the correct code is selected based on what is measured rather than how it is measured. However, some procedures are coded by method; in these cases, it is essential that you know the methodology used. In many instances, identification of method is the key to appropriate coding and reimbursement.

Pathology and Laboratory services are provided by the pathologist or by technologists under the supervision of a physician. The majority of the codes represent a technical component only, but certain codes do represent a global service — a combination of professional and technical components. If the pathologist reviews a test result or renders an opinion of a test represented by a global code, the code selected should be identified with modifier -26 to indicate that only the professional component was provided.

80002–80018
Automated Multichannel Tests

CODING INSIGHT

The list below contains those tests frequently done as groups and combinations on automated multichannel equipment. For any combination of tests among those listed below, use the appropriate code (80002–80019). For example, if three of the tests listed were performed on multichannel equipment, code 80003 would be reported. These 19 tests are specifically identified in CPT as part of the multichannel test listing.

Also listed are codes that would be used to report an individually performed test (e.g., "stat" testing). This code listing can be helpful in two ways: (1) use it as a check against reporting individual tests that should be grouped as multichannel, and (2) use it to locate the code for an individual test that was performed alone. According to CPT guidelines, "Groups of the tests listed here are distinguished from multiple tests performed individually for immediate or 'stat' reporting."

Alanine aminotransferase (ALT, SGPT)	84460
Albumin	82040
Aspartate aminotransferase (AST,	84450
Bilirubin, direct	82250
Bilirubin, total	82250
Calcium	82310
Carbon dioxide content	82374
Chloride	82435
Cholesterol	85465
Creatinine	82565
Glucose	82947
Lactate dehydrogenase (LD)	83615
Phosphatase, alkaline	84075
Phosphorous (inorganic phosphate)	84100
Potassium	84132
Protein, total	84155
Sodium	84295
Urea Nitrogen (BUN)	84520
Uric acid	84550

Many payers have unbundling software that automatically rebundles the codes listed above when two or more tests are reported on the same day. Generally, the cost is greater (depending upon any contractual terms in force) when two or more tests are reported with individual codes than when reported using a multichannel test code.

The physician should state in writing, both in the medical record and on the laboratory request, that the test(s) require immediate or "stat" testing. Acknowledgment in the medical records that the physician has seen the results of the test is also important: auditors have used the argument (and won) that if it is not clear that the test results were used for the patient's benefit, the charge is invalid.

Code	Description	Medicode RVU	50th	75th	Medicare Nat'l Avg
80002	Automated multichannel test; 1 or 2 clinical chemistry test(s)	19.50	21	27	7
-26			0	0	
80003	Automated multichannel test; 3 clinical chemistry tests	24.00	26	34	9
-26			0	0	
80004	Automated multichannel test; 4 clinical chemistry tests	25.50	27	36	10
-26			0	0	
80005	Automated multichannel test; 5 clinical chemistry tests	27.00	29	38	11
-26			0	0	
80006	Automated multichannel test; 6 clinical chemistry tests	28.00	30	39	11
-26			0	0	

Code	Description	Medicode RVU	50th	75th	Medicare Nat'l Avg
80007	Automated multichannel test; 7 clinical chemistry tests	29.00	31	40	12
-26			0	0	
80008	Automated multichannel test; 8 clinical chemistry tests	30.00	32	42	12
-26			0	0	
80009	Automated multichannel test; 9 clinical chemistry tests	31.00	33	43	12
-26			0	0	
80010	Automated multichannel test; 10 clinical chemistry tests	32.00	34	45	12
-26			0	0	
80011	Automated multichannel test; 11 clinical chemistry tests	33.00	36	46	13
-26			0	0	
80012	Automated multichannel test; 12 clinical chemistry tests	34.00	37	47	13
-26			0	0	
80016	Automated multichannel test; 13-16 clinical chemistry tests	36.00	39	50	15
-26			0	0	
80018	Automated multichannel test; 17-18 clinical chemistry tests	36.50	39	51	15
-26			0	0	

80019

CODING INSIGHT

Prior to release of *CPT '96*, many laboratories reported more than 19 multichannel tests as additional tests. However, payers frequently denied them because code 80019 specified "19 or more" in the code description. The words "or more" have been deleted from the 1996 description for code 80019. Additional tests should be reported separately and reimbursed by payers.

MEDICARE ALERT

HCFA has adopted new payment rules for automated profiles effective January 1, 1996. It has nationally standardized the list of automated test reportable under 80002–80019 by adding three tests to the CPT list of 19 tests; making the total number of tests in the list 22.. The three additional tests along with corresponding CPT codes are:

Creatine Kinase (CK, CPK)	82250
Gamma glutamyltransferase (GGT)	82977
Triglyceride	84478

Code 80019 will now only be used for Medicare when billing profiles with 19 automated tests. HCFA assigned temporary codes for use when more than 19 test in a profile are reported, they are:

G0058 Automated multichannel test, 20 clinical chemistry tests
G0059 Automated multichannel test, 21 clinical chemistry tests
G0060 Automated multichannel test, 22 clinical chemistry tests

Further, HCFA will reimburse an additional of 50 cents per test when more than 19 medically necessary tests are reported in a profile. Although the "lab industry" welcomes the additional fee, it does not feel the increase will cover the cost of running the additional test. HCFA, however, feels that it is medically necessary only in rare cases for such a high number of tests to be performed.

HCFA has control over adding, deleting, or changing the list of tests. It has tightened medical necessity requirements for profile payment and left it to local carrier discretion to limit coverage for certain tests to specific diagnoses and to require independent labs to use diagnostic codes on claims for the tests. Even tighter payment controls and the revised payment rules for automated tests will be applied March 1, 1996 (when one or more tests on the new list are reported). Previously, the threshold was three tests.

HCFA will only pay for medically necessary tests in a profile. The previous standard allowed an entire profile if at least one of the tests was medically necessary. Additionally HCFA will limit the amount paid for a profile to what would have been paid had only the medically necessary tests been ordered. Payment is not to exceed the amount for the allowed test.

Specific rules now apply when a carrier receives a claim for tests reported separately or individually. Carriers are to pay at the lesser amount for the profile if the sum of the fees exceeds that for the profile, which includes the tests. The fee for a profile cannot exceed payment for its individual tests. This rule applies whether or not a lab has the automated equipment. When one or more automated profile tests are run for a patient on the same day, carriers are to determine whether to base the payment on the automated profile or on the individual tests.

	Code	Description	Medicode RVU	50th	75th	Medicare Nat'l Avg
▲	**80019**	Automated multichannel test; 19 clinical chemistry tests	37.00	40	52	16
	-26			0	0	

80050–80092
Organ or Disease Oriented Panels

CODING INSIGHT

These panels are reported by nine codes (80050–80092) that list definitive test components. Note that these panels do not specify clinical parameters. Tests performed in addition to the procedures defined in a panel can be reported separately.

80050	General health panel
80055	Obstetric panel
80058	Hepatic function panel
80059	Hepatitis panel
80061	Lipid panel
80072	Arthritis panel
80090	TORCH antibody panel
80091	Thyroid panel
80092	Thyroid panel, with thyroid stimulating hormone (TSH)

Some payers do not cover routine physical exams; thus, a general health panel test would be denied. Others allow a well physical exam and preventive screening test(s) once per year based on their own guidelines (e.g., age). Lipid and thyroid panels may not be covered when performed as part of a routine screening, such as pregnancy. (Some hospitals do routine thyroid screening on all pregnant hospitalized patients). Payers may restrict payment for these tests to specific ICD-9 diagnoses, so always ascertain individual payer guidelines and plan benefits. Remember, auditors can request reimbursement (usually up to one year) for services paid that were not a covered plan benefit or for test(s) that do not meet clinical guidelines.

Do not report panel tests on the same day as the single test codes listed as part of the panel. An example is a hepatic function panel (code 80058), which includes five tests (82040, 82250, 84075, 84450, and 84460).

Medicare Alert

HCFA now recognizes CPT organ or disease-oriented panels (80050–80092) and differentiates them from profiles. Panels are now subject to the same payment rules as profiles.

Obstetric Panels

Laboratory tests performed in groups or combinations on automated multichannel equipment are considered part of an automated battery. When performed on the same day, the tests should be combined and coded as the appropriate multichannel test. Itemizing charges for tests that are part of an automated multichannel test is considered fragmenting.

Disease Oriented Panels

The Medicare Carriers Manual states that the payment allowance for a panel test will not exceed the sum of the applicable fees for the individual tests.

All the tests in the definitions must be included to use obstetric and disease panels. If a laboratory uses a custom panel definition that includes other tests in addition to those in the CPT definition, the additional tests are to be reported separately and in addition.

Code	Description	Medicode RVU	50th	75th	Medicare Nat'l Avg
80050	General health panel This panel must include the following:	55.00	64	81	0
-26	Automated chemistries, 12 or more (80012-80019) Hemogram, automated, and manual differential WBC count (CBC) (85022) OR Hemogram and platelet count, automated, and automated complete differential WBC count (CBC) (85025) Thyroid stimulating hormone (TSH) (84443)		0	0	
80055	Obstetric panel This panel must include the following:	63.00	74	93	0
-26	Hemogram, automated, and manual differential WBC count (CBC) (85022) OR Hemogram and platelet count, automated, and automated complete differential WBC count (CBC) (85025) Hepatitis B surface antigen (HBsAg) (86287) Antibody, rubella (86762) Syphilis test, qualitative (eg, VDRL, RPR, ART) (86592) Antibody screen, RBC, each serum technique (86850) Blood typing, ABO (86900) AND Blood typing, Rh (D) (86901)		0	0	
80058	Hepatic function panel This panel must include the following:	31.00	36	46	0
-26	Albumin, serum (82040) Bilirubin, total or direct (82250) Phosphatase, alkaline (84075) Transferase, aspartate amino (AST) (SGOT) (84450) Transferase, alanine amino (ALT) (SGPT) (84460)		0	0	
80059	Hepatitis panel This panel must include the following: Hepatitis	94.00	110	139	0
-26	B surface antigen (HBsAg) (86287) Hepatitis B surface antibody (HBsAb) (86291) Hepatitis B core antibody (HBcAb), IgG and IgM (86289) Hepatitis A antibody (HAAb), IgG and IgM (86296) Hepatitis s antibody (86302)		0	0	
80061	Lipid panel This panel must include the following: Cholesterol,	38.50	45	57	0
-26	serum, total (82465) Lipoprotein, direct measurement, high density cholesterol (HDL cholesterol) (83718) Triglycerides (84478)		0	0	

Code	Description	Medicode RVU	50th	75th	Medicare Nat'l Avg
80072	Arthritis panel This panel must include the following: Uric acid, blood, chemical (84550) Sedimentation rate, erythrocyte, non-automated (85651) Fluorescent antibody, screen, each antibody (86255) Rheumatoid factor, qualitative (86430)	54.00	63	80	0
-26			0	0	
80090	TORCH antibody panel This panel must include the following tests: Antibody, cytomegalovirus (CMV) (86644) Antibody, herpes simplex, non-specific type test (86694) Antibody, rubella (86762) Antibody, toxoplasma (86777)	75.00	88	111	0
-26			0	0	
80091	Thyroid panel This panel must include the following tests: Thyroxine, total (84436) Triiodothyronine (T-3), resin uptake (84479);	34.00	40	50	0
-26			0	0	
80092	Thyroid panel This panel must include the following tests: Thyroxine, total (84436) Triiodothyronine (T-3), resin uptake (84479); with thyroid stimulating hormone (TSH) (84443)	65.00	76	96	0
-26			0	0	

80100–80103
Drug Testing

Coding Insight
The Drug Testing subsection lists codes (80100–80103) for qualitative screens, which are usually followed by confirmation by a second technique. Thirteen drugs or classes of drugs are listed as examples of commonly assayed qualitative screens.

Alcohols

Amphetamines

Barbiturates

Benzodiazepines

Cocaine and metabolites

Methadones

Methaqualones

Opiates

Phencyclidines

Phenothiazines

Propoxyphenes

Tetrahydrocannabinoids

Tricyclic antidepressants

Coding for Drug Screens
Qualitative screens should be coded when testing for the presence of a particular substance or substances. Coding for qualitative screening tests is based on procedure, not method or analyte. For example, if confirmation of five drugs requires three procedures, code 80102 *Drug confirmation, each procedure* is identified three times. Confirmed drugs may also be quantitated. Codes in the Chemistry section (82000–84999) and Therapeutic Drug Assay section (80150–80299) are used to identify quantitation of drugs screened.

Code	Description	Medicode RVU	50th	75th	Medicare Nat'l Avg
80100	Drug, screen; multiple drug classes, each procedure	44.00	51	65	21
-26			0	0	
80101	Drug, screen; single drug class, each drug class	35.00	41	52	19
-26			0	0	
80102	Drug, confirmation, each procedure	50.00	58	74	19
-26			0	0	
80103	Tissue preparation for drug analysis	25.00	29	37	–
-26			0	0	

80150–80299
Therapeutic Drug Assays

Coding Insight

The Therapeutic Drug Assays subsection (80150–80299) lists codes for quantitative assays. Several of these codes were previously listed in the Chemistry and Toxicology subsection of CPT, which had referenced both quantitative and qualitative tests. Unless stated in the code description, the Therapeutic Drug Assays and Chemistry subsections list codes for quantitative tests only.

Payers may have established criteria (e.g., frequency) for payment of frequently performed drug levels such as lithium and digoxin, so it is important to determine their guidelines.

Coding for Drug Assays

Codes listed under Therapeutic Drug Assays or Chemistry should be used when a drug is quantitated, or measured. Screening may be used to detect a substance, but it is not a prerequisite for quantitation. For example, screening is not necessary when a known drug has been overdosed. Coding for quantitative assays is based on the substance tested. Unless the code description notes otherwise, the examination material may be from any source.

Medicare Alert

Refer to the new "Correct Coding Initiative" for Medicare policy regarding coding for drug assays.

Code	Description	Medicode RVU	50th	75th	Medicare Nat'l Avg
80150	Amikacin	45.00	53	66	21
-26			0	0	
80152	Amitriptyline	50.00	58	74	25
-26			0	0	
80154	Benzodiazepines	50.00	58	74	26
-26			0	0	
80156	Carbamazepine	40.00	47	59	21
-26			0	0	
80158	Cyclosporine	60.00	70	89	26
-26			0	0	
80160	Desipramine	50.00	58	74	24
-26			0	0	

Code	Description	Medicode RVU	50th	75th	Medicare Nat'l Avg
80162	Digoxin	38.00	44	56	19
-26			0	0	
80164	Dipropylacetic acid (valproic acid)	40.00	47	59	19
-26			0	0	
80166	Doxepin	50.00	58	74	22
-26			0	0	
80168	Ethosuximide	45.00	53	66	23
-26			0	0	
80170	Gentamicin	40.00	47	59	23
-26			0	0	
80172	Gold	40.00	47	59	23
-26			0	0	
80174	Imipramine	50.00	58	74	24
-26			0	0	
80176	Lidocaine	40.00	47	59	21
-26			0	0	
80178	Lithium	23.00	27	34	9
-26			0	0	
80182	Nortriptyline	50.00	58	74	19
-26			0	0	
80184	Phenobarbital	40.00	47	59	16
-26			0	0	
80185	Phenytoin; total	38.00	44	56	19
-26			0	0	
80186	Phenytoin; free	40.00	47	59	20
-26			0	0	
80188	Primidone	40.00	47	59	23
-26			0	0	
80190	Procainamide;	40.00	47	59	24
-26			0	0	
80192	Procainamide; with metabolites (eg, n-acetyl procainamide)	55.00	64	81	24
-26			0	0	
80194	Quinidine	40.00	47	59	21
-26			0	0	
80196	Salicylate	24.00	28	35	10
-26			0	0	
80198	Theophylline	38.00	44	56	20
-26			0	0	
80200	Tobramycin	45.00	53	66	23
-26			0	0	
80202	Vancomycin	40.00	47	59	19
-26			0	0	
80299	Quantitation of drug, not elsewhere specified	50.00	58	74	19
-26			0	0	

80400–80440
Evocative/Suppression Testing

Coding Insight
The Evocative/Suppression Testing section was added to CPT in 1994. These 24 codes represent the technical component of the measurement of effects of administered drugs or evocative agents upon the patient. The physician's administration of the evocative or suppressive agent is reported separately using 90780–90784. To report physician attendance and monitoring during the testing, refer to the appropriate evaluation and management codes; prolonged care codes may be used if required, but prolonged physician care should not be reported separately when these tests involve prolonged infusions. Instead, CPT specifies they should be "reported with 90780 and 90781." Drugs and supplies are identified separately with 99070.

80400	ACTH stimulation panel; for adrenal insufficiency
80402	for 21 hydroxylase deficiency
80406	for 3 beta-hydroxydehydrogenase deficiency
80408	Aldosterone suppression evaluation panel (eg, saline infusion)
80410	Calcium-pentagastrin stimulation panel**
80412	Corticotropic releasing hormone (CRH) stimulation panel
80414	Chorionic gonadotropin stimulation panel; testosterone response
80415	estradiol response
80416	Renal vein renin stimulation panel (eg, captopril)*
80417	Peripheral vein renin stimulation panel (eg, captopril)*
80418	Combined rapid anterior pituitary evaluation panel
80420	Dexamethasone suppression panel, 48 hour
80422	Glucagon tolerance panel; for insulinoma
80424	for pheochromocytoma
80426	Gonadotropin releasing hormone stimulation panel
80428	Growth hormone stimulation panel (eg, arginine infusion, l-dopa administration)
80430	Growth hormone suppression panel (glucose administration)
80432	Insulin-induced C-peptide suppression panel
80434	Insulin tolerance panel; for ACTH insufficiency
80435	for growth hormone deficiency
80436	Metyrapone panel
80438	Thyrotropin releasing hormone (TRH) stimulation panel; one hour
80439	two hours
80440	for hyperprolactemia

* New CPT code for 1996

** Revised CPT code for 1996

CPT provides some information on the testing required for the use of a code by referencing analyte tests in other sections of the book. For instance, following 80415 *Chorionic gonadotrophin stimulation panel; estradiol response* is the note, "This panel must include the following: Estradiol (82670 x 2 on three pooled blood samples)," indicating that an estradiol test must be performed twice on three pooled blood samples to complete the test.

A cortisol code (82533) may be reimbursed by payers when reported with an ACTH stimulation panel code (80400). The ACTH stimulation panel must include two cortisols, but if both codes are reported it may be assumed that three cortisol levels were measured. This practice is consistent with recommended protocols for ACTH stimulation testing.

	Code	Description	Medicode RVU	50th	75th	Medicare Nat'l Avg
	80400 **-26**	ACTH stimulation panel; for adrenal insufficiency This panel must include the following: Cortisol (82533 x 2)	94.00	110 0	139 0	0
	80402 **-26**	ACTH stimulation panel; for 21 hydroxylase deficiency This panel must include the following: Cortisol (82533 x 2) 17 hydroxyprogesterone (83498 x 2)	173.0	202 0	255 0	0
	80406 **-26**	ACTH stimulation panel; for 3 beta-hydroxydehydrogenase deficiency This panel must include the following: Cortisol (82533 x 2) 17 hydroxypregnenolone (84143 x 2)	161.0	188 0	237 0	0
	80408 **-26**	Aldosterone suppression evaluation panel (eg, saline infusion) This panel must include the following: Aldosterone (82088 x 2) Renin (84244 x 2)	216.0	252 0	319 0	0
▲	**80410** **-26**	Calcitonin stimulation panel (eg, calcium, pentagastrin)	193.0	225 0	285 0	0
	80412 **-26**	Corticotropic releasing hormone (CRH) stimulation panel This panel must include the following: Cortisol (82533 x 6) Adrenocorticotropic hormone (ACTH) (82024 x 6)	480.0	561 0	708 0	0
	80414 **-26**	Chorionic gonadotropin stimulation panel; testosterone response This panel must include the following: Testosterone (84403 x 2 on three pooled blood samples)	71.00	83 0	105 0	0
	80415 **-26**	Chorionic gonadotropin stimulation panel; estradiol response This panel must include the following: Estradiol (82670 x 2 on three pooled blood samples)	71.00	83 0	105 0	0
●	**80416** **-26**	Renal vein renin stimulation panel (eg, captopril)	224.0	262 0	330 0	–
●	**80417** **-26**	Peripheral vein renin stimulation panel (eg, captopril)	96.00	112 0	142 0	–
	80418 **-26**	Combined rapid anterior pituitary evaluation panel This panel must include the following: Adrenocorticotropic hormone (ACTH) (82024 x 4) Luteinizing hormone (LH) (83002 x 4) Follicle stimulating hormone (FSH) (83001 x 4) Prolactin (84146 x 4) Human growth hormone (HGH) (83003 x 4) Cortisol (82533 x 4) Thyroid stimulating hormone (TSH) (84443 x 4)	1337	156 2 0	197 2 0	0
	80420 **-26**	Dexamethasone suppression panel, 48 hour This panel must include the following: Free cortisol, urine (82530 x 2) Cortisol (82533 x 2) Volume measurement for timed collection (81050 x 2) (For single dose dexamethasone, use 82533)	170.0	199 0	251 0	0
	80422 **-26**	Glucagon tolerance panel; for insulinoma This panel must include the following: Glucose (82947 x 3) Insulin (83525 x 3)	106.0	124 0	156 0	0
	80424 **-26**	Glucagon tolerance panel; for pheochromocytoma This panel must include the following: Catecholamines, fractionated (82384 x 2)	103.0	120 0	152 0	0

Code	Description	Medicode RVU	50th	75th	Medicare Nat'l Avg
80426	Gonadotropin releasing hormone stimulation panel This panel must include the following: Follicle stimulating hormone (FSH) (83001 x 4) Luteinizing hormone (LH) (83002 x 4)	250.0	292	369	0
-26			0	0	
80428	Growth hormone stimulation panel (eg, arginine infusion, l-dopa administration) This panel must include the following: Human growth hormone (HGH) (83003 x 4)	125.0	146	184	0
-26			0	0	
80430	Growth hormone suppression panel (glucose administration) This panel must include the following: Glucose (82947 x 3) Human growth hormone (HGH) (83003 x 4)	152.0	178	224	0
-26			0	0	
80432	Insulin-induced s-peptide suppression panel This panel must include the following: Insulin (83525) s-peptide (84681 x 5) Glucose (82947 x 5)	271.0	317	400	0
-26			0	0	
80434	Insulin tolerance panel; for ACTH insufficiency This panel must include the following: Cortisol (82533 x 5) Glucose (82947 x 5)	180.0	210	266	0
-26			0	0	
80435	Insulin tolerance panel; for growth hormone deficiency This panel must include the following: Glucose (82947 x 5) Human growth hormone (HGH) (83003 x 5)	191.0	223	282	0
-26			0	0	
80436	Metyrapone panel This panel must include the following: Cortisol (82533 x 2) 11 deoxycortisol (82634 x 2)	176.0	206	260	0
-26			0	0	
80438	Thyrotropin releasing hormone (TRH) stimulation panel; one hour This panel must include the following: Thyroid stimulating hormone (TSH) (84443 x 3)	84.00	98	124	0
-26			0	0	
80439	Thyrotropin releasing hormone (TRH) stimulation panel; two hour This panel must include the following: Thyroid stimulating hormone (TSH) (84443 x 4)	105.0	123	155	0
-26			0	0	
80440	Thyrotropin releasing hormone (TRH) stimulation panel; for hyperprolactinemia This panel must include the following: Prolactin (84146 x 3)	100.0	117	148	0
-26			0	0	

80500–80502
Consultation (Clinical Pathology)

Coding Insight
Two consultation codes (80500 and 80502) are reserved for the pathologist only and indicate a service, not a test. The pathology consultation is done at the request of an attending physician and requires a written report.

Code 80500 is a limited service without review of the patient's history and medical records, and 80502 is a comprehensive service for a complex diagnostic problem, with review of the patient's history and medical records.

The parenthetical phrases or notes preceding or following code(s) contain valuable information on how to use the code(s); they may add information or cross-reference another code that may more accurately describe the procedure performed. For example; two phrases appear in CPT after code 80502: "(These codes may also be used for pharmacokinetic consultations)" and "(For consultations involving the examination and evaluation of the patient, see 99241–99275)."

Medicare Alert

Note the following guidelines for Medicare and consultations:

1. The clinical pathology consultation must be requested by the patient's attending physician, and there must be specific documentation in the medical record.
2. The clinical pathology consultation must relate to test results that lie outside the clinically significant normal or expected range in view of the patient's condition.
3. The results of the clinical pathology consultation must result in a written narrative report, which is included in the patient's medical record.
4. Require the "excercise of medical judgement" by the consulting physician.
5. Routine conversations a laboratory directory may have with an attending physician about test orders or results are not a consultation unless the four requirements preceding are met.

Code	Description	Medicode RVU	50th	75th	Medicare Nat'l Avg
80500	Clinical pathology consultation; limited, without review of	41.00	50	62	21
-26	patient's history and medical records		50	62	
80502	Clinical pathology consultation; comprehensive, for a complex	80.00	97	120	58
-26	diagnostic problem, with review of patient's history and medical records		97	120	

81000–81099
Urinalysis

Coding Insight

Codes 81000–81099 are used for specific analysis of one or more components of urinalysis. Select the appropriate code for what is actually being performed.

81000 Urinalysis, by dip stick or tablet reagent for bilirubin, glucose, hemoglobin, ketones, leukocytes, nitrite, pH, protein, specific gravity, urobilinogen, any number of these constituents; with microscopy

81001 automated, with microscopy*

81002 without microscopy, non-automated

81003 without microscopy; automated

* New code in *CPT '96*

These codes continue to be waived from the government's CLIA regulations.

Code 81015, a microscopic urinalysis code, should not be reported with a two- or three-glass test code (81020) because microscopic examination of urine is included in either procedure.

Code 81005 *Urinalysis; qualitative or semi-quantitative, except immunoassays* may be denied when reported in addition to codes 81000, 81002, and 81003. It may be assumed that code 81005 refers to alternate methods for determination of one or more of the constituents commonly measured in a routine urinalysis.

Code	Description	Medicode RVU	50th	75th	Medicare Nat'l Avg
▲ **81000**	Urinalysis, by dip stick or tablet reagent for bilirubin, glucose, hemoglobin, ketones, leukocytes, nitrite, pH, protein, specific gravity, urobilinogen, any number of these constituents; non-automated, with microscopy	11.50	14	17	4
-26			0	0	
● **81001**	Urinalysis, by dip stick or tablet reagent for bilirubin, glucose, hemoglobin, ketones, leukocytes, nitrite, pH, protein, specific gravity, urobilinogen, any number of these constituents; automated, with microscopy	11.50	14	17	–
-26			0	0	
81002	Urinalysis, by dip stick or tablet reagent for bilirubin, glucose, hemoglobin, ketones, leukocytes, nitrite, pH, protein, specific gravity, urobilinogen, any number of these constituents; non-automated, without microscopy	9.00	11	13	4
-26			0	0	
81003	Urinalysis, by dip stick or tablet reagent for bilirubin, glucose, hemoglobin, ketones, leukocytes, nitrite, pH, protein, specific gravity, urobilinogen, any number of these constituents; automated, without microscopy	9.00	11	13	3
-26			0	0	
81005	Urinalysis; qualitative or semiquantitative, except immunoassays	8.00	9	12	3
-26			0	0	
81007	Urinalysis; bacteriuria screen, by non-culture technique, commercial kit (specify type)	12.00	14	17	4
-26			0	0	
81015	Urinalysis; microscopic only	9.00	11	13	4
-26			0	0	
81020	Urinalysis; two or three glass test	11.00	13	16	5
-26			0	0	
81025	Urine pregnancy test, by visual color comparison methods	17.00	20	25	9
-26			0	0	
81050	Volume measurement for timed collection, each	8.00	9	12	4
-26			0	0	
81099	Unlisted urinalysis procedure	0.00	0	0	–

82000–83887
Chemistry

Coding Insight

Qualitative screens are reported by the four Drug Testing codes (80100–80103), and Chemistry codes now report only quantitative tests — unless the description specifies otherwise, as is the case with the chromatography codes (82486–82491).

Certain procedures within Chemistry are identified with a series of codes. Either one code or a series of codes may be used for appropriate reporting, such as the codes for glucose testing:

82947	Glucose; quantitative
82948	blood, reagent strip
82950	post glucose dose (includes glucose)
82951	tolerance (GTT), three specimens (includes glucose)
82952	tolerance test, each additional beyond three specimens

Code 82951 is used to report a three specimen glucose tolerance test (GTT). This code includes obtaining the fasting blood sample, supplying and administering the oral glucose dose, and obtaining the next two samples (e.g., at one-half hour and one hour). Code 82952 is used to report additional samples beyond the first three. Use codes 82951 and 82952 twice to report a three-hour GTT where specimens are obtained at 0, 1/2, 1, 2, and 3 hours.

When selecting codes for services involving multiple tests, read the code descriptions carefully. Contact the AMA and/or your payers for clarification of CPT codes and descriptions as needed.

A cortisol code (82533) may be reimbursed when it is reported twice on the same date of service. However, when a cortisol code is reported three times, two codes may be rebundled into the ACTH stimulation panel code (80400) along with an additional cortisol code (82533).

There are a number of clinical situations where cortisol may be performed twice on the same day that do not involve the infusion of ACTH into the patient (e.g., when morning and afternoon cortisol levels are measured). More than two cortisol levels in one day, however, is consistent with an evocative test.

There is not a single test for an Alpha-Feto Protein (AFP) "Triple Test" (a test run on a pregnant woman's serum). When this test is performed an AFP (code 82105), b-HCG (code 82677), and Estriol (code 84702) should be reported. AFP levels in pregnancy are used to screen for neural tube defects such as spina bifida in the fetus (high AFP levels) and for Down Syndrome (low AFP levels). The predictive value for the low AFP levels for Down Syndrome is much improved when combined with the results of HCG and Estriol on the same sample.

Subsidiary Codes

Subsidiary codes have relative values that require no further adjustment:

82952 is "in addition" to 82951

Because these are subsidiary or "in addition to" codes, reimbursement reduction and modifier -51 do not apply.

Code	Description	Medicode RVU	50th	75th	Medicare Nat'l Avg
82000	Acetaldehyde, blood	46.00	50	68	18
-26			0	0	
82003	Acetaminophen	45.00	49	67	29
-26			0	0	
82009	Acetone or other ketone bodies, serum; qualitative	10.00	11	15	6
-26			0	0	
82010	Acetone or other ketone bodies, serum; quantitative	20.00	22	30	12
-26			0	0	
82013	Acetylcholinesterase	40.00	44	59	16
-26			0	0	
82024	Adrenocorticotropic hormone (ACTH)	90.00	98	133	55
-26			0	0	
82030	Adenosine, 5'-monophosphate, cyclic (cyclic AMP)	70.00	76	103	37
-26			0	0	
82040	Albumin; serum	13.00	14	19	7
-26			0	0	
82042	Albumin; urine, quantitative	16.00	17	24	7
-26			0	0	
82043	Albumin; urine, microalbumin, quantitative	35.00	38	52	8
-26			0	0	

Code	Description	Medicode RVU	50th	75th	Medicare Nat'l Avg
82044	Albumin; urine, microalbumin, semiquantitative (eg, reagent	18.00	20	27	6
-26	strip assay)		0	0	
82055	Alcohol (ethanol); any specimen except breath	30.00	33	44	15
-26			0	0	
82075	Alcohol (ethanol); breath	18.00	20	27	17
-26			0	0	
82085	Aldolase	30.00	33	44	14
-26			0	0	
82088	Aldosterone	80.00	87	118	58
-26			0	0	
82101	Alkaloids, urine, quantitative	50.00	55	74	42
-26			0	0	
82103	Alpha-1-antitrypsin; total	40.00	44	59	19
-26			0	0	
82104	Alpha-1-antitrypsin; phenotype	55.00	60	81	20
-26			0	0	
82105	Alpha-fetoprotein; serum	47.00	51	69	24
-26			0	0	
82106	Alpha-fetoprotein; amniotic fluid	47.00	51	69	24
-26			0	0	
82108	Aluminum	60.00	65	89	36
-26			0	0	
82128	Amino acids, qualitative	29.00	32	43	20
-26			0	0	
82130	Amino acids, urine or plasma, chromatographic fractionation	150.0	164	222	38
-26			0	0	
82131	Amino acids, quantitation, each	135.0	147	200	24
-26			0	0	
82135	Aminolevulinic acid, delta (ALA)	44.00	48	65	23
-26			0	0	
82140	Ammonia	35.00	38	52	21
-26			0	0	
82143	Amniotic fluid scan (spectrophotometric)	37.00	40	55	10
-26			0	0	
82145	Amphetamine or methamphetamine	50.00	55	74	22
-26			0	0	
82150	Amylase	16.00	17	24	9
-26			0	0	
82154	Androstanediol glucuronide	65.00	71	96	41
-26			0	0	
82157	Androstenedione	60.00	65	89	41
-26			0	0	
82160	Androsterone	65.00	71	96	35
-26			0	0	
82163	Angiotensin II	60.00	65	89	29
-26			0	0	
82164	Angiotensin I - converting enzyme (ACE)	50.00	55	74	21
-26			0	0	

Code	Description	Medicode RVU	50th	75th	Medicare Nat'l Avg
82172	Apolipoprotein, each	33.00	36	49	22
-26			0	0	
82175	Arsenic	55.00	60	81	27
-26			0	0	
82180	Ascorbic acid (Vitamin s), blood	29.00	32	43	14
-26			0	0	
82190	Atomic absorption spectroscopy, each analyte	60.00	65	89	21
-26			0	0	
82205	Barbiturates, not elsewhere specified	40.00	44	59	16
-26			0	0	
82232	Beta-2 microglobulin	55.00	60	81	23
-26			0	0	
82239	Bile acids; total	32.00	35	47	24
-26			0	0	
82240	Bile acids; cholylglycine	71.00	77	105	38
-26			0	0	
82250	Bilirubin; total OR direct	14.00	15	21	7
-26			0	0	
82251	Bilirubin; total AND direct	19.50	21	29	8
-26			0	0	
82252	Bilirubin; feces, qualitative	9.00	10	13	6
-26			0	0	
82270	Blood, occult; feces screening, 1-3 simultaneous determinations	10.00	11	15	4
-26			0	0	
82273	Blood, occult; other sources, qualitative	10.00	11	15	5
-26			0	0	
82286	Bradykinin	80.00	87	118	10
-26			0	0	
82300	Cadmium	55.00	66	83	33
-26			0	0	
82306	Calcifediol (25-OH Vitamin D-3)	75.00	91	113	42
-26			0	0	
82307	Calciferol (Vitamin D)	75.00	91	113	46
-26			0	0	
82308	Calcitonin	77.00	93	116	38
-26			0	0	
82310	Calcium; total	13.00	16	20	7
-26			0	0	
82330	Calcium; ionized	37.00	45	56	19
-26			0	0	
82331	Calcium; after calcium infusion test	16.00	19	24	7
-26			0	0	
82340	Calcium; urine quantitative, timed specimen	16.00	19	24	9
-26			0	0	
82355	Calculus (stone); qualitative analysis	35.00	42	53	16
-26			0	0	
82360	Calculus (stone); quantitative analysis, chemical	38.00	46	57	18
-26			0	0	

Code	Description	Medicode RVU	50th	75th	Medicare Nat'l Avg
82365	Calculus (stone); infrared spectroscopy	38.00	46	57	18
-26			0	0	
82370	Calculus (stone); x-ray diffraction	35.00	42	53	18
-26			0	0	
82374	Carbon dioxide (bicarbonate)	13.00	16	20	7
-26			0	0	
82375	Carbon monoxide, (carboxyhemoglobin); quantitative	34.00	41	51	17
-26			0	0	
82376	Carbon monoxide, (carboxyhemoglobin); qualitative	12.00	14	18	8
-26			0	0	
82378	Carcinoembryonic antigen (CEA)	52.00	63	79	27
-26			0	0	
82380	Carotene	30.00	36	45	13
-26			0	0	
82382	Catecholamines; total urine	52.00	63	79	24
-26			0	0	
82383	Catecholamines; blood	75.00	91	113	35
-26			0	0	
82384	Catecholamines; fractionated	75.00	91	113	36
-26			0	0	
82387	Cathepsin-D	70.00	84	106	29
-26			0	0	
82390	Ceruloplasmin	32.00	39	48	15
-26			0	0	
82397	Chemiluminescent assay	37.00	45	56	20
-26			0	0	
82415	Chloramphenicol	50.00	60	76	18
-26			0	0	
82435	Chloride; blood	13.00	16	20	7
-26			0	0	
82436	Chloride; urine	14.00	17	21	7
-26			0	0	
82438	Chloride; other source	14.00	17	21	7
-26			0	0	
82441	Chlorinated hydrocarbons, screen	36.00	43	54	9
-26			0	0	
82465	Cholesterol, serum, total	13.50	16	20	6
-26			0	0	
82480	Cholinesterase; serum	24.00	29	36	11
-26			0	0	
82482	Cholinesterase; RBC	36.00	43	54	11
-26			0	0	
82485	Chondroitin B sulfate, quantitative	60.00	72	91	29
-26			0	0	
82486	Chromatography, qualitative; column (eg, gas liquid or high	56.00	68	85	26
-26	performance liquid chromatography), analyte not elsewhere specified		0	0	
82487	Chromatography, qualitative; paper, 1-dimensional, analyte not	44.00	53	66	23
-26	elsewhere specified		0	0	

Code	Description	Medicode RVU	50th	75th	Medicare Nat'l Avg
82488	Chromatography, qualitative; paper, 2-dimensional, analyte not elsewhere specified	59.00	71	89	30
-26			0	0	
82489	Chromatography, qualitative; thin layer, analyte not elsewhere specified	44.00	53	66	26
-26			0	0	
82491	Chromatography, quantitative, column (eg, gas liquid or high performance liquid chromatography), analyte not elsewhere specified	50.00	60	76	26
-26			0	0	
82495	Chromium	60.00	72	91	29
-26			0	0	
82507	Citrate	75.00	91	113	39
-26			0	0	
82520	Cocaine or metabolite	50.00	60	76	21
-26			0	0	
82525	Copper	40.00	48	60	18
-26			0	0	
82528	Corticosterone	60.00	72	91	32
-26			0	0	
82530	Cortisol; free	55.00	66	83	24
-26			0	0	
82533	Cortisol; total	47.00	57	71	23
-26			0	0	
82540	Creatine	14.50	18	22	7
-26			0	0	
82550	Creatine kinase (CK), (CPK); total	15.00	18	23	9
-26			0	0	
82552	Creatine kinase (CK), (CPK); isoenzymes	40.00	48	60	19
-26			0	0	
82553	Creatine kinase (CK), (CPK); MB fraction only	18.50	22	28	16
-26			0	0	
82554	Creatine kinase (CK), (CPK); isoforms	35.00	42	53	16
-26			0	0	
82565	Creatinine; blood	13.00	16	20	7
-26			0	0	
82570	Creatinine; other source	16.00	19	24	7
-26			0	0	
82575	Creatinine; clearance	29.00	35	44	13
-26			0	0	
82585	Cryofibrinogen	20.00	24	30	12
-26			0	0	
82595	Cryoglobulin	20.00	24	30	9
-26			0	0	
82600	Cyanide	40.00	48	60	27
-26			0	0	
82607	Cyanocobalamin (Vitamin B-12);	40.00	48	60	21
-26			0	0	
82608	Cyanocobalamin (Vitamin B-12); unsaturated binding capacity	46.00	56	69	20
-26			0	0	
82615	Cystine and homocystine, urine, qualitative	30.00	36	45	12
-26			0	0	

Code	Description	Medicode RVU	50th	75th	Medicare Nat'l Avg
82626	Dehydroepiandrosterone (DHEA)	69.50	79	101	36
-26			0	0	
82627	Dehydroepiandrosterone-sulfate (DHEA-S)	60.00	69	87	31
-26			0	0	
82633	Desoxycorticosterone, 11-	80.00	91	116	44
-26			0	0	
82634	Deoxycortisol, 11-	70.00	80	102	41
-26			0	0	
82638	Dibucaine number	28.00	32	41	17
-26			0	0	
82646	Dihydrocodeinone	50.00	57	73	29
-26			0	0	
82649	Dihydromorphinone	50.00	57	73	36
-26			0	0	
82651	Dihydrotestosterone (DHT)	60.00	69	87	37
-26			0	0	
82652	Dihydroxyvitamin D, 1,25-	80.00	91	116	54
-26			0	0	
82654	Dimethadione	50.00	57	73	20
-26			0	0	
82664	Electrophoretic technique, not elsewhere specified	46.00	53	67	49
-26			0	0	
82666	Epiandrosterone	60.00	69	87	30
-26			0	0	
82668	Erythropoietin	65.00	74	95	26
-26			0	0	
82670	Estradiol	47.00	54	68	40
-26			0	0	
82671	Estrogens; fractionated	84.00	96	122	46
-26			0	0	
82672	Estrogens; total	60.00	69	87	31
-26			0	0	
82677	Estriol	43.00	49	63	34
-26			0	0	
82679	Estrone	65.00	74	95	35
-26			0	0	
82690	Ethchlorvynol	33.00	38	48	24
-26			0	0	
82693	Ethylene glycol	50.00	57	73	21
-26			0	0	
82696	Etiocholanolone	70.00	80	102	33
-26			0	0	
82705	Fat or lipids, feces; qualitative	15.00	17	22	7
-26			0	0	
82710	Fat or lipids, feces; quantitative	56.00	64	81	24
-26			0	0	
82715	Fat differential, feces, quantitative	24.00	27	35	24
-26			0	0	

Code	Description	Medicode RVU	50th	75th	Medicare Nat'l Avg
82725	Fatty acids, nonesterified	24.00	27	35	19
-26			0	0	
82728	Ferritin	37.00	42	54	19
-26			0	0	
82735	Fluoride	43.00	49	63	26
-26			0	0	
82742	Flurazepam	50.00	57	73	28
-26			0	0	
82746	Folic acid; serum	41.00	47	60	21
-26			0	0	
82747	Folic acid; RBC	49.00	56	71	25
-26			0	0	
82757	Fructose, semen	26.00	30	38	25
-26			0	0	
82759	Galactokinase, RBC	32.00	37	47	30
-26			0	0	
82760	Galactose	33.00	38	48	16
-26			0	0	
82775	Galactose-1-phosphate uridyl transferase; quantitative	42.00	48	61	30
-26			0	0	
82776	Galactose-1-phosphate uridyl transferase; screen	13.50	15	20	12
-26			0	0	
82784	Gammaglobulin; IgA, IgD, IgG, IgM, each	34.00	39	49	13
-26			0	0	
82785	Gammaglobulin; IgE	43.00	49	63	23
-26			0	0	
82787	Gammaglobulin; immunoglobulin subclasses, (IgG1, 2, 3, and 4)	107.0	122	156	47
-26			0	0	
82800	Gases, blood, pH only	26.00	30	38	12
-26			0	0	
82803	Gases, blood, any combination of pH, pCO2, pO2, CO2, HCO2	51.00	58	74	27
-26	(including calculated O2 saturation);		0	0	
82805	Gases, blood, any combination of pH, pCO2, pO2, CO2, HCO2	55.00	63	80	40
-26	(including calculated O2 saturation); with O2 saturation, by direct measurement, except pulse oximetry		0	0	
82810	Gases, blood, O2 saturation only, by direct measurement,	28.00	32	41	12
-26	except pulse oximetry		0	0	
82820	Hemoglobin-oxygen affinity (pO2 for 50% hemoglobin	35.00	40	51	14
-26	saturation with oxygen)		0	0	
82926	Gastric acid, free and total, each specimen	16.00	18	23	8
-26			0	0	
82928	Gastric acid, free or total; each specimen	15.00	17	22	9
-26			0	0	
82938	Gastrin after secretin stimulation	49.00	56	71	25
-26			0	0	
82941	Gastrin	49.00	56	71	25
-26			0	0	
82943	Glucagon	59.00	67	86	20
-26			0	0	

Code	Description	Medicode RVU	50th	75th	Medicare Nat'l Avg
82946	Glucagon tolerance test	33.00	38	48	21
-26			0	0	
82947	Glucose; quantitative	13.00	15	19	6
-26			0	0	
82948	Glucose; blood, reagent strip	10.00	11	15	4
-26			0	0	
82950	Glucose; post glucose dose (includes glucose)	17.00	19	25	7
-26			0	0	
82951	Glucose; tolerance test (GTT), three specimens (includes	37.00	42	54	18
-26	glucose)		0	0	
82952	Glucose; tolerance test, each additional beyond three	10.00	11	15	6
-26	specimens		0	0	
82953	Glucose; tolbutamide tolerance test	43.00	49	63	21
-26			0	0	
82955	Glucose-6-phosphate dehydrogenase (G6PD); quantitative	38.00	43	55	14
-26			0	0	
82960	Glucose-6-phosphate dehydrogenase (G6PD); screen	20.00	23	29	9
-26			0	0	
82962	Glucose, blood by glucose monitoring device(s) cleared by the	10.00	11	15	4
-26	FDA specifically for home use		0	0	
82963	Glucosidase, beta	50.00	57	73	30
-26			0	0	
82965	Glutamate dehydrogenase	14.00	16	20	11
-26			0	0	
82975	Glutamine (glutamic acid amide)	34.00	39	49	22
-26			0	0	
82977	Glutamyltransferase, gamma (GGT)	13.00	15	19	10
-26			0	0	
82978	Glutathione	35.00	40	51	20
-26			0	0	
82979	Glutathione reductase, RBC	25.00	29	36	10
-26			0	0	
82980	Glutethimide	50.00	57	73	26
-26			0	0	
82985	Glycated protein	21.00	24	31	21
-26			0	0	
83001	Gonadotropin; follicle stimulating hormone (FSH)	50.00	57	73	26
-26			0	0	
83002	Gonadotropin; luteinizing hormone (LH)	50.00	57	73	26
-26			0	0	
83003	Growth hormone, human (HGH) (somatotropin)	50.00	57	73	24
-26			0	0	
83008	Guanosine monophosphate (GMP), cyclic	60.00	69	87	24
-26			0	0	
83010	Haptoglobin; quantitative	37.00	41	53	18
-26			0	0	
83012	Haptoglobin; phenotypes	40.00	45	58	24
-26			0	0	

Code	Description	Medicode RVU	50th	75th	Medicare Nat'l Avg
83015	Heavy metal (arsenic, barium, beryllium, bismuth, antimony, mercury); screen	66.00	74	95	27
-26			0	0	
83018	Heavy metal (arsenic, barium, beryllium, bismuth, antimony, mercury); quantitative, each	70.00	78	101	31
-26			0	0	
83020	Hemoglobin, electrophoresis (eg, A2, S, s)	37.50	42	54	18
-26			0	0	
83026	Hemoglobin; by copper sulfate method, non-automated	9.00	10	13	3
-26			0	0	
83030	Hemoglobin; F(fetal), chemical	26.00	29	38	12
-26			0	0	
83033	Hemoglobin; F(fetal), qualitative (APT) test, fecal	15.00	17	22	8
-26			0	0	
83036	Hemoglobin; glycated	29.00	32	42	14
-26			0	0	
83045	Hemoglobin; methemoglobin, qualitative	10.00	11	14	7
-26			0	0	
83050	Hemoglobin; methemoglobin, quantitative	12.00	13	17	10
-26			0	0	
83051	Hemoglobin; plasma	13.00	15	19	10
-26			0	0	
83055	Hemoglobin; sulfhemoglobin, qualitative	16.50	18	24	7
-26			0	0	
83060	Hemoglobin; sulfhemoglobin, quantitative	23.00	26	33	12
-26			0	0	
83065	Hemoglobin; thermolabile	8.00	9	12	10
-26			0	0	
83068	Hemoglobin; unstable, screen	11.00	12	16	12
-26			0	0	
83069	Hemoglobin; urine	8.00	9	12	6
-26			0	0	
83070	Hemosiderin; qualitative	12.00	13	17	7
-26			0	0	
83071	Hemosiderin; quantitative	12.00	13	17	10
-26			0	0	
83088	Histamine	77.00	86	111	42
-26			0	0	
83150	Homovanillic acid (HVA)	50.00	56	72	27
-26			0	0	
83491	Hydroxycorticosteroids, 17- (17-OHCS)	59.00	66	85	25
-26			0	0	
83497	Hydroxyindolacetic acid, 5-(HIAA)	47.00	52	68	18
-26			0	0	
83498	Hydroxyprogesterone, 17-d	68.00	76	98	38
-26			0	0	
83499	Hydroxyprogesterone, 20-	53.50	60	77	36
-26			0	0	
83500	Hydroxyproline; free	50.00	56	72	32
-26			0	0	

Code	Description	Medicode RVU	50th	75th	Medicare Nat'l Avg
83505	Hydroxyproline; total	65.00	72	94	34
-26			0	0	
83516	Immunoassay for analyte other than antibody or infectious agent antigen, qualitative or semiquantitative; multiple step method	32.00	36	46	0
-26			0	0	
83518	Immunoassay for analyte other than antibody or infectious agent antigen, qualitative or semiquantitative; single step method (eg, reagent strip)	20.00	22	29	0
-26			0	0	
83519	Immunoassay, analyte, quantitative; by radiopharmaceutical technique (eg, RIA)	42.00	47	61	19
-26			0	0	
83520	Immunoassay, analyte, quantitative; not otherwise specified	36.00	40	52	18
-26			0	0	
83525	Insulin; total	39.00	43	56	16
-26			0	0	
83527	Insulin; free	44.00	49	64	18
-26			0	0	
83528	Intrinsic factor	52.00	58	75	23
-26			0	0	
83540	Iron	13.00	15	19	9
-26			0	0	
83550	Iron binding capacity	17.50	20	25	12
-26			0	0	
83570	Isocitric dehydrogenase (IDH)	24.00	27	35	13
-26			0	0	
83582	Ketogenic steroids, fractionation	41.00	46	59	20
-26			0	0	
83586	Ketosteroids, 17- (17-KS); total	40.00	45	58	18
-26			0	0	
83593	Ketosteroids, 17- (17-KS); fractionation	88.00	98	127	37
-26			0	0	
83605	Lactate (lactic acid)	32.00	36	46	15
-26			0	0	
83615	Lactate dehydrogenase (LD), (LDH);	13.50	15	19	9
-26			0	0	
83625	Lactate dehydrogenase (LD), (LDH); isoenzymes, separation and quantitation	40.00	45	58	18
-26			0	0	
83632	Lactogen, human placental (HPL) human chorionic somatomammotropin	64.00	71	92	29
-26			0	0	
83633	Lactose, urine; qualitative	12.00	13	17	8
-26			0	0	
83634	Lactose, urine; quantitative	22.00	25	32	16
-26			0	0	
83655	Lead	25.00	28	36	17
-26			0	0	
83661	Lecithin-sphingomyelin ratio (L/S ratio); quantitative	86.20	96	124	31
-26			0	0	
83662	Lecithin-sphingomyelin ratio (L/S ratio); foam stability test	25.00	28	36	27
-26			0	0	

Code	Description	Medicode RVU	50th	75th	Medicare Nat'l Avg
83670	Leucine aminopeptidase (LAP)	36.00	40	52	13
-26			0	0	
83690	Lipase	23.00	26	33	10
-26			0	0	
83715	Lipoprotein, blood; electrophoretic separation and quantitation	31.00	35	45	16
-26			0	0	
83717	Lipoprotein, blood; ultracentrifugation and quantitation	39.00	43	56	35
-26			0	0	
83718	Lipoprotein, direct measurement; high density cholesterol (HDL	19.00	21	27	12
-26	cholesterol)		0	0	
83719	Lipoprotein, direct measurement; VLDL cholesterol	21.00	23	30	16
-26			0	0	
83721	Lipoprotein, direct measurement; LDL cholesterol	20.00	22	29	13
-26			0	0	
83727	Luteinizing releasing factor (LRH)	55.00	61	79	24
-26			0	0	
83735	Magnesium	14.00	16	21	9
-26			0	0	
83775	Malate dehydrogenase	23.00	27	34	10
-26			0	0	
83785	Manganese	60.00	69	89	35
-26			0	0	
83805	Meprobamate	50.00	58	74	25
-26			0	0	
83825	Mercury, quantitative	52.00	60	77	23
-26			0	0	
83835	Metanephrines	52.00	60	77	24
-26			0	0	
83840	Methadone	50.00	58	74	23
-26			0	0	
83857	Methemalbumin	30.00	35	45	15
-26			0	0	
83858	Methsuximide	50.00	58	74	21
-26			0	0	
83864	Mucopolysaccharides, acid; quantitative	30.00	35	45	28
-26			0	0	
83866	Mucopolysaccharides, acid; screen	19.00	22	28	14
-26			0	0	
83872	Mucin, synovial fluid (Ropes test)	13.00	15	19	8
-26			0	0	
83873	Myelin basic protein, CSF	55.00	64	82	24
-26			0	0	
83874	Myoglobin	45.00	52	67	18
-26			0	0	
83883	Nephelometry, each analyte not elsewhere specified	37.00	43	55	19
-26			0	0	
83885	Nickel	53.50	62	80	35
-26			0	0	

Code	Description	Medicode RVU	50th	75th	Medicare Nat'l Avg
83887	Nicotine	50.00	58	74	34
-26			0	0	

83890–84999
Molecular Diagnostics

Coding Insight

Molecular diagnostics (analysis of nucleic acids) are listed within the chemistry section of CPT. Tests in this series are coded, as stated in CPT, "by procedure rather than analyte" and should be coded "separately for each procedure used in an analysis."

Payers may restrict payment for tests such as thyroid, lipids, and triglycerides without a definitive diagnosis. Routine screening may not be a covered benefit.

The thyroid panel code (80091) should not be reported with the codes for thyroxine, total (84436), triiodothyronine (T-3), resin uptake (84479). CPT guidelines specify that a thyroid panel includes those two tests.

Code	Description	Medicode RVU	50th	75th	Medicare Nat'l Avg
83890	Nuclear molecular diagnostics; molecular isolation or extraction	25.00	29	37	6
-26			0	0	
83892	Nuclear molecular diagnostics; enzymatic digestion	20.00	23	30	6
-26			0	0	
83894	Nuclear molecular diagnostics; separation (eg, dot blot,	35.00	41	52	6
-26	electrophoresis)		0	0	
83896	Nuclear molecular diagnostics; nucleic acid probe, each	35.00	41	52	6
-26			0	0	
83898	Nuclear molecular diagnostics; nucleic acid probe with	74.00	86	110	39
-26	amplification, eg, polymerase chain reaction (PCR), each		0	0	
83912	Nuclear molecular diagnostics; interpretation and report	33.00	38	49	6
-26			19	25	20
83915	Nucleotidase 5'-	28.00	32	42	16
-26			0	0	
83916	Oligoclonal immunoglobulin (oligoclonal bands)	48.00	56	71	28
-26			0	0	
83918	Organic acids, quantitative	75.00	87	111	23
-26			0	0	
83925	Opiates, (eg, morphine, meperidine)	50.00	58	74	28
-26			0	0	
83930	Osmolality; blood	15.00	17	22	9
-26			0	0	
83935	Osmolality; urine	22.00	25	33	10
-26			0	0	
83937	Osteocalcin (bone g1a protein)	72.00	83	107	42
-26			0	0	
83945	Oxalate	36.00	42	54	18
-26			0	0	

Code	Description	Medicode RVU	50th	75th	Medicare Nat'l Avg
83970	Parathormone (parathyroid hormone)	80.00	93	119	58
-26			0	0	
83986	pH, body fluid, except blood	11.00	13	16	5
-26			0	0	
83992	Phencyclidine (PCP)	50.00	58	74	21
-26			0	0	
84022	Phenothiazine	41.00	47	61	22
-26			0	0	
84030	Phenylalanine (PKU), blood	14.00	16	21	8
-26			0	0	
84035	Phenylketones, qualitative	10.00	12	15	5
-26			0	0	
84060	Phosphatase, acid; total	25.00	29	37	11
-26			0	0	
84061	Phosphatase, acid; forensic examination	28.00	32	42	10
-26			0	0	
84066	Phosphatase, acid; prostatic	33.00	38	49	14
-26			0	0	
84075	Phosphatase, alkaline;	13.50	16	20	7
-26			0	0	
84078	Phosphatase, alkaline; heat stable (total not included)	24.50	28	36	10
-26			0	0	
84080	Phosphatase, alkaline; isoenzymes	43.00	50	64	21
-26			0	0	
84081	Phosphatidylglycerol	60.00	69	89	23
-26			0	0	
84085	Phosphogluconate, 6-, dehydrogenase, RBC	26.00	30	39	10
-26			0	0	
84087	Phosphohexose isomerase	28.00	32	42	15
-26			0	0	
84100	Phosphorus inorganic (phosphate);	13.00	15	19	7
-26			0	0	
84105	Phosphorus inorganic (phosphate); urine	16.00	19	24	7
-26			0	0	
84106	Porphobilinogen, urine; qualitative	19.00	22	28	6
-26			0	0	
84110	Porphobilinogen, urine; quantitative	25.00	29	37	12
-26			0	0	
84119	Porphyrins, urine; qualitative	26.00	30	39	12
-26			0	0	
84120	Porphyrins, urine; quantitation and fractionation	47.00	54	70	21
-26			0	0	
84126	Porphyrins, feces; quantitative	45.00	52	67	36
-26			0	0	
84127	Porphyrins, feces; qualitative	13.00	15	19	15
-26			0	0	
84132	Potassium; serum	13.00	15	19	7
-26			0	0	

Code	Description	Medicode RVU	50th	75th	Medicare Nat'l Avg
84133	Potassium; urine	14.00	16	21	6
-26			0	0	
84134	Prealbumin	30.00	35	45	21
-26			0	0	
84135	Pregnanediol	50.00	58	74	27
-26			0	0	
84138	Pregnanetriol	50.00	58	74	27
-26			0	0	
84140	Pregnenolone	60.00	69	89	29
-26			0	0	
84143	17-hydroxypregnenolone	60.00	69	89	32
-26			0	0	
84144	Progesterone	50.00	58	74	30
-26			0	0	
84146	Prolactin	50.00	58	74	27
-26			0	0	
84150	Prostaglandin, each	55.00	64	82	35
-26			0	0	
84153	Prostate specific antigen (PSA)	50.00	58	74	26
-26			0	0	
84155	Protein; total, except refractometry	16.00	19	24	5
-26			0	0	
84160	Protein; refractometric	10.00	12	15	7
-26			0	0	
84165	Protein; electrophoretic fractionation and quantitation	36.00	42	54	15
-26			8	11	20
84181	Protein; Western Blot, with interpretation and report, blood or	55.00	64	82	24
-26	other body fluid		19	25	20
84182	Protein; Western Blot, with interpretation and report, blood or	80.00	93	119	25
-26	other body fluid, immunological probe for band identification, each		28	36	20
84202	Protoporphyrin, RBC; quantitative	32.00	37	48	20
-26			0	0	
84203	Protoporphyrin, RBC; screen	17.50	20	26	12
-26			0	0	
84206	Proinsulin	75.00	87	111	25
-26			0	0	
84207	Pyridoxal phosphate (Vitamin B-6)	75.00	87	111	40
-26			0	0	
84210	Pyruvate	36.00	42	54	15
-26			0	0	
84220	Pyruvate kinase	30.00	35	45	13
-26			0	0	
84228	Quinine	40.00	46	59	16
-26			0	0	
84233	Receptor assay; estrogen	71.00	82	106	91
-26			0	0	
84234	Receptor assay; progesterone	71.00	82	106	92
-26			0	0	

Code	Description	Medicode RVU	50th	75th	Medicare Nat'l Avg
84235	Receptor assay; endocrine, other than estrogen or	71.00	82	106	74
-26	progesterone (specify hormone)		0	0	
84238	Receptor assay; non-endocrine (eg, acetylcholine) (specify	100.0	116	149	52
-26	receptor)		0	0	
84244	Renin	64.00	74	95	31
-26			0	0	
84252	Riboflavin (Vitamin B-2)	42.00	49	62	29
-26			0	0	
84255	Selenium	50.00	58	74	36
-26			0	0	
84260	Serotonin	92.00	106	137	44
-26			0	0	
84270	Sex hormone binding globulin (SHBG)	53.00	61	79	31
-26			0	0	
84275	Sialic acid	32.00	37	48	19
-26			0	0	
84285	Silica	68.00	79	101	33
-26			0	0	
84295	Sodium; serum	13.00	15	19	7
-26			0	0	
84300	Sodium; urine	14.00	16	21	7
-26			0	0	
84305	Somatomedin	75.00	87	111	28
-26			0	0	
84307	Somatostatin	55.00	64	82	23
-26			0	0	
84311	Spectrophotometry, analyte not elsewhere specified	22.00	25	33	10
-26			0	0	
84315	Specific gravity (except urine)	7.00	8	10	4
-26			0	0	
84375	Sugars, chromatographic, TLC or paper chromatography	40.00	46	59	28
-26			0	0	
84392	Sulfate, urine	0.00			–
84402	Testosterone; free	57.00	68	86	37
-26			0	0	
84403	Testosterone; total	47.00	56	71	37
-26			0	0	
84425	Thiamine (Vitamin B-1)	55.00	65	83	30
-26			0	0	
84430	Thiocyanate	35.00	42	53	16
-26			0	0	
84432	Thyroglobulin	50.00	59	75	23
-26			0	0	
84436	Thyroxine; total	18.00	21	27	10
-26			0	0	
84437	Thyroxine; requiring elution (eg, neonatal)	20.00	24	30	9
-26			0	0	

Code	Description	Medicode RVU	50th	75th	Medicare Nat'l Avg
84439	Thyroxine; free	30.00	36	45	13
-26			0	0	
84442	Thyroxine binding globulin (TBG)	35.00	42	53	21
-26			0	0	
84443	Thyroid stimulating hormone (TSH)	42.00	50	63	24
-26			0	0	
84445	Thyroid stimulating immunoglobulins (TSI)	130.0	154	196	67
-26			0	0	
84446	Tocopherol alpha (Vitamin E)	40.00	47	60	20
-26			0	0	
84449	Transcortin (cortisol binding globulin)	48.00	57	72	26
-26			0	0	
84450	Transferase; aspartate amino (AST) (SGOT)	14.00	17	21	7
-26			0	0	
84460	Transferase; alanine amino (ALT) (SGPT)	14.00	17	21	7
-26			0	0	
84466	Transferrin	35.00	42	53	19
-26			0	0	
84478	Triglycerides	14.00	17	21	8
-26			0	0	
84479	Triiodothyronine (T-3); resin uptake	18.00	21	27	9
-26			0	0	
84480	Triiodothyronine (T-3); total (TT-3)	40.00	47	60	20
-26			0	0	
84481	Triiodothyronine (T-3); free	53.00	63	80	24
-26			0	0	
84482	Triiodothyronine (T-3); reverse	45.00	53	68	24
-26			0	0	
84485	Trypsin; duodenal fluid	20.00	24	30	11
-26			0	0	
84488	Trypsin; feces, qualitative	13.00	15	20	10
-26			0	0	
84490	Trypsin; feces, quantitative, 24-hour collection	15.00	18	23	11
-26			0	0	
84510	Tyrosine	26.00	31	39	15
-26			0	0	
84520	Urea nitrogen; quantitative	13.00	15	20	6
-26			0	0	
84525	Urea nitrogen; semiquantitative (eg, reagent strip test)	10.00	12	15	5
-26			0	0	
84540	Urea nitrogen, urine	16.00	19	24	7
-26			0	0	
84545	Urea nitrogen, clearance	20.00	24	30	9
-26			0	0	
84550	Uric acid; blood	13.00	15	20	6
-26			0	0	

Code	Description	Medicode RVU	50th	75th	Medicare Nat'l Avg
84560	Uric acid; other source	16.00	19	24	7
-26			0	0	
84577	Urobilinogen, feces, quantitative	20.00	24	30	18
-26			0	0	
84578	Urobilinogen, urine; qualitative	9.00	11	14	5
-26			0	0	
84580	Urobilinogen, urine; quantitative, timed specimen	19.00	23	29	10
-26			0	0	
84583	Urobilinogen, urine; semiquantitative	9.00	11	14	7
-26			0	0	
84585	Vanillylmandelic acid (VMA), urine	50.00	59	75	22
-26			0	0	
84586	Vasoactive intestinal peptide (VIP)	77.00	91	116	50
-26			0	0	
84588	Vasopressin (antidiuretic hormone, ADH)	82.00	97	123	48
-26			0	0	
84590	Vitamin A	47.00	56	71	16
-26			0	0	
84597	Vitamin K	46.00	55	69	19
-26			0	0	
84600	Volatiles (eg, acetic anhydride, carbon tetrachloride,	35.00	42	53	23
-26	dichloroethane, dichloromethane, diethylether, isopropyl alcohol, methanol)		0	0	
84620	Xylose absorption test, blood and/or urine	44.00	52	66	17
-26			0	0	
84630	Zinc	40.00	47	60	16
-26			0	0	
84681	s-peptide	60.00	71	90	29
-26			0	0	
84702	Gonadotropin, chorionic (hCG); quantitative	40.00	47	60	21
-26			0	0	
84703	Gonadotropin, chorionic (hCG); qualitative	23.00	27	35	11
-26			0	0	
84830	Ovulation tests, by visual color comparison methods for human	25.00	30	38	14
-26	luteinizing hormone		0	0	
84999	Unlisted chemistry procedure	0.00	0	0	–

85002–85999
Hematology and Coagulation

CODING INSIGHT

The Hematology and Coagulation subsection (85002–85999) lists those procedures specific to hematology, including various codes for complete blood counts, with or without differentials.

Note that a new code, 85652 *Sedimentation rate, erythrocyte; automated* was added to CPT in 1996.

Some payers reimburse 85007 *Blood count; manual differential WBC count . . .* with 85025 *Blood count; hemogram and platelet count, automated, and manual differential WBC count (CBC)*.

A bone marrow aspiration only code (85095) should not be reported with the code for a bone marrow biopsy, needle or trocar (85102).

SUBSIDAIARY CODES

Subsidiary codes have relative values that require no further adjustment:

85029, 85030 is "in addition" to 85021-85027

Because these are subsidiary or "in addition to" codes, reimbursement reduction and modifier -51 do not apply.

Code	Description	Medicode RVU	50th	75th	Medicare Nat'l Avg
85002	Bleeding time	21.00	26	33	6
-26			0	0	
85007	Blood count; manual differential WBC count (includes RBC	12.00	15	19	5
-26	morphology and platelet estimation)		0	0	
85008	Blood count; manual blood smear examination without	8.00	10	12	5
-26	differential parameters		0	0	
85009	Blood count; differential WBC count, buffy coat	12.00	15	19	5
-26			0	0	
85013	Blood count; spun microhematocrit	9.00	11	14	3
-26			0	0	
85014	Blood count; other than spun hematocrit	9.00	11	14	3
-26			0	0	
85018	Blood count; hemoglobin	9.00	11	14	3
-26			0	0	
85021	Blood count; hemogram, automated (RBC, WBC, Hgb, Hct and	15.00	19	23	8
-26	indices only)		0	0	
85022	Blood count; hemogram, automated, and manual differential	17.50	22	27	8
-26	WBC count (CBC)		0	0	
85023	Blood count; hemogram and platelet count, automated, and	22.00	27	34	12
-26	manual differential WBC count (CBC)		0	0	
85024	Blood count; hemogram and platelet count, automated, and	18.00	22	28	12
-26	automated partial differential WBC count (CBC)		0	0	
85025	Blood count; hemogram and platelet count, automated, and	18.50	23	29	11
-26	automated complete differential WBC count (CBC)		0	0	
85027	Blood count; hemogram and platelet count, automated	17.50	22	27	9
-26			0	0	
85029	Additional automated hemogram indices (eg, red cell	2.00	2	3	7
-26	distribution width (RDW), mean platelet volume (MPV), red blood cell histogram, platelet histogram, white blood cell histogram); one to three indices		0	0	
85030	Additional automated hemogram indices (eg, red cell	2.50	3	4	6
-26	distribution width (RDW), mean platelet volume (MPV), red blood cell histogram, platelet histogram, white blood cell histogram); four or more indices		0	0	
85031	Blood count; hemogram, manual, complete CBC (RBC, WBC,	18.50	23	29	8
-26	Hgb, Hct, differential and indices)		0	0	
85041	Blood count; red blood cell (RBC) only	8.50	11	13	4
-26			0	0	

Code	Description	Medicode RVU	50th	75th	Medicare Nat'l Avg
85044	Blood count; reticulocyte count, manual	15.00	19	23	6
-26			0	0	
85045	Blood count; reticulocyte count, flow cytometry	14.00	17	22	6
-26			0	0	
85048	Blood count; white blood cell (WBC)	10.00	12	16	4
-26			0	0	
85060	Blood smear, peripheral, interpretation by physician with written report	35.00	43	54	23
-26			43	54	
85095	Bone marrow; aspiration only	106.0	124	155	62
-26			124	155	
85097	Bone marrow; smear interpretation only, with or without differential cell count	90.00	106	132	51
-26			85	105	
85102	Bone marrow biopsy, needle or trocar	130.0	153	190	73
-26			137	171	
85130	Chromogenic substrate assay	30.00	35	44	17
-26			0	0	
85170	Clot retraction	10.50	12	15	5
-26			0	0	
85175	Clot lysis time, whole blood dilution	20.00	23	29	6
-26			0	0	
85210	Clotting; factor II, prothrombin, specific	30.00	35	44	18
-26			0	0	
85220	Clotting; factor V (AcG or proaccelerin), labile factor	60.00	70	88	25
-26			0	0	
85230	Clotting; factor VII (proconvertin, stable factor)	60.00	70	88	25
-26			0	0	
85240	Clotting; factor VIII (AHG), one stage	65.00	76	95	25
-26			0	0	
85244	Clotting; factor VIII related antigen	80.00	94	117	29
-26			0	0	
85245	Clotting; factor VIII, VW factor, ristocetin cofactor	50.00	59	73	32
-26			0	0	
85246	Clotting; factor VIII, VW factor antigen	80.00	94	117	32
-26			0	0	
85247	Clotting; factor VIII, Von Willebrand's factor, multimetric analysis	80.00	94	117	32
-26			0	0	
85250	Clotting; factor IX (PTC or Christmas)	65.00	76	95	27
-26			0	0	
85260	Clotting; factor X (Stuart-Prower)	60.00	70	88	25
-26			0	0	
85270	Clotting; factor XI (PTA)	65.00	76	95	25
-26			0	0	
85280	Clotting; factor XII (Hageman)	65.00	76	95	27
-26			0	0	
85290	Clotting; factor XIII (fibrin stabilizing)	60.00	70	88	23
-26			0	0	
85291	Clotting; factor XIII (fibrin stabilizing), screen solubility	29.00	34	42	13
-26			0	0	

Code	Description	Medicode RVU	50th	75th	Medicare Nat'l Avg
85292	Clotting; prekallikrein assay (Fletcher factor assay)	60.00	70	88	27
-26			0	0	
85293	Clotting; high molecular weight kininogen assay (Fitzgerald	60.00	70	88	27
-26	factor assay)		0	0	
85300	Clotting inhibitors or anticoagulants; antithrombin III, activity	53.00	62	78	17
-26			0	0	
85301	Clotting inhibitors or anticoagulants; antithrombin III, antigen	50.00	59	73	15
-26	assay		0	0	
85302	Clotting inhibitors or anticoagulants; protein s, antigen	55.00	65	81	17
-26			0	0	
85303	Clotting inhibitors or anticoagulants; protein s, activity	60.00	70	88	20
-26			0	0	
85305	Clotting inhibitors or anticoagulants; protein S, total	65.00	76	95	16
-26			0	0	
85306	Clotting inhibitors or anticoagulants; protein S, free	65.00	76	95	22
-26			0	0	
85335	Factor inhibitor test	27.00	32	40	18
-26			0	0	
85337	Thrombomodulin	50.00	59	73	14
-26			0	0	
85345	Coagulation time; Lee and White	10.00	12	15	6
-26			0	0	
85347	Coagulation time; activated	10.00	12	15	6
-26			0	0	
85348	Coagulation time; other methods	16.00	19	23	5
-26			0	0	
85360	Euglobulin lysis	32.00	38	47	12
-26			0	0	
85362	Fibrin(ogen) degradation (split) products (FDP)(FSP);	22.00	26	32	10
-26	agglutination slide, semiquantitative		0	0	
85366	Fibrin(ogen) degradation (split) products (FDP)(FSP);	32.00	38	47	12
-26	paracoagulation		0	0	
85370	Fibrin(ogen) degradation (split) products (FDP)(FSP); quantitative	32.00	38	47	16
-26			0	0	
85378	Fibrin degradation products, D-dimer; semiquantitative	26.00	31	38	11
-26			0	0	
85379	Fibrin degradation products, D-dimer; quantitative	30.00	35	44	14
			0	0	
85384	Fibrinogen; activity	20.00	23	29	12
			0	0	
85385	Fibrinogen; antigen	25.00	29	37	12
			0	0	
85390	Fibrinolysins or coagulopathy screen, interpretation and report	25.00	29	37	7
-26			15	18	20
85400	Fibrinolytic factors and inhibitors; plasmin	48.00	56	70	13
			0	0	
85410	Fibrinolytic factors and inhibitors; alpha-2 antiplasmin	48.00	56	70	11
			0	0	

Code	Description	Medicode RVU	50th	75th	Medicare Nat'l Avg
85415	Fibrinolytic factors and inhibitors; plasminogen activator	37.00	43 0	54 0	24
85420	Fibrinolytic factors and inhibitors; plasminogen, except antigenic assay	48.00	56 0	70 0	9
85421	Fibrinolytic factors and inhibitors; plasminogen, antigenic assay	60.00	70 0	88 0	14
85441	Heinz bodies; direct	9.00	11 0	13 0	6
85445	Heinz bodies; induced, acetyl phenylhydrazine	14.00	16 0	21 0	10
85460	Hemoglobin or RBCs, fetal, for fetomaternal hemorrhage; differential lysis (Kleihauer-Betke)	27.00	32 0	40 0	11
85461	Hemoglobin or RBCs, fetal, for fetomaternal hemorrhage; rosette	27.00	32 0	40 0	0
85475	Hemolysin, acid	34.00	40 0	50 0	13
85520	Heparin assay	40.00	47 0	59 0	19
85525	Heparin neutralization	40.00	47 0	59 0	17
85530	Heparin-protamine tolerance test	40.00	47 0	59 0	20
85535	Iron stain (RBC or bone marrow smears)	17.00	20 0	25 0	9
85540	Leukocyte alkaline phosphatase with count	25.00	29 0	37 0	12
85547	Mechanical fragility, RBC	23.00	27 0	34 0	12
85549	Muramidase	51.00	60 0	75 0	27
85555	Osmotic fragility, RBC; unincubated	25.00	29 0	37 0	9
85557	Osmotic fragility, RBC; incubated	50.00	59 0	73 0	19
85576 **-26**	Platelet; aggregation (in vitro), each agent	50.00	59 12	73 15	30 20
85585	Platelet; estimation on smear, only	8.00	9 0	12 0	5
85590	Platelet; manual count	12.00	14 0	18 0	6
85595	Platelet; automated count	12.00	14 0	18 0	6
85597	Platelet neutralization	35.00	41 0	51 0	25
85610	Prothrombin time;	14.00	16 0	21 0	6
85611	Prothrombin time; substitution, plasma fractions, each	15.00	18 0	22 0	6

Code	Description	Medicode RVU	50th	75th	Medicare Nat'l Avg
85612	Russell viper venom time (includes venom); undiluted	28.00	33 0	41 0	14
85613	Russell viper venom time (includes venom); diluted	33.00	39 0	48 0	14
85635	Reptilase test	20.00	23 0	29 0	14
85651	Sedimentation rate, erythrocyte; non-automated	12.50	15 0	18 0	5
● **85652**	Sedimentation rate, erythrocyte; automated	12.50	15 0	18 0	–
85660	Sickling of RBC, reduction	14.00	16 0	21 0	8
85670	Thrombin time; plasma	19.00	22 0	28 0	8
85675	Thrombin time; titer	21.00	25 0	31 0	10
85705	Thromboplastin inhibition; tissue	38.00	45 0	56 0	12
85730	Thromboplastin time, partial (PTT); plasma or whole blood	17.00	20 0	25 0	9
85732	Thromboplastin time, partial (PTT); substitution, plasma fractions, each	20.00	23 0	29 0	9
85810	Viscosity	23.00	27 0	34 0	17
85999	Unlisted hematology and coagulation procedure	0.00	0	0	–

86000–86849
Immunology

Coding Insight

The immunology subsection (86000–86849) identifies codes for antibody studies and blood bank physician services. The following are several high-volume procedures in this subsection:

86147	Cardiolipin (phospholipid) antibody
86160	Complement; antigen, each component
86161	Complement; functional activity, each component
86226	Deoxyribonucleic acid (DNA) antibody; single stranded
86302	Hepatitis C antibody
86306	Hepatitis, delta agent
86309	Heterophile antibodies; titer
86588	Streptococcus, screen, direct

Note that the term "semiquantitative" has been added and the words "each panel of up to 12 allergens" has been changed to "each allergen" in the 1996 description for code 86003. Code 86005 has also been revised, with the addition of the word "paddle" to the nomenclature.

Code	Description	Medicode RVU	50th	75th	Medicare Nat'l Avg
86000	Agglutinins, febrile (eg, Brucella, Francisella, Murine typhus, Q fever, Rocky Mountain spotted fever, scrub typhus), each antigen	23.00	26 0	33 0	10
▲ 86003	Allergen specific IgE; quantitative or semiquantitative, each allergen	11.00	12 0	16 0	0
▲ 86005	Allergen specific IgE; qualitative, multiallergen screen (dipstick, paddle or disk)	5.00	6 0	7 0	0
86021	Antibody identification; leukocyte antibodies	60.00	67 0	87 0	21
86022	Antibody identification; platelet antibodies	91.00	102 0	132 0	26
86023	Antibody identification; platelet associated immunoglobulin assay	50.00	56 0	73 0	15
86038	Antinuclear antibodies (ANA);	35.00	39 0	51 0	17
86039	Antinuclear antibodies (ANA); titer	35.00	39 0	51 0	16
86060	Antistreptolysin 0; titer	24.00	27 0	35 0	10
86063	Antistreptolysin 0; screen	18.00	20 0	26 0	8
86077 -26	Blood bank physician services; difficult cross match and/or evaluation of irregular antibody(s), interpretation and written report	63.00	71 71	92 92	25
86078 -26	Blood bank physician services; investigation of transfusion reaction including suspicion of transmissible disease, interpretation and written report	73.00	82 82	106 106	45
86079 -26	Blood bank physician services; authorization for deviation from standard blood banking procedures (eg, use of outdated blood, transfusion of Rh incompatible units), with written report	45.00	51 51	65 65	25
86140	s-reactive protein	19.00	21 0	28 0	7
86147	Cardiolipin (phospholipid) antibody	70.00	79 0	102 0	37
86155	Chemotaxis assay, specify method	27.00	30 0	39 0	16
86156	Cold agglutinin; screen	18.00	20 0	26 0	9
86157	Cold agglutinin; titer	23.00	26 0	33 0	11
86160	Complement; antigen, each component	44.00	49 0	64 0	17
86161	Complement; functional activity, each component	44.00	49 0	64 0	17
86162	Complement; total hemolytic (CH50)	62.00	70 0	90 0	29
86171	Complement fixation tests, each antigen	29.00	33 0	42 0	14
86185	Counterimmunoelectrophoresis, each antigen	28.00	31 0	41 0	13

Code	Description	Medicode RVU	50th	75th	Medicare Nat'l Avg
86215	Deoxyribonuclease, antibody	39.00	44 0	57 0	19
86225	Deoxyribonucleic acid (DNA) antibody; native or double stranded	43.00	48 0	63 0	19
86226	Deoxyribonucleic acid (DNA) antibody; single stranded	43.00	48 0	63 0	17
86235	Extractable nuclear antigen, antibody to, any method (eg, nRNP, SS-A, SS-B, Sm, RNP, Sc170, J01), each antibody	38.00	43 0	55 0	25
86243	Fc receptor	47.00	53 0	68 0	29
86255	Fluorescent antibody; screen, each antibody	35.00	39 0	51 0	17 20
86256	Fluorescent antibody; titer, each antibody	43.00	48 0	63 0	17 20
86277	Growth hormone, human (HGH), antibody	35.00	39 0	51 0	22
86280	Hemagglutination inhibition test (HAI)	29.00	33 0	42 0	12
86287	Hepatitis B surface antigen (HBsAg)	29.00	33 0	42 0	15
86289	Hepatitis B core antibody (HBcAb); IgG and IgM	35.00	39 0	51 0	17
86290	Hepatitis B core antibody (HBcAb); IgM antibody	38.00	43 0	55 0	17
86291	Hepatitis B surface antibody (HBsAb)	31.00	35 0	45 0	15
86293	Hepatitis Be antigen (HBeAg)	34.00	38 0	49 0	16
86295	Hepatitis Be antibody (HBeAb)	34.00	38 0	49 0	16
86296	Hepatitis A antibody (HAAb); IgG and IgM	37.00	42 0	54 0	18
86299	Hepatitis A antibody (HAAb); IgM antibody	35.00	39 0	51 0	15
86302	Hepatitis s antibody;	49.00	52 0	66 0	20
86303	Hepatitis s antibody; confirmatory test (eg, immunoblot)	70.00	75 0	95 0	0
86306	Hepatitis, delta agent	38.00	41 0	52 0	23
86308	Heterophile antibodies; screening	17.00	18 0	23 0	7
86309	Heterophile antibodies; titer	22.00	24 0	30 0	9
86310	Heterophile antibodies; titers after absorption with beef cells and guinea pig kidney	25.00	27 0	34 0	10
86311	HIV, antigen	47.00	50 0	64 0	25

Code	Description	Medicode RVU	50th	75th	Medicare Nat'l Avg
86313	Immunoassay for infectious agent antigen, qualitative or semiquantitative; multiple step method	22.00	24 0	30 0	0
86315	Immunoassay for infectious agent antigen, qualitative or semiquantitative; single step method (eg, reagent strip)	22.00	24 0	30 0	0
86316	Immunoassay for tumor antigen (eg, cancer antigen 125), each	52.00	56 0	71 0	29
86317	Immunoassay for infectious agent antibody, quantitative, not elsewhere specified	24.00	26 0	33 0	21
86318	Immunoassay for infectious agent antibody, qualitative or semiquantitative, single step method (eg, reagent strip)	24.00	26 0	33 0	18
86320 **-26**	Immunoelectrophoresis; serum	63.00	67 13	85 17	32 20
86325 **-26**	Immunoelectrophoresis; other fluids (eg, urine, CSF) with concentration	65.00	69 14	88 18	32 20
86327 **-26**	Immunoelectrophoresis; crossed (2-dimensional assay)	50.00	53 11	68 14	32 20
86329	Immunodiffusion; not elsewhere specified	48.00	51 0	65 0	20
86331	Immunodiffusion; gel diffusion, qualitative (Ouchterlony), each antigen or antibody	45.00	48 0	61 0	17
86332	Immune complex assay	57.00	61 0	77 0	34
86334 **-26**	Immunofixation electrophoresis	54.00	58 12	73 15	32 20
86337	Insulin antibodies	63.00	67 0	85 0	30
86340	Intrinsic factor antibodies	44.00	47 0	60 0	21
86341	Islet cell antibody	35.00	37 0	47 0	28
86343	Leukocyte histamine release test (LHR)	43.00	50 0	63 0	18
86344	Leukocyte phagocytosis	25.00	29 0	37 0	11
86353	Lymphocyte transformation, mitogen (phytomitogen) or antigen induced blastogenesis	140.0	162 0	206 0	69
86359	T cells; total count	66.00	76 0	97 0	53
86360	T cells; T4 and T8, including ratio	100.0	116 0	147 0	66
86376	Microsomal antibodies (eg, thyroid or liver-kidney), each	42.00	49 0	62 0	21
86378	Migration inhibitory factor test (MIF)	45.00	52 0	66 0	28
86382	Neutralization test, viral	46.00	53 0	68 0	24
86384	Nitroblue tetrazolium dye test (NTD)	35.00	41 0	51 0	16

Code	Description	Medicode RVU	50th	75th	Medicare Nat'l Avg
86403	Particle agglutination; screen, each antibody	16.00	19 0	24 0	14
86406	Particle agglutination; titer, each antibody	18.50	21 0	27 0	0
86430	Rheumatoid factor; qualitative	19.00	22 0	28 0	8
86431	Rheumatoid factor; quantitative	22.00	26 0	32 0	8
86485	Skin test; candida	15.00	17 0	22 0	14
86490	Skin test; coccidioidomycosis	14.00	16 0	21 0	10
86510	Skin test; histoplasmosis	15.00	17 0	22 0	11
86580	Skin test; tuberculosis, intradermal	13.00	15 0	19 0	9
86585	Skin test; tuberculosis, tine test	10.00	12 0	15 0	7
86586	Skin test; unlisted antigen, each	15.00	17 0	22 0	8
86588	Streptococcus, screen, direct	16.00	19 0	24 0	13
86590	Streptokinase, antibody	18.00	21 0	26 0	16
86592	Syphilis test; qualitative (eg, VDRL, RPR, ART)	13.00	15 0	19 0	6
86593	Syphilis test; quantitative	14.00	16 0	21 0	6
86602	Antibody; actinomyces	40.00	46 0	59 0	14
86603	Antibody; adenovirus	40.00	46 0	59 0	18
86606	Antibody; Aspergillus	44.00	51 0	65 0	21
86609	Antibody; bacterium, not elsewhere specified	55.00	64 0	81 0	18
86612	Antibody; Blastomyces	44.00	51 0	65 0	19
86615	Antibody; Bordetella	50.00	58 0	74 0	19
86617	Antibody; Borrelia burgdorferi (Lyme disease) confirmatory test (eg, Western blot or immunoblot)	53.00	61 0	78 0	0
86618	Antibody; Borrelia burgdorferi (Lyme disease)	50.00	58 0	74 0	24
86619	Antibody; Borrelia (relapsing fever)	40.00	46 0	59 0	19
86622	Antibody; Brucella	30.00	35 0	44 0	14

Code	Description	Medicode RVU	50th	75th	Medicare Nat'l Avg
86625	Antibody; Campylobacter	50.00	58 0	74 0	19
86628	Antibody; Candida	48.00	56 0	71 0	18
86631	Antibody; Chlamydia	35.00	41 0	51 0	18
86632	Antibody; Chlamydia, IgM	39.00	45 0	57 0	18
86635	Antibody; Coccidioides	48.00	56 0	71 0	16
86638	Antibody; Coxiella Brunetii (Q fever)	40.00	46 0	59 0	18
86641	Antibody; Cryptococcus	30.00	35 0	44 0	21
86644	Antibody; cytomegalovirus (CMV)	46.00	53 0	68 0	20
86645	Antibody; cytomegalovirus (CMV), IgM	51.00	59 0	75 0	25
86648	Antibody; Diphtheria	44.00	51 0	65 0	22
86651	Antibody; encephalitis, California (La Crosse)	40.00	46 0	59 0	19
86652	Antibody; encephalitis, Eastern equine	40.00	46 0	59 0	19
86653	Antibody; encephalitis, St. Louis	40.00	46 0	59 0	19
86654	Antibody; encephalitis, Western equine	40.00	46 0	59 0	19
86658	Antibody; enterovirus (eg, coxsackie, echo, polio)	40.00	46 0	59 0	19
86663	Antibody; Epstein-Barr (EB) virus, early antigen (EA)	48.00	56 0	71 0	19
86664	Antibody; Epstein-Barr (EB) virus, nuclear antigen (EBNA)	48.00	56 0	71 0	22
86665	Antibody; Epstein-Barr (EB) virus, viral capsid (VCA)	52.00	60 0	76 0	26
86668	Antibody; Francisella Tularensis	30.00	35 0	44 0	15
86671	Antibody; fungus, not elsewhere specified	55.00	64 0	81 0	18
86674	Antibody; Giardia Lamblia	40.00	46 0	59 0	21
86677	Antibody; Helicobacter Pylori	54.00	63 0	79 0	21
86682	Antibody; helminth, not elsewhere specified	55.00	64 0	81 0	19
86684	Antibody; Hemophilus influenza	50.00	58 0	74 0	22

Code	Description	Medicode RVU	50th	75th	Medicare Nat'l Avg
86687	Antibody; HTLV I	40.00	46 0	59 0	12
86688	Antibody; HTLV-II	38.00	44 0	56 0	19
86689	Antibody; HTLV or HIV antibody, confirmatory test (eg, Western Blot)	53.00	61 0	78 0	27
86692	Antibody; hepatitis, delta agent	50.00	58 0	74 0	24
86694	Antibody; herpes simplex, non-specific type test	44.00	51 0	65 0	20
86695	Antibody; herpes simplex, type I	44.00	51 0	65 0	19
86698	Antibody; histoplasma	40.00	46 0	59 0	18
86701	Antibody; HIV-1	34.00	39 0	50 0	13
86702	Antibody; HIV-2	50.00	58 0	74 0	19
86703	Antibody; HIV-1 and HIV-2, single assay	34.00	39 0	50 0	20
86710	Antibody; influenza virus	33.00	38 0	49 0	20
86713	Antibody; Legionella	48.00	56 0	71 0	21
86717	Antibody; Leishmania	40.00	46 0	59 0	18
86720	Antibody; Leptospira	40.00	46 0	59 0	19
86723	Antibody; Listeria monocytogenes	40.00	46 0	59 0	19
86727	Antibody; lymphocytic choriomeningitis	40.00	46 0	59 0	18
86729	Antibody; Lymphogranuloma Venereum	40.00	46 0	59 0	17
86732	Antibody; mucormycosis	40.00	46 0	59 0	19
86735	Antibody; mumps	40.00	46 0	59 0	19
86738	Antibody; Mycoplasma	40.00	46 0	59 0	19
86741	Antibody; Neisseria meningitidis	40.00	46 0	59 0	19
86744	Antibody; Nocardia	40.00	46 0	59 0	19
86747	Antibody; parvovirus	50.00	58 0	74 0	21
86750	Antibody; Plasmodium (malaria)	40.00	46 0	59 0	19

Code	Description	Medicode RVU	50th	75th	Medicare Nat'l Avg
86753	Antibody; protozoa, not elsewhere specified	55.00	64 0	81 0	18
86756	Antibody; respiratory syncytial virus	40.00	46 0	59 0	18
86759	Antibody; rotavirus	40.00	46 0	59 0	19
86762	Antibody; rubella	23.00	27 0	34 0	20
86765	Antibody; rubeola	50.00	58 0	74 0	18
86768	Antibody; Salmonella	40.00	46 0	59 0	19
86771	Antibody; Shigella	40.00	46 0	59 0	19
86774	Antibody; tetanus	50.00	58 0	74 0	21
86777	Antibody; Toxoplasma	38.00	44 0	56 0	20
86778	Antibody; Toxoplasma, IgM	47.00	54 0	69 0	21
86781	Antibody; Treponema Pallidum, confirmatory test (eg, FTA-abs)	34.00	39 0	50 0	19
86784	Antibody; trichinella	40.00	46 0	59 0	18
86787	Antibody; varicella-zoster	44.00	51 0	65 0	18
86790	Antibody; virus, not elsewhere specified	55.00	64 0	81 0	18
86793	Antibody; Yersinia	40.00	46 0	59 0	19
86800	Thyroglobulin antibody	43.00	50 0	63 0	23
86805	Lymphocytotoxicity assay, visual crossmatch; with titration	148.0	172 0	218 0	74
86806	Lymphocytotoxicity assay, visual crossmatch; without titration	49.00	57 0	72 0	67
86807	Serum screening for cytotoxic percent reactive antibody (PRA); standard method	49.00	57 0	72 0	56
86808	Serum screening for cytotoxic percent reactive antibody (PRA); quick method	55.00	64 0	81 0	42
86812	HLA typing; A, B, or s (eg, A10, B7, B27), single antigen	70.00	81 0	103 0	37
86813	HLA typing; A, B, or s, multiple antigens	100.0	116 0	147 0	82
86816	HLA typing; DR/DQ, single antigen	95.00	110 0	140 0	39
86817	HLA typing; DR/DQ, multiple antigens	273.0	316 0	402 0	91

Code	Description	Medicode RVU	50th	75th	Medicare Nat'l Avg
86821	HLA typing; lymphocyte culture, mixed (MLC)	213.0	247 0	313 0	80
86822	HLA typing; lymphocyte culture, primed (PLC)	70.00	81 0	103 0	52
86849	Unlisted immunology procedure	0.00	0	0	–

86850–86999
Transfusion Medicine

CODING INSIGHT

Once listed in Immunology, most blood bank codes are now grouped together under the Transfusion Medicine subsection (86850–86999). Since more blood bank procedures are likely to be performed on an outpatient basis, this subsection may expand in the future.

Although antibody screening, autologous blood or component collection, processing and storage, blood typing, and blood preparation are usually covered by payers, the cost of the blood itself may not be a covered benefit. Some payers require blood to be replaced, when the unit given is replaceable, instead of paid. Not all payers cover the cost of blood components such as albumin, plasma, or plasmanate. There may also be restrictions on procedures involving pheresis. Check with individual payers regarding prior authorization and allowables.

SUBSIDIARY CODES

Subsidiary codes have relative values that require no further adjustment:

86911 is "in addition" to 86910

Because these are subsidiary or "in addition to" codes, reimbursement reduction and CPT modifier -51 do not apply.

Code	Description	Medicode RVU	50th	75th	Medicare Nat'l Avg
86850	Antibody screen, RBC, each serum technique	20.00	23 0	29 0	–
86860	Antibody elution (RBC), each elution	20.00	23 0	29 0	–
86870	Antibody identification, RBC antibodies, each panel for each serum technique	35.00	41 0	51 0	–
86880	Antihuman globulin test (Coombs test); direct, each antiserum	11.00	13 0	16 0	8
86885	Antihuman globulin test (Coombs test); indirect, qualitative, each antiserum	14.00	16 0	21 0	8
86886	Antihuman globulin test (Coombs test); indirect, titer, each antiserum	18.00	21 0	26 0	7
86890	Autologous blood or component, collection processing and storage; predeposited	80.00	93 0	118 0	–
86891	Autologous blood or component, collection processing and storage; intra- or postoperative salvage	125.0	145 0	184 0	–

Code	Description	Medicode RVU	50th	75th	Medicare Nat'l Avg
86900	Blood typing; ABO	11.00	130	160	4
86901	Blood typing; Rh (D)	10.00	120	150	–
86903	Blood typing; antigen screening for compatible blood unit using reagent serum, per unit screened	16.00	190	240	13
86904	Blood typing; antigen screening for compatible unit using patient serum, per unit screened	15.00	170	220	13
86905	Blood typing; RBC antigens, other than ABO or Rh (D), each	12.00	140	180	5
86906	Blood typing; Rh phenotyping, complete	17.00	200	250	11
86910	Blood typing, for paternity testing, per individual, ABO, Rh and MN;	22.00	260	320	26
86911	Blood typing, for paternity testing, per individual, ABO, Rh and MN; each additional antigen system	17.00	200	250	7
86915	Bone marrow, modification or treatment to eliminate cell (eg, T-cells, metastatic carcinoma)	105.0	1220	1540	–
86920	Compatibility test each unit; immediate spin technique	22.00	260	320	–
86921	Compatibility test each unit; incubation technique	20.00	230	290	–
86922	Compatibility test each unit; antiglobulin technique	12.00	140	180	–
86927	Fresh frozen plasma, thawing, each unit	11.00	130	160	–
86930	Frozen blood, preparation for freezing, each unit;	100.0	1160	1470	–
86931	Frozen blood, preparation for freezing, each unit; with thawing	110.0	1270	1620	–
86932	Frozen blood, preparation for freezing, each unit; with freezing and thawing	120.0	1390	1770	–
86940	Hemolysins and agglutinins, auto, screen, each;	21.00	240	310	12
86941	Hemolysins and agglutinins, auto, screen, each; incubated	22.00	260	320	17
86945	Irradiation of blood product, each unit	30.00	350	440	–
86950	Leukocyte transfusion	55.00	640	810	–
86965	Pooling of platelets or other blood products	14.00	160	210	–
86970	Pretreatment of RBC's for use in RBC antibody detection, identification, and/or compatibility testing; incubation with chemical agents or drugs, each	16.00	190	240	–
86971	Pretreatment of RBC's for use in RBC antibody detection, identification, and/or compatibility testing; incubation with enzymes, each	16.00	190	240	–

Code	Description	Medicode RVU	50th	75th	Medicare Nat'l Avg
86972	Pretreatment of RBC's for use in RBC antibody detection, identification, and/or compatibility testing; by density gradient separation	15.00	17 0	22 0	–
86975	Pretreatment of serum for use in RBC antibody identification; incubation with drugs, each	10.00	12 0	15 0	–
86976	Pretreatment of serum for use in RBC antibody identification; by dilution	8.00	9 0	12 0	–
86977	Pretreatment of serum for use in RBC antibody identification; incubation with inhibitors, each	10.00	12 0	15 0	–
86978	Pretreatment of serum for use in RBC antibody identification; by differential red cell absorption using patient RBC's or RBC's of known phenotype, each absorption	22.00	26 0	32 0	–
86985	Splitting of blood or blood products, each unit	21.00	24 0	31 0	–
86999	Unlisted transfusion medicine procedure	0.00	0	0	–

87001–87999
Microbiology

CODING INSIGHT

The microbiology codes (87001–87999) identify services performed in microbiology and include cultures, identification, and sensitivity studies. Some examples are:

87075	Culture, bacterial, any source; anaerobic
87076	definitive identification, each anaerobic organism, including gas chromatography
87181	Sensitivity studies, antibiotic; agar diffusion method, per antibiotic

SUBSIDIARY CODES

Subsidiary codes have relative values that require no further adjustment:

87088 is "in addition" to 87086–87087
87106 is "in addition" to 87101–87103
87163 is "in addition" to 87040–87158
87187 is "in addition" to 87186, 87188
87253 is "in addition" to 87250, 87252
88280 is "in addition" to 88245–88269
88283 is "in addition" to 88245–88269
88285 is "in addition" to 88245–88269
88289 is "in addition" to 88245–88269
88312 is "in addition" to 87015, 88177, 87205, 87206, 87208–87211
88313 is "in addition" to 87015, 88177, 87205, 87206, 87208–87211

Because these are subsidiary or "in addition to" codes, reimbursement reduction and CPT modifier -51 do not apply.

Code	Description	Medicode RVU	50th	75th	Medicare Nat'l Avg
87001	Animal inoculation, small animal; with observation	27.00	30 0	39 0	19
87003	Animal inoculation, small animal; with observation and dissection	40.00	45 0	57 0	24
87015	Concentration (any type), for parasites, ova, or tubercle bacillus (TB, AFB)	21.00	23 0	30 0	9
87040	Culture, bacterial, definitive; blood (includes anaerobic screen)	28.00	31 0	40 0	15
87045	Culture, bacterial, definitive; stool	33.00	37 0	47 0	13
87060	Culture, bacterial, definitive; throat or nose	18.00	20 0	26 0	11
87070	Culture, bacterial, definitive; any other source	27.00	30 0	39 0	12
87072	Culture or direct bacterial identification method, each organism, by commercial kit, any source except urine	18.00	20 0	26 0	11
87075	Culture, bacterial, any source; anaerobic (isolation)	28.00	31 0	40 0	13
87076	Culture, bacterial, any source; definitive identification, each anaerobic organism, including gas chromatography	31.00	35 0	44 0	18
87081	Culture, bacterial, screening only, for single organisms	16.00	18 0	23 0	9
87082	Culture, presumptive, pathogenic organisms, screening only, by commercial kit (specify type); for single organisms	16.00	18 0	23 0	10
87083	Culture, presumptive, pathogenic organisms, screening only, by commercial kit (specify type); multiple organisms	20.00	22 0	29 0	12
87084	Culture, presumptive, pathogenic organisms, screening only, by commercial kit (specify type); with colony estimation from density chart	20.00	22 0	29 0	12
87085	Culture, presumptive, pathogenic organisms, screening only, by commercial kit (specify type); with colony count	22.00	25 0	31 0	12
87086	Culture, bacterial, urine; quantitative, colony count	25.00	28 0	36 0	11
87087	Culture, bacterial, urine; commercial kit	19.00	21 0	27 0	9
87088	Culture, bacterial, urine; identification, in addition to quantitative or commercial kit	24.00	27 0	34 0	11
87101	Culture, fungi, isolation (with or without presumptive identification); skin	21.00	23 0	30 0	11
87102	Culture, fungi, isolation (with or without presumptive identification); other source (except blood)	26.00	29 0	37 0	12
87103	Culture, fungi, isolation (with or without presumptive identification); blood	30.00	34 0	43 0	13
87106	Culture, fungi, definitive identification of each fungus (use in addition to codes 87101, 87102, or 87103 when appropriate)	27.00	30 0	39 0	15
87109	Culture, mycoplasma, any source	57.50	64 0	82 0	22
87110	Culture, chlamydia	40.00	45 0	57 0	28

Code	Description	Medicode RVU	50th	75th	Medicare Nat'l Avg
87116	Culture, tubercle or other acid-fast bacilli (eg, TB, AFB, mycobacteria); any source, isolation only	32.00	36 0	46 0	15
87117	Culture, tubercle or other acid-fast bacilli (eg, TB, AFB, mycobacteria); concentration plus isolation	42.00	47 0	60 0	16
87118	Culture, mycobacteria, definitive identification of each organism	26.00	29 0	37 0	15
87140	Culture, typing; fluorescent method, each antiserum	16.00	18 0	23 0	8
87143	Culture, typing; gas liquid chromatography (GLC) method	38.00	42 0	54 0	18
87145	Culture, typing; phage method	20.00	22 0	29 0	14
87147	Culture, typing; serologic method, agglutination grouping, per antiserum	14.00	16 0	20 0	7
87151	Culture, typing; serologic method, speciation	14.00	16 0	20 0	8
87155	Culture, typing; precipitin method, grouping, per antiserum	14.00	16 0	20 0	7
87158	Culture, typing; other methods	13.50	15 0	19 0	7
87163	Culture, any source, additional identification methods required (use in addition to primary culture code)	20.00	22 0	29 0	16
87164 **-26**	Dark field examination, any source (eg, penile, vaginal, oral, skin); includes specimen collection	30.00	35 28	44 35	15 20
87166	Dark field examination, any source (eg, penile, vaginal, oral, skin); without collection	25.00	29 0	37 0	16
87174	Endotoxin, bacterial (pyrogens); chemical	22.00	25 0	32 0	12
87175	Endotoxin, bacterial (pyrogens); biological assay (eg, Limulus lysate)	41.00	47 0	60 0	15
87176	Endotoxin, bacterial (pyrogens); homogenization, tissue, for culture	18.00	21 0	27 0	8
87177	Ova and parasites, direct smears, concentration and identification	30.00	35 0	44 0	13
87178	Microbial identification, nucleic acid probes, each probe used;	40.00	46 0	59 0	24
87179	Microbial identification, nucleic acid probes, each probe used; with amplification, eg, polymerase chain reaction (PCR)	80.00	92 0	118 0	24
87181	Sensitivity studies, antibiotic; agar diffusion method, per antibiotic	17.00	20 0	25 0	7
87184	Sensitivity studies, antibiotic; disk method, per plate (12 or less disks)	20.00	23 0	30 0	10
87186	Sensitivity studies, antibiotic; microtiter, minimum inhibitory concentration (MIC), any number of antibiotics	23.00	26 0	34 0	12
87187	Sensitivity studies, antibiotic; minimum bactericidal concentration (MBC) (use in addition to 87186 or 87188)	23.00	26 0	34 0	15
87188	Sensitivity studies, antibiotic; macrotube dilution method, each antibiotic	23.00	26 0	34 0	9

Code	Description	Medicode RVU	50th	75th	Medicare Nat'l Avg
87190	Sensitivity studies, antibiotic; tubercle bacillus (TB, AFB), each drug	15.00	17 0	22 0	8
87192	Sensitivity studies, antibiotic; fungi, each drug	23.00	26 0	34 0	13
87197	Serum bactericidal titer (Schlicter test)	32.00	37 0	47 0	21
87205	Smear, primary source, with interpretation; routine stain for bacteria, fungi, or cell types	13.00	15 0	19 0	6
87206	Smear, primary source, with interpretation; fluorescent and/or acid fast stain for bacteria, fungi, or cell types	23.00	26 0	34 0	8
87207	Smear, primary source, with interpretation; special stain for inclusion bodies or intracellular parasites (eg, malaria, kala azar, herpes)	21.00	24 0	31 0	8 20
87208	Smear, primary source, with interpretation; direct or concentrated, dry, for ova and parasites	14.00	16 0	21 0	8
87210	Smear, primary source, with interpretation; wet mount with simple stain, for bacteria, fungi, ova, and/or parasites	12.00	14 0	18 0	6
87211	Smear, primary source, with interpretation; wet and dry mount, for ova and parasites	18.00	21 0	27 0	7
87220	Tissue examination for fungi (eg, KOH slide)	15.00	17 0	22 0	6
87230	Toxin or antitoxin assay, tissue culture (eg, Clostridium difficile toxin)	45.00	52 0	66 0	28
87250	Virus identification; inoculation of embryonated eggs, or small animal, includes observation and dissection	54.00	62 0	80 0	28
87252	Virus identification; tissue culture inoculation and observation	50.00	58 0	74 0	37
87253	Virus identification; tissue culture, additional studies (eg, hemabsorption, neutralization) each isolate	50.00	58 0	74 0	29
87999	Unlisted microbiology procedure	0.00	0	0	–

88000–88299
Anatomic Pathology

Coding Insight

Anatomic Pathology (codes 88000–88299) includes postmortem examinations. Also included in this section is cytopathology (e.g., fluids, washing or brushing, fine needle aspirations, flow cytometry, etc.) and cytogenetic studies (e.g., tissue cultures for chromosome studies, etc.).

Screening Pap smears are usually covered by payers. The allowed frequency of the testing depends upon the criteria they have used to establish their guidelines.

Subsidiary Codes

Subsidiary codes have relative values that require no further adjustment:

88312 is "in addition" to 88104–88108, 88151, 88157, 88161–88162, and 88170–88172
88313 is "in addition" to 88104–88108, 88151, 88157, 88161–88162, and 88170–88172

Because these are subsidiary or "in addition to" codes, reimbursement reduction and CPT modifier -51 do not apply.

Code	Description	Medicode RVU	50th	75th	Medicare Nat'l Avg
88000	Necropsy (autopsy), gross examination only; without CNS	252.0	329	379	–
-26			329	379	
88005	Necropsy (autopsy), gross examination only; with brain	280.0	366	421	–
-26			366	421	
88007	Necropsy (autopsy), gross examination only; with brain and	308.0	402	463	–
-26	spinal cord		402	463	
88012	Necropsy (autopsy), gross examination only; infant with brain	232.0	303	349	–
-26			303	349	
88014	Necropsy (autopsy), gross examination only; stillborn or	232.0	303	349	–
-26	newborn with brain		303	349	
88016	Necropsy (autopsy), gross examination only; macerated	282.0	368	424	–
-26	stillborn		368	424	
88020	Necropsy (autopsy), gross and microscopic; without CNS	362.0	473	544	–
-26			473	544	
88025	Necropsy (autopsy), gross and microscopic; with brain	390.0	509	586	–
-26			509	586	
88027	Necropsy (autopsy), gross and microscopic; with brain and	418.0	546	628	–
-26	spinal cord		546	628	
88028	Necropsy (autopsy), gross and microscopic; infant with brain	232.0	303	349	–
-26			303	349	
88029	Necropsy (autopsy), gross and microscopic; stillborn or	232.0	303	349	–
-26	newborn with brain		303	349	
88036	Necropsy (autopsy), limited, gross and/or microscopic; regional	150.0	196	225	–
-26			196	225	
88037	Necropsy (autopsy), limited, gross and/or microscopic; single	110.0	144	165	–
-26	organ		144	165	
88040	Necropsy (autopsy); forensic examination	600.0	784	902	–
-26			784	902	
88045	Necropsy (autopsy); coroner's call	50.00	65	75	–
-26			65	75	
88099	Unlisted necropsy (autopsy) procedure	0.00	0	0	–
88104	Cytopathology, fluids, washings or brushings, except cervical	50.00	63	74	35
-26	or vaginal; smears with interpretation		50	59	27
88106	Cytopathology, fluids, washings or brushings, except cervical	44.00	55	65	33
-26	or vaginal; filter method only with interpretation		44	52	-26
88107	Cytopathology, fluids, washings or brushings, except cervical	63.00	79	93	43
-26	or vaginal; smears and filter preparation with interpretation		63	75	34
88108	Cytopathology, fluids, washings or brushings, except cervical	57.00	72	84	37
-26	or vaginal; concentration technique, smears and interpretation (eg, Saccomanno technique)		57	67	28
88125	Cytopathology, forensic (eg, sperm)	40.00	50	59	13
-26			45	53	12
88130	Sex chromatin identification; Barr bodies	25.00	31	37	21
-26			3	4	

Code	Description	Medicode RVU	50th	75th	Medicare Nat'l Avg
88140	Sex chromatin identification; peripheral blood smear, polymorphonuclear "drumsticks"	20.00	25 0	30 0	11
88150	Cytopathology, smears, cervical or vaginal, up to three smears; screening by technician under physician supervision	17.00	21 0	25 0	7
88151 **-26**	Cytopathology, smears, cervical or vaginal, up to three smears; requiring interpretation by physician	17.50	22 15	26 18	7 25
88155 **-26**	Cytopathology, smears, cervical or vaginal, up to three smears; with definitive hormonal evaluation (eg, maturation index, karyopyknotic index, estrogenic index)	18.75	24 5	28 6	8
88156	Cytopathology, smears, cervical or vaginal, (the Bethesda System (TBS)), up to three smears; screening by technician under physician supervision	17.00	21 0	25 0	7
88157 **-26**	Cytopathology, smears, cervical or vaginal, (the Bethesda System (TBS)), up to three smears; requiring interpretation by physician	17.50	22 15	26 18	7 25
88160 **-26**	Cytopathology, smears, any other source; screening and interpretation	35.00	44 31	52 36	29 23
88161 **-26**	Cytopathology, smears, any other source; preparation, screening and interpretation	40.00	50 30	59 36	31 24
88162 **-26**	Cytopathology, smears, any other source; extended study involving over 5 slides and/or multiple stains	67.00	84 51	99 59	55 42
88170 **-26**	Fine needle aspiration with or without preparation of smears; superficial tissue (eg, thyroid, breast, prostate)	92.00	116 93	136 109	56 40
88171 **-26**	Fine needle aspiration with or without preparation of smears; deep tissue under radiologic guidance	125.0	157 134	185 157	86 63
88172	Evaluation of fine needle aspirate with or without preparation of smears; immediate cytohistologic study to determine adequacy of specimen(s)	72.00	91 0	106 0	47 35
88173 **-26**	Evaluation of fine needle aspirate with or without preparation of smears; interpretation and report	94.00	118 101	139 118	68 55
88180 **-26**	Flow cytometry; each cell surface marker	91.00	114 23	135 27	27 20
88182 **-26**	Flow cytometry; cell cycle or DNA analysis	254.0	320 64	376 75	60 44
88199	Unlisted cytopathology procedure	0.00	0	0	–
88230	Tissue culture for chromosome analysis; lymphocyte	108.0	131 0	160 0	165
88233	Tissue culture for chromosome analysis; skin or other solid tissue biopsy	41.00	50 0	61 0	199
88235	Tissue culture for chromosome analysis; amniotic fluid or chorionic villus cells	230.0	279 0	340 0	208
88237	Tissue culture for chromosome analysis; bone marrow (myeloid) cells	177.0	215 0	262 0	179
88239	Tissue culture for chromosome analysis; other tissue	70.00	85 0	104 0	209
88245 **-26**	Chromosome analysis for breakage syndromes; score 25 cells (SCE study), count 5 cells, 1 karyotype, with banding (eg, Bloom syndrome)	150.0	182 18	222 22	211

Code	Description	Medicode RVU	50th	75th	Medicare Nat'l Avg
88248 -26	Chromosome analysis for breakage syndromes; score 100 cells, count 20 cells, 2 karyotypes, with banding (eg, ataxia telangiectasia, Fanconi anemia)	300.0	365 36	444 44	245
88250 -26	Chromosome analysis for fragile X associated with fragile X-linked mental retardation, score 100 cells, count 20 cells, 2 karyotypes, with banding	339.0	412 41	502 50	214
88260 -26	Chromosome analysis; count 5 cells, screening, with banding	275.0	334 33	407 41	158
88261 -26	Chromosome analysis; count 5 cells, 1 karyotype, with banding	290.0	352 35	429 43	250
88262 -26	Chromosome analysis; count 15-20 cells, 2 karyotypes, with banding	350.0	425 43	518 52	176
88263 -26	Chromosome analysis; count 45 cells for mosaicism, 2 karyotypes, with banding	360.0	437 44	533 53	213
88267 -26	Chromosome analysis, amniotic fluid or chorionic villus, count 15 cells, 1 karyotype, with banding	395.0	480 48	585 58	254
88269 -26	Chromosome analysis, in situ for amniotic fluid cells, count cells from 6-12 colonies, 1 karyotype, with banding	347.0	422 42	514 51	235
88280 -26	Chromosome analysis; additional karyotypes, each study	114.0	139 14	169 17	36
88283 -26	Chromosome analysis; additional specialized banding technique (eg, NOR, s-banding)	90.00	109 11	133 13	97
88285 -26	Chromosome analysis; additional cells counted, each study	105.0	128 13	155 16	27
88289 -26	Chromosome analysis; additional high resolution study	75.00	91 9	111 11	49
88299	Unlisted cytogenetic study	0.00	0	0	–

88300–88399
Surgical Pathology

CODING INSIGHT

The primary surgical pathology codes (88300–88309) describe gross and microscopic examination of specimens submitted for pathologic evaluation.

Since 1985, the definitions of these codes have required pathologists to decide which codes best describe the level of service provided based on assessment of the complexity of each case. A specimen is defined as tissue or tissues submitted for individual and separate attention, requiring individual examination and pathologic diagnosis. CPT includes a specimen coding system for codes 88300 through 88309. Code 88300 is to be used for specimens that the pathologist feels can be accurately diagnosed by gross examination only. Codes 88302 through 88309 are organized in a hierarchy that describes five levels of service in which gross and microscopic examinations are required to make an accurate diagnosis. Each code is defined by the list of specimens assigned to the code. Specific specimens are assigned to each code or level of service, resulting in a uniform specimen coding system.

Surgical pathology codes for preparation and interpretation of pathology slide(s) (88302–88309, 88314, 88331, and 88332) should not be reported with a code for Mohs' micrographic surgery (17304–17310).

Subsidiary Codes

Subsidiary codes have relative values that require no further adjustment:

88311 is "in addition" to 88302–88309
88312 is "in addition" to 88302–88309, 88323–88325, and 88355–88358
88313 is "in addition" to 88302–88309, 88323–88325, and 88355–88358
88314 is "in addition" to 88302–88309, and 88331–88332
88332 is "in addition" to 88331

Because these are subsidiary or "in addition to" codes, reimbursement reduction and CPT modifier -51 do not apply.

Code	Description	Medicode RVU	50th	75th	Medicare Nat'l Avg
88300	LEVEL I - Surgical pathology, gross examination only	28.00	32	40	12
-26			22	28	8
88302	LEVEL II - Surgical pathology, gross and microscopic examination Appendix, Incidental Fallopian Tube, Sterilization Fingers/Toes, Amputation, Traumatic Foreskin, Newborn Hernia Sac, Any Location Hydrocele Sac Nerve Skin, Plastic Repair Sympathetic Ganglion Testis, Castration Vaginal Mucosa, Incidental Vas Deferens, Sterilization	55.00	62	80	23
-26			37	48	17
88304	LEVEL III - Surgical pathology, gross and microscopic examination Abortion, Induced Abscess Aneurysm - Arterial/Ventricular Anus, Tag Appendix, Other than Incidental Artery, Atheromatous Plaque Bartholin's Gland Cyst Bone Fragment(s), Other than Pathologic Fracture Bursa/Synovial Cyst Carpal Tunnel Tissue Cartilage, Shavings Cholesteatoma Colon, Colostomy Stoma Conjunctiva - Biopsy/Pterygium Cornea Diverticulum - Esophagus/Small Bowel Dupuytren's Contracture Tissue Femoral Head, Other than Fracture Fissure/Fistula Foreskin, Other than Newborn Gallbladder Ganglion Cyst Hematoma Hemorrhoids Hydatid of Morgagni Intervertebral Disc Joint, Loose Body Meniscus Mucocele, Salivary Neuroma - Morton's/Traumatic Pilonidal Cyst/Sinus Polyps, Inflammatory - Nasal/Sinusoidal Skin - Cyst/Tag/Debridement Soft Tissue, Debridement Soft Tissue, Lipoma Spermatocele Tendon/Tendon Sheath Testicular Appendage Thrombus or Embolus Tonsil and/or Adenoids Varicocele Vas Deferens, Other than Sterilization Vein, Varicosity	72.00	81	104	32
-26			49	62	24

Code	Description	Medicode RVU	50th	75th	Medicare Nat'l Avg
88305 **-26**	LEVEL IV - Surgical pathology, gross and microscopic examination Abortion - Spontaneous/Missed Artery, Biopsy Bone Marrow, Biopsy Bone Exostosis Brain/Meninges, Other than for Tumor Resection Breast, Biopsy Breast, Reduction Mammoplasty Bronchus, Biopsy Cell Block, Any Source Cervix, Biopsy Colon, Biopsy Duodenum, Biopsy Endocervix, Curettings/Biopsy Endometrium, Curettings/Biopsy Esophagus, Biopsy Extremity, Amputation, Traumatic Fallopian Tube, Biopsy Fallopian Tube, Ectopic Pregnancy Femoral Head, Fracture Fingers/Toes, Amputation, Non-traumatic Gingiva/Oral Mucosa, Biopsy Heart Valve Joint, Resection Kidney, Biopsy Larynx, Biopsy Leiomyoma(s), Uterine Myomectomy - without Uterus Lip, Biopsy/Wedge Resection Lung, Transbronchial Biopsy Lymph Node, Biopsy Muscle, Biopsy Nasal Mucosa, Biopsy Nasopharynx/Oropharynx, Biopsy Nerve, Biopsy Odontogenic/Dental Cyst Omentum, Biopsy Ovary with or without Tube, Non-neoplastic Ovary, Biopsy/Wedge Resection Parathyroid Gland Peritoneum, Biopsy Pituitary Tumor Placenta, Other than Third Trimester Pleura/Pericardium - Biopsy/Tissue Polyp, Cervical/Endometrial Polyp, Colorectal Polyp, Stomach/Small Bowel Prostate, Needle Biopsy Prostate, TUR Salivary Gland, Biopsy Sinus, Paranasal Biopsy Skin, Other than Cyst/Tag/Debridement/Plastic Repair Small Intestine, Biopsy Soft Tissue, Other than Tumor/Mass/Lipoma/Debridement Spleen Stomach, Biopsy Synovium Testis, Other than Tumor/Biopsy/Castration Thyroglossal Duct/Brachial Cleft Cyst Tongue, Biopsy Tonsil, Biopsy Trachea, Biopsy Ureter, Biopsy Urethra, Biopsy Urinary Bladder, Biopsy Uterus, with or without Tubes & Ovaries, for Prolapse Vagina, Biopsy Vulva/Labia, Biopsy	104.0	118 82	150 105	65 49
88307 **-26**	LEVEL V - Surgical pathology, gross and microscopic examination Adrenal, Resection Bone - Biopsy/Curettings Bone Fragment(s), Pathologic Fracture Brain, Biopsy Brain/Meninges, Tumor Resection Breast, Mastectomy - Partial/Simple Cervix, Conization Colon, Segmental Resection, Other than for Tumor Extremity, Amputation, Non-traumatic Eye, Enucleation Kidney, Partial/Total Nephrectomy Larynx, Partial/Total Resection Liver, Biopsy - Needle/Wedge Liver, Partial Resection Lung, Wedge Biopsy Lymph Nodes, Regional Resection Mediastinum, Mass Myocardium, Biopsy Odontogenic Tumor Ovary with or without Tube, Neoplastic Pancreas, Biopsy Placenta, Third Trimester Prostate, Except Radical Resection Salivary Gland Small Intestine, Resection, Other than for Tumor Soft Tissue Mass (except Lipoma) - Biopsy/Simple Excision Stomach - Subtotal/Total Resection, Other than for Tumor Testis, Biopsy Thymus, Tumor Thyroid, Total/Lobe Ureter, Resection Urinary Bladder, TUR Uterus, with or without Tubes & Ovaries, Other than Neoplastic/Prolapse	167.0	189 142	241 181	109 86
88309 **-26**	LEVEL VI - Surgical pathology, gross and microscopic examination Bone Resection Breast, Mastectomy - with Regional Lymph Nodes Colon, Segmental Resection for Tumor Colon, Total Resection Esophagus, Partial/Total Resection Extremity, Disarticulation Fetus, with Dissection Larynx, Partial/Total Resection - with Regional Lymph Nodes Lung - Total/Lobe/Segment Resection Pancreas, Total/Subtotal Resection Prostate, Radical Resection Small Intestine, Resection for Tumor Soft Tissue Tumor, Extensive Resection Stomach - Subtotal/Total Resection for Tumor Testis, Tumor Tongue/Tonsil - Resection for Tumor Urinary Bladder, Partial/Total Resection Uterus, with or without Tubes & Ovaries, Neoplastic Vulva, Total/Subtotal Resection	232.0	262 197	335 252	148 119
88311 **-26**	Decalcification procedure (List separately in addition to code for surgical pathology examination)	27.00	31 24	39 31	18 12

Code	Description	Medicode RVU	50th	75th	Medicare Nat'l Avg
88312 **-26**	Special stains (List separately in addition to code for surgical pathology examination); Group I for microorganisms (eg, Gridley, acid fast, methenamine silver), each	40.00	45 36	58 46	27 23
88313 **-26**	Special stains (List separately in addition to code for surgical pathology examination); Group II, all other, (eg, iron, trichrome), except immunocytochemistry and immunoperoxidase stains, each	30.00	34 27	43 35	16 12
88314 **-26**	Special stains (List separately in addition to code for surgical pathology examination); histochemical staining with frozen section(s)	55.00	62 44	80 56	40 29
88318 **-26**	Determinative histochemistry to identify chemical components (eg, copper, zinc)	44.00	50 40	64 51	23 19
88319 **-26**	Determinative histochemistry or cytochemistry to identify enzyme constituents, each	68.00	77 62	98 79	38 28
88321 **-26**	Consultation and report on referred slides prepared elsewhere	90.00	102 102	130 130	57
88323 **-26**	Consultation and report on referred material requiring preparation of slides	105.0	119 95	152 121	72 60
88325 **-26**	Consultation, comprehensive, with review of records and specimens, with report on referred material	140.0	158 158	202 202	91
88329 **-26**	Pathology consultation during surgery;	66.00	75 75	95 95	38
88331 **-26**	Pathology consultation during surgery; with frozen section(s), single specimen	127.0	144 108	184 138	80 62
88332 **-26**	Pathology consultation during surgery; each additional tissue block with frozen section(s)	76.00	86 64	110 82	40 31
88342 **-26**	Immunocytochemistry (including tissue immunoperoxidase), each antibody	100.0	113 90	145 116	54 42
88346 **-26**	Immunofluorescent study, each antibody; direct method	73.00	83 66	106 84	51 41
88347 **-26**	Immunofluorescent study, each antibody; indirect method	78.00	88 71	113 90	46 36
88348 **-26**	Electron microscopy; diagnostic	300.0	339 238	434 304	142 101
88349 **-26**	Electron microscopy; scanning	203.0	230 161	294 205	84 56
88355 **-26**	Morphometric analysis; skeletal muscle	239.0	270 203	346 259	128 98
88356 **-26**	Morphometric analysis; nerve	220.0	249 187	318 239	200 155
88358 **-26**	Morphometric analysis; tumor	198.0	224 168	286 215	181 139
88362 **-26**	Nerve teasing preparations	135.0	153 115	195 146	146 110
88365 **-26**	Tissue in situ hybridization, interpretation and report	70.00	79 63	101 81	61 48
88371 **-26**	Protein analysis of tissue by Western Blot, with interpretation and report;	60.00	68 14	87 17	31 20
88372 **-26**	Protein analysis of tissue by Western Blot, with interpretation and report; immunological probe for band identification, each	85.00	96 19	123 25	32 20

Code	Description	Medicode RVU	50th	75th	Medicare Nat'l Avg
88399	Unlisted surgical pathology procedure	0.00	0	0	–

89050–89399
Other Procedures

Coding Insight

Other procedures (89050–89399) contain important codes that do not fit into the other 14 subsections in the Pathology and Laboratory section (e.g., codes 89135–89140 and 89360). Codes for semen analysis are also found in this subsection.

Code 89250 *Culture and fertilization of oocyte(s)* is a new code added to CPT in 1996.

Medicare and Pathology & Laboratory Codes

CLIA Regulations

Recent changes to Pathology and Laboratory accommodate requirements set by the Clinical Laboratory Improvement Amendments of 1988 (CLIA). CLIA requirements impose varying levels of federal regulation on providers of clinical laboratory procedures.

CLIA regulations redefine laboratory testing in regard to laboratory certification and accreditation, proficiency testing, quality assurance, personnel standards, and program administration. Laboratory tests are classified as waived, moderately complex, and highly complex. Six microscopy tests, which are of moderate complexity, are largely unregulated.

Waived Tests

The nine waived tests listed below require CLIA certification but are not subject to routine inspection. Laboratories performing only these tests may request a waiver from CLIA regulations. The $100 Certificate of Waiver covers a two-year period. The waived tests are:

- Blood glucose by flucose monitoring devices cleared by FDA for home use.
- Automated hemoglobin tests using single analyte instruments with self-contained specimen-reagent interaction and direct measurement and readout
- Dip stick or tablet reagent urinalysis (nonautomated) for bilirubin, glucose, hemoglobin, ketones, leukocytes, nitrite, pH, protein, specific gravity, or urobilinogen
- Fecal occult blood
- Ovulation tests — visual color comparison tests
- Urine pregnancy tests — visual color comparison tests
- Erythrocyte sedimentation rate (nonautomated)
- Hemoglobin by copper sulfate method
- Spun microhematocrit

Moderately Complex Tests

Tests of moderate complexity require limited manual intervention or are automated procedures that do not require operator intervention during the analytic process. This category accounts for approximately 75 percent of all laboratory procedures. For CLIA certification, each laboratory performing moderately complex tests must have a laboratory director, a technical supervisor, a clinical consultant, and testing personnel.

Highly Complex Tests

Tests pertaining to cytogenetics, histopathology, histocompatibility, and cytology fall into the high complexity category. Regulations and personnel standards for highly complex tests are much more rigorous than for the other categories. Each laboratory must have a laboratory director, technical supervisor for each specialty or subspecialty, general supervisor, clinical consultant, and testing personnel. Separate regulations that apply to cytology laboratories allow limited "grandfathering" of testing personnel and generally require personnel to be cytotechnologists.

Microscopy Unregulated Tests

A new, largely unregulated category for physician-performed microscopy procedures was recently approved. While the following moderately complex tests are not waived procedures, they do not require routine inspection because no effective quality-control measures currently apply:

- Wet mounts, including preparations for vaginal, cervical, or skin specimens
- KOH preparations
- Pinworm preparations
- Fern tests
- Urine sediment exams
- Postcoital exams

Be sure to submit claims for specimen collection (e.g., venipuncture), codes 36400–36425, and for handling and/or conveyance of specimens, codes 99000–99001. Billing for these codes is discussed in the individual code section.

MEDICARE ALERT

HCPCS code G0001 *Routine venipuncture for collection of specimen(s)* should be used to report a routine venipuncture. However, CPT code 36415 should be used when the specimen is obtained by a routine capillary stick (e.g., finger/heel/ear stick).

Code	Description	Medicode RVU	50th	75th	Medicare Nat'l Avg
89050	Cell count, miscellaneous body fluids (eg, CSF, joint fluid), except blood;	16.00	19 0	24 0	7
89051	Cell count, miscellaneous body fluids (eg, CSF, joint fluid), except blood; with differential count	19.00	23 0	28 0	8
89060	Crystal identification by light microscopy with or without polarizing lens analysis, any body fluid (except urine)	19.00	23 0	28 0	10 20
89100 **-26**	Duodenal intubation and aspiration; single specimen (eg, simple bile study or afferent loop culture) plus appropriate test procedure	70.00	84 84	103 103	37
89105 **-26**	Duodenal intubation and aspiration; collection of multiple fractional specimens with pancreatic or gallbladder stimulation, single or double lumen tube	90.00	108 108	132 132	32
89125	Fat stain, feces, urine, or sputum	15.00	18 0	22 0	6
89130 **-26**	Gastric intubation and aspiration, diagnostic, each specimen, for chemical analyses or cytopathology;	30.00	36 36	44 44	31
89132 **-26**	Gastric intubation and aspiration, diagnostic, each specimen, for chemical analyses or cytopathology; after stimulation	30.00	36 36	44 44	14

Code	Description	Medicode RVU	50th	75th	Medicare Nat'l Avg
89135	Gastric intubation, aspiration, and fractional collections (eg, gastric secretory study); one hour	48.00	57	71	48
-26			57	71	
89136	Gastric intubation, aspiration, and fractional collections (eg, gastric secretory study); two hours	48.00	57	71	15
-26			57	71	
89140	Gastric intubation, aspiration, and fractional collections (eg, gastric secretory study); two hours including gastric stimulation (eg, histalog, pentagastrin)	70.00	84	103	62
-26			84	103	
89141	Gastric intubation, aspiration, and fractional collections (eg, gastric secretory study); three hours, including gastric stimulation	70.00	84	103	56
-26			84	103	
89160	Meat fibers, feces	9.00	11	13	5
			0	0	
89190	Nasal smear for eosinophils	14.00	17	21	7
			0	0	
● **89250**	Culture and fertilization of oocyte(s)	673.0	806	989	–
			0	0	
89300	Semen analysis; presence and/or motility of sperm including Huhner test	35.00	42	51	12
			0	0	
89310	Semen analysis; motility and count	33.00	40	49	12
			0	0	
89320	Semen analysis; complete (volume, count, motility and differential)	50.00	60	74	17
			0	0	
89325	Sperm antibodies	85.00	102	125	15
			0	0	
89329	Sperm evaluation; hamster penetration test	225.0	269	331	30
			0	0	
89330	Sperm evaluation; cervical mucus penetration test, with or without spinnbarkeit test	57.00	68	84	14
			0	0	
89350	Sputum, obtaining specimen, aerosol induced technique (separate procedure)	21.00	25	31	14
			0	0	
89355	Starch granules, feces	10.00	12	15	5
			0	0	
89360	Sweat collection by iontophoresis	40.00	48	59	16
			0	0	
89365	Water load test	24.00	29	35	8
			0	0	
89399	Unlisted miscellaneous pathology test	0.00	0	0	–

Medicine Codes 90700–99199

The majority of codes reported to Medicare and other payers are Evaluation and Management codes and Medicine codes. Correct use of these codes is very important because they represent the "bread and butter" of most physician practices.

Among the many diagnostic and therapeutic services included under Medicine are immunizations, injections, specialty specific codes, and special services.

Guidelines in this section begin with instructions on reporting multiple procedures. Instructions state that each procedure should be reported separately. (Note that examples given of "procedures" include medical and/or evaluation and management services), and that although the coder is not instructed to use modifier -51 as they are in Surgery guidelines (multiple procedures), modifier -51 is listed in and therefore should be applied to the Medicine section.

The wording in the multiple procedure guidelines produces a billing dilemma because modifier -51 may result in a reduction of the traditional 100 percent usually allowed for Medicine services. It may be wise to report without using modifier -51 or use it sparingly. Pay close attention to contracts and EOBs to determine payer guidelines. If a payer reduces a second code, it may be a good idea to negotiate future contracts based on what constitutes a procedure versus a service in the Medicine section.

Historically, no reduction for multiple services has been applied by payers to multiple medical services performed at the same session or to combinations of medical and surgical services. Multiple procedure reductions have historically been applied when multiple surgical procedures are performed during the same operative session.

90700–90799
Injections

Coding Insight

Immunizations are usually performed in conjunction with a medical service. According to CPT guidelines, a minimal office visit (99211) may be listed with an immunization. However, if both the physician and the nurse provide medical services on the same day, only one procedure code is used to identify the E/M service for that day. Remember, immunization codes include the supply of drugs and materials.

Fees charged by providers for immunizations include the cost of giving the immunization as well as the medication. When figuring the charge, double check the rate you are paying for the medication over a period of time and see which supplier offers the best price. HMO and other managed care companies will usually allow payment for immunizations, but the contract rate for the immunization may be low. Getting the best rate possible when purchasing various immunizations will, in the long run, enhance profitability.

Diagnostic and therapeutic infusion codes require the physician to be present during the infusion. If service time is greater than one hour, to use two codes (90780 and 90781) to identify the service. Prolonged attendance and infusion therapy codes for administration of routine medications through intravenous lines should not be reported with these codes. The drugs that are injected are not included in the code and should be reported separately. If the drugs are supplied by the physician, report 99070 (or the appropriate HCPCS Level II J code) for some commercial insurance companies, but Medicare will only accept the Level II code.

Therapeutic or diagnostic injection codes (90782–90799) do not include the supply of materials. List the charge for the drug separately, using 99070 for commercial payers.

Nota Bene: Surgical injection codes are found in the specific anatomical listings within the surgery section. Evaluation and Management codes and supplies should be reported separately.

Subsidiary Codes

Subsidiary codes have relative values that require no further adjustment:

90781 is "in addition" to 90780

Because these are subsidiary or "in addition to" codes, reimbursement reduction and modifier -51 do not apply.

Medicare Alert

Medicare bundles the administration of the medication into the E/M service, but they allow separate payment for the drug. Each Medicare and Medicaid carrier has individual requirements for the use of HCPCS Level II codes to describe the drug administered. Some carriers require the use of the CPT code and the HCPCS Level II J code, while others use only the J code and require a modifier to designate the method of administration. Check with your Medicare carrier for its policy.

Medicare rebundles certain codes in the medicine section when the listed codes are considered a component of a more comprehensive service.

36000 will not be reimbursed when reported with 90780–90781, 90784

Code	Description	Medicode RVU	50th	75th	Medicare Nat'l Avg
90700	Immunization, active; diphtheria, tetanus toxoids, and acellular pertussis vaccine (DTaP)	22.00	32	38	–
90701	Immunization, active; diphtheria and tetanus toxoids and pertussis vaccine (DTP)	18.00	26	31	–
90702	Immunization, active; diphtheria and tetanus toxoids (DT)	12.00	17	21	–
90703	Immunization, active; tetanus toxoid	10.50	15	18	–
90704	Immunization, active; mumps virus vaccine, live	20.00	29	35	–
90705	Immunization, active; measles virus vaccine, live, attenuated	18.00	26	31	–
90706	Immunization, active; rubella virus vaccine, live	19.00	27	33	–
90707	Immunization, active; measles, mumps and rubella virus vaccine, live	25.00	36	43	–
90708	Immunization, active; measles and rubella virus vaccine, live	22.00	32	38	–

Code	Description	Medicode RVU	50th	75th	Medicare Nat'l Avg
90709	Immunization, active; rubella and mumps virus vaccine, live	23.00	33	40	–
90710	Immunization, active; measles, mumps, rubella, and varicella vaccine	30.00	43	52	–
90711	Immunization, active; diphtheria, tetanus toxoids, and pertussis (DPT) and injectable poliomyelitis vaccine	23.50	34	41	–
90712	Immunization, active; poliovirus vaccine, live, oral (any type(s))	15.00	22	26	–
90713	Immunization, active; poliomyelitis vaccine	19.00	27	33	–
90714	Immunization, active; typhoid vaccine	15.50	22	27	–
90716	Immunization, active; varicella (chicken pox) vaccine	30.00	43	52	–
90717	Immunization, active; yellow fever vaccine	29.00	42	50	–
90718	Immunization, active; tetanus and diphtheria toxoids absorbed, for adult use (Td)	11.00	16	19	–
90719	Immunization, active; diphtheria toxoid	18.00	26	31	–
90720	Immunization, active; diphtheria, tetanus toxoids, and pertussis (DPT) and Hemophilus influenza B (HIB) vaccine	32.00	46	55	–
● 90721	Immunization, active; diphtheria, tetanus toxoids, and acellular pertussis vaccine (DTaP) and Hemophilus influenza B (HIB) vaccine	32.00	46	55	–
90724	Immunization, active; influenza virus vaccine	10.75	16	19	–
90725	Immunization, active; cholera vaccine	13.00	19	22	–
90726	Immunization, active; rabies vaccine	60.00	87	104	–
90727	Immunization, active; plague vaccine	18.00	26	31	–
90728	Immunization, active; BCG vaccine	105.0	152	181	–
90730	Immunization, active; hepatitis A vaccine	14.00	20	24	–
90732	Immunization, active; pneumococcal vaccine, polyvalent	16.00	23	28	–
90733	Immunization, active; meningococcal polysaccharide vaccine (any group(s))	35.00	51	60	–
90735	Immunization, active; encephalitis virus vaccine	14.50	21	25	–
90737	Immunization, active; Hemophilus influenza B	21.00	30	36	–
90741	Immunization, passive; immune serum globulin, human (ISG)	17.00	25	29	–

	Code	Description	Medicode RVU	50th	75th	Medicare Nat'l Avg
	90742	Immunization, passive; specific hyperimmune serum globulin (eg, hepatitis B, measles, pertussis, rabies, Rho(D), tetanus, vaccinia, varicella-zoster)	40.00	58	69	–
●	**90744**	Immunization, active, hepatitis B vaccine; newborn to 11 years	22.00	32	38	–
●	**90745**	Immunization, active, hepatitis B vaccine; 11-19 years	24.50	35	42	–
●	**90746**	Immunization, active, hepatitis B vaccine; 20 years and above	27.00	39	47	–
●	**90747**	Immunization, active, hepatitis B vaccine; dialysis or immunosuppressed patient, any age	27.00	39	47	–
	90749	Unlisted immunization procedure	0.00	0	0	–
	90780	IV infusion for therapy/diagnosis, administered by physician or under direct supervision of physician; up to one hour	68.00	87	115	39
	90781	IV infusion for therapy/diagnosis, administered by physician or under direct supervision of physician; each additional hour, up to eight (8) hours	68.00	87	115	21
	90782	Therapeutic or diagnostic injection (specify material injected); subcutaneous or intramuscular	13.00	17	22	4
	90783	Therapeutic or diagnostic injection (specify material injected); intra-arterial	29.00	37	49	16
	90784	Therapeutic or diagnostic injection (specify material injected); intravenous	27.00	34	46	17
	90788	Intramuscular injection of antibiotic (specify)	14.00	18	24	4
	90799	Unlisted therapeutic or diagnostic injection	0.00	0	0	–

90801–90899
Psychiatry

Coding Insight

Some of the codes in the psychiatry section of CPT are also used for reporting by psychologists and social workers. In fact, in managed care situations psychiatrists often are used only for pharmacologic management or inpatient treatment of mental disorders. Payers generally reimburse providers other than psychiatrists a percentage of the allowable for the code — typically 60 percent for psychologists and 40 percent for social workers.

Providers of mental health services should consider negotiating contracts with provisions made for patients who miss appointments. Co-pays should be collected at the time of service, unless the patient has a secondary insurer, in which case it must be determined whether it is worth the time and effort to report secondary insurers or to have the patient pay the co-pay and provide them with a bill.

For psychiatry services, code the initial interview and intake as 90801. Code the evaluation of hospital records separately as 90825 when the physician must evaluate extensive data about a patient in developing a treatment plan in addition to the initial interview intake or E/M service.

Hospital service codes (99221–99233) are used when the physician is involved in the medical management of inpatients (e.g., when the attending physician reviews laboratory and other diagnostic tests or initiates, alters, and re-evaluates the patient's treatment plan). The patient's clinical record must verify that a medical examination was performed and must document the level of care provided.

Both medical and psychiatric codes should be identified when other procedures are provided in addition to hospital care services. Some payers will not reimburse a procedure such as electroconvulsive therapy (90870–90871) when combined with an E/M code; others will not reimburse psychotherapy (90841–90889) performed on the same day as the electroconvulsive service. Appealing denials is usually beneficial. Send a cover letter referring to the notes in CPT and include a copy of the patient's medical record so the payer can verify the services provided.

Medicare Alert

One of the proposed changes to the 1996 physician fee schedule is that the payment for codes 90825 and 90877 be bundled into the payment for other psychiatric codes. If this proposal is adopted separate payment would no longer be made for these codes.

	Code	Description	Medicode RVU	50th	75th	Medicare Nat'l Avg
	90801	Psychiatric diagnostic interview examination including history, mental status, or disposition (may include communication with family or other sources, ordering and medical interpretation of laboratory or other medical diagnostic studies. In certain circumstances other informants will be seen in lieu of the patient)	101.0	129	164	100
	90820	Interactive medical psychiatric diagnostic interview examination	111.0	142	181	92
	90825	Psychiatric evaluation of hospital records, other psychiatric reports, psychometric and/or projective tests, and other accumulated data for medical diagnostic purposes	92.00	117	150	46
	90835	Narcosynthesis for psychiatric diagnostic and therapeutic purposes (eg, sodium amobarbital (Amytal) interview)	100.0	141	165	116
▲	90841	Individual medical psychotherapy by a physician, with continuing medical diagnostic evaluation, and drug management when indicated, including insight oriented, behavior modifying or supportive psychotherapy (face-to-face with the patient); time unspecified	0.00	0	0	–
▲	90842	Individual medical psychotherapy by a physician, with continuing medical diagnostic evaluation, and drug management when indicated, including insight oriented, behavior modifying or supportive psychotherapy; approximately 75 to 80 minutes	95.00	134	156	134
▲	90843	Individual medical psychotherapy by a physician, with continuing medical diagnostic evaluation, and drug management when indicated, including insight oriented, behavior modifying or supportive psychotherapy; approximately 20 to 30 minutes	53.00	75	87	51
▲	90844	Individual medical psychotherapy by a physician, with continuing medical diagnostic evaluation, and drug management when indicated, including insight oriented, behavior modifying or supportive psychotherapy; approximately 45 to 50 minutes	67.50	95	111	80
	90845	Medical psychoanalysis	82.00	115	135	75

Code	Description	Medicode RVU	50th	75th	Medicare Nat'l Avg
90846	Family medical psychotherapy (without the patient present)	67.00	94	110	86
90847	Family medical psychotherapy (conjoint psychotherapy) by a physician, with continuing medical diagnostic evaluation, and drug management when indicated	71.00	100	117	95
90849	Multiple-family group medical psychotherapy by a physician, with continuing medical diagnostic evaluation, and drug management when indicated	69.00	97	114	29
90853	Group medical psychotherapy (other than of a multiple-family group) by a physician, with continuing medical diagnostic evaluation and drug management when indicated	44.00	62	72	26
90855	Interactive individual medical psychotherapy	71.50	101	118	85
90857	Interactive group medical psychotherapy	60.00	84	99	21
90862	Pharmacologic management, including prescription, use, and review of medication with no more than minimal medical psychotherapy	45.00	62	73	45
90870	Electroconvulsive therapy (includes necessary monitoring); single seizure	158.0	217	257	85
90871	Electroconvulsive therapy (includes necessary monitoring); multiple seizures, per day	200.0	274	325	126
90880	Medical hypnotherapy	76.00	104	124	98
90882	Environmental intervention for medical management purposes on a psychiatric patient's behalf with agencies, employers, or institutions	79.00	108	128	–
90887	Interpretation or explanation of results of psychiatric, other medical examinations and procedures, or other accumulated data to family or other responsible persons, or advising them how to assist patient	75.00	103	122	63
90889	Preparation of report of patient's psychiatric status, history, treatment, or progress (other than for legal or consultative purposes) for other physicians, agencies, or insurance carriers	68.00	93	111	–
90899	Unlisted psychiatric service or procedure	0.00	0	0	–

90900–90915
Biofeedback

Coding Insight
Biofeedback may require prior authorization before treatment. If the payer does not cover biofeedback, enlist the help of the medical director or prior authorization (or utilization) review nurses to get the service covered. It may require some documentation (articles or printed research material on the benefits of biofeedback), but the time spent would be well worth the effort.

Code	Description	Medicode RVU	50th	75th	Medicare Nat'l Avg
90900	Biofeedback training; by electromyogram application (eg, in tension headache, muscle spasm)	65.00	91	110	64
90902	Biofeedback training; in conduction disorder (eg, arrhythmia)	54.00	76	91	54
90904	Biofeedback training; regulation of blood pressure (eg, in essential hypertension)	53.00	74	89	44
90906	Biofeedback training; regulation of skin temperature or peripheral blood flow	55.00	77	93	89
90908	Biofeedback training; by electroencephalogram application (eg, in anxiety, insomnia)	63.00	88	106	62
90910	Biofeedback training; by electro-oculogram application (eg, in blepharospasm)	64.00	90	108	57
90911	Biofeedback training; anorectal, including EMG and/or manometry	100.0	140	169	121
90915	Biofeedback training; other	50.00	70	84	59

90918–90999
Dialysis

CODING INSIGHT

Dialysis codes (90918–90999) are separated into hemodialysis, peritoneal dialysis, and miscellaneous dialysis procedures. These codes designate single physician evaluations and repeated evaluations. The repeated evaluation code is used whether or not the dialysis prescription is changed.

An instructional note in CPT states that office and hospital visits may be reported in addition to dialysis procedures only when they are unrelated to the dialysis and cannot be rendered during the dialysis session. For a level of service to be reimbursed with dialysis treatment on the same day, a separate diagnosis supporting the level of service must be reported.

Procedures for other medical problems and complications are not included in the monthly maintenance service. The documentation in the patient's chart substantiates the codes used. Payers often require physician participation in these monthly maintenance services.

Nota Bene: Some payers are interested in outpatient contracts that include the facility and professional component of dialysis, and HMOs are becoming more interested in buying equipment for use at home and utilization of more home health nurses because of the expense of the outpatient services. If the trend in your area is headed in this direction, it should be a consideration when negotiating contracts; otherwise, you may find your profitability suffering. Do some of the same research HMOs and other payers do (e.g., check prices of home dialysis equipment and depreciate it over the number of years expected from the equipment). Include an estimated cost of repairs as well as medication, tubing, and the cost of home health nursing visits, and so forth. Then, if you can offer a better rate, negotiate fairly with the payer. Remember, once payers start moving in this direction it is hard to stop the trend. Consider working with your hospital or outpatient dialysis facility and pharmacy to offer a package incentive with good rates on all aspects of dialysis — including drugs.

Medicare Alert

Medicare's policy for home glucose monitors no longer requires a patient to be "subject to poor diabetic control" in order to be eligible for Medicare coverage. In addition, the revised policy also allows any responsible individual, not just a family member, to be trained to use the equipment and monitor the patient if the patient is not able to do so. The policy changes are effective for services performed on or after April 27, 1995.

	Code	Description	Medicode RVU	50th	75th	Medicare Nat'l Avg
	90918	End stage renal disease (ESRD) related services per full month; for patients under 2 years of age to include monitoring for the adequacy of nutrition, assessment of growth and development, and counseling of parents	380.0	494	646	298
▲	**90919**	End stage renal disease (ESRD) related services per full month; for patients between two and eleven years of age to include monitoring for the adequacy of nutrition, assessment of growth and development, and counseling of parents	339.0	441	576	253
▲	**90920**	End state renal disease (ESRD) related services per full month; for patients between twelve and nineteen years of age to include monitoring for the adequacy of nutrition, assessment of growth and development, and counseling of parents	303.0	394	515	231
	90921	End stage renal disease (ESRD) related services per full month; for patients twenty years of age and over	248.0	322	421	183
▲	**90922**	End stage renal disease (ESRD) related services (less than full month), per day; for patients under two years of age	23.00	30	39	6
●	**90923**	End stage renal disease (ESRD) related services (less than full month), per day; for patients between two and eleven years of age	22.00	29	37	–
●	**90924**	End stage renal disease (ESRD) related services (less than full month), per day; for patients between twelve and nineteen years of age	21.00	27	36	–
●	**90925**	End stage renal disease (ESRD) related services (less than full month), per day; for patients twenty years of age and over	20.00	26	34	–
	90935	Hemodialysis procedure with single physician evaluation	170.0	221	289	103
	90937	Hemodialysis procedure requiring repeated evaluation(s) with or without substantial revision of dialysis prescription	270.0	351	459	190
	90945	Dialysis procedure other than hemodialysis (eg, peritoneal, hemofiltration), with single physician evaluation	160.0	208	272	94
	90947	Dialysis procedure other than hemodialysis (eg, peritoneal, hemofiltration) requiring repeated evaluations, with or without substantial revision of dialysis prescription	250.0	325	425	157
	90989	Dialysis training, patient, including helper where applicable, any mode, completed course	457.0	594	776	–
	90993	Dialysis training, patient, including helper where applicable, any mode, course not completed, per training session	77.00	100	131	–
	90997	Hemoperfusion (eg, with activated charcoal or resin)	190.0	247	323	150
	90999	Unlisted dialysis procedure, inpatient or outpatient	0.00	0	0	–

91000–91299
Gastroenterology

Coding Insight
Most gastroenterology procedures can be reported with other evaluation and management codes. However, confirmatory consults would only provide an opinion or advice and as such would not be reported with procedure codes. For information on reporting procedures, see the 40000s code range of the surgery section.

Medicare Alert
Medicare rebundles certain codes in the medicine section when the listed codes are considered a component of a more comprehensive service.

91105 will not be reimbursed when reported with 99291–99292

Code	Description	Medicode RVU	50th	75th	Medicare Nat'l Avg
91000	Esophageal intubation and collection of washings for cytology,	56.00	73	95	56
-26	including preparation of specimens (separate procedure)		58	76	54
91010	Esophageal motility study;	208.0	270	353	141
-26			216	283	114
91011	Esophageal motility study; with mecholyl or similar stimulant	240.0	312	408	165
-26			250	326	130
91012	Esophageal motility study; with acid perfusion studies	250.0	325	425	179
-26			260	340	140
91020	Esophagogastric manometric studies	175.0	228	297	157
-26			182	238	128
91030	Esophagus, acid perfusion (Bernstein) test for esophagitis	95.00	124	161	62
-26			111	145	54
91032	Esophagus, acid reflux test, with intraluminal pH electrode for	165.0	215	280	126
-26	detection of gastroesophageal reflux;		172	224	100
91033	Esophagus, acid reflux test, with intraluminal pH electrode for	245.0	319	416	170
-26	detection of gastroesophageal reflux; prolonged recording		255	333	123
91052	Gastric analysis test with injection of stimulant of gastric	110.0	143	187	88
-26	secretion (eg, histamine, insulin, pentagastrin, calcium and secretin)		129	168	77
91055	Gastric intubation, washings, and preparing slides for cytology	70.00	91	119	72
-26	(separate procedure)		73	95	62
91060	Gastric saline load test	65.00	85	110	42
-26			68	88	34
91065	Breath hydrogen test (eg, for detection of lactase deficiency)	126.0	164	214	47
-26			131	171	33
91100	Intestinal bleeding tube, passage, positioning and monitoring	68.00	88	116	57
91105	Gastric intubation, and aspiration or lavage for treatment (eg, for ingested poisons)	67.00	87	114	33
91122	Anorectal manometry	181.0	235	308	154
-26			188	246	116
91299	Unlisted diagnostic gastroenterology procedure	0.00	0	0	–

92002–92499
Ophthalmic Services

Coding Insight

Payer coverage of services in this section may be based on a contracted amount with the subscriber having only a percentage benefit instead of a full benefit for services. Watch contracted amounts and co-pay issues. When contracted, payment and co-pays will be at the allowed amount, and charges to the member cannot be up to the fee-for-service rate.

Medical examination and evaluation codes (92002–92014) are divided into new and established patient categories, and the three-year rule of determining the category applies. (See under E/M codes for a complete definition.) Unlike E/M codes, there is no reference to the key components or time, and these services do not include counseling or coordination of care.

Special Ophthalmological Services

Refractions

Code 92015 is for "determination of a refractive state." Many payers allow this service as a covered benefit. Medicare, however, does not cover this service and considers it "medically unnecessary." This distinguishing factor allows the patient to be billed directly for this service.

With 92015, it is unnecessary to use modifiers to indicate the refraction. Simply list the eye examination code on the first line of the HCFA-1500 form, and the refraction second.

Visual Fields

Gross visual field testing is considered integral to the general ophthalmic services and is not reported separately.

Subsidiary Codes

Subsidiary codes have relative values that require no further adjustment:

95920 is "in addition" to 92280

Because these are subsidiary or "in addition to" codes, reimbursement reduction and modifier -51 do not apply.

Medicare Alert

Modifier -50 is not applicable to visual field testing because the codes are listed as unilateral or bilateral. Medical diagnostic evaluation is included in these tests and should not be reported separately. Some codes, such as 92225 and 92226, are unilateral.

Code	Description	Medicode RVU	50th	75th	Medicare Nat'l Avg
92002	Ophthalmological services: medical examination and evaluation with initiation of diagnostic and treatment program; intermediate, new patient	41.00	57	65	54
92004	Ophthalmological services: medical examination and evaluation with initiation of diagnostic and treatment program; comprehensive, new patient, one or more visits	54.00	75	85	76
92012	Ophthalmological services: medical examination and evaluation, with initiation or continuation of diagnostic and treatment program; intermediate, established patient	39.00	53	60	43

	Code	Description	Medicode RVU	50th	75th	Medicare Nat'l Avg
	92014	Ophthalmological services: medical examination and evaluation, with initiation or continuation of diagnostic and treatment program; comprehensive, established patient, one or more visits	48.00	65	74	55
	92015	Determination of refractive state	13.50	17	22	
	92018	Ophthalmological examination and evaluation, under general anesthesia, with or without manipulation of globe for passive range of motion or other manipulation to facilitate diagnostic examination; complete	140.0	178	225	71
	92019	Ophthalmological examination and evaluation, under general anesthesia, with or without manipulation of globe for passive range of motion or other manipulation to facilitate diagnostic examination; limited	65.00	83	104	63
▲	**92020**	Gonioscopy (separate procedure)	27.00	34	43	24
▲	**92060**	Sensorimotor examination with multiple measurements of ocular deviation (eg, restrictive or paretic muscle with diplopia) with interpretation and report (separate procedure)	40.00	51	64	32
	92065	Orthoptic and/or pleoptic training, with continuing medical direction and evaluation	0.00	0	0	25
	92070	Fitting of contact lens for treatment of disease, including supply of lens	0.00	0	0	72
▲	**92081**	Visual field examination, unilateral or bilateral, with interpretation and report; limited examination (eg, tangent screen, Autoplot, arc perimeter, or single stimulus level automated test, such as Octopus 3 or 7 equivalent)	27.00	34	43	25
▲	**92082**	Visual field examination, unilateral or bilateral, with medical diagnostic evaluation; intermediate examination (eg, at least 2 isopters on Goldmann perimeter, or semiquantitative, automated suprathreshold screening program, Humphrey suprathreshold automatic diagnostic test, Octopus program 33)	46.00	58	74	36
▲	**92083**	Visual field examination, unilateral or bilateral, with medical diagnostic evaluation; extended examination (eg, Goldmann visual fields with at least 3 isopters plotted and static determination within the central 30, or quantitative, automated threshold perimetry, Octopus program G-1, 32 or 42, Humphrey visual field analyzer full threshold programs 30-2, 24-2, or 30/60-2)	70.00	89	112	55
▲	**92100**	Serial tonometry (separate procedure) with multiple measurements of intraocular pressure over an extended time period with interpretation and report, same day (eg, diurnal curve or medical treatment of acute elevation of intraocular pressure)	25.00	32	40	37
▲	**92120**	Tonography with interpretation and report, recording indentation tonometer method or perilimbal suction method	30.00	38	48	37
	92130	Tonography with water provocation	30.00	38	48	45
▲	**92140**	Provocative tests for glaucoma, with interpretation and report, without tonography	29.50	37	47	28
▲	**92225**	Ophthalmoscopy, extended, with retinal drawing (eg, for retinal detachment, melanoma), with interpretation and report; initial	43.00	57	75	36

	Code	Description	Medicode RVU	50th	75th	Medicare Nat'l Avg
▲	92226	Ophthalmoscopy, extended, with retinal drawing (eg, for retinal detachment, melanoma), with medical diagnostic evaluation; subsequent	37.00	49	64	31
▲	92230	Fluorescein angioscopy with interpretation and report	52.00	69	90	46
▲	92235	Fluorescein angiography (includes multiframe imaging) with interpretation and report	136.0	181	236	92
▲	92250	Fundus photography with interpretation and report	43.00	57	75	32
	92260	Ophthalmodynamometry	50.00	67	87	38
▲	92265	Needle oculoelectromyography, one or more extraocular muscles, one or both eyes, with interpretation and report	100.0	133	173	40
▲	92270	Electro-oculography with interpretation and report	100.0	133	173	54
▲	92275	Electroretinography with interpretation and report	100.0	133	173	69
	92283	Color vision examination, extended, eg, anomaloscope or equivalent	37.00	49	64	20
▲	92284	Dark adaptation examination, with interpretation and report	53.00	70	92	30
▲	92285	External ocular photography with interpretation and report for documentation of medical progress (eg, close-up photography, slit lamp photography, goniophotography, stereophotography)	29.00	39	50	19
▲	92286	Special anterior segment photography with interpretation and report; with specular endothelial microscopy and cell count	140.0	186	243	74
▲	92287	Special anterior segment photography with medical diagnostic evaluation; with fluorescein angiography	175.0	233	303	84
	92310	Prescription of optical and physical characteristics of and fitting of contact lens, with medical supervision of adaptation; corneal lens, both eyes, except for aphakia	88.00	117	153	–
	92311	Prescription of optical and physical characteristics of and fitting of contact lens, with medical supervision of adaptation; corneal lens for aphakia, one eye	76.00	101	132	71
	92312	Prescription of optical and physical characteristics of and fitting of contact lens, with medical supervision of adaptation; corneal lens for aphakia, both eyes	100.0	133	173	86
	92313	Prescription of optical and physical characteristics of and fitting of contact lens, with medical supervision of adaptation; corneoscleral lens	126.0	168	218	64
	92314	Prescription of optical and physical characteristics of contact lens, with medical supervision of adaptation and direction of fitting by independent technician; corneal lens, both eyes, except for aphakia	90.00	120	156	–
	92315	Prescription of optical and physical characteristics of contact lens, with medical supervision of adaptation and direction of fitting by independent technician; corneal lens for aphakia, one eye	84.00	112	146	41
	92316	Prescription of optical and physical characteristics of contact lens, with medical supervision of adaptation and direction of fitting by independent technician; corneal lens for aphakia, both eyes	139.0	185	241	58

Code	Description	Medicode RVU	50th	75th	Medicare Nat'l Avg
92317	Prescription of optical and physical characteristics of contact lens, with medical supervision of adaptation and direction of fitting by independent technician; corneoscleral lens	90.00	120	156	30
92325	Modification of contact lens (separate procedure), with medical supervision of adaptation	47.50	63	82	14
92326	Replacement of contact lens	52.00	69	90	56
92330	Prescription, fitting, and supply of ocular prosthesis (artificial eye), with medical supervision of adaptation	0.00	0	0	81
92335	Prescription of ocular prosthesis (artificial eye) and direction of fitting and supply by independent technician, with medical supervision of adaptation	0.00	0	0	87
92340	Fitting of spectacles, except for aphakia; monofocal	51.50	69	89	–
92341	Fitting of spectacles, except for aphakia; bifocal	56.00	74	97	–
92342	Fitting of spectacles, except for aphakia; multifocal, other than bifocal	77.00	102	133	–
92352	Fitting of spectacle prosthesis for aphakia; monofocal	23.00	31	40	23
92353	Fitting of spectacle prosthesis for aphakia; multifocal	25.00	33	43	32
92354	Fitting of spectacle mounted low vision aid; single element system	0.00	0	0	290
92355	Fitting of spectacle mounted low vision aid; telescopic or other compound lens system	0.00	0	0	141
92358	Prosthesis service for aphakia, temporary (disposable or loan, including materials)	0.00	0	0	33
92370	Repair and refitting spectacles; except for aphakia	75.00	100	130	–
92371	Repair and refitting spectacles; spectacle prosthesis for aphakia	124.0	165	215	21
92390	Supply of spectacles, except prosthesis for aphakia and low vision aids	0.00	0	0	–
92391	Supply of contact lenses, except prosthesis for aphakia	0.00	0	0	–
92392	Supply of low vision aids (A low vision aid is any lens or device used to aid or improve visual function in a person whose vision cannot be normalized by conventional spectacle correction. Includes reading additions up to 4D.)	0.00	0	0	–
92393	Supply of ocular prosthesis (artificial eye)	0.00	0	0	–
92395	Supply of permanent prosthesis for aphakia; spectacles	0.00	0	0	–
92396	Supply of permanent prosthesis for aphakia; contact lenses	0.00	0	0	–
92499	Unlisted ophthalmological service or procedure	0.00	0	0	–

92502–92599
Otorhinolaryngologic (ENT) Services

CODING INSIGHT

Otorhinolaryngology/audiology codes 92502–92599 contain procedures that are among the most misunderstood in CPT. While some codes speak for themselves, such as 92507 *Speech, language or hearing therapy, with continuing medical supervision, individual*; codes like 92543 *Caloric vestibular test, each irrigation (binaural, bithermal stimulation constitutes four tests), with recording* are unclear. What are all of these mysterious codes and under what circumstances are they used?

Those responsible for prior authorization must be especially careful about which codes to use when requesting a test. Written protocols for these types of procedures may be nonexistent, and new code additions can be especially confusing. Here are some tips that may help.

- If questioned on a test or a new code, offer to supply a definition of what the test is and for what type of disorder(s) the test is indicated. This may clarify the issue for prior authorization, physicians and other providers, and your definitions may become part of the protocol for the tests.
- If a screening test is performed and further testing is warranted, attach a standard definition and test indication statement to the prior authorization request. It issurprising how often papers like these become part of prior authorization efforts to have material available to order appropriate tests.
- If contracts with payers are in place, contact them as soon as new codes are added. Give the new code, its description, the cost of the test at your fee-for-service and contract rate, and ask for an addendum to the contract. Although many contracts are written to handle situations where a code is not included in the contract, it can be at a percent of fee-for-service. If the contract is negotiated with an 80 percent of fee-for-service rate and is written so that you receive only 75 percent of reported charges for procedures not on the fee schedule, the reimbursement may not cover the costs of the test.
- When first payments are received for new tests always check contract rates with the payer to determine if payment was made according to the contract and that your charges are in line with allowables from noncontracted payers.

ENT codes (92502–92599) identify the special diagnostic and treatment services not usually included in the comprehensive otorhinolaryngologic evaluation, including audiologic function tests.

Audiologic function tests are reported only if calibrated electronic equipment is used. Use of a tuning fork is not reported separately. Hearing tests are bilateral except for 92590 through 92595, which are identified as monaural (one ear) or binaural (both ears). If only one ear is tested, other than the exceptions noted above, a reduced service must be reported using modifier -52.

SUBSIDIARY CODES

Subsidiary codes have relative values that require no further adjustment:

95920 is "in addition" to 95925

Because these are subsidiary or "in addition to" codes, reimbursement reduction and modifier -51 do not apply.

MEDICARE ALERT

Medicare rebundles certain codes in the medicine section when the listed codes are considered a component of a more comprehensive service.

69210, 92552–92553, 92556 will not be reimbursed when reported with 92557

	Code	Description	Medicode RVU	50th	75th	Medicare Nat'l Avg
	92502	Otolaryngologic examination under general anesthesia	172.0	224	295	93
	92504	Binocular microscopy (separate diagnostic procedure)	25.50	33	44	17
▲	**92506**	Evaluation of speech, language, voice, communication, auditory processing, and/or aural rehabilitation status	96.50	125	166	49
▲	**92507**	Treatment of speech, language, voice, communication, and/or auditory processing disorder (includes aural rehabilitation); individual	46.00	60	79	30
▲	**92508**	Treatment of speech, language, voice, communication, and/or auditory processing disorder (includes aural rehabilitation); group, two or more individuals	35.00	46	60	16
●	**92510**	Aural rehabilitation following cochlear implant (includes evaluation of aural rehabilitation status and hearing, therapeutic services) with or without speech processor programming	0.00	0	0	–
	92511	Nasopharyngoscopy with endoscope (separate procedure)	100.0	130	172	71
	92512	Nasal function studies (eg, rhinomanometry)	72.00	94	123	37
▲	**92516**	Facial nerve function studies (eg, electroneuronography)	79.00	103	135	30
	92520	Laryngeal function studies	155.0	202	266	48
●	**92525**	Evaluation of swallowing and oral function for feeding	148.0	192	254	–
●	**92526**	Treatment of swallowing dysfunction and/or oral function for feeding	74.50	97	128	–
	92531	Spontaneous nystagmus, including gaze	23.00	30	39	–
	92532	Positional nystagmus	27.00	35	46	–
	92533	Caloric vestibular test, each irrigation (binaural, bithermal stimulation constitutes four tests)	43.00	56	74	–
	92534	Optokinetic nystagmus	19.00	25	33	–
	92541	Spontaneous nystagmus test, including gaze and fixation nystagmus, with recording	57.00	74	98	41
	-26			59	78	32
	92542	Positional nystagmus test, minimum of 4 positions, with recording	51.00	66	87	35
	-26			53	70	27
	92543	Caloric vestibular test, each irrigation (binaural, bithermal stimulation constitutes four tests), with recording	66.00	86	113	45
	-26			69	91	29
	92544	Optokinetic nystagmus test, bidirectional, foveal or peripheral stimulation, with recording	31.00	40	53	27
	-26			32	43	20

	Code	Description	Medicode RVU	50th	75th	Medicare Nat'l Avg
	92545	Oscillating tracking test, with recording	31.00	40	53	23
	-26			32	43	16
▲	**92546**	Sinusoidal vertical axis rotational testing	49.00	64	84	30
	-26			51	67	22
	92547	Use of vertical electrodes in any or all of above tests counts as one additional test	30.00	39	51	21
	-26			31	41	
	92551	Screening test, pure tone, air only	13.00	18	22	–
	92552	Pure tone audiometry (threshold); air only	19.00	27	32	16
	92553	Pure tone audiometry (threshold); air and bone	29.00	41	49	24
▲	**92555**	Speech audiometry threshold;	15.00	21	26	14
▲	**92556**	Speech audiometry threshold; with speech recognition	25.00	35	43	21
▲	**92557**	Comprehensive audiometry threshold evaluation and speech recognition (92553 and 92556 combined)	51.00	71	87	43
	92559	Audiometric testing of groups	42.00	59	71	–
	92560	Bekesy audiometry; screening	25.00	35	43	–
	92561	Bekesy audiometry; diagnostic	50.00	70	85	26
	92562	Loudness balance test, alternate binaural or monaural	12.50	17	21	15
	92563	Tone decay test	22.00	31	37	14
	92564	Short increment sensitivity index (SISI)	22.00	31	37	17
	92565	Stenger test, pure tone	18.00	25	31	15
	92567	Tympanometry (impedance testing)	20.00	28	34	19
	92568	Acoustic reflex testing	17.00	24	29	14
	92569	Acoustic reflex decay test	18.00	25	31	15
	92571	Filtered speech test	27.00	38	46	14
	92572	Staggered spondaic word test	22.00	31	37	3
	92573	Lombard test	14.00	20	24	13
	92575	Sensorineural acuity level test	22.00	31	37	11
	92576	Synthetic sentence identification test	20.00	28	34	16

	Code	Description	Medicode RVU	50th	75th	Medicare Nat'l Avg
	92577	Stenger test, speech	18.00	25	31	26
●	92579	Visual reinforcement audiometry (VRA)	35.00	49	60	–
	92582	Conditioning play audiometry	38.00	53	65	26
	92583	Select picture audiometry	25.00	35	43	32
	92584	Electrocochleography	147.0	206	250	91
▲	92585	Auditory evoked potentials for evoked response audiometry and/or testing of the central nervous system	172.0	240	293	139
	-26			120	146	83
	92587	Evoked otoacoustic emissions; limited (single stimulus level, either transient or distortion products)	36.00	50	61	55
▲	92588	Evoked otoacoustic emissions; comprehensive or diagnostic evaluation (comparison of transient and/or distortion product otoacoustic emissions at multiple levels and frequencies)	51.00	71	87	75
	92589	Central auditory function test(s) (specify)	31.00	43	53	20
	92590	Hearing aid examination and selection; monaural	50.00	70	85	–
	92591	Hearing aid examination and selection; binaural	75.00	105	128	–
	92592	Hearing aid check; monaural	22.00	31	37	–
	92593	Hearing aid check; binaural	33.00	46	56	–
	92594	Electroacoustic evaluation for hearing aid; monaural	24.00	34	41	–
	92595	Electroacoustic evaluation for hearing aid; binaural	36.00	50	61	–
	92596	Ear protector attenuation measurements	18.00	25	31	21
●	92597	Evaluation for use and/or fitting of voice prosthetic or augmentative/alternative communication device to supplement oral speech	0.00	0	0	–
●	92598	Modification of voice prosthetic or augmentative/alternative communication device to supplement oral speech	0.00	0	0	–
	92599	Unlisted otorhinolaryngological service or procedure	0.00	0	0	–

92950–93799
Cardiovascular Services

CODING INSIGHT

Therapeutic (92950–92996)
Percutaneous transluminal coronary angioplasty (PTCA) dilates the artery by flattening plaque obstructing an artery. Atherectomy involves use of cutting mechanisms to remove plaque and either store the fragments in a chamber to be emptied outside the body or removed with a vacuum mechanism.

In some cases, the physician will be unable to achieve the desired opening of the artery with atherectomy alone, and a balloon angioplasty will be needed to provide additional reduction in the degree of blockage in the artery.

Because 92995 and 92996 describe atherectomy with or without balloon angioplasty, 92982 and 92984 should not be reported in addition to the atherectomy.

Nota Bene: There may be circumstances in which multiple coronary arteries are treated at a single setting using different techniques. For example, a patient undergoes atherectomy of a proximal left anterior descending coronary artery and a balloon angioplasty of the left circumflex coronary artery. The atherectomy for the left anterior descending coronary artery would be identified with 92995, and the balloon angioplasty of the left circumflex coronary artery would be coded using 92982-51. Submit an operative report showing that two separate services were performed.

Medicare and Therapeutic Services
Placement of intracoronary stents is covered by Medicare. Two codes added to CPT '95 report percutaneous placement of an intracoronary stent(s): 92980 and 92981. These codes include the work of angioplasty or arthrectomy on the vessel(s) in which the stent is placed. If additional vessels are treated without stent placement, 92984 and/or 92986 should be used. If you have any questions contact your local Medicare carrier.

Cardiovascular Stress Tests (93015–93018)
Code 93015 identifies the total service (global) for cardiovascular stress test and includes the following components:

- The recording (the technical component only)
- Supervision of the procedure (a portion of the professional component)
- Interpretation and report (a portion of the professional component)

To report services separately use the following subordinate codes:

- 93016–93018 are not global codes, and each one represents a portion of the professional component of the total service for cardiovascular stress test.
- Use 93016 when a physician provides supervision only
- Use 93017 when a physician provides a tracing only
- Use 93018 when a physician provides interpretation and report only

Nota Bene: Payers consider the physician use of 93016 and 93018 instead of identifying 93015-26 as unbundling (identifying separate components instead of using the available combination code). It may be flagged for audit because reimbursement could be higher by using 93016 and 93018.

To determine payment for component parts of a global fee payers usually break the allowable into percentages. As an example, 93015 may be broken out into 40 percent of the allowable for the professional component and 60 percent of the allowable for the technical component.

Other codes, which already represent components, are assigned their own fee; for example:

- 93016 represents 100 percent professional component
- 93017 represents 100 percent technical component
- 93018 represents 100 percent professional component
- Modifier -51 is used when multiple procedures are performed on the same day or at the same session. The major procedure or service (the service with the highest value) may be identified and listed as secondary, additional, or lesser procedure(s) or service(s) and may be identified with modifier -51 added. Historically, no reduction for multiple services has been applied by payers to multiple medical services performed at the same session or combinations of medical and surgical services. Multiple procedure reductions have historically been applied when multiple surgical procedures are performed during the same operative session

Nuclear medicine codes (78460, 78461, 78464, 78465; 78472, 78473; 78481, and 78483) should be reported separately when performed with cardiovascular stress tests.

Medicare and Cardiovascular Stress Tests

Physicians were instructed by HCFA in 1993 to use 93015-26 to report the physician supervision and performance of interpretation for cardiovascular stress test. The 1994 Medicare Fee Schedule "deleted" the professional component (which represented the physician supervision, interpretation, and report) of code 93015. Code 93016 represents the physician supervision only of a cardiovascular stress test, and 93018 represents the physician interpretation and report of a cardiovascular stress test.

When a physician supervises the test and provides an interpretation and report, the physician may report and be paid for both 93016 and 93018.

Medicare will continue to consider whether there are efficiencies in the provision of nonsurgical procedures which should result in reduced payment when more that one service category is provided on the same day to a beneficiary. Any changes where payment reduction is deemed appropriate by Medicare would be announced in the Federal Register for public comment before a final decision is made.

Phonocardiography (93201-93210)

Phonocardiography is a graphic recording of heart sounds and pulse waves and their reaction to time. Indications for phonocardiography include the identification and timing of various sounds and murmurs.

Vectorcardiography (93220-93222)

Vectorcardiography is a three-dimensional view of the electrical forces of the heart. Indications for vectorcardiography include the need for amplified understanding of the ECG/EKG, or when more information is needed than that provided in ECG/EKG.

Holter Monitor (93224–93237)

Holter monitor involves an ambulatory record of the heart's activity continually during the patient's normal routine for a 12, 24, or 48-hour period.

Indications include:

- Diagnosis for suspected dysrhythmia
- To diagnose unexplained symptoms (dizziness, syncope, or palpitations)

- To diagnose chest pain episodes
- To evaluate effectiveness of anti-arrhythmic drugs
- Evaluation of pacemaker function

Medicare and Monitors

Conventional tape type monitors and real-time devices which use data compression techniques to produce a full-disclosure printout are used for long-term ECG monitoring. To be reimbursed by Medicare, such monitoring needs to be related to a disease process documented by signs and/or symptoms such as palpitations or near syncope. Long-term ECG monitoring for the routine assessment of pacemaker function is not usually reimbursed by Medicare. A monitoring period of up to 24 hours is generally considered adequate to provide essential diagnostic information, and the medical necessity of longer periods must be documented.

Signal averaged electrocardiogram (SAECG) is a computerized, noninvasive diagnostic method for determining patients at risk for life-threatening ventricular arrhythmias. It is used to identify late potentials, which refer to areas of delayed or fragmented ventricular depolarization. These abnormalities are felt to be indicators of a diseased myocardium that has the potential of initiating a life-threatening ventricular tachycardia or fibrillation. Medicare will cover SAECG only in patients who have had a recent myocardial infarction (MI) and who have a documented ventricular ejection fraction (EF) of less than or equal to 40 percent.

HCFA states they have been informed that some suppliers of these types of services have decided that, since their devices provide both pre-symptom memory loop and post-symptom recording, they may report for two codes, e.g., G0006 and G0015, to increase their payments. This is incorrect and represents a duplicate reporting for the services furnished. All of these devices provide post-symptom recording. Therefore, the codes denoting pre-symptom memory loop (G0004–G0007) also include payment for post-symptom recording. The whole basis for having G0015 and G0016 is for the description of services in which the device used does not have the capacity for pre-symptom memory loop recording.

Echocardiography (93307–93350)

Echocardiography codes represent a global procedure. When the physician provides only supervision and interpretation, modifier -26 is added. In echocardiography, ultrasonic waves directed at the heart and great vessels provide a hard copy recording that serves as a diagnostic tool. Code 93325 for color flow mapping is never reported alone; it is always listed as an additional line item to echocardiography (76825–76828, 93307, 93308, 93312, 93314, 93320, and 93321).

Echocardiography records ultrasonic waves reflected from the heart and allows visualization of heart size and shape, myocardial wall thickness, motion, cardiac valve structure, and function. Check with your local Medicare carrier for policy guidelines.

Transesophageal Echocardiography (TEE) (93312–93314)

Transesophageal echocardiography involves a small ultrasonic devise attached to tip of a gastroscope and is guided by the physician into the patient's esophagus, where it rests behind the heart. Check with your local Medicare carrier for policy guidelines.

Doppler (93320–93321)

Doppler echocardiography provides continuous waves but also uses a sound or frequency ultrasound to record direction of blood flow through the heart chambers.

If a Doppler echocardiogram is performed in addition to a 2-D echocardiogram (93307–93314), it may be reported separately.

After an initial study, follow-up Doppler echocardiograms by the same provider or provider group are usually covered when: (a) there are new, significantly changing symptoms for the conditions listed above, or (b) at reasonable intervals when progression is expected in one of these conditions. Routine follow-up testing that does not meet this criteria will not be covered. To code for a follow-up echocardiogram, use 93308 (2-D) and 93321 (Doppler), if applicable.

Color Flow Mapping (93325)
Color flow mapping converts recorded flow frequencies into different colors. These color images are superimposed on M-mode or 2-D echoes, allowing more detailed evaluation of disorders.

Code 93325 for color flow mapping is never reportable alone; it is always listed with an echocardiogram code or with 76825–76828.

Check with your local Medicare carrier for policy guidelines.

Cardiac Catheterization (93501–93562)
If an injection procedure is performed in conjunction with a heart catheterization, the introduction of the catheter is not included in the injection procedure code, although repositioning of the catheter and automatic power injectors are.

Supervision and interpretation codes related to cardiac catheterization (93555 and 93556) were added to use with imaging done as part of cardiac catheterization procedures. The plural presentation of the word "procedure(s)" as well as the "and/or" terminology in the codes' descriptions suggest the codes include imaging of one or more areas.

Cardiac catheterizations are invasive procedures used to visualize the heart's chambers, valves, great vessels, and coronary arteries. Pressure measurements and blood volumes are done with the catheter procedures and are used to evaluate cardiac function and provide information regarding valve patency. Cardiac catheterization is the most definitive procedure for diagnosis and evaluation of coronary disease.

Cardiac catheterization includes the following services:

- Intravenous pressure
- Intracardiac pressure
- Arterial blood sample for blood gas studies
- Cardiac output (93561)
- Ergometer (to exercise patient)
- Electrode catheter (temporary pacemaker)
- Swan-Ganz insertion
- Arterial/venous cutdown
- Placement or repositioning of catheters and use of automatic power injectors

The following services may be included in a cardiac catheterization and would not be identified separately:

- Introduction (percutaneous or cutdown) and positioning or repositioning of catheters (venous codes 36000, 36010, 36013, 36014, 36015, 36400, 36400, 36405, 36406, 36410, 36415, 36420, 36425, 36488, 36489, 36490, 36491, and arterial codes 36120, 36140, 36200, 36200, 36215, 36216, 36217, 36218, 36620, 36625). Catheters may include (1) electrode catheters for sensing or pacing (93610, 93612, 33210, 33211), (2) platinum tipped catheters for sensing reducing substances, (3) angiographic catheters for delivery of contrast material, transducer-tipped catheters for measuring pressure at the catheter tip, (4) single end-hole catheters for recording pulmonary capillary wedge pressure, right heart pressures, and blood sampling from the right heart, and (5) flow direct (balloon tipped or Swan-Ganz) catheters for measuring right heart, pulmonary artery, and pulmonary capillary wedge pressure (93503).

- Monitoring and recording of cardiac rhythm (codes 93040, 93041, 93042)
- Fluoroscopic guidance for positioning and repositioning of catheters (codes 76000 and 76001)
- Recording of pressures in all cardiac chambers and great vessels through which the catheter passes (codes 93603, 93607, 93770)
- Obtaining blood samples from the various chambers and great vessels through which the catheter passes
- Cardiac output determination by Fick method, indicator dilution method, and/or thermodilution method (codes 94681, 93561, 93562)

Additional special procedures that may be performed during cardiac catheterization include:

- Passive or active supine exercise to determine the physiologic effect of exercise in the presence of various anomalies
- Intracardiac phonocardiography (code 93210)
- Intracardiac electrocardiography
- Pharmacologic interventions, e.g., isoproterenol, ergonovine (codes 93024, 90783, 90784)

Cardiac catheterization excludes the following services:

- Introduction of the catheter for an injection procedure performed in conjunction with a catheterization
- Technical details of angiography, supervision and interpretation

Right heart catheterization is necessary when the patient's clinical condition requires one or more of the following: measurements of right sided pressures, right heart angiography, or myocardial biopsy.

Code 93501 refers to right heart catheterization done as a diagnostic procedure. If the right heart catheter remains in the patient for monitoring purposes (e.g., Swan-Ganz), it should be coded 93503.

Contraindications include a patient whose cardiac diagnosis is uncertain but in whom cardiac surgery would be deferred because of debilitating illness (e.g., severe cardiomegaly or extreme obesity).

Nota Bene: Cardiac output is the measurement of the volume of blood ejected by ventricles of the heart. It is usually measured by a catheter with an opening in the right atrium and pulmonary artery. The minimum time that should elapse after MI before performing a cardiac catheterization is three weeks.

Aortography

Aortic root aortography involves the injection of a large bolus of dye into the proximal ascending aorta, just above the aortic valve. This procedure, when performed in addition to left ventricular angiography, coronary angiography, and/or visualization of coronary bypass grafts, may be covered under Medicare for the following diagnoses:

- Known or suspected aortic valvular disease
- Dysfunction of a prosthetic aortic valve
- Aortic aneurysms

Claims for aortic root aortography with a diagnosis different from those listed above must have documentation clearly indicating the medical necessity of the procedure. This documentation must be maintained in the patient's file and made available to a Medicare post-payment analyst upon request. Aortic root aortography is not routinely indicated in the evaluation of ischemic heart disease.

When thoracic aortography is performed without a cardiac catheterization it should be reported using procedure 36200 and the appropriate radiologic supervision/interpretation (75600 or 75605). Code 36200 should not be reported with 93546–9353, which already include introduction of the catheter.

Electrophysiologic Studies (EPS) (93600–93660)

Electrophysiologic studies (EPS) are performed to evaluate the electrical conduction system of the heart. An electrode is placed and the patient is monitored constantly with both intracardiac EKG and external EKG leads to record the cardiac response. Programmed electrical stimulation is delivered through an electrode catheter to evaluate electrical conduction pathways, formation of dysrhythmia, and automaticity and refractoriness of myocardial cells. This procedure is designed to reproduce any dysrhythmia so the origin of the conduction problem can be isolated.

Indications for electrophysiologic studies include sinus node disorders, AV or intraventricular block, previous cardiac arrest, tachycardia over 200 beats per minute, and unexplained syncope.

Contraindications include underlying cardiac disease such that the risk of inducing dysrhythmia can lead to sudden death, and/or conditions that create findings unrepresentative of the patient's usual state of health (e.g., electrolyte imbalance or drug toxicity).

Complications can include any of the following:

- Atrial fibrillation
- Ventricular tachycardia
- Ventricular fibrillation
- Pulmonary emboli
- Thrombosis
- Hemorrhage
- Phlebitis
- Infection
- Cardiac perforation leading to tamponade

Myocardial Biopsy

Myocardial biopsy is biopsy of the inside and middle layers of the heart. It may be done in surgery or the cardiac catheterization lab and is usually performed under local anesthesia. The procedure generally lasts approximately 15 minutes and the biopsy is usually taken from the right or left ventricle.

Note that the patient is monitored constantly with both intracardiac ECG/EKG and external ECG/EKG leads to record cardiac response.

Subsidiary Codes

Subsidiary codes have relative values that require no further adjustment:

92981 is "in addition" to 92980
92984 is "in addition" to 92980–92982

92996 is "in addition" to 92980–92981, 92985
93325 is "in addition" to 93307–93308, 93312, 93314, 93320–93321
93539 is "in addition" to 93510–93529
93541–93542 is "in addition" to 93501, 93503, 93524–93529
93543–93545 is "in addition" to 93510–93529
93555 is "in addition" to 93501, 93510–93529, 93542–93543
93556 is "in addition" to to 93501, 93510–93529, 93539–93541, 93544–93545
93623 is "in addition" to 93620–93622

Because these are subsidiary or "in addition to" codes, reimbursement reduction and modifier -51 do not apply.

Medicare Alert

Medicare rebundles certain codes in the medicine section when the listed codes are considered a component of a more comprehensive service.

33210, 36140 will not be reimbursed when reported with 92982
33210, 36000, 36010, 36140, 36489, 36491, 76000, 93561–93562 will not be reimbursed when reported with 93501
33210, 36140, 36600, 36620, 36625, 76000, 93561–93562 will not be reimbursed when reported with 93510
33210, 36000, 36010, 36013–36015, 36489, 36491, 36600, 36620, 36625, 76000, 93501, 93510, 93561–93562 will not be reimbursed when reported with 93526
33210, 36140, 36489, 36491, 36600, 36620, 36625, 92950, 92960, 93562, 93603, 93610, 93612 will not be reimbursed when reported with 93618
36000, 36010, 76000 will not be reimbursed when reported with 93505
36140, 36489, 36600, 36620 will not be reimbursed when reported with 93536
43200, 43234, 93313, 93314 will not be reimbursed when reported with 93312
43200, 43234, 93314 will not be reimbursed when reported with 93313
92982 will not be reimbursed when reported with 92995–92996
93017–93018 will not be reimbursed when reported with 93015
93308 will not be reimbursed when reported with 93307
96013–96015 will not be reimbursed when reported with 93527–93529
93731, 93733–93736 will not be reimbursed when reported with 93732
93731, 93734–93736 will not be reimbursed when reported with 93733
93734–93735 will not be reimbursed when reported with 93736

Code	Description	Medicode RVU	50th	75th	Medicare Nat'l Avg
92950	Cardiopulmonary resuscitation (eg, in cardiac arrest)	270.0	388	446	209
92953	Temporary transcutaneous pacing	75.00	108	124	62
92960	Cardioversion, elective, electrical conversion of arrhythmia, external	225.0	324	371	150
92970	Cardioassist-method of circulatory assist; internal	250.0	360	413	252
92971	Cardioassist-method of circulatory assist; external	75.00	108	124	101
92975	Thrombolysis, coronary; by intracoronary infusion, including selective coronary angiography	822.0	1182	1357	465
92977	Thrombolysis, coronary; by intravenous infusion	417.0	600	688	278

Code	Description	Medicode RVU	50th	75th	Medicare Nat'l Avg
92980	Transcatheter placement of an intracoronary stent(s), percutaneous, with or without other therapeutic intervention, any method; single vessel	1753	2521	2894	1108
-26			2521	2894	
92981	Transcatheter placement of an intracoronary stent(s), percutaneous, with or without other therapeutic intervention, any method; each additional vessel	546.0	785	901	345
-26			785	901	
92982	Percutaneous transluminal coronary balloon angioplasty; single vessel	1775	2552	2931	1023
-26			2552	2931	
92984	Percutaneous transluminal coronary balloon angioplasty; each additional vessel	670.0	963	1106	310
-26			963	1106	
92986	Percutaneous balloon valvuloplasty; aortic valve	1700	2445	2807	1138
-26			2445	2807	
● **92987**	Percutaneous balloon valvuloplasty; mitral valve	1870	2689	3087	–
-26			-2689	3087	
92990	Percutaneous balloon valvuloplasty; pulmonary valve	1400	2013	2311	919
-26			2013	2311	
92992	Atrial septectomy or septostomy; transvenous method, balloon, Rashkind type (includes cardiac catheterization)	2629	3781	4340	1367
92993	Atrial septectomy or septostomy; blade method (Park septostomy) (includes cardiac catheterization)	1842	2649	3041	1425
92995	Percutaneous transluminal coronary atherectomy, with or without balloon angioplasty; single vessel	1900	2732	3137	1087
-26			2732	3137	
92996	Percutaneous transluminal coronary atherectomy, with or without balloon angioplasty; each additional vessel	855.0	1229	1412	326
-26			1229	1412	
93000	Electrocardiogram, routine ECG with at least 12 leads; with interpretation and report	39.00	60	71	27
-26			24	28	
93005	Electrocardiogram, routine ECG with at least 12 leads; tracing only, without interpretation and report	29.00	45	53	18
-26			0	0	
93010	Electrocardiogram, routine ECG with at least 12 leads; interpretation and report only	19.50	30	36	12
-26			30	36	
93012	Telephonic transmission of post-symptom electrocardiogram rhythm strip(s), per 30 day period of time; tracing only	26.00	40	47	84
-26			0	0	
93014	Telephonic transmission of post-symptom electrocardiogram rhythm strip(s), per 30 day period of time; physician review with interpretation and report only	22.00	34	40	33
-26			34	40	
93015	Cardiovascular stress test using maximal or submaximal treadmill or bicycle exercise, continous electrocardiographic monitoring, and/or pharmacological stress; with physician supervision, with interpretation and report	183.0	282	334	115
-26			141	167	
93016	Cardiovascular stress test using maximal or submaximal treadmill or bicycle exercise, continous electrocardiographic monitoring, and/or pharmacological stress; physician supervision only, without interpretation and report	50.00	77	91	30
-26			77	91	
93017	Cardiovascular stress test using maximal or submaximal treadmill or bicycle exercise, continous electrocardiographic monitoring, and/or pharmacological stress; tracing only, without interpretation and report	122.0	188	223	59
-26			0	0	
93018	Cardiovascular stress test using maximal or submaximal treadmill or bicycle exercise, continous electrocardiographic monitoring, and/or pharmacological stress; interpretation and report only	62.00	96	113	32
-26			96	113	

Code	Description	Medicode RVU	50th	75th	Medicare Nat'l Avg
93024	Ergonovine provocation test	209.0	322	381	136
-26			193	229	98
93040	Rhythm ECG, one to three leads; with interpretation and	24.00	37	44	15
-26	report		24	28	
93041	Rhythm ECG, one to three leads; tracing only without	12.00	18	22	6
-26	interpretation and report		0	0	
93042	Rhythm ECG, one to three leads; interpretation and report	16.00	25	29	10
-26	only		25	29	
93201	Phonocardiogram with or without ECG lead; with	76.00	117	139	52
-26	supervision during recording with interpretation and report (when equipment is supplied by the physician)		53	62	
93202	Phonocardiogram with or without ECG lead; tracing only,	42.00	65	77	28
-26	without interpretation and report (eg, when equipment is supplied by the hospital, clinic)		0	0	
93204	Phonocardiogram with or without ECG lead; interpretation	34.00	52	62	25
-26	and report		52	62	
93205	Phonocardiogram with ECG lead, with indirect carotid artery	145.0	223	264	48
-26	and/or jugular vein tracing, and/or apex cardiogram; with interpretation and report		112	132	
93208	Phonocardiogram with ECG lead, with indirect carotid artery	75.00	116	137	12
-26	and/or jugular vein tracing, and/or apex cardiogram; tracing only, without interpretation and report		0	0	
93209	Phonocardiogram with ECG lead, with indirect carotid artery	70.00	108	128	36
-26	and/or jugular vein tracing, and/or apex cardiogram; interpretation and report only		108	128	
93210	Phonocardiogram, intracardiac	140.0	216	255	95
-26			119	140	61
93220	Vectorcardiogram (VCG), with or without ECG; with	102.0	157	186	47
-26	interpretation and report		63	74	
93221	Vectorcardiogram (VCG), with or without ECG; tracing only,	61.00	94	111	21
-26	without interpretation and report		0	0	
93222	Vectorcardiogram (VCG), with or without ECG;	41.00	63	75	24
-26	interpretation and report only		63	75	
93224	Electrocardiographic monitoring for 24 hours by continuous	249.0	384	454	172
-26	original ECG waveform recording and storage, with visual superimposition scanning; includes recording, scanning analysis with report, physician review and interpretation		153	182	
93225	Electrocardiographic monitoring for 24 hours by continuous	81.00	125	148	44
-26	original ECG waveform recording and storage, with visual superimposition scanning; recording (includes hook-up, recording, and disconnection)		0	0	
93226	Electrocardiographic monitoring for 24 hours by continuous	90.00	139	164	77
-26	original ECG waveform recording and storage, with visual superimposition scanning; scanning analysis with report		0	0	
93227	Electrocardiographic monitoring for 24 hours by continuous	95.00	146	173	49
-26	original ECG waveform recording and storage, with visual superimposition scanning; physician review and interpretation		146	173	

Code	Description	Medicode RVU	50th	75th	Medicare Nat'l Avg
93230	Electrocardiographic monitoring for 24 hours by continuous original ECG waveform recording and storage without superimposition scanning utilizing a device capable of producing a full miniaturized printout; includes recording, microprocessor-based analysis with report, physician review and interpretation	243.0	374	443	181
-26			150	177	
93231	Electrocardiographic monitoring for 24 hours by continuous original ECG waveform recording and storage without superimposition scanning utilizing a device capable of producing a full miniaturized printout; recording (includes hook-up, recording, and disconnection)	75.00	116	137	54
-26			0	0	
93232	Electrocardiographic monitoring for 24 hours by continuous original ECG waveform recording and storage without superimposition scanning utilizing a device capable of producing a full miniaturized printout; microprocessor-based analysis with report	99.00	153	181	78
-26			0	0	
93233	Electrocardiographic monitoring for 24 hours by continuous original ECG waveform recording and storage without superimposition scanning utilizing a device capable of producing a full miniaturized printout; physician review and interpretation	90.00	139	164	52
-26			139	164	
93235	Electrocardiographic monitoring for 24 hours by continuous computerized monitoring and non-continuous recording, and real-time data analysis utilizing a device capable of producing intermittent full-sized waveform tracings, possibly patient activated; includes monitoring and real time data analysis with report, physician review and interpretation	225.0	347	410	140
-26			139	164	
93236	Electrocardiographic monitoring for 24 hours by continuous computerized monitoring and non-continuous recording, and real-time data analysis utilizing a device capable of producing intermittent full-sized waveform tracings, possibly patient activated; monitoring and real-time data analysis with report	154.0	237	281	92
-26			0	0	
93237	Electrocardiographic monitoring for 24 hours by continuous computerized monitoring and non-continuous recording, and real-time data analysis utilizing a device capable of producing intermittent full-sized waveform tracings, possibly patient activated; physician review and interpretation	87.00	134	159	46
-26			134	159	
93268	Patient demand single or multiple event recording with presymptom memory loop, per 30 day period of time; includes transmission, physician review and interpretation	225.0	347	410	160
-26			139	164	33
93270	Patient demand single or multiple event recording with presymptom memory loop, per 30 day period of time; recording (includes hook-up, recording and disconnection)	45.50	70	83	43
-26			0	0	
93271	Patient demand single or multiple event recording with presymptom memory loop, per 30 day period of time; monitoring, receipt of transmissions, and analysis	89.50	138	163	84
-26			0	0	
93272	Patient demand single or multiple event recording with presymptom memory loop, per 30 day period of time; physician review and interpretation only	90.00	139	164	33
-26			139	164	
93278	Signal-averaged electrocardiography (SAECG), with or without ECG	127.0	196	232	80
-26			78	93	34
93307	Echocardiography, real-time with image documentation (2D) with or without M-mode recording; complete	258.0	369	458	205
-26			148	183	76

Code	Description	Medicode RVU	50th	75th	Medicare Nat'l Avg
93308	Echocardiography, real-time with image documentation (2D) with or without M-mode recording; follow-up or limited study	144.0	206	256	114
-26			82	102	48
93312	Echocardiography, real time with image documentation (2D) (with or without M-Mode recording), transesophageal; including probe placement, image acquisition, interpretation and report	370.0	529	657	251
-26			238	296	122
93313	Echocardiography, real time with image documentation (2D) (with or without M-Mode recording), transesophageal; placement of transesophageal probe only	128.0	183	227	57
-26			183	227	
93314	Echocardiography, real time with image documentation (2D) (with or without M-Mode recording), transesophageal; image acquisition, interpretation and report only	263.0	376	467	191
-26			150	187	57
93320	Doppler echocardiography, pulsed wave and/or continuous wave with spectral display; complete	158.0	226	280	97
-26			90	112	41
93321	Doppler echocardiography, pulsed wave and/or continuous wave with spectral display; follow-up or limited study	94.80	136	168	55
-26			54	67	17
93325	Doppler color flow velocity mapping (list separately in addition to code for echocardiography 76825, 76826, 76827, 76828, 93307, 93308, 93312, 93314, 93320, 93321)	112.0	160	199	106
-26			64	80	14
93350	Echocardiography, real-time with image documentation (2D), with or without M-mode recording, during rest and cardiovascular stress test using maximal or submaximal treadmill, bicycle exercise and/or pharmacologically induced stress, including electrocardiographic monitoring, with interpretation and report	460.0	658	817	162
-26			-263	327	82
93501	Right heart catheterization	624.0	802	1035	826
-26			361	466	256
93503	Insertion and placement of flow directed catheter (eg, Swan-Ganz) for monitoring purposes	342.0	440	567	188
93505	Endomyocardial biopsy	550.0	707	912	339
-26			389	502	273
93510	Left heart catheterization, retrograde, from the brachial artery, axillary artery or femoral artery; percutaneous	653.0	840	1083	1541
-26			378	487	307
93511	Left heart catheterization, retrograde, from the brachial artery, axillary artery or femoral artery; by cutdown	700.0	900	1161	1513
-26			405	522	276
93514	Left heart catheterization by left ventricular puncture	818.0	1052	1356	1888
-26			473	610	468
93524	Combined transseptal and retrograde left heart catheterization	1091	1403	1809	2042
-26			631	814	414
93526	Combined right heart catheterization and retrograde left heart catheterization	1131	1454	1875	2055
-26			655	844	467
93527	Combined right heart catheterization and transseptal left heart catheterization through intact septum (with or without retrograde left heart catheterization)	1312	1687	2175	2115
-26			759	979	566
93528	Combined right heart catheterization with left ventricular puncture (with or without retrograde left heart catheterization)	1546	1988	2562	2076
-26			894	1153	521
93529	Combined right heart catheterization and left heart catheterization through existing septal opening (with or without retrograde left heart catheterization)	1188	1528	1970	1902
-26			688	886	282

Code	Description	Medicode RVU	50th	75th	Medicare Nat'l Avg
93536	Percutaneous insertion of intra-aortic balloon catheter	765.0	984	1268	471
93539	Injection procedure during cardiac catheterization; for selective opacification of arterial conduits (eg, internal mammary), whether native or used for bypass	237.0	305	393	88
-26			305	393	
93540	Injection procedure during cardiac catheterization; for selective opacification of aortocoronary venous bypass grafts, one or more coronary arteries	247.0	318	410	95
-26			318	410	
93541	Injection procedure during cardiac catheterization; for pulmonary angiography	234.0	301	388	80
-26			301	388	
93542	Injection procedure during cardiac catheterization; for selective right ventricular or right atrial angiography	209.0	269	347	69
-26			-269	347	
93543	Injection procedure during cardiac catheterization; for selective left ventricular or left atrial angiography	209.0	269	347	58
-26			-269	347	
93544	Injection procedure during cardiac catheterization; for aortography	241.5	311	400	60
-26			311	400	
93545	Injection procedure during cardiac catheterization; for selective coronary angiography (injection of radiopaque material may be by hand)	376.0	484	623	108
-26			484	623	
93555	Imaging supervision, interpretation and report for injection procedure(s) during cardiac catheterization; ventricular and/or atrial angiography	452.0	581	749	252
-26			87	112	40
93556	Imaging supervision, interpretation and report for injection procedure(s) during cardiac catheterization; pulmonary angiography, aortography, and/or selective coronary angiography including venous bypass grafts and arterial conduits (whether native or used in bypass)	608.0	782	1008	383
-26			117	151	49
93561	Indicator dilution studies such as dye or thermal dilution, including arterial and/or venous catheterization; with cardiac output measurement (separate procedure)	283.0	364	469	89
-26			146	188	70
93562	Indicator dilution studies such as dye or thermal dilution, including arterial and/or venous catheterization; subsequent measurement of cardiac output	139.0	179	230	42
-26			72	92	31
93600	Bundle of His recording	376.0	516	637	244
-26			284	350	182
93602	Intra-atrial recording	214.0	294	362	176
-26			161	199	141
93603	Right ventricular recording	243.0	333	411	213
-26			183	226	158
93607	Left ventricular recording	243.0	333	411	245
-26			183	226	194
93609	Intraventricular and/or intra-atrial mapping of tachycardia site(s) with catheter manipulation to record from multiple sites to identify origin of tachycardia	845.0	1159	1431	581
-26			638	787	488
93610	Intra-atrial pacing	270.0	370	457	235
-26			204	251	193
93612	Intraventricular pacing	317.0	435	537	249
-26			239	295	196
93615	Esophageal recording of atrial electrogram with or without ventricular electrogram(s);	35.00	48	59	59
-26			-26	33	48

Code	Description	Medicode RVU	50th	75th	Medicare Nat'l Avg
93616	Esophageal recording of atrial electrogram with or without ventricular electrogram(s); with pacing	155.0	213	262	112
-26			117	144	101
93618	Induction of arrhythmia by electrical pacing	900.0	1235	1524	488
-26			679	838	377
93619	Comprehensive electrophysiologic evaluation with right atrial pacing and recording, right ventricular pacing and recording, His bundle recording, including insertion and repositioning of multiple electrode catheters; without induction of arrhythmia (This code is to be used when 93600 is combined with 93602, 93603, 93610, 93612)	1466	2011	2482	907
-26			1106	1365	682
93620	Comprehensive electrophysiologic evaluation with right atrial pacing and recording, right ventricular pacing and recording, His bundle recording, including insertion and repositioning of multiple electrode catheters; with induction of arrhythmia (This code is to be used when 93618 is combined with 93619)	1868	2563	3163	1219
-26			1410	1739	938
93621	Comprehensive electrophysiologic evaluation with right atrial pacing and recording, right ventricular pacing and recording, His bundle recording, including insertion and repositioning of multiple electrode catheters; with left atrial recordings from coronary sinus or left atrium, with or without pacing	2125	2916	3598	2008
-26			1604	1979	998
93622	Comprehensive electrophysiologic evaluation with right atrial pacing and recording, right ventricular pacing and recording, His bundle recording, including insertion and repositioning of multiple electrode catheters; with left ventricular recordings, with or without pacing	2125	2916	3598	1828
-26			1604	1979	984
93623	Programmed stimulation and pacing after intravenous drug infusion (Use this code with 93620, 93621, 93622)	482.0	661	816	375
-26			364	449	205
93624	Electrophysiologic follow-up study with pacing and recording to test effectiveness of therapy, including induction or attempted induction of arrhythmia	1177	1615	1993	348
-26			888	1096	292
93631	Intra-operative epicardial and endocardial pacing and mapping to localize the site of tachycardia or zone of slow conduction for surgical correction	0.00	0	0	715
-26			0	0	524
93640	Electrophysiologic evaluation of cardioverter-defibrillator leads (includes defibrillation threshold testing and sensing function) at time of initial implantation or replacement;	993.0	1362	1681	589
-26			749	925	393
93641	Electrophysiologic evaluation of cardioverter-defibrillator leads (includes defibrillation threshold testing and sensing function) at time of initial implantation or replacement; with testing of cardioverter-defibrillator pulse generator	1225	1681	2074	702
-26			924	1141	507
93642	Electrophysiologic evaluation of cardioverter-defibrillator (includes defibrillation threshold evaluation, induction of arrhythmia, evaluation of sensing and pacing for arrhythmia termination, and programming or reprogramming of sensing or therapeutic parameters)	1476	2025	2499	653
-26			1114	1374	458
93650	Intracardiac catheter ablation of atrioventricular node function, atrioventricular conduction for creation of complete heart block, with or without temporary pacemaker placement	2305	3162	3902	941
-26			1739	2146	
93651	Intracardiac catheter ablation of arrhythmogenic focus; for treatment of supraventricular tachycardia by ablation of fast or slow atrioventricular pathways, accessory atrioventricular connections or other atrial foci, singly or in combination	2350	3224	3979	1246
-26			1773	2188	

Code	Description	Medicode RVU	50th	75th	Medicare Nat'l Avg
93652 -26	Intracardiac catheter ablation of arrhythmogenic focus; for treatment of ventricular tachycardia	2350	3224 1773	3979 2188	1293
▲ 93660 -26	Evaluation of cardiovascular function with tilt table evaluation, with continuous ECG monitoring and intermittent blood pressure monitoring, with or without pharmacological intervention	0.00	0 0	0 0	221 120
93720 -26	Plethysmography, total body; with interpretation and report	106.0	145 58	179 72	44
93721 -26	Plethysmography, total body; tracing only, without interpretation and report	75.00	103 0	127 0	25
93722 -26	Plethysmography, total body; interpretation and report only	40.00	55 55	68 68	17
93724 -26	Electronic analysis of antitachycardia pacemaker system (includes electrocardiographic recording, programming of device, induction and termination of tachycardia via implanted pacemaker, and interpretation of recordings)	64.00	88 18	108 22	411 273
93731 -26	Electronic analysis of dual-chamber pacemaker system (includes evaluation of programmable parameters at rest and during activity where applicable, using electrocardiographic recording and interpretation of recordings at rest and during exercise, analysis of event markers and device response); without reprogramming	86.00	118 24	146 29	44 28
93732 -26	Electronic analysis of dual-chamber pacemaker system (includes evaluation of programmable parameters at rest and during activity where applicable, using electrocardiographic recording and interpretation of recordings at rest and during exercise, analysis of event markers and device response); with reprogramming	83.00	114 46	141 56	64 46
93733 -26	Electronic analysis of dual chamber internal pacemaker system (may include rate, pulse amplitude and duration, configuration of wave form, and/or testing of sensory function of pacemaker), telephonic analysis	52.00	71 14	88 18	40 15
93734 -26	Electronic analysis of single chamber pacemaker system (includes evaluation of programmable parameters at rest and during activity where applicable, using electrocardiographic recording and interpretation of recordings at rest and during exercise, analysis of event markers and device response); without reprogramming	66.50	91 18	113 23	37 25
93735 -26	Electronic analysis of single chamber pacemaker system (includes evaluation of programmable parameters at rest and during activity where applicable, using electrocardiographic recording and interpretation of recordings at rest and during exercise, analysis of event markers and device response); with reprogramming	70.00	96 38	119 47	56 40
93736 -26	Electronic analysis of single chamber internal pacemaker system (may include rate, pulse amplitude and duration, configuration of wave form, and/or testing of sensory function of pacemaker), telephonic analysis	44.00	60 24	74 30	37 15
93737 -26	Electronic analysis of cardioverter/defibrillator only (interrogation, evaluation of pulse generator status); without reprogramming	55.00	75 45	93 56	43 25
93738 -26	Electronic analysis of cardioverter/defibrillator only (interrogation, evaluation of pulse generator status); with reprogramming	70.00	96 67	119 83	64 46
93740 -26	Temperature gradient studies	100.0	137 27	169 34	23 17

Code	Description	Medicode RVU	50th	75th	Medicare Nat'l Avg
93760	Thermogram; cephalic	134.0	184	227	–
-26			37	45	
93762	Thermogram; peripheral	197.0	270	334	–
-26			54	67	
93770	Determination of venous pressure	15.00	21	25	13
-26			8	10	13
93784	Ambulatory blood pressure monitoring, utilizing a system such as magnetic tape and/or computer disk, for 24 hours or longer; including recording, scanning analysis, interpretation and report	245.0	336	415	–
-26			134	166	
93786	Ambulatory blood pressure monitoring, utilizing a system such as magnetic tape and/or computer disk, for 24 hours or longer; recording only	36.50	50	62	–
-26			0	0	
93788	Ambulatory blood pressure monitoring, utilizing a system such as magnetic tape and/or computer disk, for 24 hours or longer; scanning analysis with report	110.0	151	186	–
-26			0	0	
93790	Ambulatory blood pressure monitoring, utilizing a system such as magnetic tape and/or computer disk, for 24 hours or longer; physician review with interpretation and report	107.0	147	181	–
-26			147	181	
93797	Physician services for outpatient cardiac rehabilitation; without continuous ECG monitoring (per session)	40.00	55	68	19
-26			55	68	
93798	Physician services for outpatient cardiac rehabilitation; with continuous ECG monitoring (per session)	51.00	70	86	30
-26			70	86	
93799	Unlisted cardiovascular service or procedure	0.00	0	0	–

93875–93990
Noninvasive Vascular Diagnostic Studies

Coding Insight

Noninvasive vascular studies codes include the patient care required to perform the studies as well as the professional and technical components. All codes in this series are bilateral; to report a unilateral series use modifier -52 or 09952.

A duplex scan (93880) is defined as an ultrasonic scanning procedure with display of both two-dimensional structure and motion with time and Doppler ultrasonic signal documentation with spectral analysis and/or color flow velocity mapping or imaging.

A clear directive is found in CPT indicating that a vascular study must provide a hard copy with analysis for the patient's record, including bidirectional vascular flow or imaging, when provided. The simple hand-held (screening) devices not meeting these requirements are part of the patient examination and are not reported separately.

Medicare Alert

Medicare rebundles certain codes in the medicine section when the listed codes are considered a component of a more comprehensive service.

93325 will not be reimbursed when reported with 93875–93990
93882 will not be reimbursed when reported with 93880
93888 will not be reimbursed when reported with 93886
93926 will not be reimbursed when reported with 93925

93931 will not be reimbursed when reported with 93930
93971 will not be reimbursed when reported with 93970
93976 will not be reimbursed when reported with 93975, 93978
93981 will not be reimbursed when reported with 93980
93926–93931, 93970–93971 will not be reimbursed when reported with 93990

Code	Description	Medicode RVU	50th	75th	Medicare Nat'l Avg
93875	Noninvasive physiologic studies of extracranial arteries, complete bilateral study (eg, periorbital flow direction with arterial compression, ocular pneumoplethysmography, Doppler ultrasound spectral analysis)	129.0	179	225	68
-26			72	90	28
93880	Duplex scan of extracranial arteries; complete bilateral study	245.0	340	427	171
-26			136	171	44
93882	Duplex scan of extracranial arteries; unilateral or limited study	176.0	244	307	128
-26			98	123	34
93886	Transcranial Doppler study of the intracranial arteries; complete study	271.0	376	472	199
-26			150	189	48
93888	Transcranial Doppler study of the intracranial arteries; limited study	162.0	225	282	133
-26			90	113	32
93922	Noninvasive physiologic studies of upper or lower extremity arteries, single level, bilateral (eg, ankle/brachial indices, Doppler waveform analysis, volume plethysmography, transcutaneous oxygen tension measurement)	155.0	215	270	78
-26			86	108	28
93923	Non-invasive physiologic studies of upper or lower extremity arteries, multiple levels or with provocative functional maneuvers, complete bilateral study (eg, segmental blood pressure measurements, segmental Doppler waveform analysis, segmental volume plethysmography, segmental transcutaneous oxygen tension measurements, measurements with postural provocative tests, measurements with reactive hyperemia)	180.0	250	314	117
-26			100	125	41
93924	Non-invasive physiologic studies of lower extremity arteries, at rest and following treadmill stress testing, complete bilateral study	170.0	236	296	124
-26			94	118	44
93925	Duplex scan of lower extremity arteries or arterial bypass grafts; complete bilateral study	231.0	320	402	169
-26			128	161	35
93926	Duplex scan of lower extremity arteries or arterial bypass grafts; unilateral or limited study	138.0	191	240	113
-26			77	96	23
93930	Duplex scan of upper extremity arteries or arterial bypass grafts; complete bilateral study	227.0	315	395	173
-26			126	158	31
93931	Duplex scan of upper extremity arteries or arterial bypass grafts; unilateral or limited study	118.0	164	206	115
-26			65	82	20
93965	Non-invasive physiologic studies of extremity veins, complete bilateral study (eg, Doppler waveform analysis with responses to compression and other maneuvers, phleborheography, impedance plethysmography)	145.0	201	253	72
-26			80	101	32
93970	Duplex scan of extremity veins including responses to compression and other maneuvers; complete bilateral study	222.0	308	387	187
-26			123	155	39
93971	Duplex scan of extremity veins including responses to compression and other maneuvers; unilateral or limited study	138.0	191	240	125
-26			77	96	-26
93975	Duplex scan of arterial inflow and venous outflow of abdominal, pelvic, and/or retroperitoneal organs; complete study	197.0	273	343	246
-26			109	137	78

Code	Description	Medicode RVU	50th	75th	Medicare Nat'l Avg
93976	Duplex scan of arterial inflow and venous outflow of abdominal,	127.0	176	221	165
-26	pelvic, and/or retroperitoneal organs; limited study		70	88	52
93978	Duplex scan of aorta, inferior vena cava, iliac vasculature, or	210.0	291	366	176
-26	bypass grafts; complete study		117	146	37
93979	Duplex scan of aorta, inferior vena cava, iliac vasculature, or	126.0	175	219	117
-26	bypass grafts; unilateral or limited study		70	88	25
93980	Duplex scan of arterial inflow and venous outflow of penile	188.0	261	328	218
-26	vessels; complete study		104	131	93
93981	Duplex scan of arterial inflow and venous outflow of penile	124.0	172	216	153
-26	vessels; follow-up or limited study		69	86	37
93990	Duplex scan of hemodialysis access (including arterial inflow,	115.0	160	200	106
-26	body of access and venous outflow)		64	80	16

94010–94799
Pulmonary Services

CODING INSIGHT
When requesting prior authorization for pulmonary testing, be specific about the procedures you intend to perform; certain combinations of tests may seem similar to prior authorization personnel and claims reviewers. The differences in the tests and the purpose of the information to be gathered by use of a particular test may seem vague. If you are ordering tests for a patient and are unsure about which test would be performed for the problem, contact the pulmonary laboratory for clarification and exact CPT code numbers.

List hospital inpatient visits, consultations, emergency department services, or office visits separately when performed on the same date as a diagnostic pulmonary service.

Spirometry
Codes for spirometry (94010–94070) vary according to the extent of the test performed. Code 94010 refers to the measurement of the lung's capacity and flow measurements with a spirometer. This machine must produce a graphic record or hard copy for the patient's record, and the time necessary for exhaling the total volume of inhaled air must be recorded. Expiratory flow rate is calculated from these measurements, generally in terms of liters per second. Maximal voluntary ventilation is also included in this service.

Bronchospasm
Bronchospasm evaluation (94060) covers spirometry before and after the use of a bronchodilator (either aerosol or parenteral) or after exercise. The final code in this series (94070) is for prolonged tests and is a process involving multiple determinations.

MEDICARE ALERT
Medicare rebundles certain codes in the medicine section when the listed codes are considered a component of a more comprehensive service.

94160, 94200 will not be reimbursed when reported with 94010

Code	Description	Medicode RVU	50th	75th	Medicare Nat'l Avg
94010	Spirometry, including graphic record, total and timed vital capacity, expiratory flow rate measurement(s), and/or maximal voluntary ventilation	50.50	69	90	31
-26			28	36	17
94060	Bronchospasm evaluation: spirometry as in 94010, before and after bronchodilator (aerosol or parenteral) or exercise	77.50	106	138	57
-26			42	55	25
94070	Prolonged postexposure evaluation of bronchospasm with multiple spirometric determinations after test dose of bronchodilator (aerosol only) antigen, exercise, cold air, methocholine or other chemical agent, with spirometry as in 94010	160.0	219	285	84
-26			88	114	35
94150	Vital capacity, total (separate procedure)	16.50	23	29	11
-26			9	12	8
94160	Vital capacity screening tests: total capacity, with timed forced expiratory volume (state duration), and peak flow rate	24.00	33	43	19
-26			13	17	13
94200	Maximum breathing capacity, maximal voluntary ventilation	39.00	53	69	19
-26			11	14	10
94240	Functional residual capacity or residual volume: helium method, nitrogen open circuit method, or other method	61.00	83	109	41
-26			17	22	18
94250	Expired gas collection, quantitative, single procedure (separate procedure)	15.00	21	27	14
-26			4	5	9
94260	Thoracic gas volume	56.00	77	100	32
-26			15	20	13
94350	Determination of maldistribution of inspired gas: multiple breath nitrogen washout curve including alveolar nitrogen or helium equilibration time	57.00	78	101	36
-26			16	20	17
94360	Determination of resistance to airflow, oscillatory or plethysmographic methods	58.00	79	103	48
-26			16	21	16
94370	Determination of airway closing volume, single breath tests	54.00	74	96	24
-26			15	19	14
94375	Respiratory flow volume loop	60.00	82	107	35
-26			16	21	18
94400	Breathing response to CO2 (CO2 response curve)	120.0	164	213	46
-26			33	43	34
94450	Breathing response to hypoxia (hypoxia response curve)	96.00	131	171	36
-26			-26	34	23
94620	Pulmonary stress testing, simple or complex	215.0	294	382	107
-26			59	77	56
94640	Nonpressurized inhalation treatment for acute airway obstruction	21.00	29	37	15
94642	Aerosol inhalation of pentamidine for pneumocystis carinii pneumonia treatment or prophylaxis	93.50	128	166	38
94650	Intermittent positive pressure breathing (IPPB) treatment, air or oxygen, with or without nebulized medication; initial demonstration and/or evaluation	22.00	30	39	14
94651	Intermittent positive pressure breathing (IPPB) treatment, air or oxygen, with or without nebulized medication; subsequent	18.00	25	32	13
94652	Intermittent positive pressure breathing (IPPB) treatment, air or oxygen, with or without nebulized medication; newborn infants	33.00	45	59	17

Code	Description	Medicode RVU	50th	75th	Medicare Nat'l Avg
94656	Ventilation assist and management, initiation of pressure or volume preset ventilators for assisted or controlled breathing; first day	152.0	208	270	87
94657	Ventilation assist and management, initiation of pressure or volume preset ventilators for assisted or controlled breathing; subsequent days	81.00	111	144	51
94660	Continuous positive airway pressure ventilation (CPAP), initiation and management	115.0	157	205	53
94662	Continuous negative pressure ventilation (CNP), initiation and management	75.00	103	133	37
94664	Aerosol or vapor inhalations for sputum mobilization, bronchodilation, or sputum induction for diagnostic purposes; initial demonstration and/or evaluation	25.00	34	44	18
94665	Aerosol or vapor inhalations for sputum mobilization, bronchodilation, or sputum induction for diagnostic purposes; subsequent	20.00	27	36	17
94667	Manipulation chest wall, such as cupping, percussing, and vibration to facilitate lung function; initial demonstration and/or evaluation	30.00	41	53	20
94668	Manipulation chest wall, such as cupping, percussing, and vibration to facilitate lung function; subsequent	24.00	33	43	13
94680	Oxygen uptake, expired gas analysis; rest and exercise, direct, simple	80.00	109	142	41
-26			44	57	23
94681	Oxygen uptake, expired gas analysis; including CO2 output, percentage oxygen extracted	150.0	205	267	72
-26			82	107	23
94690	Oxygen uptake, expired gas analysis; rest, indirect (separate procedure)	30.00	41	53	23
-26			16	21	5
94720	Carbon monoxide diffusing capacity, any method	65.00	89	116	47
-26			36	46	18
94725	Membrane diffusion capacity	115.0	157	205	75
-26			63	82	17
94750	Pulmonary compliance study, any method	92.00	126	164	38
-26			50	65	19
94760	Noninvasive ear or pulse oximetry for oxygen saturation; single determination	21.00	29	37	10
-26			0	0	
94761	Noninvasive ear or pulse oximetry for oxygen saturation; multiple determinations (eg, during exercise)	35.00	48	62	24
-26			0	0	
94762	Noninvasive ear or pulse oximetry for oxygen saturation; by continuous overnight monitoring (separate procedure)	44.00	60	78	42
-26			0	0	
94770	Carbon dioxide, expired gas determination by infrared analyzer	60.00	82	107	24
-26			33	43	12
94772	Circadian respiratory pattern recording (pediatric pneumogram), 12 to 24 hour continuous recording, infant	0.00	0	0	258
-26			0	0	98
94799	Unlisted pulmonary service or procedure	0.00	0	0	–

95004–95199
Allergy and Clinical Immunology

CODING INSIGHT
Allergy testing and immunology treatment is performed according to the patient's history, physical findings, and clinical judgment. Codes 95004–95024, and 95028–95052 are defined according to type of test. Specify the number of tests performed in the unit area of the claim or electronic billing. Many payers require a report of the exact number of tests performed since their allowable is based on a per-test amount. Ask your commonly billed payers for their requirements.

Observe the following guidelines when coding allergen immunotherapy services:

- All allergen immunotherapy codes (95115–95199) include the necessary professional services. Nursing services for observation and medical instruction are also included as an integral part of administering extracts or antigens. Use office visit codes in addition to an allergen immunotherapy code only if another identifiable service was provided at that time. (Some payers unbundle E/M services in this range unless modifier -25 is appended.)
- Codes 95115 and 95117 are different from all other allergen immunotherapy codes in that they do not include the provision of allergenic extracts. Use these codes when the patient supplies the allergenic extracts and the service performed is the injection only
- Codes 95120–95134 describe the supervision and provision of single or multiple antigens in single-use vials. Use these codes when a vial is prepared for a single treatment, and specify the number of vials. These codes also include the antigen injections
- Codes 95145–95165 describe the supervision and provision of allergen immunotherapy using single or multiple-dose vials. These codes do not include the antigen injections. Codes 95145–95149 are used for insect venoms. Specify the number of doses. Code 95165 describes the supervision of allergen immunotherapy with provision of single or multiple antigens using multiple-dose vials. Specify the number of doses. Code 95170 is for whole body extracts of biting insects or other arthropods

MEDICARE ALERT
Medicare rebundles certain codes in the medicine section when the listed codes are considered a component of a more comprehensive service.

95150 will not be reimbursed when reported with 95155

Payment System Changes for Antigen Therapy
Since implementation of the Medicare Fee Schedule in 1992, payment for antigen therapy has been split between the fee schedule and the original reasonable charge system (i.e., the system that requires calculation of customary and prevailing charges based on physicians' actual charging patterns).

While the injection portion of antigen therapy has been paid under the fee schedule, the antigen itself and its preparation has been paid under the reasonable charges system. For CPT codes representing both the injection and antigen, payment for these "complete service" codes has also been based on reasonable charges. Now, due to provisions in the Omnibus Budget Reconciliation Act of 1993, this payment structure is changed. The antigen/antigen preparation codes and the complete service codes fall under the Medicare Fee Schedule.

The following chart and explaining text, taken from a letter that the Health Care Financing Administration sent to Medicare carriers, depicts what the payment system change means in terms of the CPT codes that report antigen therapy.

Type	*Codes*	*Payment*
Injection Codes	95115–95117	Fee schedule
Antigen/antigen prep codes	95144–95170	Fee Schedule

Codes 95145–95149 and 95170 are antigen/antigen preparation codes for stinging/biting insects. All other antigen/antigen preparation services (e.g., dust, pollens, etc.) are reported under the remaining codes: 95144 for single dose vials and 95165 for multiple dose vials.

Certain antigen codes are not listed above. HCPCS Level II J codes that identify antigens are not listed because they are deleted in the 1995 HCPCS. Deleted J codes are:

J0220 Injection, allergy desensitization, aqueous preparation
J0230 Injection, allergy desensitization, Allpyral
J0240 Injection, allergy desensitization, emulsion not specified
J0710 Vial of allergy vaccine, single dose
J0720 Vial of allergy vaccine, multiple dose

These codes were used infrequently and do not represent a significant number of Medicare allowed charges. Because they are deleted in the 1995 HCPCS, the codes will no longer be used by HCFA as part of the payment policy for antigen therapy.

Other codes not listed above are referred to as "complete service" antigen codes. These codes, 95120–95134, represent both the injection and the antigen/antigen preparation services. No Medicare payment will be made for these codes. This decision was made because, in HCFA's judgment, accurate payment cannot be guaranteed under the complete service codes. Those codes can represent more than one way to deliver antigen services (i.e., through single or multiple dose vials) and one delivery method (i.e., single dose vials) costs more than the other (i.e., multiple dose vials.)

Component Billing
The new payment policy for antigen therapy means that allergists providing both components of the service must now do component billing. They do not have the option of using a complete service code. Instead of using any code in the series 95120–95134, the allergist must, as appropriate, report one of the injection codes (95115 or 95117) and one of the antigen/antigen preparation codes (95145, 95146, 95147, 95148, 95149, 95165, or 95170). Note that 95144, the single dose vial antigen/antigen preparation code, is not listed as one of the components to be reported by an allergist performing a complete service. This is because the code, although its language is not explicit in this regard, is not to be used by allergists providing both the injection and antigen/antigen preparation services. Single dose vials of antigens, which are more costly to produce than multiple dose vials, should be used only when an allergist is preparing extract to be injected by another physician. Medicare will pay an allergist reporting both an injection service and either 95144 or 95165 based on the injection fee plus the fee for 95165, the multiple dose vial code.

Vial Preparation
Requiring physicians to use the above listed antigen/antigen preparation codes has caused some concern among allergists who use treatment boards and who, therefore, do not create vials. The listed antigen/antigen preparation codes all have wording which assumes vial preparation, while the complete service codes, which will not longer be recognized, do not. Allergists who use treatment boards, who formerly used complete service codes, are to use the extract/extract preparation vial codes (i.e., 95145–95149, 95165 and 95170) even though they

prepare no vials. Therefore, like all other allergists furnishing a complete service, they must report it on a component basis. Treatment board allergists are not expected to use extract/extract preparation 95144, the single dose vial code. They should report the appropriate injection code plus 95165. As noted above, under our claims processing system, HCFA will pay for the injection plus the amount for 95165, regardless of whether the physician reports 95144 or 95165.

HCFA hopes to have coding changes starting in 1996 which will clarify that 95144 (the single dose vial code) is to be used only when the allergist has prepared the extract for injection by another physician. Also, HCFA hopes to clarify in the wording for 95165 that it represents antigens and antigen preparation in multiple dose vials or through treatment boards.

Payment for Antigen Services

Because of varying definitions that have been used in making payment for antigen services over the years, HCFA will begin paying for antigens at the full fee schedule level beginning in 1996. This means that fee schedule variations in payment for antigen services, from one place to another, will be based solely on the index known as the Geographic Practice Cost Index. This is the index used in each fee schedule calculation to factor in variations in practice costs from one area to another. Without factoring in practice cost variations, average allowance level, in 1995, was as follows:

Code	*Average allowance level*
95115	$13.50
95117	$17.31
95144	$ 6.92 @ dose/vial
95145	$14.88 @ dose
95146	$24.23 @ dose
95147	$34.62 @ dose
95148	$34.62 @ dose
95149	$42.58 @ dose
95165	$ 5.88 @ dose
95170	$15.23 @ dose

These average payment amounts were derived by using relative value units recommended by the Joint Council of Allergy and Immunology. In CPT the antigen/antigen prep codes require the biller to specify the number of doses for which he or she is reporting. HCFA's payment amounts for these codes are calculated on a per dose basis. HCFA will calculate payments by multiplying the per dose allowance by the number of doses reported. When submitting Medicare claims, specify that number of doses in the units field of the HCFA-1500 (paper claims or electronic format). If you are an allergist who has prepared a multidose vial of antigens (e.g., a vial with seven doses), and you inject one dose, report the seven doses of antigen and the one injection service. When you or another physician injects the remaining six doses at subsequent times, only injection services are to be reported.

Some individuals have expressed concern about the use of doses in HCFA's payment calculations. They are concerned about the potential for abuse if physicians change their practice patterns by routinely reducing the amounts of antigen that they provide in a "dose" and thereby increase the number of doses they can get from a multiple dose vial. This would essentially result in Medicare and beneficiaries paying more for the same amount of service/item. HCFA does not expect this kind of behavior change but plans to monitor for dose volume changes.

Remember, the amounts listed above are national averages. Your Medicare carrier can provide the specific fee disclosure material that tells you precisely what the Medicare allowance is for your payment locality for antigen therapy codes as well as others. Refer to those materials to obtain your precise allowance amounts.

	Code	Description	Medicode RVU	50th	75th	Medicare Nat'l Avg
	95004	Percutaneous tests (scratch, puncture, prick) with allergenic extracts, immediate type reaction, specify number of tests	2.50	3	4	3
	95010	Percutaneous tests (scratch, puncture, prick) sequential and incremental, with drugs, biologicals or venoms, immediate type reaction, specify number of tests	3.80	5	6	9
	95015	Intracutaneous (intradermal) tests, sequential and incremental, with drugs, biologicals, or venoms, immediate type reaction, specify number of tests	7.00	10	12	9
	95024	Intracutaneous (intradermal) tests with allergenic extracts, immediate type reaction, specify number of tests	4.25	6	7	5
	95027	Skin end point titration	0.00	0	0	5
	95028	Intracutaneous (intradermal) tests with allergenic extracts, delayed type reaction, including reading, specify number of tests	7.25	10	12	8
	95044	Patch or application test(s) (specify number of tests)	9.75	13	16	7
	95052	Photo patch test(s) (specify number of tests)	13.00	18	21	8
	95056	Photo tests	3.50	5	6	6
	95060	Ophthalmic mucous membrane tests	15.00	21	25	12
	95065	Direct nasal mucous membrane test	12.50	17	21	7
	95070	Inhalation bronchial challenge testing (not including necessary pulmonary function tests); with histamine, methacholine, or similar compounds	100.0	138	165	74
	95071	Inhalation bronchial challenge testing (not including necessary pulmonary function tests); with antigens or gases, specify	100.0	138	165	95
	95075	Ingestion challenge test (sequential and incremental ingestion of test items, eg, food, drug or other substance such as metabisulfite)	79.00	109	130	100
	95078	Provocative testing (eg, Rinkel test)	40.00	55	66	9
	95115	Professional services for allergen immunotherapy not including provision of allergenic extracts; single injection	8.00	11	13	13
▲	**95117**	Professional services for allergen immunotherapy not including provision of allergenic extracts; two or more injections	12.00	16	20	17
	95120	Professional services for allergen immunotherapy in prescribing physician's office or institution, including provision of allergenic extract; single injection	11.00	15	18	–
▲	**95125**	Professional services for allergen immunotherapy in prescribing physician's office or institution, including provision of allergenic extract; two or more injections	13.50	18	22	–
	95130	Professional services for allergen immunotherapy in prescribing physician's office or institution, including provision of allergenic extract; single stinging insect venom	19.00	26	31	–

Code	Description	Medicode RVU	50th	75th	Medicare Nat'l Avg
95131	Professional services for allergen immunotherapy in prescribing physician's office or institution, including provision of allergenic extract; two stinging insect venoms	24.00	33	39	–
95132	Professional services for allergen immunotherapy in prescribing physician's office or institution, including provision of allergenic extract; three stinging insect venoms	29.00	39	47	–
95133	Professional services for allergen immunotherapy in prescribing physician's office or institution, including provision of allergenic extract; four stinging insect venoms	35.00	47	57	–
95134	Professional services for allergen immunotherapy in prescribing physician's office or institution, including provision of allergenic extract; five stinging insect venoms	42.00	57	68	–
95144	Professional services for the supervision and provision of antigens for allergen immunotherapy, single or multiple antigens, single dose vials (specify number of vials)	29.00	41	50	7
▲ 95145	Professional services for the supervision and provision of antigens for allergen immunotherapy (specify number of doses); single stinging insect venom	22.00	31	38	15
▲ 95146	Professional services for the supervision and provision of antigens for allergen immunotherapy (specify number of doses); two single stinging insect venoms	27.00	38	47	24
▲ 95147	Professional services for the supervision and provision of antigens for allergen immunotherapy (specify number of doses); three single stinging insect venoms	32.00	46	56	34
▲ 95148	Professional services for the supervision and provision of antigens for allergen immunotherapy (specify number of doses); four single stinging insect venoms	38.00	54	66	34
▲ 95149	Professional services for the supervision and provision of antigens for allergen immunotherapy (specify number of doses); five single stinging insect venoms	45.00	64	78	42
▲ 95165	Professional services for the supervision and provision of antigens for allergen immunotherapy; single or multiple antigens (specify number of doses)	0.00	0	0	6
95170	Professional services for the supervision and provision of antigens for allergen immunotherapy; whole body extract of biting insect or other arthropod (specify number of doses)	0.00	0	0	15
95180	Rapid desensitization procedure, each hour (eg, insulin, penicillin, horse serum)	108.0	154	187	71
95199	Unlisted allergy/clinical immunologic service or procedure	0.00	0	0	–

95805–95999
Neurology and Neuromuscular Services

CODING INSIGHT

Codes 95805–95999 cover the services listed in the neurology section. The electroencephalogram (EEG) codes (95816–95827) include both the technical (tracing) and professional (interpretation and report) components. When only interpretation is performed, indicate the service with modifier -26.

Take special note of codes that are anatomical site-specific. For example, 95831–95834 cover muscle testing of the extremity or trunk, but 95831 excludes the hand, while 95832 is specific to the hand. Codes 95833 and 95834 report total body evaluation with the exception that 95833 excludes the hands. Note, that electromyography codes 95860–95864 relate to the number of extremities evaluated and include the related paraspinal areas.

SUBSIDIARY CODES

Subsidiary codes have relative values that require no further adjustment:

95957 is "in addition" to 95816, 95819, 95954
95962 is "in addition" to 95961

Because these are subsidiary or "in addition to" codes, reimbursement reduction and modifier -51 do not apply.

MEDICARE ALERT

Medicare rebundles certain codes in the medicine section when the listed codes are considered a component of a more comprehensive service.

95816, 95822 will not be reimbursed when reported with 95819
95860 will not be reimbursed when reported with 95861

Code	Description	Medicode RVU	50th	75th	Medicare Nat'l Avg
95805	Multiple sleep latency testing (MSLT), recording, analysis and interpretation of physiological measurements of sleep during multiple nap opportunities	376.0	508	646	266
-26			203	258	87
95807	Sleep study, 3 or more parameters of sleep other than sleep staging, attended by a technologist	281.0	380	482	304
-26			152	193	129
95808	Polysomnography; sleep staging with 1-3 additional parameters of sleep, attended by a technologist	316.0	427	543	333
-26			171	217	156
95810	Polysomnography; sleep staging with 4 or more additional parameters of sleep, attended by a technologist	339.0	458	582	357
-26			183	233	177
95812	Electroencephalogram (EEG) extended monitoring; up to one hour	34.00	46	58	103
-26			18	23	54
95813	Electroencephalogram (EEG) extended monitoring; greater than one hour	0.00	0	0	127
-26			0	0	78
95816	Electroencephalogram (EEG) including recording awake and drowsy, with hyperventilation and/or photic stimulation	156.0	211	268	92
-26			84	107	47
95819	Electroencephalogram (EEG) including recording awake and asleep, with hyperventilation and/or photic stimulation	166.0	224	285	101
-26			90	114	53
95822	Electroencephalogram (EEG); sleep only	160.0	216	275	119
-26			86	110	57
95824	Electroencephalogram (EEG); cerebral death evaluation only	135.0	182	232	61
-26			73	93	47
95827	Electroencephalogram (EEG); all night sleep only	200.0	270	343	149
-26			108	137	70
95829	Electrocorticogram at surgery (separate procedure)	325.0	439	558	232
-26			439	558	227
95830	Insertion by physician of sphenoidal electrodes for electroencephalographic (EEG) recording	116.0	157	199	88
-26			157	199	
95831	Muscle testing, manual (separate procedure); extremity (excluding hand) or trunk, with report	30.50	41	52	21

Code	Description	Medicode RVU	50th	75th	Medicare Nat'l Avg
95832	Muscle testing, manual (separate procedure); hand (with or without comparison with normal side)	34.50	47	59	20
95833	Muscle testing, manual (separate procedure); total evaluation of body, excluding hands	80.00	108	137	33
95834	Muscle testing, manual (separate procedure); total evaluation of body, including hands	88.00	119	151	44
95851	Range of motion measurements and report (separate procedure); each extremity (excluding hand) or each trunk section (spine)	32.00	43	55	19
95852	Range of motion measurements and report (separate procedure); hand, with or without comparison with normal side	32.00	43	55	13
95857	Tensilon test for myasthenia gravis;	65.00	88	112	39
95858	Tensilon test for myasthenia gravis; with electromyographic recording	187.5	253	322	91
-26			51	64	77
95860	Needle electromyography, one extremity and related paraspinal areas	130.0	176	223	76
-26			70	89	62
95861	Needle electromyography, two extremities and related paraspinal areas	169.0	228	290	126
-26			91	116	100
95863	Needle electromyography, three extremities and related paraspinal areas	220.0	297	378	152
-26			119	151	118
95864	Needle electromyography, four extremities and related paraspinal areas	286.0	386	491	196
-26			155	196	135
95867	Needle electromyography, cranial nerve supplied muscles, unilateral	135.0	182	232	65
-26			73	93	45
95868	Needle electromyography, cranial nerve supplied muscles, bilateral	236.0	319	405	123
-26			128	162	97
95869	Needle electromyography, limited study of specific muscles (eg, thoracic spinal muscles)	100.0	135	172	35
-26			54	69	27
▲ **95872**	Needle electromyography using single fiber electrode, with quantitative measurement of jitter, blocking and/or fiber density, any/all sites of each muscle studied	231.0	312	397	98
-26			125	159	77
95875	Ischemic limb exercise with needle electromyography, with lactic acid determination	46.00	62	79	70
-26			25	32	55
▲ **95900**	Nerve conduction, amplitude and latency/velocity study, each nerve, any/all site(s) along the nerve; motor, without F-wave study	74.50	101	128	37
-26			40	51	28
● **95903**	Nerve conduction, amplitude and latency/velocity study, each nerve, any/all site(s) along the nerve; motor, with F-wave study	82.00	111	141	–
-26			44	56	
▲ **95904**	Nerve conduction, amplitude and latency/velocity study, each nerve, any/all site(s) along the nerve; sensory	74.50	101	128	33
-26			40	51	25
95920	Intraoperative neurophysiology testing, per hour	243.0	328	417	170
-26			328	417	125
▲ **95925**	Short-latency somatosensory evoked potential study, stimulation of any/all peripheral nerves or skin sites, recording from the central nervous system; in upper limbs	211.5	286	363	114
-26			114	145	65
● **95926**	Short-latency somatosensory evoked potential study, stimulation of any/all peripheral nerves or skin sites, recording from the central nervous system; in lower limbs	211.5	286	363	–
-26			114	145	

	Code	Description	Medicode RVU	50th	75th	Medicare Nat'l Avg
●	**95927** **-26**	Short-latency somatosensory evoked potential study, stimulation of any/all peripheral nerves or skin sites, recording from the central nervous system; in the trunk or head	211.5	286 114	363 145	–
●	**95930** **-26**	Visual evoked potential (VEP) testing central nervous system, checkerboard or flash	100.0	135 68	172 86	–
	95933 **-26**	Orbicularis oculi (blink) reflex, by electrodiagnostic testing	85.00	115 46	146 58	66 39
●	**95934** **-26**	H-reflex, amplitude and latency study; record gastrocnemius/soleus muscle	84.00	113 45	144 58	–
●	**95936** **-26**	H-reflex, amplitude and latency study; record muscle other than gastrocnemius/soleus muscle	84.00	113 45	144 58	–
	95937 **-26**	Neuromuscular junction testing (repetitive stimulation, paired stimuli), each nerve, any one method	79.00	107 43	136 54	50 39
	95950 **-26**	Monitoring for identification and lateralization of cerebral seizure focus by attached electrodes; electroencephalographic (eg, 8 channel EEG) recording and interpretation, each 24 hours	400.0	540 216	687 275	320 102
	95951 **-26**	Monitoring for identification and lateralization of cerebral seizure focus by attached electrodes; combined electroencephalographic (EEG) and video recording and interpretation, each 24 hours	514.0	694 278	883 353	449 186
	95953 **-26**	Monitoring for localization of cerebral seizure focus by computerized portable 16 or more channel EEG; electroencephalographic (EEG) recording and interpretation, each 24 hours	462.0	624 250	793 317	368 150
	95954 **-26**	Pharmacological or physical activation requiring physician attendance during EEG recording of activation phase (eg, thiopental activation test)	100.0	135 135	172 172	172 150
	95955 **-26**	Electroencephalogram (EEG) during nonintracranial surgery (eg, carotid surgery)	180.0	243 243	309 309	144 75
	95956 **-26**	Monitoring for localization of cerebral seizure focus by cable or radio, 16 or more channel telemetry, electroencephalographic (EEG) recording and interpretation, each 24 hours	462.0	624 250	793 317	382 162
	95957 **-26**	Digital analysis of electroencephalogram (EEG) (eg, for epileptic spike analysis) (list separately in addition to code for primary procedure)	0.00	0 0	0 0	150 91
	95958 **-26**	Wada activation test for hemispheric function, including electroencephalographic (EEG) monitoring	285.0	385 154	489 196	328 267
	95961 **-26**	Functional cortical mapping by stimulation of electrodes on brain surface, or of depth electrodes, to provoke seizures or identify vital cortex; initial hour of physician attendance	300.0	405 405	515 515	199 155
	95962 **-26**	Functional cortical mapping by stimulation of electrodes on brain surface, or of depth electrodes, to provoke seizures or identify vital cortex; each additional hour of physician attendance	200.0	270 270	343 343	207 163
	95999	Unlisted neurological or neuromuscular diagnostic procedure	0.00	0	0	–

96400–96549
Chemotherapy Administration

Coding Insight
Chemotherapy codes (96400–96549), according to the instructional note in CPT, are independent of a patient's visit; the service no longer qualifies as an office visit. You can report inpatient and outpatient medical services, in addition to the chemotherapy procedure, when they occur on the same day. (Currently, federal regulations require that a physician be on the premises in order for the services of a nonphysician employee to be reported as "incident to" the physician's services.)

CPT guidelines state further: "Placement of the intra-arterial catheter should be reported using the appropriate code from the Cardiovascular Surgery section," i.e., 36620–36640. Codes 96440, 96445, and 96450 include the access procedure. Thoracentesis, peritoneocentesis, and lumbar puncture are not reported separately.

Chemotherapy codes include preparation of the chemotherapy agent(s) and are distinguished by technique (push or infusion), by agent preparation (premixed or requiring mixing), and by time required for administration.

Code special filter needles and infusion sets used to mix and administer the chemotherapy agent separately. HCPCS Level II "A" codes specify supplies and materials, and "J" codes identify chemotherapy agents. Use HCPCS Level II codes when billing Medicare. For commercial insurance payers, 96545 indicates provision of the chemotherapy agent or drug, and 99070 in the Special Services and Reports section reports the supplies. Since the HCFA-1500 form no longer allows space for a descriptor, eliminate questions from your payers by including an attachment indicating the exact drug and supplies used. It might even be a good idea to include a current drug invoice to eliminate questions regarding the drug's cost.

Subsidiary Codes
Subsidiary codes have relative values that require no further adjustment:

96412 is "in addition" to 96410
96423 is "in addition" to 96422

Because these are subsidiary or "in addition to" codes, reimbursement reduction and modifier -51 do not apply.

Medicare Alert
Payment will not be made for 96400–96425 chemotherapy administration services in a hospital setting, and claims for these services with a modifier -26 will not be recognized. Separate payment will be made for each chemotherapeutic agent furnished on the day of chemotherapy administration. Only one "push" technique code may be reported when multiple drugs are furnished by this technique.

Medicare rebundles certain codes in the medicine section when the listed codes are considered a component of a more comprehensive service.

36000 will not be reimbursed when reported with 96408–96412, 96440–96450
32002, 32005 will not be reimbursed when reported with 96440
49080–49081 will not be reimbursed when reported with 96445
62270–62272 will not be reimbursed when reported with 96450

Code	Description	Medicode RVU	50th	75th	Medicare Nat'l Avg
96400	Chemotherapy administration, subcutaneous or intramuscular, with or without local anesthesia	30.00	41	51	8
96405	Chemotherapy administration, intralesional; up to and including 7 lesions	48.00	65	81	36
96406	Chemotherapy administration, intralesional; more than 7 lesions	72.00	97	122	55
96408	Chemotherapy administration, intravenous; push technique	53.00	72	90	34
96410	Chemotherapy administration, intravenous; infusion technique, up to one hour	81.00	110	137	54
96412	Chemotherapy administration, intravenous; infusion technique, one to 8 hours, each additional hour	67.00	91	114	40
96414	Chemotherapy administration, intravenous; infusion technique, initiation of prolonged infusion (more than 8 hours), requiring the use of a portable or implantable pump	94.00	127	159	47
96420	Chemotherapy administration, intra-arterial; push technique	67.00	91	114	44
96422	Chemotherapy administration, intra-arterial; infusion technique, up to one hour	99.00	134	168	45
96423	Chemotherapy administration, intra-arterial; infusion technique, one to 8 hours, each additional hour	77.00	104	131	18
96425	Chemotherapy administration, intra-arterial; infusion technique, initiation of prolonged infusion (more than 8 hours), requiring the use of a portable or implantable pump	119.0	161	202	50
96440	Chemotherapy administration into pleural cavity, requiring and including thoracentesis	175.0	237	297	108
96445	Chemotherapy administration into peritoneal cavity, requiring and including peritoneocentesis	175.0	237	297	111
96450	Chemotherapy administration, into CNS (eg, intrathecal), requiring and including lumbar puncture	154.5	209	262	96
96520	Refilling and maintenance of portable pump	45.00	61	76	31
96530	Refilling and maintenance of implantable pump or reservoir	45.00	61	76	38
96542	Chemotherapy injection, subarachnoid or intraventricular via subcutaneous reservoir, single or multiple agents	110.0	149	186	90
96545	Provision of chemotherapy agent	0.00	0	0	–
96549	Unlisted chemotherapy procedure	0.00	0	0	21

96100–96117
Central Nervous System

	Code	Description	Medicode RVU	50th	75th	Medicare Nat'l Avg
●	96100	Psychological testing (includes psychodiagnostic assessment of personality, psychopathology, emotionality, intellectual abilities, eg, WAIS-R, Rorschach, MMPI) with interpretation and report, per hour	105.0	142	178	–
●	96105	Assessment of aphasia (includes assessment of expressive and receptive speech and language function, language comprehension, speech production ability, reading, spelling, writing, eg, by Boston Diagnostic Aphasia Examination) with interpretation and report, per hour	146.0	198	247	–
●	96110	Developmental testing; limited (eg, Developmental Screening Test II, Early Language Milestone Screen), with interpretation and report	98.00	133	166	–
●	96111	Developmental testing; extended (includes assessment of motor, language, social, adaptive and/or cognitive functioning by standardized developmental instruments, eg, Bayley Scales of Infant Development) with interpretation and report, per hour	117.5	159	199	–
●	96115	Neurobehavorial status exam (clinical assessment of thinking, reasoning and judgment, eg, acquired knowledge, attention, memory, visual spatial abilities, language functions, planning) with interpretation and report, per hour	108.5	147	184	–
●	96117	Neuropsychological testing battery (eg, Halstead-Reitan, Luria, WAIS-R) with interpretation and report, per hour	102.5	139	174	–

96900–96999
Special Dermatological Procedures

Coding Insight

Dermatologists are frequently asked to accept a capitated contract with managed care payers. Refer to the chapter "Reimbursement Issues" for some points to consider when entering into a capitated agreement.

Code	Description	Medicode RVU	50th	75th	Medicare Nat'l Avg
96900	Actinotherapy (ultraviolet light)	19.00	28	33	13
96910	Photochemotherapy; tar and ultraviolet B (Goeckerman treatment) or petrolatum and ultraviolet B	22.00	33	38	20
96912	Photochemotherapy; psoralens and ultraviolet A (PUVA)	25.50	38	44	23
96913	Photochemotherapy (Goeckerman and/or PUVA) for severe photoresponsive dermatoses requiring at least four to eight hours of care under direct supervision of the physician (includes application of medication and dressings)	0.00	0	0	47
96999	Unlisted special dermatological service or procedure	0.00	0	0	–

97010–97799
Physical Medicine Services

Coding Insight
The new range of modalities and procedures that were added to *CPT '95* that comprise physical medicine (97032–97736) require that a physician or therapist be in constant attendance. Codes 97010–97039 indicate the application of a supervised treatment modality to one or more areas at one session. Codes 97010–97028 can only be listed once.

Codes 97110–97139 also indicate treatment to one anatomical area but are further defined with an initial time of 15 minutes. If fewer than 15 minutes are performed, use modifier -52 to designate a reduced service. If reporting one hour of treatment, you may use a code from 97110 through 97139 for each additional 15 minutes (chosen by the specific treatment performed), or enter a "2" in the unit box.

Additional codes in ranges 97530–97542 and 97703–97770 also have time components in 15-minute units. The codes describing "each additional" are never stand-alone codes; they are reported secondary to the primary code.

Significant changes and additions to the Physical Medicine section were affected in *CPT '95*. Read the guidelines to this section carefully when using these codes.

Subsidiary Codes
Subsidiary codes have relative values that require no further adjustment:

97261 is "in addition" to 97260
97501 is "in addition" to 97500
97521 is "in addition" to 97520

Because these are subsidiary or "in addition to" codes, reimbursement reduction and modifier -51 do not apply.

Medicare Alert
Medicare recently updated its payment policy for outpatient services furnished by a physical or occupational therapist in independent practice. The update addresses the base payment on the physician fee schedule and deletes the words "reasonable charge." The policy is as follows:

- Claims for outpatient services provided by a speech pathologist in independent practice are not covered. Outpatient physical or occupational therapy services of a qualified therapist in independent practice are covered
- The base payment on the physician's fee schedule is less any coinsurance and deductible amounts. The payment limit on expenses incurred for each type of therapy in a calendar year is $900. Thus, where the beneficiary has satisfied the deductible, the maximum payable under the physical therapy benefit is $720, i.e., 80 percent of $900. The maximum amount payable under the occupational therapy benefit is $720

When billing Medicare be sure to include the name of the attending physician, the date the patient was last seen by the physician, and the therapist's certification that the plan of treatment is on file and was in effect when the services were furnished.

Make certain that the services provided were covered therapy services and consistent with the diagnosis. When a review of the therapist's clinical records are necessary, verify that the services provided were in accordance with the plan of treatment and that the plan was reviewed by the physician if the services extend over a period of time. When services are furnished beyond the initial estimate of need, a revision of the plan and documentation of the extended need is required.

Medicare Physical and Occupational Therapy

Procedure Codes

Physicians may report general Evaluation and Management (E/M) codes for services provided the same day as CPT therapy codes were provided only if they provide separately identifiable services that meet the definition of a visit. Independent therapists cannot report the general E/M visit codes to Medicare; however, independent therapists may use procedure codes M005–M008 to report an office visit that includes at least one modality. Osteopathic Manipulation Therapy (OMT) (98925–98929) is considered a procedure performed only by a physician. Procedures and an E/M service will not be paid on the same day unless the E/M service is a significant, separately identifiable evaluation and management service by the same physician. Modifier -25 is used with the code for the E/M service.

HCFA has established two new temporary HCPCS Level II alphanumeric codes for physical therapy: Q0103 Physical therapy evaluation, initial, and Q0104 Physical therapy re-evaluation, periodic.

Code Q0103 must be used by the physician or physical therapist to report the initial physical therapy evaluation before a plan of care has been established. This evaluation is for the purpose of evaluating the patient's condition and establishing a physical therapy plan of care. Code Q0104 must be used by the physician or physical therapist to report the re-evaluation of a patient who has been under a plan of care established by a physician or physical therapist. This evaluation is for the purpose of evaluating the patient's condition and establishing a physical therapy plan of care under which he or she will be treated.

General Guidelines

Physical and occupational therapy services are paid under the physician fee schedule. Payment for physical therapy services furnished in provider settings (e.g., hospital and nursing facility) will continue to be part of the payment to that provider and not separately paid to the practitioner furnishing the therapy services.

Independent physical therapists and/or physicians may report physical therapy to Medicare using CPT therapy codes 97010–97999. Independent physical therapists can use CPT codes not in the 97000 range such as 95842, 95900, and 95860 through 95867 to report the technical component of services. They cannot report the professional component.

Outpatient Limitation

Therapy services furnished by an independently practicing physical or occupational therapist have a $900 limitation on allowed charges per calendar year. Coverage is limited to services provided in the therapist's office or the beneficiary's home. Reimbursement for these services is based on the reasonable charge less co-insurance and any deductible amounts due. Thus, where the beneficiary has already satisfied the Part B deductible, the maximum amount presently payable under this benefit would be $720 (80 percent of $900).

Coverage Requirements for PT/OT

To be a covered physical or occupational therapy service, the patient must be under the care of a physician. The attending physician may be the patient's private physician or a physician associated with an institution. There must be evidence in the clinical record maintained by the therapist that the patient has been seen by the physician at least every 30 days, and the therapist must indicate on the claim the name of the physician and the date the patient was last seen by the physician.

The therapy must be furnished under a written plan of treatment established by the physician or therapist caring for the patient. The plan must be established (i.e., in written form either by the physician who makes the plan available to the therapist or by the therapist) and incorporated into the therapist's permanent record for the patient.

The plan must relate the type, amount, frequency, and duration of the therapy services to be furnished and indicate the diagnosis and anticipated goals. Any changes should be made in writing and signed by the physician or by the therapist. Changes made pursuant to verbal orders from the attending physician must be immediately recorded in the patient's records and signed by the therapist receiving the orders. While the physician may change a plan of treatment established by the therapist providing such service, the therapist may not alter a plan of treatment established by a physician.

The plan must be reviewed by the physician, in consultation with the therapist, at such intervals as the severity of the patient's condition requires, but at least every 30 days. Each review of the plan should contain the initials of the physician and the date of review. The patient's plan normally is not forwarded for review. The plan of treatment and the therapist's clinical records concerning the beneficiary will be retained by the therapist but must be available. The therapist must certify on the reporting form that the plan is on file and was in effect at the time the services were rendered.

Generally speaking, therapy services designed to improve function are considered reasonable and necessary only where an expectation exists that the therapy will result in significant practical improvement in the individual's level of functioning within a reasonable period of time. Where the improvement potential is less significant in relation to the extent and duration of time required to achieve improvement, such services would not be considered reasonable and necessary and thus not covered.

If a valid expectation of improvement exists at the time the therapy program is instituted, the services would be covered even though the expectation may not be realized. However, in such situations, the services would be covered only up to the time at which it would have been reasonable to conclude that the patient was not going to improve. Once a patient has reached the point where no further significant practical improvement can be expected, the skills of a therapist are not required to carry out any activity and/or exercise program to maintain function at the level to which it has been restored. Consequently, while the services of a therapist in designing a maintenance program and making infrequent but periodic evaluation of its effectiveness would be covered, carrying out the program is not considered reasonable and necessary, and such services would not be covered.

To be considered reasonable and necessary, the following conditions must be met:

- The services must be considered to be a specific and effective treatment for the patient's condition
- The services must be of such a level of complexity or the condition of the patient must be such that the services required can be safely and effectively performed only by a qualified therapist, or under his/her supervision. Services that do not require the performance or supervision of a therapist are not considered reasonable or necessary therapy services
- There must be an expectation that the condition will improve significantly in a reasonable amount of time, or the services must be necessary to the establishment of a safe and effective maintenance program required in connection with a specific disease state
- The amount, frequency, and duration of the services must be reasonable

Code	Description	Medicode RVU	50th	75th	Medicare Nat'l Avg
97010	Application of a modality to one or more areas; hot or cold packs	14.00	19	23	13
97012	Application of a modality to one or more areas; traction, mechanical	16.00	21	27	16

	Code	Description	Medicode RVU	50th	75th	Medicare Nat'l Avg
	97014	Application of a modality to one or more areas; electrical stimulation (unattended)	15.75	21	26	14
	97016	Application of a modality to one or more areas; vasopneumatic devices	19.50	26	32	16
	97018	Application of a modality to one or more areas; paraffin bath	16.00	21	27	14
	97020	Application of a modality to one or more areas; microwave	15.50	21	26	12
	97022	Application of a modality to one or more areas; whirlpool	15.50	21	26	16
	97024	Application of a modality to one or more areas; diathermy	16.00	21	27	13
	97026	Application of a modality to one or more areas; infrared	15.00	20	25	12
	97028	Application of a modality to one or more areas; ultraviolet	15.00	20	25	14
	97032	Application of a modality to one or more areas; electrical stimulation (manual), each 15 minutes	14.50	19	24	15
	97033	Application of a modality to one or more areas; iontophoresis, each 15 minutes	21.00	28	35	16
	97034	Application of a modality to one or more areas; contrast baths, each 15 minutes	14.00	19	23	12
	97035	Application of a modality to one or more areas; ultrasound, each 15 minutes	14.25	19	24	12
	97036	Application of a modality to one or more areas; Hubbard tank, each 15 minutes	23.00	31	38	20
	97039	Unlisted modality (specify type and time if constant attendance)	0.00	0	0	19
	97110	Therapeutic procedure, one or more areas, each 15 minutes; therapeutic exercises to develop strength and endurance, range of motion and flexibility	23.50	27	34	20
	97112	Therapeutic procedure, one or more areas, each 15 minutes; neuromuscular reeducation of movement, balance, coordination, kinesthetic sense, posture, and proprioception	23.00	27	34	20
	97113	Therapeutic procedure, one or more areas, each 15 minutes; aquatic therapy with therapeutic exercises	26.00	30	38	21
▲	**97116**	Therapeutic procedure, one or more areas, each 15 minutes; gait training (includes stair climbing)	20.75	24	30	18
	97122	Therapeutic procedure, one or more areas, each 15 minutes; traction, manual	18.00	21	26	18
	97124	Therapeutic procedure, one or more areas, each 15 minutes; massage, including effleurage, petrissage and/or tapotement (stroking, compression, percussion)	15.50	18	23	16
	97139	Therapeutic procedure, one or more areas, each 15 minutes; unlisted therapeutic procedure (specify)	0.00	0	0	15
	97150	Therapeutic procedure(s), group (2 or more individuals)	0.00	0	0	17
	97250	Myofascial release/soft tissue mobilization, one or more regions	25.00	32	36	29

	Code	Description	Medicode RVU	50th	75th	Medicare Nat'l Avg
	97260	Manipulation (cervical, thoracic, lumbosacral, sacroiliac, hand, wrist) (separate procedure), performed by physician; one area	21.00	27	31	15
	97261	Manipulation (cervical, thoracic, lumbosacral, sacroiliac, hand, wrist) (separate procedure), performed by physician; each additional area	14.75	19	22	9
	97265	Joint mobilization, one or more areas (peripheral or spinal)	25.00	32	36	29
	97500	Orthotics training (dynamic bracing, splinting), upper and/or lower extremities; initial 30 minutes, each visit	33.00	42	48	22
	97501	Orthotics training (dynamic bracing, splinting), upper and/or lower extremities; each additional 15 minutes	16.50	21	24	12
	97520	Prosthetic training; initial 30 minutes, each visit	37.00	47	54	25
	97521	Prosthetic training; each additional 15 minutes	18.50	24	27	14
	97530	Therapeutic activities, direct (one on one) patient contact by the provider (use of dynamic activities to improve functional performance), each 15 minutes	17.00	22	25	21
●	**97535**	Self care/home management training (eg, activities of daily living (ADL) and compensatory training, meal preparation, safety procedures, and instructions in use of adaptive equipment) direct one on one contact by provider, each 15 minutes	15.00	19	22	–
●	**97537**	Community/work reintegration training (eg, shopping, transportation, money management, avocational activities and/or work environment/modification analysis, work task analysis), direct one on one contact by provider, each 15 minutes	16.50	21	24	–
●	**97542**	Wheelchair management/propulsion training, each 15 minutes	14.00	18	20	–
	97545	Work hardening/conditioning; initial 2 hours	84.00	107	122	90
	97546	Work hardening/conditioning; each additional hour	33.50	43	49	45
●	**97703**	Checkout for orthotic/prosthetic use, established patient, each 15 minutes	19.00	26	32	–
	97750 **-26**	Physical performance test or measurement (eg, musculoskeletal, functional capacity), with written report, each 15 minutes	32.00	44 9	54 11	25
	97770	Development of cognitive skills to improve attention, memory, problem solving, includes compensatory training and/or sensory integrative activities, direct (one on one) patient contact by the provider, each 15 minutes	0.00	0	0	25
	97799	Unlisted physical medicine/rehabilitation service or procedure	0.00	0	0	–

98925–98929
Osteopathic Manipulative Treatment

Coding Insight
Codes 98925–98929 were added for inpatient or outpatient Osteopathic Manipulative Treatment (OMT). Instructional notes state osteopathic manipulative treatment is a form of manual treatment applied by a physician to eliminate or alleviate somatic dysfunction and related disorders. Conditions include:

- Disorders in the skeletal, arthrodial, myofascial, and visceral structures as well as related vascular, lymphatic, and neural elements
- Palpatory findings such as tenderness, asymmetry, range of motion abnormalities, and tissue texture changes

Osteopathic Manipulative Treatment may be accomplished by a variety of techniques including, but not limited to:

- Soft tissue techniques such as stretch, gentle range of motion, and kneading
- Direct techniques such as joint mobilization, thrust, and muscle energy
- Indirect techniques such as myofascial release, strain/counter-strain, and cranial osteopathy

The five codes are differentiated by the number of body regions involved in the treatment. CPT guidelines refer to the following body regions:

- Head
- Cervical
- Thoracic
- Lumbar
- Sacral
- Pelvic
- Lower extremities
- Upper extremities
- Rib cage
- Abdomen and viscera

These regions are common to osteopathic physicians but may apply to regions used by nonphysicians and surgeons.

Osteopathic Manipulative Treatment includes a component of E/M service to ascertain the effectiveness of the therapy. An E/M service may be identified separately when (1) a physician diagnoses the condition requiring manipulative therapy and provides it during the same visit, (2) the condition requiring manipulative therapy fails to respond to the therapy or the condition significantly changes or intensifies, consequently requiring E/M services beyond those considered included in the manipulation codes, and (3) the physician treats a condition unrelated to the condition requiring manipulative therapy during the same visit.

For an E/M service to be paid separately when performed on the same day as OMT, identify the E/M service with modifier -25 (significant, separately identifiable evaluation and management service by the same physician on the day of a procedure).

Code	Description	Medicode RVU	50th	75th	Medicare Nat'l Avg
98925	Osteopathic manipulative treatment (OMT); one to two body regions involved	27.00	37	46	24
98926	Osteopathic manipulative treatment (OMT); three to four body regions involved	35.50	49	60	37
98927	Osteopathic manipulative treatment (OMT); five to six body regions involved	42.00	58	71	45
98928	Osteopathic manipulative treatment (OMT); seven to eight body regions involved	46.00	63	78	51
98929	Osteopathic manipulative treatment (OMT); nine to ten body regions involved	48.00	66	81	55

99000–99090
Special Services and Reports

CODING INSIGHT

Special services and reports codes (99000–99090) allow supplemental reimbursement for "services that are an adjunct to the basic services rendered." To justify use of these codes, identify the medical necessity of special circumstances. Document the information clearly and completely in the patient's medical record. Payers have individual guidelines for use of these codes.

Codes 99050–99058 identify emergency office calls and services provided after hours, on Sundays, or on holidays. Other codes in this category identify medical testimony, unusual travel requirements (e.g., escorting a patient on a trip of more than ten miles), and educational services.

There are also codes identifying transportation of specimens; for example, 99001 *Handling and/or conveyance of specimen for transfer from the patient in other than a physician's office to a laboratory (distance may be indicated).*

Code	Description	Medicode RVU	50th	75th	Medicare Nat'l Avg
99000	Handling and/or conveyance of specimen for transfer from the physician's office to a laboratory	7.50	10	13	–
99001	Handling and/or conveyance of specimen for transfer from the patient in other than a physician's office to a laboratory (distance may be indicated)	8.50	12	15	–
99002	Handling, conveyance, and/or any other service in connection with the implementation of an order involving devices (eg, designing, fitting, packaging, handling, delivery or mailing) when devices such as orthotics, protectives, prosthetics are fabricated by an outside laboratory or shop but which items have been designed, and are to be fitted and adjusted by the attending physician	12.25	17	22	–
99024	Postoperative follow-up visit, included in global service	0.00	0	0	–
99025	Initial (new patient) visit when starred (*) surgical procedure constitutes major service at that visit	34.50	47	61	–
99050	Services requested after office hours in addition to basic service	23.00	31	40	–

Code	Description	Medicode RVU	50th	75th	Medicare Nat'l Avg
99052	Services requested between 10:00 PM and 8:00 AM in addition to basic service	23.00	31	40	–
99054	Services requested on Sundays and holidays in addition to basic service	23.00	31	40	–
99056	Services provided at request of patient in a location other than physician's office which are normally provided in the office	30.00	41	53	–
99058	Office services provided on an emergency basis	31.00	42	54	–
99070	Supplies and materials (except spectacles), provided by the physician over and above those usually included with the office visit or other services rendered (list drugs, trays, supplies, or materials provided)	0.00	0	0	–
99071	Educational supplies, such as books, tapes, and pamphlets, provided by the physician for the patient's education at cost to physician	0.00	0	0	–
99075	Medical testimony	0.00	0	0	–
99078	Physician educational services rendered to patients in a group setting (eg, prenatal, obesity, or diabetic instructions)	0.00	0	0	–
99080	Special reports such as insurance forms, more than the information conveyed in the usual medical communications or standard reporting form	0.00	0	0	–
99082	Unusual travel (eg, transportation and escort of patient)	0.00	0	0	11
99090	Analysis of information data stored in computers (eg, ECGs, blood pressures, hematologic data)	0.00	0	0	–

99100–99140
Qualifying Circumstances for Anesthesia

Coding Insight
These circumstances, when present, add significantly to the amount the anesthesiologist reports for services.

Code	Description	Medicode RVU	50th	75th	Medicare Nat'l Avg
99100	Anesthesia for patient of extreme age, under one year and over seventy	0.00	0	0	–
99116	Anesthesia complicated by utilization of total body hypothermia	0.00	0	0	–
99135	Anesthesia complicated by utilization of controlled hypotension	0.00	0	0	–
99140	Anesthesia complicated by emergency conditions (specify)	0.00	0	0	–

99175–99199
Other Services

Code	Description	Medicode RVU	50th	75th	Medicare Nat'l Avg
99175	Ipecac or similar administration for individual emesis and continued observation until stomach adequately emptied of poison	38.00	49	60	48
99183	Physician attendance and supervision of hyperbaric oxygen therapy, per session	220.0	282	349	14
-26			282	349	1
99185	Hypothermia; regional	26.00	33	41	22
-26			13	17	
99186	Hypothermia; total body	125.0	160	198	74
-26			64	79	
99190	Assembly and operation of pump with oxygenator or heat exchanger (with or without ECG and/or pressure monitoring); each hour	611.0	783	969	–
-26			313	388	
99191	Assembly and operation of pump with oxygenator or heat exchanger (with or without ECG and/or pressure monitoring); 3/4 hour	458.0	587	726	–
-26			235	291	
99192	Assembly and operation of pump with oxygenator or heat exchanger (with or without ECG and/or pressure monitoring); 1/2 hour	305.5	392	485	–
-26			157	194	
99195	Phlebotomy, therapeutic (separate procedure)	40.00	51	63	17
99199	Unlisted special service or report	0.00	0	0	–

Appendix: Conversion Factors

MEDICARE LOCALITIES

The Medicare localities below include a brief delineation of the locality (cities, towns, geographic regions, etc.) and a factor by which the national Medicare amounts from the supplied fee data can be multiplied to approximate the allowable for the specific locality.

Alabama	
Birmingham	0.948
Mobile	0.927
North central	0.916
Northwest	0.930
Southeast	0.918
Rest of Alabama	0.904
Alaska	1.151
Arizona	
Flagstaff (city)	0.969
Phoenix	1.012
Prescott (city)	0.963
Tucson (city)	0.990
Yuma (city)	0.970
Rest of Arizona	0.984
Arkansas	0.881
California	
Anaheim/Santa Ana	1.119
Bakersfield	1.024
Fresno/Madera	0.998
Kings/Tulare	0.986
Los Angeles	1.123
Marin/Napa/Solano	1.091
Merced/surr. cntys	1.003
Monterey/Santa Cruz	1.064
N Coastal cntys	1.037
NE Rural	0.983
Oakland/Berkeley	1.123
Riverside	1.041
Sacramento/surr. cntys	1.046
San Bernardino/East central	1.043
San Diego/Imperial	1.049
San Francisco	1.168
San Mateo	1.157
Santa Barbara	1.052
Santa Clara	1.157
Stockton/surr. cntys	1.019
Ventura	1.090
Colorado	0.971
Connecticut	
Eastern	1.050
NW and North central	1.065
South central	1.097
SW	1.126
Delaware	1.010
District of Columbia	
DC, MD/VA suburbs	1.107
Florida	
Fort Lauderdale	1.033
Miami	1.090
N and North central cities	0.975
Rest of Florida	0.949
Georgia	
Atlanta	0.999
Small GA cities 02	0.935
Small GA cities 03	0.918
Rest Of Georgia	0.903
Hawaii/Guam	1.070
Idaho	
North	0.918
South	0.930
Illinois	
Champaign/Urbana	0.939
Chicago	1.091
De Kalb	0.935
Decatur	0.940
East St. Louis	0.988
Kankakee	0.940
Normal	0.957
Northwest	0.919
Peoria	0.979
Quincy	0.914
Rock Island	0.947
Rockford	0.987
Southeast	0.911
Southern	0.916
Springfield	0.974
Suburban Chicago	1.057
Inidana	
Metropolitan Indiana	0.947
Urban Indiana	0.915
Rest of Indiana	0.907
Iowa	0.922
Kansas	
Kansas City	0.980
Rest of Kansas	0.934
Kentucky	
Lexington/Louisville	0.940
Small cities	0.914
Rest of Kentucky	0.902

Louisiana	
Alexandria	0.923
Baton Rouge	0.956
Lafayette	0.932
Lake Charles	0.937
Monroe	0.920
New Orleans	0.991
Shreveport	0.948
Rest of Louisiana	0.917
Maine	
Central	0.925
Northern	0.927
Southern	0.974
Maryland	
Baltimore/surr. cntys	1.030
S and E shore	0.987
Western	0.977
Massachusetts	
Suburbs/rural cities	1.038
Urban	1.071
Michigan	
Detroit	1.124
Rest of Michigan	1.007
Minnesota	
(Blue Shield)	0.966
(Travelers)	0.966
Mississippi	
Urban (city limits)	0.915
Rest of Mississippi	0.884
Missouri	
Jackson County (K.C.)	0.982
Clay/Platte cntys	0.982
Rural NW cntys	0.917
Small E cities	0.903
St. Joseph	0.920
St. Louis/Lg. E cities	0.981
Rest of Missouri	0.905
Montana	0.920
Nebraska	0.895
Nevada	
Elko/Ely cities	0.996
Las Vegas	1.036
Reno	1.045
Rest of Nevada	1.026
New Hampshire	0.985
New Jersey	
Middle	1.061
Northern	1.101
Southern	1.033
New Mexico	0.939
New York	
Buffalo/surr. cntys	0.969
Manhattan	1.206
N Central cities	0.977
NYC suburbs/Long Is.	1.179
Poughkpsie/N NYC suburbs	1.040
Queens	1.179
Rochester/surr. cntys	1.004
Rest of New York	0.960
North Carolina	0.915
North Dakota	0.907
Ohio	0.971
Oklahoma	0.913
Oregon	
Eugene	0.960
Portland	0.994
Salem	0.957
SW cities	0.962
Rest of Oregon	0.953
Pennsylvania	
Large cities	1.014
Phila./Pitts.	1.041
Small cities	0.954
Rest of Pennsylvania	0.941
Puerto Rico	0.797
Rhode Island	1.031
South Carolina	0.906
South Dakota	0.886
Tennessee	0.913
Texas	
Abilene	0.908
Amarillo	0.922
Austin	0.962
Beaumont	0.962
Brazoria	0.985
Brownsville	0.908
Corpus Christi	0.938
Dallas	0.983
Denton	0.957
El Paso	0.929
Fort Worth	0.955
Galveston	0.976
Grayson	0.914
Houston	1.008
Laredo	0.899
Longview	0.922
Lubbock	0.909
Mc Allen	0.895
Midland	0.964
NE rural	0.907
Odessa	0.955
Orange	0.947
San Angelo	0.902
San Antonio	0.939
SE rural	0.917
Temple	0.916
Texarkana	0.905
Tyler	0.933
Victoria	0.937
Waco	0.914
Western	0.888
Wichita Falls	0.908
Utah	0.943
Vermont	0.937
Virginia	
Richmond/Charlottesville	0.957
Sm. town (industrial)	0.915
Tidewater/N cntys	0.967
Rest of Virginia	0.909
Virgin Islands	0.987
Washington	
Seattle/King Cnty	1.030
E central and NE	0.976
West and Southeast	0.984
West Virginia	
Charleston	0.949

Eastern valley 0.923
Ohio River valley 0.908
Southern valley 0.901
Wheeling 0.917

Wisconsin

Central 0.919
NE/Green Bay 0.944
S central/Janesville 0.937
W central La Crosse 0.940
Dane cnty/Madison 0.986
SE/Milwaukee suburbs 0.991
Milwaukee 0.997
Northwes 0.923
E central/Oshkosh 0.939
Southwest 0.919
N central/Wausau 0.928

Wyoming 0.935

MEDICODE GEOGRAPHIC ADJUSTMENT FACTORS

MEDICODE'S AREAS

Medicode calculates UCR amounts for approximately 200 areas nationwide. These areas are defined by the first three digits of the US zip code. This appendix includes a text description of the area, a list of the three digit zip codes included in the area, and a factor by which the national 50th and 75th percentile amounts can be multiplied to approximate the UCR for the specific locality.

Adj. Factor	Area Description	Zip Codes
	Alabama	
0.948	Birmingham and area	350–352
0.894	Huntsville/Tuscaloosa/Decatur	354–359, 362
0.929	Mobile/Prichard/Selma/Andalusia	364–367, 369
0.894	Montgomery/Auburn/Dothan/Phenix City	360–361, 363, 368
	Alaska	
1.152	Various	995–999
	Arizona	
0.942	Flagstaff/Prescott/Lake Havasu City	855, 859–860, 863–865
0.989	Phoenix/Mesa/Tempe/Scottsdale	850, 852–853
0.965	Tucson and Area	856–857
	Arkansas	
0.883	Jonesboro/Fayetteville/West Memphis	723–727
0.901	Little Rock and Area	720–722
0.922	Pine Bluff/Fort Smith/Hot Springs	716–719, 728–729
	California	
1.073	Bakersfield/Visalia/Lancaster	932–933, 935
1.339	Downtown Los Angeles	900–901
0.998	Fresno/Salinas/Clovis/Seaside	936–937, 939
1.160	Long Beach/Torrance/Whittier	905–908
1.102	Oakland/Berkeley/Fremont/Napa	945–949
1.161	Ontario/Pomona/W Covina/Alhambra	917–918
1.057	Oxnard/Santa Barbara/Simi Valley	930–931, 934
1.161	Pasadena/Glendale/Van Nuys	910–916
1.081	Riverside/San Bernardino/Palm Springs	922–925
1.059	Sacramento/Davis/Woodland	942, 956–958
1.044	San Diego/Chula Vista/Oceanside	919–921
1.178	San Francisco/Sunnyvale/Palo Alto	940–941, 943–944
1.117	San Jose/Santa Clara/Santa Cruz	950–951
1.163	Santa Ana/Anaheim/Newport Beach	926–928
1.288	Santa Monica/Inglewood/Redondo Beach	902–904
0.973	Santa Rosa/Redding/Chico/Yuba City	954–955, 959–961
1.012	Stockton/Modesto/Merced/Lodi	952–953

Adj. Factor	Area Description	Zip Codes
	Colorado	
0.966	Colorado Springs and area	808–809
1.007	Denver/Boulder/Arvada/Westminster	800–804
0.892	Fort Collins/Loveland/Greeley	805–807
0.890	Pueblo/Grand Junction/Durango	810–816
	Connecticut	
1.169	Bridgeport/New Haven/Waterbury	064–067
1.142	Hartford/New Britain/Norwich	060–063
1.257	Stamford/Danbury	068–069
	Delaware	
1.102	Various	197–199
	District of Columbia	
1.236	Various	200–205
	Florida	
1.098	Fort Lauderdale/Tamarac	333
1.150	Hialeah/Hollywood/Miramar	330, 340
1.026	Jacksonville	322
1.230	Miami and area	331–332
0.986	Orlando/Melbourne/Titusville	327–329, 347, 349
0.914	St. Petersburg/Clearwater/Lakeland	335, 337–339, 342, 346
0.897	Tallahassee/Gainesville/Pensacola	320–321, 323–326, 344
0.953	Tampa	336
1.036	West Palm Beach/Boca Raton/Delray Beach	334
	Georgia	
0.940	Albany/Valdosta/Waycross/Statesboro	304, 315–317
1.078	Atlanta	303, 311
0.957	Augusta/Athens/Gainsville	305–306, 308–309
0.993	Columbus/Macon/Warner Robins	310, 312, 318–319
1.000	Marietta/Rome/Dalton/Griffin	300–302, 307
1.020	Savannah and area	313–314
	Hawaii	
1.128	Various	967–968
	Idaho	
0.910	Boise	837
0.870	Idaho Falls/Pocatello/Nampa/Lewiston	832–836, 838
	Illinois	
1.020	Aurora/Naperville/Joliet/Oak Lawn	604–605
0.814	Carbondale/Centralia/Effingham	624, 628–629
1.098	Champaign/Danville/Urbana	618–619
1.170	Chicago	606–608
0.885	East St. Louis/Belleville/Alton	620, 622
1.040	Elgin/Evanston/Schaumburg/De Kalb	601–603
0.866	Peoria/Bloomington/Kankakee/Moline	609, 612–617
0.967	Rockford/Freeport/Dixon	610–611
0.929	Springfield/Decatur/Quincy	623, 625–627
1.059	Waukegan/Arlington Heights/Skokie	600
	Indiana	
0.891	Anderson/Muncie/Indianapolis area	460–461, 473
0.860	Bloomington/Terre Haute/New Albany	470–472, 474, 478
0.852	Evansville/Vincennes/Washington	475–477
0.889	Fort Wayne/Huntington	467–468
0.951	Gary/Hammond/East Chicago	463–464
1.017	Indianapolis/Lawrence	462
0.951	Kokomo/Lafayette/Marion	469, 479
0.840	South Bend/Mishawaka/Elkhart/Goshen	465–466

Adj. Factor	Area Description	Zip Codes
	Iowa	
0.857	Cedar Rapids/Dubuque/Sioux City	504–508, 510–516, 520–521, 523–527
0.900	Des Moines and area/Davenprt/Iowa City	500–503, 522, 528
	Kansas	
0.800	Emporia/Manhattan/Independence	664–665, 667–668, 673
0.954	Kansas City/Topeka/Overland Park	660–662, 666
0.850	Salina/Dodge City/Garden City/Hays	669, 674, 676–679
0.930	Wichita/Hutchinson/Winfield	670–672, 675
	Kentucky	
0.893	Lexington/Frankfort/Covington	403–406, 410
0.912	Louisville/Ft. Knox/Pleasure Ridge Park	400–402
0.875	Owensboro/Bowling Green/Hopkinsville	407–409, 411–418, 420–427
	Louisiana	
0.913	Baton Rouge/Slidell/Hammond	704, 707–708
0.892	Lafayette/Lake Charles/Alexandria	703, 705–706, 713–714
1.036	New Orleans/Metairie/Kenner	700–701
0.914	Shreveport/Bossier City/Monroe	710–712
	Maine	
0.938	Various	039–049
	Maryland	
1.099	Baltimore/Columbia/Annapolis	210–212, 214
0.904	Frederick/Hagerstown/Cumberland	215–219
1.150	Maryland suburbs of D.C.	206–209
	Massachusetts	
1.149	Boston/Cambridge/Quincy/Newton	021–022
1.089	Brockton/Fall River/New Bedford	020, 023–027
1.138	Lawrence/Lowell/Lynn/Marlborough	017–019
1.009	Springfield/Chicopee/Pittsfield	010–013
1.104	Worcester/Fitchburg/Leominster	014–016
	Michigan	
1.000	Detroit/Ann Arbor/Livonia/Dearborn	481–482
0.916	Grand Rapids/Muskegon/Holland	493–495
0.878	Kalamazoo/Battle Creek/Jackson	490–492
0.910	Lansing/Saginaw/Bay City	486–489
0.859	Marquette/Traverse City/Cadillac	496–499
1.094	Warren/Flint/Sterling Heights/Troy	480, 483–485
	Minnesota	
1.005	Duluth/northern Minnesota	556–558, 564–567
1.051	Minneapolis/Bloomington/Edina	554
1.116	Rochester/Winona/Austin	559
0.972	St. Cloud/southwestern Minnesota	560–563
1.012	St. Paul/Minnetonka/Burnsville	550–551, 553, 555
	Mississippi	
0.879	Various	386–397
	Missouri	
0.806	Cape Girardeau/Poplar Bluff/Sikeston	636–639, 654–655
0.794	Columbia and area	652
0.945	Florissant/St.. Charles	630, 633
0.826	Jefferson City/Sedalia/Marshall	650–651, 653
0.960	Kansas City/Independence	640–641
0.842	Springfield/Joplin	647–648, 656–658
0.832	St. Joseph/Kirksville/Hannibal	634–635, 644–646
1.001	St. Louis and area	631
	Montana	
0.862	Various	590–599

Adj. Factor	Area Description	Zip Codes
	Nebraska	
0.843	Omaha/Lincoln	681, 685
0.785	Various	680, 683–684, 686–693
	Nevada	
1.109	Las Vegas and area	889–891
0.968	Reno/various	893–895, 897–898
	New Hampshire	
0.985	Various	030–038
	New Jersey	
1.188	Newark and area	070–073
1.151	Paterson/Hackensack	074–076
1.115	Red Bank/Lakewood	077, 087
1.117	South Jersey	080–084
1.158	Trenton/New Brunswick	078–079, 085–086, 088–089
	New Mexico	
0.944	Various	870–875, 877–885
	New York	
1.014	Albany/Schenectady/Poughkeepsie	120–129
0.902	Binghamton/Elmira/Ithaca	137–139, 148–149
0.826	Buffalo/Rochester/Irondequoit	140–147
1.619	Manhattan	100–102
1.245	Nassau and Suffolk counties	115–119
1.376	Staten Island/Bronx/Brooklyn/Queens	103–104, 110–114
0.925	Syracuse/Utica/Auburn/Watertown	130–136
1.208	Westchester-Orange-Rockland counties	105–109
	North Carolina	
0.859	Asheville/Hickory/Western N.C.	286–289
0.986	Charlotte/Gastonia/Kannapolis	280–282
0.911	Fayetteville/Jacksonville/Wilmington	278–279, 283–285
0.815	Greensboro/Winston-Salem/High Point	270–274
1.032	Raleigh/Durham/Goldsboro	275–277
	North Dakota	
0.981	Various	580–588
	Ohio	
0.859	Canton/Massillon/Zanesville	437–438, 446–447, 457
0.915	Cincinnati/Hamilton/Portsmouth	450–452, 456
0.996	Cleveland/Parma/Lakewood/Euclid	441
0.933	Columbus and area	430–432
0.907	Dayton/Springfield/Beaver Creek	453–455
0.832	Mansfield/Marion/Findlay/Lima	433, 448–449, 458
0.899	Toledo/Bowling Green	434–436
0.929	Youngstown/Akron/Warren/Steubenville	439–440, 442–445
	Oklahoma	
0.889	Lawton/Enid/Muskogee/Mcalester/Altus	734–739, 743–749
0.948	Oklahoma City/Norman/Edmond	730–731
0.935	Tulsa/Bartlesville/Stillwater	740–741
	Oregon	
0.866	Altamont/Bend/Klamath Falls/Pendelton	976–979
0.936	Eugene/Medford/Springfield	974–975
0.955	Portland/Beaverton/Hillsboro	970–972
0.934	Salem/Corvallis/Albany	973
	Pennsylvania	
1.015	Allentown/Scranton/Wilkes-Barre	180–188
0.962	Erie/Johnstown/New Castle/Sharon	153–155, 157–165
0.940	Harrisburg/Reading/Altoona	166–171, 177–179, 195–196
0.862	Lancaster/York	172–176
1.019	Norristown/Warminster/West Chester	189, 193–194

Adj. Factor	Area Description	Zip Codes
1.250	Philadelphia	191
1.072	Philadelphia area/Leavittown/Upper Darby	190
1.005	Pittsburgh/Beaver Valley/Greensburg	150–152, 156
	Puerto Rico	
0.958	Puerto Rico and Virgin Islands	006–009
	Rhode Island	
1.049	Various	028–029
	South Carolina	
0.910	Columbia/Charleston	292, 294
0.888	Various	290–291, 293, 295–299
	South Dakota	
0.852	Various	570–577
	Tennessee	
0.912	Knoxville/Chattanooga/Concord	373–374, 376–379, 385
0.975	Memphis/Jackson/Union City/Dyersburg	380–383
0.944	Nashville/Clarksville/Columbia	370–372, 384
	Texas	
0.906	Amarillo/Lubbock/Abilene	790–796
0.987	Austin/San Marcos/La Grange	786–787, 789
0.984	Beaumont/Pasadena/Baytown/Galveston	773–775, 777
0.930	Corpus Christi/Brownsville/Mc Allen	783–785
1.004	Dallas	752–753
0.963	El Paso/San Angelo/Midland/Odessa	768–769, 788, 797–799
0.947	Fort Worth/ Arlington/Wichita Falls	760–764
0.991	Garland/Irving/Sherman/Denison	750–751
1.017	Houston	770, 772
0.891	Longview/Texarkana/Tyler	754–759, 776
0.948	San Antonio	782
0.904	San Antonio area/Laredo/Victoria	779–781
1.225	Waco/College Station/Bryan/Killeen	765–767, 778
	Utah	
0.775	Ogden/Logan/Brigham City	842–844
0.802	Provo/Cedar City/St.. George/Moab	845–847
0.850	Salt Lake City	841
0.786	Sandy/Orem/West Jordan/Layton	840
	Vermont	
0.918	Various	050–054, 056–059
	Virginia	
0.909	Charlottesvlle/Harrisonbrg/Winchester	226–229, 244
0.998	Richmond/Petersburg/Fredericksburg	224–225, 230–232, 238
0.941	Roanoke/Lynchburg/Danville	239–243, 245–246
0.975	Virginia Beach/Norfolk/Newport News	233–237
1.114	Virginia suburbs of D.C.	220–223
	Washington	
1.033	Seattle/Bellevue/Edmonds	980–981
0.947	Spokane/Kennewick/Yakima	988–994
0.995	Tacoma/Olympia/Everett	982–986
	West Virginia	
0.988	Charleston/Huntington/Southwestern	247–248, 250–253, 255–259
0.904	Morgantown/Wheeling/Parkersburg	249, 254, 260–268
	Wisconsin	
0.950	Appleton/Oshkosh/Fond Du Lac	549
0.935	Green Bay/Eau Claire/Northern	540–543, 545, 547–548
0.993	Janesville/Beloit/Southwest	535, 538
1.007	Kenosha/Waukesha/Sheboygan	530–531
1.030	La Crosse/Wausau	539, 544, 546
1.118	Madison	537
1.078	Milwaukee/Racine	532, 534

Adj. Factor	Area Description	Zip Codes
	Wyoming	
0.845	Various	820–831